F

Magnetoelectric Devices

TRANSDUCERS, TRANSFORMERS, AND MACHINES

Magnetoelectric Devices

TRANSDUCERS, TRANSFORMERS, AND MACHINES

Gordon R. Slemon

Professor and Head, Department of Electrical Engineering
University of Toronto

John Wiley and Sons, Inc.   New York · London · Sydney

Library of Congress Catalog Card Number: 66-21039
Printed in the United States of America

PREFACE

This book is concerned with understanding, modeling, analyzing, and designing those devices that are used to convert, transform, and control electrical energy. Included are transducers, actuators, transformers, magnetic amplifiers, and rotating machines. In introducing the generic term "magnetoelectric" to denote this group of devices, I have sought to emphasize their predominantly magnetic nature, while distinguishing them from other well-established groupings such as electronic and microwave devices.

Chapter 1 is devoted to a study of some of the basic energy conversion processes and to an examination of the properties of the important materials used in exploiting these processes. Particular emphasis is placed on a study of ferromagnetism, including the mechanism of force production between sections of ferromagnetic material.

Chapter 2 introduces some of the concepts that are useful in devising approximate analytical models for nonlinear magnetic elements. The derivation of equivalent electric circuits to represent multilimbed magnetic systems is discussed.

In Chapter 3, the modeling concepts of Chapter 2 are applied in analyzing the performance of transformers, saturable reactors, and other static magnetic devices.

Chapters 4 and 5 are devoted to rotating electric machines. General equivalent circuit models are developed for two broad classes of machines, namely commutator and polyphase machines. Specific machine types—such as shunt, series, compound, induction, synchronous, reluctance, polyphase commutator, single-phase, and synchro machines—are analyzed by adaptation of the two basic equivalent circuit models. A feature of the analytical approach is that the effects of magnetic nonlinearity can be included approximately in any of the models.

It is my conviction that the essence of engineering is design. The ultimate objective of each phase of preparatory study should therefore be to increase the students' capability to design useful components and systems. The route to this ultimate objective has four distinct but interrelated aspects: an understanding of the physical processes, the derivation of approximate models, techniques of analysis, and, finally, design.

The first objective of this book is the development of a physical understanding of the forces and energies arising from electric and magnetic phenomena. To appreciate the implications of this objective, consider, for example, the force tending to close an air gap in a ferromagnetic core. This force can be determined by use of the principles of energy conservation and virtual displacement. While this method is analytically simple, it gives little physical appreciation of the origin and area of action of the force. In Chapter 1, this force is developed from direct interaction of magnetic moments in the material and is also deduced indirectly from energy considerations. The first approach is intended to give a qualitative physical understanding; the second approach is intended for quantitative analysis.

A large part of the book is devoted to developing models for devices. All models are by nature approximate in that they retain only that information which is considered necessary for prediction of performance. Thus, engineering judgment is required in choosing an adequate model for each situation. Various kinds of model (e.g., simultaneous equations, linear graphs, block diagrams) can be used to represent magnetoelectric devices. I have chosen to emphasize the use of equivalent circuit models because these are also encountered in parallel studies of other electric and electronic systems. A familiarity with methods of analysis for linear and nonlinear electric circuits can be reasonably assumed. A further advantage of equivalent circuits is that individual parameters generally can be related directly to the dimensions and material properties of the device.

Much has been written in recent years about generalized models for electric machines. In many of the proposed models, linearity has been assumed. But most electrical devices have important operating regions for which magnetic nonlinearity is significant. Thus the purely linear models have been highly restricted in the generality of their engineering usefulness. In the models that appear in this book, provision has been made for the inclusion of magnetic nonlinearity while retaining general models that can be adapted to represent various classes of machines.

Since most of the models are in the form of equivalent circuits, very little space has been given to methods of analysis of these models. It has been assumed that parallel courses in electric circuits, differential equations, computer programming, and system analysis will have provided an adequate range of analytical techniques. Some analysis is included to derive typical operating characteristics. Most of the models derived in this book are appropriate for the solution of either dynamic or steady-state performance. They can therefore be integrated directly into representations of systems either in the form of equivalent circuits or as transfer functions. The methods of control system analysis have not been included, since it is assumed that most curricula provide for a general course in control systems.

The process of design is dependent on concepts obtained from the understanding, modeling, and analysis phases. It also requires an exercise of engineering judgment which initially may be somewhat disconcerting to the beginning student. The objective in most of the design problems is limited to choosing a reasonable set of principal dimensions for a device. The resulting device may be larger and costlier than the optimized design of an expert, but it is generally workable.

A number of problems have been included at the end of each chapter. These problems draw on all the concepts of understanding, modeling, analysis, and design. Many typical device applications have been described in the problem sections rather than in the text. Answers have been included for some sections of most problems to reassure the student in his progress. In design problems, approximate answers have been suggested to indicate to the student whether he is "within the ball park."

The student using this book should have previous familiarity with electrical physics (particularly electric and magnetic fields) and circuit analysis (preferably including elementary Laplace transforms). At the University of Toronto, the study of magnetoelectric devices is given somewhat greater emphasis than is usual in current American curricula. All the material in the book, with the exception of Section 5.5.5 to Section 5.7.4 and Section 5.8.5 to Section 5.9.3, is currently presented in about 60 lecture hours, partly in the third year and partly in the fourth year. If only 35–45 lecture hours are available, part or all of the following sections may be omitted without loss of continuity: Section 1.3.4 to 1.4.1, 1.6.6 and 1.6.7, 2.5, 3.2.3 to 3.4.5, 4.4.3 and 4.4.4, 4.5.2 to 4.5.7, 4.6.2 to 4.8, 5.2.3 to 5.2.5, 5.4.5 and 5.4.6, 5.5.5 to 5.9.3. Significant parts of Chapter 1 may be considered elsewhere in some curricula.

I wish to thank my colleagues at the University of Toronto for their many helpful suggestions, criticism, and discussion. In particular, I wish to acknowledge the encouragement and assistance given to me by Professor J. M. Ham, Dean-elect of the Faculty of Applied Science and Engineering. To the many undergraduate and postgraduate students who have studied with me during the development and final preparation of this book, I am particularly grateful. It is to you that this book is dedicated.

Gordon R. Slemon

Toronto, Canada
June, 1966

CONTENTS

Magnetoelectric Devices

TRANSDUCERS, TRANSFORMERS, AND MACHINES

Chapter 1

ELECTRIC ENERGY CONVERSION PROCESSES

1.1 THE PURPOSE AND SCOPE OF THIS BOOK

This book is concerned with electrical devices that are used for the conversion of electric energy to or from mechanical energy, or to electric energy in a different form. Let us look first at some of the needs for electrical devices or machines since it is only by appreciating the functions which they must perform and the environment in which they operate that we can assess the properties which will be significant.

Electrical devices are required for the following.

1. The production of large amounts of electric power from hydraulic or steam turbines. (Need for these machines may be partially superseded in the future by the development of direct methods for converting thermal energy to electrical form.)

2. The transformation of electric energy to a voltage suitable for bulk transmission and its retransformation to voltages suitable for distribution and use.

3. The conversion of available electric power to other desired forms involving a change of frequency, source characteristics, etc.

4. The production of mechanical energy with relatively constant mechanical speed for a majority of the applications of electric motors, large and small.

5. The control, with varying degrees of accuracy, of the speed and position of mechanical systems.

6. The measurement of mechanical quantities by the production of proportional electric signals.

If electrical machines predominate in all these roles, it is because they allow economical centralized production of power, relatively simple distribution, economical reconversion to useful form, and a high degree of control and automation.

To contrive a useful device, various materials must be assembled in

1

such a way as to exploit some physical phenomenon. Chapter 1 of this book is devoted to a study of some of the basic energy conversion processes on which electrical devices are based and to an examination of the properties of the more important materials that are used.

The concepts of electric and magnetic fields are very useful in reaching an understanding of these basic energy conversion processes. But when these processes are exploited in complex machines, the wealth of information contained in the field approach generally becomes unwieldy. It is usually possible to extract only a few descriptive parameters through which the important operational properties of the machine may be adequately described. In many instances this extraction results in an equivalent electric circuit; in others, a set of equations is produced. When making this step from the field to the circuit point of view for purposes of easy analysis, we should keep in mind that the machine designer must reverse this process, and, starting with the required terminal properties of the machine, must specify its dimensions. Chapter 2 covers methods by which simple models such as equivalent circuits may be produced for magnetic systems. These models are then used in Chapter 3 to analyze the properties of transformers and some other stationary electrical-to-electrical conversion devices.

The remainder of the book is devoted to rotating machines and to systems of these machines. Although these machines are, for convenience, divided into a number of categories, they are all based on a small and essentially common set of energy conversion phenomena. The appropriate parameters of these machines are developed from a knowledge of the dimensions and materials. These parameters are then incorporated into analytical models, usually in the form of equivalent circuits. From an analysis of these models, the behavior of these machines may be predicted and their applications studied.

Thus the purposes of this book are to introduce the reader to those physical principles that have been most widely exploited by engineers to produce electrical devices and machines, to show how materials are arranged to produce the device and how the performance is limited by the physical limits of the material properties, to develop means by which the behavior of the machine may be readily predicted in various applications, and to provide some background for the understanding and even for the invention of new devices. Throughout the book, numerous approximations are made to provide the maximum simplicity and yet to retain enough information for the problem under study. Naturally, these approximate analyses neglect various secondary factors which may be significant in certain circumstances. A further purpose of the book is the development of that pragmatic approach by which the engineer seeks to obtain the maximum utility in his design and analysis with the minimum expenditure of effort.

1.2 SOME ENERGY CONVERSION PHENOMENA

In this section let us examine, in a qualitative manner, some of the electrical phenomena that result in the production of mechanical force. Figure 1.1 shows the familiar forces of repulsion between similarly

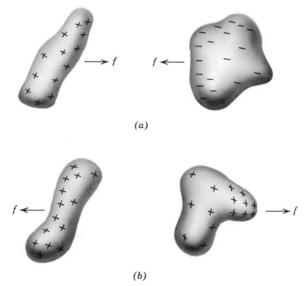

(a)

(b)

Fig. 1.1 Force between electrically charged bodies. (a) Opposite charges. (b) Like charges.

charged bodies. If in Fig. 1.1a the two bodies are allowed to move in response to these forces, mechanical work is done. During this motion some of the energy which was originally used to separate the positive charge from the negative is converted to mechanical energy. To pull apart the bodies in Fig. 1.1a requires an input of mechanical energy that is converted into an electrical form. By generalizing from this simple example, it follows that any system exhibiting mechanical forces of electrical origin is capable of both electrical-to-mechanical and mechanical-to-electrical energy conversion.

Figure 1.2a shows the forces that exist on parallel current-carrying

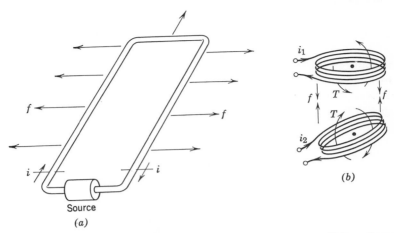

Fig. 1.2 Forces between electrical currents. (a) Force between parallel conductors. (b) Force and torque between two current-carrying coils.

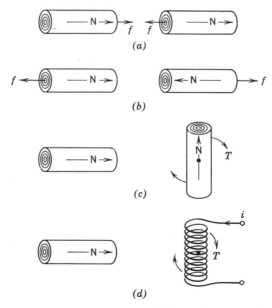

Fig. 1.3 Forces and torques with permanent magnets.

conductors. Displacement of the conductors in the direction of the forces results in conversion of energy from electrical form to mechanical form. The two current-carrying coils of Fig. 1.2b exhibit both forces of attraction and torques tending to align the two coils. The torque produced in this arrangement provides for the development of mechanical energy in rotary form.

Another familiar set of forces and torques are those between permanent magnets, as shown in Fig. 1.3. Replacement of one of the magnets by a

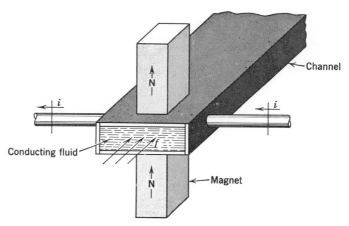

Fig. 1.4   Force on a conducting fluid.

current-carrying coil produces forces and torques of the same nature, as indicated in Fig. 1.3d. Furthermore, insertion of a magnetic (but not necessarily a permanent magnetic) material inside the coil of Fig. 1.3d augments the torque. All these simple experiments suggest that a common theoretical basis can be developed for both forces between current-carrying conductors and forces between bodies made of various magnetic materials.

Figure 1.4 demonstrates another form of the force on current-carrying conductors. In this instance the conductor is a fluid, either liquid or gaseous. When a current i is passed through this fluid across a region of the channel that is also within a magnetic field, a force acts on the fluid, tending to move it along the channel. Conversely, motion of the fluid along the channel through the magnetic field causes a current i to flow through the electrical system connected to the sides of the channel.

Figure 1.5 shows the magnetostrictive forces that are established within

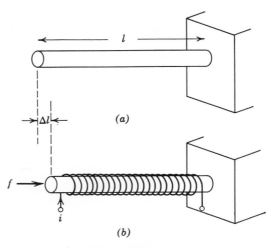

Fig. 1.5   Magnetostriction force in nickel bar.

certain types of magnetic material when magnetized. In the nickel bar
shown, passage of a current in either direction around the bar causes it to
contract in length. If the bar is restrained to some extent from contracting,
a mechanical force is produced, and mechanical energy can be extracted.
In some magnetic materials the action is to elongate rather than contract
the bar. The change in length is always very small (less than 0.01 %),
but the force that can be produced is relatively large.

Piezoelectric forces that are set up within certain crystalline insulating
materials, such as Rochelle Salt or quartz, are demonstrated in highly
exaggerated form in Fig. 1.6. Electric charges placed on or near two
opposite faces of the crystal may cause an increase in its thickness; reversal
of the polarity of the charges on the same crystal causes a decrease in
thickness. Restraint of this motion results in mechanical forces. As in

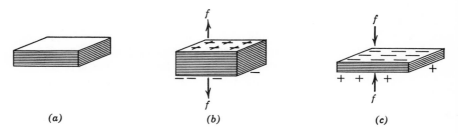

Fig. 1.6   Piezoelectric forces in crystal.

magnetostriction, the change in dimension is very small, but the forces may be large.

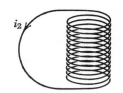

All the physical phenomena we have discussed until now have been associated with mechanical force and electromechanical energy conversion. Figure 1.7 demonstrates the induced forces that can cause the motion of electric charges in conductors. A current i_1, which is increasing with time, causes a current i_2 of electric charge to flow in an adjacent, but physically separate, closed coil. In an open coil, the same forces exist and act on the charges in the conductor in such a way as to accumulate positive charge at one terminal and negative charge at the other. This process of induction allows the transfer of electric energy from a source connected to one coil to a load connected to another coil, and is the basis for electrical-to-electrical transformation of energy.

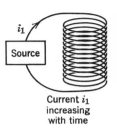

Current i_1 increasing with time

Now that we have reviewed these energy conversion processes qualitatively, let us consider the methods by which each of these processes may be described and analyzed quantitatively.

1.3 ENERGY CONVERSION USING ELECTROSTATIC FORCES

Fig. 1.7 Induced forces arising from increasing current i_1 causing motion of charge in other coils.

The system of Fig. 1.8 consists of two parallel conducting plates having equal but opposite charges of Q coulombs. From our qualitative approach in Section 1.2, we expect a force $\vec{f}$ of attraction between the plates, and we also expect mechanical work to be done if the plates are allowed to come closer together. In this section we consider some of the methods by which this force and the resultant work may be evaluated.

The first method is simple in principle, but is numerically very lengthy. It is based on Coulomb's law, which states that the magnitude f of the force between two concentrated or point charges Q_a and Q_b in vacuum is proportional to the product of the charges and inversely proportional to the square of the separation distance d.

$$f = \frac{Q_a Q_b}{4\pi\epsilon_0 d^2} \qquad \text{newtons} \qquad (1.1)$$

where $\epsilon_0 = 8.854 \times 10^{-12}$ coulombs^2/newton-meter If the distribution of the charge over the surfaces of the two conductors were known, each surface could be divided into a large number N of incremental areas ΔA, and the charge ΔQ on each area ΔA would be known. Suppose we regard each charge increment ΔQ as an approximate point charge. Each charge increment ΔQ on the positively charged plate experiences an incremental force component $\Delta \vec{f}$ directed toward each of the N charge increments on

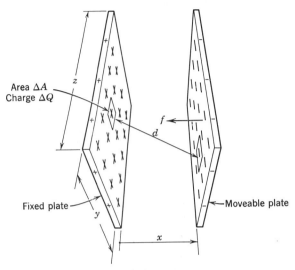

Fig. 1.8   Two parallel charged conducting plates.

the negative plate; the magnitude of each component is found by use of eq. 1.1. The total force $\vec{f}$ may then be determined by vectorial addition of the N^2 incremental force vectors.*

$$\vec{f} = \sum \Delta \vec{f} \qquad \text{newtons} \tag{1.2}$$

Since the distribution of the charge on the conductor surfaces is generally not known, it must be found by using a summation of force increments for each incremental surface charge. The force component parallel to the conductor surface acting on each incremental charge ΔQ is zero, since otherwise the charge would move until this was so. If this force component is evaluated in terms of the N unknown charge increments ΔQ and equated to zero for each area, the result is N simultaneous equations, which may be solved to obtain the charge distribution.

* Throughout this book vector quantities are denoted by an arrow over the symbol (for example, $\vec{f}$). The magnitude of a vector quantity is denoted by the symbol with no arrow (for example, f).

The reason that this method of analysis is almost never used for manual calculations may be appreciated from this brief discussion. The method is, however, suitable for solution on a digital computer for which the repetition of the simple steps in the method presents no difficulty.

To determine the work that is done as the right-hand plate in Fig. 1.8 moves between two positions x_1 and x_2, it is necessary to evaluate the force $\vec{f}$ for a number of values of x between x_1 and x_2. When the force vector $\vec{f}$ for each vectorial increment of motion $d\vec{x}$ is known with sufficient accuracy the work W is given by*

$$W = \int_{x_1}^{x_2} \vec{f} \cdot \qquad \text{joules} \qquad (1.3)$$

Although the work is expressed here as an integral, a summation over finite increments of x is normally made in numerical calculations.

The intention in introducing this method first is not so much to develop an ability to calculate forces as to examine the thought process involved in qualitatively assessing such questions as; How is the charge distributed? In what direction does the net force act? How does the force change as the spacing is changed?

1.3.1   Electric Field Approach

In a system such as that of Fig. 1.8, the use of the somewhat more abstract concepts of an electric field and a few judicious assumptions leads to a much simpler method of calculating forces and energies. This approach depends on the determination of the electric field intensity $\vec{\mathscr{E}}$ which is defined by the property that an increment of concentrated charge ΔQ placed into the electric field at the point where the field intensity is $\vec{\mathscr{E}}$ experiences a force $\Delta \vec{f}$ of

$$\Delta \vec{f} = \Delta Q \vec{\mathscr{E}} \qquad \text{newtons} \qquad (1.4)$$

The electric field intensity is related to another vector, the electric flux density $\vec{D}$ by

$$\vec{D} = \epsilon_0 \vec{\mathscr{E}} \qquad \text{coulombs/meter} \qquad (1.5)$$

for vacuum and, for all practical purposes, for air or other gases. The electric flux density may be considered as emanating from a charged body. By Gauss's theorem, the total electric flux emanating from the area A of a closed surface is numerically equal to the charge Q enclosed

---

* The scalar or dot product of these two vectors is a scalar quantity equal to the product of the magnitude f of the force, the magnitude dx of the directed length, and the cosine of the angle between these two vectors.

within that surface. Thus

$$\int_{\substack{\text{closed} \\ \text{surface}}} \vec{D} \cdot d\vec{A} = Q_{\text{enclosed}} \quad \text{coulombs} \tag{1.6}$$

If the spacing x in Fig. 1.8 is much less than either of the dimensions y or z, it is reasonably accurate to assume that the charges are distributed uniformly over the inside surfaces of the plates. Actually, there will be a denser charge distribution near the edges, but the region of highly nonuniform distribution is assumed to be only a small part of the total area.

Figure 1.9 shows the assumed uniform sheet of charge from the left-hand plate of Fig. 1.8. A field of electric flux density $\vec{D}$ of constant magnitude emerges uniformly and perpendicularly from the surfaces of this sheet. This field is assumed to remain constant in magnitude and direction for some distance outward from the sheet. These assumptions of uniformity allow us to evaluate the integral in eq. 1.6. For a closed surface around the plate in Fig. 1.9, we find that $\int \vec{D} \cdot d\vec{A} = D\,2yz = Q$, from which

$$D = \frac{Q}{2yz} \quad \text{coulombs/meter}^2 \tag{1.7}$$

From eq. 1.5, the electric field intensity $\vec{\mathscr{E}}$ arising from the charge on the left-hand plate has a magnitude $\mathscr{E}$ of

$$\mathscr{E} = \frac{D}{\epsilon_0}$$

$$= \frac{Q}{2yz\epsilon_0} \quad \text{newtons/coulomb} \tag{1.8}$$

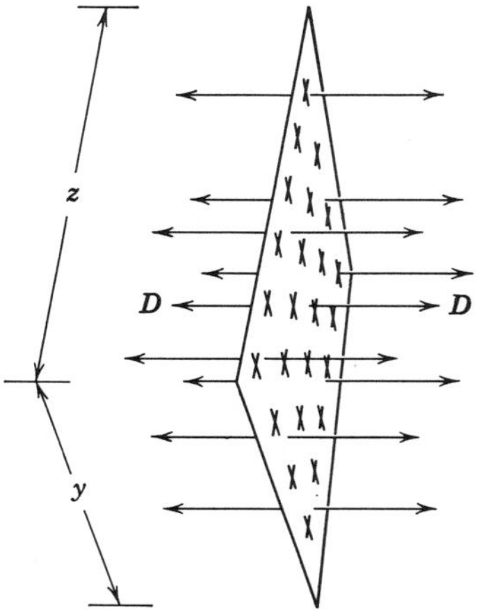

Fig. 1.9 Electric flux density field assumed to exist around a uniform sheet of charge.

It is now assumed that the whole of the negative charge Q on the right-hand plate of Fig. 1.8 is placed in this uniform electric field intensity of magnitude $\mathscr{E}$. The magnitude of the force on this right-hand plate is then given by

$$f = Q\mathscr{E}$$

$$= \frac{Q^2}{2yz\epsilon_0} \tag{1.9}$$

This force is directed to the left.

To the extent that the assumptions made are valid, eq. 1.9 shows that the force $\vec{f}$ is independent of the plate spacing x. The work W done by this force in moving the plate from a spacing x_1 to a spacing x_2 is obtained by evaluation of eq. 1.3.

$$W = \int_{x_1}^{x_2} \vec{f} \cdot d\vec{x}$$

$$= \frac{Q^2}{2yz\epsilon_0}(x_1 - x_2) \qquad \text{joules} \qquad (1.10)$$

If $x_1 > x_2$, the work W is positive, and mechanical energy is supplied to the mechanical system attached to the movable plate.

The assumption of uniformity of charge distribution could have been made in the method of analysis based on Coulomb's law in Section 1.3. Although this would have eliminated one step in the calculation, the calculation and summation of force increments in eq. 1.2 would still have been required. Thus, the field approach allows a fuller exploitation of the assumption of uniformity than does the numerical summation approach. On the other hand, unless there is some symmetry in the physical charged object that permits assumptions leading to an easy evaluation of the integral in eq. 1.6, the numerical complexity in determining the flux density $\vec{D}$ at all significant points may be as great as that of the earlier method described in Section 1.3.

Since the electric field approach gives solutions which are functional rather than numerical, it provides a better appreciation of the relations between forces or energies and the dimensions of the object. To exploit this approach, it is usual to replace the physical object under study by one or more idealized charge distributions (such as that of Fig. 1.9) for which the electric field is readily calculable.

1.3.2 Approach through the Conservation of Energy

Consider any device having provision for the input of energy and the output of useful energy, as is shown in Fig. 1.10. Within the device there are generally several ways in which energy can be stored and by which energy can be lost or rendered useless. If we suppose that all the energy must be in one of these categories, it follows from the law of conservation of energy that

$$\begin{array}{c}\text{Energy} \\ \text{input}\end{array} = \begin{array}{c}\text{Energy} \\ \text{lost}\end{array} + \begin{array}{c}\text{Increase in} \\ \text{energy stored}\end{array} + \begin{array}{c}\text{Energy} \\ \text{output}\end{array} \qquad (1.11)$$

Suppose now that the device is electromechanical with an input of electric energy and an output of mechanical energy. If we allow an infinitesimal increment dx in mechanical displacement, the corresponding increments of energy input, loss, storage, and output are related by

$$dW_{\substack{\text{electrical}\\ \text{input}}} = dW_{\text{loss}} + dW_{\text{stored}} + dW_{\substack{\text{mechanical}\\ \text{output}}} \tag{1.12}$$

The force f_x exerted by the mechanical member in the direction of the displacement dx is

$$f_x = \frac{dW_{\text{mech. output}}}{dx} \tag{1.13}$$

If the input, loss, and stored energy terms in eq. 1.12 can be evaluated, the mechanical energy output is then known and may be used in eq. 1.13 to determine the force.

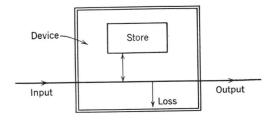

Fig. 1.10   Energy flow in a device.

Although this method on first examination may appear to be more involved than a direct determination of force, it often leads to simple and general expressions for force. Consider, for example, the system of two parallel charged conductors in Fig. 1.8. An electrical source may once have been connected to the plates in order to place on them the separated charge of Q coulombs; but since this source is not now connected, there can be no electrical input. Displacement of one plate relative to the other may cause some redistribution of charge, and, as this charge flows through the imperfectly conducting material of the plates, some energy may be lost. But, since the charge distribution remains reasonably constant, this loss may safely be neglected, particularly if the motion is reasonably slow. Let us further assume that the energy loss due to friction is part of the mechanical output. It therefore follows, for this system, that the mechanical energy output is equal to the amount of the decrease in stored energy. Thus we have

$$dW_{\substack{\text{mech.}\\ \text{output}}} = -dW_{\text{stored}} \tag{1.14}$$

and, from eq. 1.13, we have

$$f_x = -\left.\frac{\partial W_{\text{stored}}}{\partial x}\right|_{Q=\text{const.}} \qquad \text{newtons} \tag{1.15}$$

The stored energy of a two-conductor electrostatic system may be expressed in terms of its capacitance C and its stored charge Q as

$$W_{\text{stored}} = \frac{Q^2}{2C} \quad \text{joules} \tag{1.16}$$

Substituting into eq. 1.15 gives

$$f_x = \frac{Q^2}{2C^2} \frac{\partial C}{\partial x}\bigg|_{Q=\text{const.}} \quad \text{newtons} \tag{1.17}$$

This reduces the problem to one of finding the system capacitance C as a function of x. One method of accomplishing this would be the experimental measurement of the capacitance at a sufficient number of values of x. Alternatively, the capacitance can be calculated as

$$C = \frac{Q}{e} \quad \text{farads} \tag{1.18}$$

where e is the electric potential difference between the plates and is given by

$$e = \int_0^x \vec{\mathscr{E}} \cdot d\vec{x} \quad \text{volts (joules/coulomb)} \tag{1.19}$$

For the parallel-plate arrangement of Fig. 1.8, the assumption of uniform charge distribution on the inside plate surfaces results in a uniform electric flux density between the plates of magnitude

$$D = \frac{Q}{yz} \quad \text{coulombs/meter}^2 \tag{1.20}$$

The vector quantity $\vec{D}$ is directed to the right. It is noted that the quantity D in eq. 1.20 has twice the value of eq. 1.7, because the fields of both charged plates are considered simultaneously. From eqs. 1.19 and 1.20, we have

$$e = \frac{Qx}{yz\epsilon_0} \quad \text{volts}$$

$$C = \frac{yz\epsilon_0}{x} \quad \text{farads} \tag{1.21}$$

and the force in the direction of positive x is

$$f_x = \frac{Q^2}{2\left(\dfrac{yz\epsilon_0}{x}\right)^2} \frac{\partial}{\partial x}\left(\frac{yz\epsilon_0}{x}\right)$$

$$= -\frac{Q^2}{2yz\epsilon_0} \quad \text{newtons} \tag{1.22}$$

The negative sign associated with the force f_x indicates that the force is directed opposite to the positive direction of x. If we consider that the same assumptions were used in determining the capacitance as were used in the electric field approach of Section 1.3.1, it is not surprising that the result of eq. 1.22 is the same as that of eq. 1.9.

Let us now consider the more general situation shown in Fig. 1.11 in which two oppositely charged conducting plates are connected to a

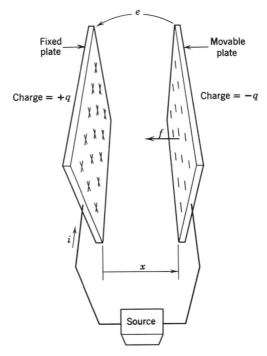

Fig. 1.11   Two plates connected to a source.

source. Suppose an incremental displacement dx of the right-hand plate is made in a time dt. During this displacement, the component of the force on the plate in the positive x direction is f_x. Then, from eq. 1.12 and 1.13, we have

$$f_x\, dx = dW_{\substack{\text{mech.}\\\text{output}}}$$

$$= dW_{\substack{\text{elect.}\\\text{input}}} - dW_{\text{loss}} - dW_{\text{stored}} \qquad (1.23)$$

The electrical energy input to the plates is

$$dW_{\substack{elect.\\input}} = ei\,dt$$
$$= e\,dq \qquad \text{joules} \qquad (1.24)$$

where dq is the charge increment delivered to the plates in the time interval dt. Let us assume that the resistive losses in the plates accompanying the redistribution of the charge q and its added increment dq are negligible. There may be a significant loss energy in the source and the leads to the plates, but this region is not included in the electrical input of eq. 1.24. Furthermore, let us assume that mechanical losses are included in the mechanical output. Then we have

$$dW_{loss} = 0 \qquad (1.25)$$

The energy stored in the system may be expressed as

$$W_{stored} = \tfrac{1}{2}qe \qquad \text{joules} \qquad (1.26)$$

Because both q and e are variables in this system,

$$dW_{stored} = \tfrac{1}{2}q\,de + \tfrac{1}{2}e\,dq \qquad \text{joules} \qquad (1.27)$$

Substituting these increments of energy into eq. 1.23 gives

$$f_x\,dx = e\,dq - \tfrac{1}{2}q\,de - \tfrac{1}{2}e\,dq$$

from which

$$f_x = \frac{1}{2}e\frac{dq}{dx} - \frac{1}{2}q\frac{de}{dx} \qquad \text{newtons} \qquad (1.28)$$

Substituting $q = Ce$ in eq. 1.28 gives the general expression for the component f_x of the force as

$$f_x = \frac{1}{2}e\left(C\frac{de}{dx} + e\frac{dC}{dx}\right) - \frac{1}{2}Ce\frac{de}{dx}$$
$$= \frac{1}{2}e^2\frac{dC}{dx} = \frac{1}{2}\frac{q^2}{C^2}\frac{dC}{dx} \qquad \text{newtons} \qquad (1.29)$$

It may be noted that this expression is that of eq. 1.17 developed for the restricted case of constant charge.

The expression of eq. 1.29 applies for any two-electrode system regardless of the shape of the charged bodies. It states that if a displacement of part of a system causes an increase in the system capacitance, there is a force component on that part of the system in the direction of the displacement.

1.3.3   A Comparison of the Methods of Analysis

We have now considered three approaches to the determination of electrostatic forces. The first was a direct determination of force using Coulomb's law. In the second, the force was viewed as the action of an electric field. In the third method, based on the principle of conservation of energy, no attempt was made to determine the mechanical quantities directly. Rather, we depended on our ability to analyze every other energy within the system and to obtain the mechanical energy and force by a process of elimination.

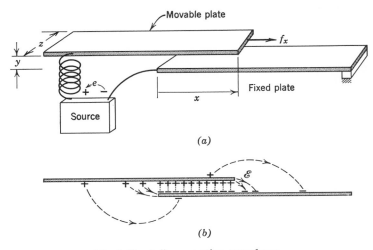

Fig. 1.12   A linear-motion transducer.

To compare these methods, consider the system of Fig. 1.12, which consists of two charged plates, one of which is free to move in the x direction. The problem is to determine whether there is a force component f_x in this direction and, if so, how much. When the source is connected to the system, the charges that flow to the plates tend to concentrate, more or less uniformly, in the region of overlap because of the forces of attraction between them. If we were to assume that the region of overlap had a uniform charge distribution with no charge outside this region, the symmetry of the charge pattern and our knowledge of the forces between parallel plates would lead us to the conclusion that the only force component is in the vertical or y direction. Figure 1.12b shows, through the medium of the electric field pattern, that there is some fringing of the electric field beyond the region of overlap. Because the positive charge on the upper plate is displaced somewhat to the left of the negative charge on the lower plate, a force on the upper plate in the positive x direction would then be expected. There appears, however, to be no easy means by which this force may be calculated either by use of Coulomb's law or by the intermediary approach using electric field concepts. Nevertheless, we may observe that motion of the plate in the x direction at constant potential difference e increases the area of the uniform field in the overlap region, while leaving the fringing field pattern essentially unchanged. We might therefore expect the force component in the x direction to be relatively independent of the position x, provided e is held constant.

Let us now consider the energy conservation approach. The general analysis of Section 1.3.2 leads to the force expression.

$$f_x = \frac{1}{2} e^2 \frac{dC}{dx} \qquad \text{newtons} \qquad (1.30)$$

The capacitance C of the system in Fig. 1.12 can be approximated by assuming that the plate charge q is made up of a uniformly distributed charge in the overlap region plus a fringing charge that is proportional to the potential difference e, but is independent of the overlap distance x. If D and $\mathscr{E}$ are the magnitudes of the electric field vectors in the region of overlap,

$$q_{\text{overlap}} = Dzx$$
$$= \epsilon_0 \mathscr{E} zx$$
$$= \epsilon_0 \frac{e}{y} zx \qquad \text{coulombs} \qquad (1.31)$$

Let

$$q_{\text{fringing}} = C_f e \qquad \text{coulombs} \qquad (1.32)$$

Then

$$C = \frac{q}{e} = \frac{q_{\text{overlap}} + q_{\text{fringing}}}{e}$$
$$= \frac{\epsilon_0 zx}{y} + C_f \qquad \text{farads} \qquad (1.33)$$

Insertion of this capacitance expression into eq. 1.30 gives

$$f_x = \frac{1}{2} \frac{\epsilon_0 e^2 z}{y} \text{ newtons} \qquad (1.34)$$

This expression is valid as long as the plates are large enough beyond the region of overlap to keep the fringing-charge pattern independent of the position x. As the overlap distance x approaches the total plate length, the capacitance C_f will decrease with increase of x eventually resulting in zero force component f_x when the plates are directly above each other.

It is significant to note that if the fringing field had been entirely neglected in developing the capacitance expression of eq. 1.33, the resulting force expression of eq. 1.34 would have been fortuitously correct, in spite of our previous reasoning that the force arises from this fringing charge! This fact emphasizes some of the strengths and weaknesses of the methods we have used. The direct approaches to the determination of force using either Coulomb's law or the electric field are most useful in obtaining a physical appreciation of a situation, but a quantitative analysis using these approaches is often difficult or tedious. The preceding example shows the ease with which functional expressions for force often may be obtained by using the energy conservation approach. But, by its nature, this approach can give no physical picture of the origin and area of action of the force. The methods are therefore often complementary rather than competitive.

1.3.4   A Rotating Electrostatic Machine

For a device in which the permitted motion is rotary rather than translational, the mechanical work is expressed in terms of the torque vector T and the angle θ of rotation. The torque component T_θ in the direction of positive angle θ is given by

$$T_\theta = \frac{dW_{\mathrm{mech.\ output}}}{d\theta} \qquad \text{newton-meters} \tag{1.35}$$

By analogy with eq. 1.30, the torque may be expressed as

$$T_\theta = \frac{1}{2}\, e^2 \frac{dC}{d\theta} \qquad \text{newton-meters} \tag{1.36}$$

That is, there is a torque component in the direction of positive angle θ if the capacitance C increases with increase of the angle θ.

Figure 1.13a shows a simple electrostatic machine with stationary or stator plates and rotating or rotor plates. If the rotor and stator axes are coincident at $\theta = 0$, the capacitance C between them may be approximated by regarding the stator and rotor sectors as complete quarter-circular disks for which

$$C_{\theta=0} = \frac{\epsilon_0 \pi r^2}{2d} \qquad \text{farads} \tag{1.37}$$

where d is the spacing between the plates. The variation of capacitance with angle is shown in Fig. 1.13b to be essentially a set of straight-line

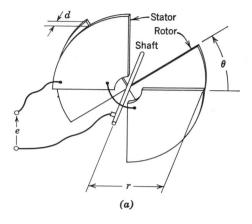

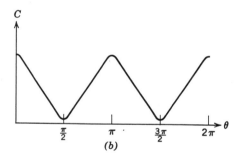

Fig. 1.13   (a) A simple rotating electrostatic machine. (b) The capacitance of the machine as a function of angular position.

segments with rounding at the intersections because of fringing fields. In the interval of $0 < \theta < \pi/2$, the capacitance C can be approximated by

$$C = \frac{\epsilon_0 \pi r^2}{2d}\left(1 - \frac{2\theta}{\pi}\right) \qquad \text{farads} \qquad (1.38)$$

If the potential difference e applied to the plates is constant at a value E, the torque, from eq. 1.36, is

$$T_\theta = -\frac{E^2 \epsilon_0 r^2}{2d} \qquad \text{newton-meters} \qquad (1.39)$$

for $0 < \theta < \pi/2$. As shown in Fig. 1.14a, this constant negative torque is followed by a constant positive torque in the interval $\pi/2 < \theta < \pi$ over which the capacitance again increases. Since the average torque over a complete revolution is zero, it is noted that this mode of operation cannot provide a continuous mechanical output. A useful unidirectional output torque can be obtained by restricting the motion to an arc not greater than $\pi/2$ radians, as in an electrostatic voltmeter.

The shape of the torque curve in Fig. 1.14a suggests that if we wish to have torque in the positive direction only, we can connect the machine to

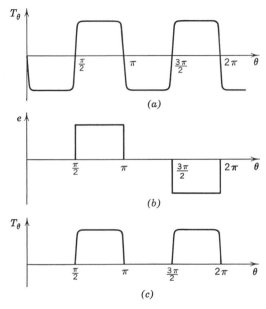

Fig. 1.14   (a) Torque of electrostatic machine with constant voltage. (b) Intermittent alternating voltage switched on to machine terminals. (c) Torque resulting from applied voltage of (b).

a source which applies a potential difference $e = E$ over the intervals of rotation $\pi/2 < \theta < \pi$ and $3\pi/2 < \theta < 2\pi$, and $e = 0$ over the remaining intervals. Because the torque is proportional to the square of the voltage, the polarity of the potential difference e is immaterial. Thus, application of the voltage e shown in Fig. 1.14b will result in the unidirectional torque of Fig. 1.14c.

Examination of the voltage wave of Fig. 1.14b suggests that this machine could produce useful torque if supplied with an alternating sinusoidal voltage e, the period of which is equal to the time required for one complete rotation. Let

$$e = \hat{E} \cos \omega t \qquad \text{volts} \qquad (1.40)$$

As we are dealing with sinusoidal functions, let us approximate the periodically varying capacitance by the first two terms of its Fourier series expansion.

$$C = C_0 + C_2 \cos 2\theta \qquad \text{farads} \qquad (1.41)$$

If the angular velocity of the rotor is ν radians/second and the angular position of the rotor at time $t = 0$ is $\theta = -\delta$,

$$\theta = \nu t - \delta \qquad \text{radians} \qquad (1.42)$$

Substitution from eq. 1.40, 1.41, and 1.42 into eq. 1.36 and manipulating trigonometrically give

$$
\begin{aligned}
T_\theta &= \tfrac{1}{2}(E \cos \omega t)^2 \frac{d}{d\theta} [C_0 + C_2 \cos 2(\nu t - \delta)] \\
&= -\tfrac{1}{2}\hat{E}^2 C_2 \{ \sin 2(\nu t - \delta) + \tfrac{1}{2} \sin [2(\omega + \nu)t - 2\delta] \\
&\qquad\qquad\qquad + \tfrac{1}{2} \sin [2(\omega - \nu)t - 2\delta] \}
\end{aligned}
\qquad (1.43)
$$

Examination of eq. 1.43 shows that all terms vary sinusoidally with time and have zero average value unless the angular velocity of the rotor is $\nu = \pm\omega$. This is consistent with our previous conclusion that the period of rotation must be equal to the period of the applied voltage. If, in eq. 1.43, ν is set equal to ω for counterclockwise or positive rotation, the average torque $\bar{T}$ is

$$\bar{T} = \tfrac{1}{4} C_2 \hat{E}^2 \sin 2\delta \qquad \text{newton-meters} \qquad (1.44)$$

This machine, operating on alternating voltage, can produce useful torque only at the forward or backward rotational velocities that correspond to the angular frequency of its supply voltage. It is therefore known as a synchronous machine. If a mechanical load is applied to this machine, the rotor momentarily slows down, thereby increasing the angle δ of its lag behind the maximum capacitance position $\theta = 0$ at the instant of maximum voltage $t = 0$. Equation 1.44 shows that this increase in angle δ results in an increase of the average torque $\bar{T}$, thus providing the required load torque as long as δ is in the range $0 < \delta < \pi/4$. Figure 1.15 shows the variation of average torque with the angle δ. The maximum average torque which the machine can produce is

$$\bar{T}_{\text{max}} = \tfrac{1}{4} C_2 \hat{E}^2 \qquad \text{newton-meters} \qquad (1.45)$$

If the load torque exceeds this value, the lag angle δ continues to increase, and the machine eventually stops.

This machine may also be used as a generator to convert mechanical energy to electrical form. If torque is applied to the shaft by a prime mover in the direction of rotation, the machine momentarily speeds up. The angle δ and the average torque both become negative, indicating that mechanical power is being absorbed by the machine and is being fed back into the electrical supply. If the prime-mover torque exceeds the value given in eq. 1.45 the machine accelerates in a runaway condition. The mechanical power output of the machine has an average value of

$$\bar{P} = \bar{T}\nu \qquad \text{watts} \qquad (1.46)$$

It is generally impractical to use air as a dielectric medium between the stator and rotor plates, because the output per unit volume is much smaller than can be obtained from other types of machine. To date no significant

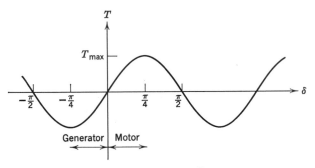

Fig. 1.15   Variation of average torque $\bar{T}$ with angle of lag δ.

area of practical application has been found for electrostatic synchronous machines. The use of vacuum, which permits a much higher electric field intensity in the machine may, however, make this type of machine competitive in the future for some applications.

1.4   PROPERTIES AND USE OF DIELECTRIC MATERIALS

Various nonconducting materials are used to provide electrical insulation, mechanical support, and electric energy storage in electrical apparatus. In this section some of the material properties that are most pertinent to energy conversion devices are examined briefly.

In Section 1.3 the discussion of electrostatic forces was restricted to conductors immersed in a vacuum. If the vacuum is replaced by a gas at normal pressure and temperature, the electric field and force relationships remain essentially unchanged. The only significant electrical difference in the gaseous media is in the electric field intensity which each medium can withstand before breakdown. Air, at normal temperature and pressure, can withstand an electric field intensity of 2.5 to 8.5 megavolts/meter without appreciable conduction, the value of breakdown stress increasing as the electrode spacing is decreased. With excessive electric stress, stray electrons in the air can achieve sufficient kinetic energy to dislodge other electrons as a result of collisions with atoms. If this ionization process is continued, a stream of conducting electrons and ions is produced between the electrodes, and breakdown occurs.

At reduced pressure, free electrons can travel longer distances in the electric field and acquire greater kinetic energy between collisions. This leads to ionization and breakdown at lower values of electric field intensity. Conversely, an increase in pressure results in an increased breakdown stress.

Theoretically, a vacuum cannot conduct because it contains no charged particles. Practically, electrical breakdown between a pair of electrodes immersed in high vacuum is almost entirely dependent on the electrode material. At sufficiently high electrical stress, gas and metal atoms are torn from the surface of the electrode material to initiate the breakdown process.

Solid and liquid insulating materials are characterized by their ability to withstand electrical stress, their electrical losses, their ability to store electrostatic energy, their thermal properties, and their stability with time. Conduction in these materials may be due to the flow of electrons, holes, or ions. Although a small amount of conduction may occur safely under normal stress, breakdown in the insulation usually occurs when the conduction becomes thermally unstable along some concentrated path between the electrodes. As the number of free charged particles increases with temperature in dielectric materials, the conductivity of these materials increases with temperature. The breakdown stress generally drops rapidly as temperature is increased. Excessive temperature may also cause structural changes, particularly in organic insulating materials, which may lead to a deterioration of both electrical and mechanical strength. Breakdown stresses in insulating materials range from 10 to 200 megavolts/meter depending on the material and its thickness.

Let us now examine the use of solid or liquid dielectric materials as electrostatic energy storage media. When a material is subjected to an electric field intensity, the electrons within each atom are displaced somewhat with respect to the positively charged nucleus (electronic polarization), ions are strained from their normal positions in the material structure (ionic polarization), and asymmetrically charged molecules are rotated toward alignment with the applied field (molecular polarization). All of these charged bodies return to their normal positions on removal of the field. Thus, energy may be stored in these various strain mechanisms and recovered as the field is removed.

In most dielectric media, the electronic, ionic, and molecular strains are directly proportional to the applied electric stress. If the whole of the volume occupied by the electric field between two electrodes is filled with dielectric material, the electrode charge q per unit of potential difference e is ϵ_r times the value with vacuum as the medium, where ϵ_r denotes the relative permittivity or dielectric constant. The capacitance C between the electrodes is

$$C_{\substack{\text{with} \\ \text{material}}} = \epsilon_r C_{\substack{\text{with} \\ \text{vacuum}}} \tag{1.47}$$

The energy stored in the material is

$$W = \tfrac{1}{2}qe$$
$$= \tfrac{1}{2}Ce^2 \quad \text{joules} \tag{1.48}$$

The ability of a material to store electrostatic energy depends on both the value of relative permittivity ϵ_r and the permissible electric stress within the material. For most materials used in electrical insulation—such as oil, paper, rubber, varnish, glass, mica, and plastics—the value of ϵ_r is between 2 and 10. Some ionic crystalline materials such as titanium oxide have values of relative permittivity greater than 100. Certain liquids also have high values of ϵ_r because of molecular polarization.

Any conduction in a dielectric material results in a power loss when an electric field is applied. Significant losses can occur however, even without conduction, when the field is changing with time or alternating. Polarized molecules are relatively sluggish bodies; their displacement in response to an applied stress is opposed by inertial and friction forces within the material. A part of the energy supplied electrically to the charged particles to cause the displacement is not recoverable when the field is removed, and appears as random molecular motion or heat.

Electrolytic capacitors consist of an aluminum foil immersed in a conducting electrolyte. The dielectric of the capacitor consists of an oxide film which forms on the aluminum. As the thickness of this film is only about 10^{-7} meter, the capacitance per unit of electrode area is very large. The film acts as an insulator only if the aluminum foil has a positive potential with respect to the electrolyte. With a reversed potential, the film conducts. For alternating-voltage operation, two aluminum electrodes are used, the film on each electrode acting as a dielectric for alternate half cycles. The power loss in the capacitor is relatively large because the stored charge must traverse the conducting electrolyte each half cycle. A major application of a-c electrolytic capacitors is in starting single-phase induction motors.

1.4.1 Piezoelectric Effect

If an electric field is applied to an insulating material, the electrons, ions, or polar molecules are displaced relative to their normal positions. As a result, the dimensions of the material are slightly altered. This effect is known as electrostriction. Although it provides a possible means of converting electric energy to mechanical energy, it does not provide for a corresponding mechanical-to-electrical conversion process.

There are, however, some types of ionic crystals—such as quartz and Rochelle salt—which exhibit a bilateral electromechanical energy conversion, known as the piezoelectric effect, as was mentioned in Section 1.2. To produce this effect, the crystal must have no center of symmetry; positive ions must not be located at the center point of a line between adjacent negative ions.

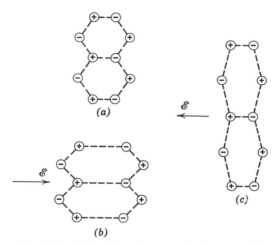

Fig. 1.16   Basic action of a piezoelectric material.

Consider, for example, a crystal having the ion arrangement shown in Fig. 1.16a. When an electric field of intensity $\vec{\mathscr{E}}$ is applied to this crystal, the positive ions are forced in the direction of $\vec{\mathscr{E}}$, while the negative ions are forced in the opposite direction. In Fig. 1.16b, the result of these forces is to reduce the height of the crystal and increase its width. When the electric field intensity is reversed in direction, as in Fig. 1.16c, the height is increased and the width reduced. These distortions of the crystal may be used to produce mechanical motion and force.

If the crystal is compressed mechanically, it becomes electrically polarized in one direction. If it is stretched, the electrical polarization is reversed. Thus the crystal is capable of mechanical-to-electrical energy conversion.

Several types of crystal distortion are possible, depending on the direction of the applied field relative to the crystal axes. Some of these are shown in highly exaggerated form in Fig. 1.17.

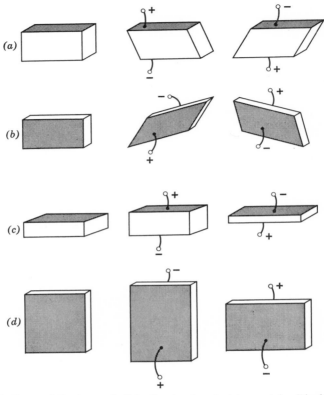

Fig. 1.17 Some of the types of distortion in piezoelectric crystals. (Shaded surfaces represent electrodes.)

The applications of piezoelectric crystals are limited by the extremely small mechanical displacements which they provide. For example, in Rochelle salt the dimensional change is about 5×10^{-10} meter/meter length of crystal per volt/meter of applied stress. The major applications for mechanical-to-electrical conversion are in microphones, headphones phonograph pickups, and accelerometers. Piezoelectric crystals are also used in the generation of ultrasonic mechanical vibrations, in electrical filters, and in oscillators where the electrical-to-mechanical energy conversion is exploited.

1.5 ENERGY CONVERSION USING MAGNETOSTATIC FORCES

Magnetostatic forces are produced between electric charges in motion. These electric charges may be moving freely in space, or they may be flowing in conductors. They may also be electrons of magnetic materials spinning about their nuclei or about their own axes. In evaluating these magnetic forces, it would be convenient to have a simple starting point, such as that provided by Coulomb's law (eq. 1.1) for electrostatic forces. But the force between two moving charges due to their motion is dependent not only on their positions but also on the magnitudes and directions of their velocities. Although an expression for this force can be developed (eq. 1.59), it is not particularly useful as an aid in visualizing the forces produced in current-carrying systems. For magnetic systems, the introduction of the field approach leads to an easier visualization of the forces and also provides a means by which they may be readily calculated.

1.5.1 Magnetic Field Approach

Any region in which a charge experiences a force by virtue of its motion is considered to have a magnetic field. This field is characterized at each point by a magnetic flux density vector $\vec{B}$, which may be defined as follows. If, as in Fig. 1.18a, a positive charge of Q coulombs has a velocity of $\vec{v}$ meters/second, directed at an angle α to the magnetic flux density

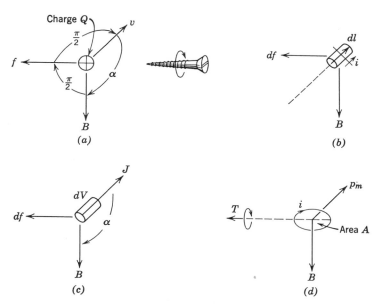

Fig. 1.18   Definition of magnetic flux density.

vector $\vec{B}$, the magnetostatic force $\vec{f}$ is*

$$\vec{f} = Q(\vec{v} \times \vec{B}) \qquad \text{newtons} \qquad (1.49)$$

If the moving charge is in a conductor, it is generally described by either the electric current i or by the electric current density $\vec{J}$. If the conductor material contains n free charges per unit volume, each one of value Q_e, and all moving with common velocity v perpendicular to the conductor cross section of area A, the current i in the conductor is

$$i = nQ_e Av \qquad \text{amperes} \qquad (1.50)$$

For the current element of length $d\vec{l}$ in Fig. 1.18b, the force $d\vec{f}$ on its charge $nQ_e A\,dl$ is

$$d\vec{f} = i(d\vec{l} \times \vec{B}) \qquad \text{newtons} \qquad (1.51)$$

In this expression the element length $d\vec{l}$ is represented by a vector directed along the conductor axis in the direction of positive current i. This expression is useful when the conductor area A can be considered as negligibly small. When the area is large, it is preferable to consider the force $d\vec{f}$ on the incremental conductor volume dV in Fig. 1.18c in which the current density $\vec{J}$ is specified. From eqs. 1.49 and 1.50 we have

$$d\vec{f} = dV(\vec{J} \times \vec{B}) \qquad \text{newtons} \qquad (1.52)$$

One further defining expression for flux density is of particular use for small coils and spinning electrons in materials. Figure 1.18d shows a small closed loop enclosing an area A and carrying a current i. The torque T on this loop can be shown to be equal to the product of the current i, the area A, the flux density B in the region of the loop, and the sine of the angle between the normal to the area A and the flux density. It is convenient to describe the area, current, and orientation of the loop by its magnetic moment $\vec{p}_m$ a vector having a magnitude

$$p_m = iA \qquad \text{ampere-meter}^2 \qquad (1.53)$$

a direction normal to the area, and a sense following the right-hand screw convention, as shown in Fig. 1.18d. The torque on the loop may then be expressed as

$$\vec{T} = \vec{p}_m \times \vec{B} \qquad \text{newton-meters} \qquad (1.54)$$

The rotational direction of the torque $\vec{T}$ in Fig. 1.18d is the same as would be followed by the turning of a right-hand screw proceeding along the direction of the torque vector $\vec{T}$.

---

* The vector or cross product ($\vec{v} \times \vec{B}$) is a vector quantity equal in magnitude to the product of the magnitudes of the two vectors and the sine of the angle α between them. It is directed perpendicularly to both $\vec{v}$ and $\vec{B}$, and its direction is the same as would be followed by a right-hand screw rotating from the first vector $\vec{v}$ to the second vector $\vec{B}$.

The magnetic flux density $\vec{B}$ is related to another vector, the magnetic field intensity $\vec{H}$, by the relation

$$\vec{B} = \mu_0 \vec{H} \qquad \text{newtons/ampere-meter} \qquad (1.55)$$

in vacuum. For engineering purposes, the relation is also valid for essentially all materials except the ferromagnetic materials to be discussed in Section 1.6. The dimensional magnetic constant μ_0, often called the permeability of free space, is

$$\mu_0 = 4\pi \times 10^{-7} \qquad \text{webers/ampere-meter} \qquad (1.56)$$

The magnetic field intensity $\vec{H}$ is considered to be produced by the moving charges or currents of the system. The incremental current

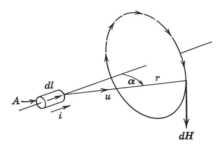

Fig. 1.19   Magnetic field intensity of a current element.

element of length $d\vec{l}$ and cross-sectional area A shown in Fig. 1.19 produces in the region around it an incremental magnetic field intensity $d\vec{H}$ given by

$$d\vec{H} = \frac{i}{4\pi r^2} (d\vec{l} \times \vec{u}) \qquad \text{amperes/meter} \qquad (1.57)$$

where $\vec{u}$ is a vector of magnitude equal to one directed from the element toward the point of interest, and r is the distance from the element to the point at which $d\vec{H}$ is specified. The field intensity $d\vec{H}$ may also be written in terms of the incremental volume dV of the element, its current density $\vec{J}$, and the unit vector $\vec{u}$ as

$$d\vec{H} = \frac{dV}{4\pi r^2} (\vec{J} \times \vec{u}) \qquad \text{amperes/meter} \qquad (1.58)$$

Combining eqs. 1.51, 1.55, and 1.57 allows the development of an expression for the force of interaction between two current elements of incremental lengths $d\vec{l}_1$ and $d\vec{l}_2$, and currents i_1 and i_2, respectively. The resulting expression for the incremental force on element $d\vec{l}_1$ is

$$d\vec{f}_1 = \frac{\mu_0}{4\pi r^2} i_1 i_2 [d\vec{l}_1 \times (d\vec{l}_2 \times \vec{u})] \qquad \text{newtons} \qquad (1.59)$$

where $\vec{u}$ is the unit vector directed from element 2 toward element 1. This expression may be used to determine the forces on any system of conductors by summation of the incremental force vectors caused by all pairs of current elements. As has been already mentioned, the expression of eq. 1.59 is not very useful as a basis for understanding the nature of the forces.

The magnetic field intensity also has the useful property that its line integral around a closed path is equal to the current enclosed by that path, that is

$$\oint \vec{H} \cdot d\vec{s} = i_{\text{enclosed}} \qquad (1.60)$$
$$\text{amperes}$$

This circuital law is very useful as a means of obtaining the magnetic field intensity in situations that have symmetry.

Let us now apply these field concepts in determining the force between the two long parallel conductors shown in Fig. 1.20. Consider an element $d\vec{l}$ of conductor 2. From eq. 1.57 it can be seen that none of the other length elements of conductor 2 can produce a magnetic field intensity in the element $d\vec{l}$, because the angle between $d\vec{l}$ and the unit vector $\vec{u}$ to these elements is either 0 or π. Thus the magnetic field in which the element $d\vec{l}$ is situated is produced only by the current in conductor 1. The intensity $\vec{H}_1$ of this magnetic field could be found by summation of eq. 1.57 over the length of conductor 1. But because of the circular symmetry of the field which is produced by conductor 1 acting alone, the circuital law can be used to evaluate the field much more simply. From eq. 1.60, we have

$$\oint \vec{H}_1 \cdot d\vec{s} = H_1 2\pi x = i_1$$

and

$$H_1 = \frac{i_1}{2\pi x} \qquad \text{ampere/meter} \qquad (1.61)$$

By using eqs. 1.51 and 1.55, the force $d\vec{f}$ on the element $d\vec{l}$ is

$$d\vec{f} = i_2(d\vec{l} \times \vec{B}_1)$$
$$= \mu_0 i_2(d\vec{l} \times \vec{H}_1)$$

The magnitude of the force is

$$df = \frac{\mu_0 i_1 i_2}{2\pi x} dl \qquad \text{newtons} \qquad (1.62)$$

Provided the conductors are long and straight for a distance much greater than x from the point of interest, the symmetry condition obtains, and the force per unit length on each conductor is constant in magnitude and direction.

Let us investigate the energy conversion properties of the system of Fig. 1.20 by pulling the conductors apart against the force of attraction

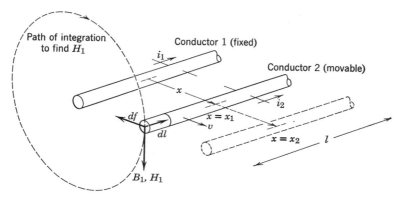

Fig. 1.20   Force between parallel conductors.

from $x = x_1$ to $x = x_2$. From eqs. 1.3 and 1.62, the mechanical energy input for a length l of conductor is

$$
\begin{aligned}
W_{\substack{\text{mech.}\\ \text{input}}} &= \int_{x_1}^{x_2} \frac{\mu_0 i_1 i_2 l}{2\pi x}\, dx \\
&= \frac{\mu_0 i_1 i_2 l}{2\pi} \ln \frac{x_2}{x_1} \qquad \text{joules}
\end{aligned}
\tag{1.63}
$$

This mechanical-input energy can also be expressed in terms of the amount of magnetic flux ϕ crossed by conductor 2 during its displacement. The magnetic flux through an area A is defined as

$$
\phi = \int_{\text{Area}} \vec{B} \cdot d\vec{A} \qquad \text{webers or joules/ampere}
\tag{1.64}
$$

The flux crossed by conductor 2 in the displacement from x_1 to x_2 is

$$
\begin{aligned}
\phi &= \int_{x_1}^{x_2} B_1 l\, dx \\
&= \frac{\mu_0 i l}{2\pi} \ln \frac{x_2}{x_1} \qquad \text{joules/ampere}
\end{aligned}
\tag{1.65}
$$

From this equation we can see that when a conductor carrying a current i sweeps across a magnetic field, the amount of energy converted is equal to the product of the current i and the magnetic flux ϕ crossed by the conductor.

$$W = i\phi_{\substack{\text{crossed by} \\ \text{conductor}}} \quad \text{joules} \tag{1.66}$$

If mechanical energy is supplied to conductor 2 in Fig. 1.20, it might be expected to appear as electric energy supplied to the source of the current i_2. As the conductor moves from x_1 to x_2 at velocity $\vec{v}$, any electric charge Q within the conductor will experience a force $\vec{f}$ of

$$\vec{f} = Q(\vec{v} \times \vec{B_1}) \quad \text{newtons} \tag{1.67}$$

In Fig. 1.20, this force is directed in such a way as to assist the current i_2. The electromotive force e_2 in a length l of conductor 2 is the energy acquired by each coulomb of charge in passing along the length.

$$e_2 = \frac{f}{Q} l$$

$$= vB_1 l \quad \text{joules/coulomb or volts} \tag{1.68}$$

Since $v = dx/dt$, it can be seen, by comparison of eqs. 1.65 and 1.68, that the electromotive force may also be expressed as

$$e_2 = \frac{d}{dt} (\phi \text{ crossed by conductor 2}) \quad \text{volts} \tag{1.69}$$

The power converted to electrical form in conductor 2 is

$$p_2 = i_2 e_2 \quad \text{watts} \tag{1.70}$$

and the electric energy produced in conductor 2 is

$$W_{\text{elec.}} = \int p_2 \, dt$$

$$= \int i_2 \frac{d\phi}{dt} \, dt = \int i_2 \, d\phi$$

$$= i_2 (\phi \text{ crossed by conductor 2}) \quad \text{joules} \tag{1.71}$$

Thus, all the mechanical input energy is converted to electric output energy in the moving conductor. If the conductor moves in the opposite direction, energy is converted from electrical to mechanical form.

1.5.2 Approach through the Conservation of Energy

Consider the simple system of conductors shown in Fig. 1.21. For any displacement of one plate relative to that other, the law of conservation of energy requires that

$$\underset{\text{input}}{\text{Energy}} = \underset{\text{lost}}{\text{Energy}} + \underset{\text{energy stored}}{\text{Increase in}} + \underset{\text{output}}{\text{Energy}} \qquad (1.72)$$

If we allow an incremental displacement dx of the movable plate in Fig. 1.21, the increments of electric input energy, loss energy, storage energy, and mechanical output energy are related by

$$\underset{\text{input}}{dW_{\text{elect.}}} = dW_{\text{loss}} + dW_{\text{stored}} + \underset{\text{output}}{dW_{\text{mech.}}} \qquad (1.73)$$

Following the same pattern as we used in Section 1.3.2 for electrostatic forces, let us attempt to find the mechanical output by evaluating all

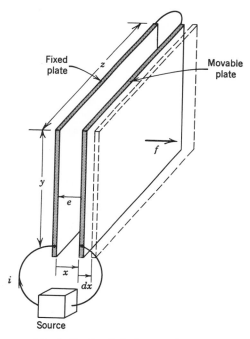

Fig. 1.21   Parallel-plate conductors.

terms in eq. 1.73, except dW mechanical output, and then by determining the force in the direction of displacement from

$$f_x = \frac{\underset{\text{output}}{dW_{\text{mech.}}}}{dx} \qquad \text{newtons} \qquad (1.74)$$

There will be resistance to the flow of the current i in the plates. Suppose we consider an equivalent system with resistanceless plates, the actual plate resistance being inserted as an element connected in series with the source. A potential difference e between the plates can then arise only from a rate of change of the magnetic flux ϕ enclosed by the plates.

$$e = \frac{d\phi_{\text{encl.}}}{dt} \qquad \text{volts} \qquad (1.75)$$

Suppose the displacement dx takes place in time dt; then the electric input energy to the resistanceless plates during this time interval is

$$\begin{aligned} dW_{\substack{\text{elec.} \\ \text{input}}} &= ie\,dt \\ &= i\,d\phi_{\text{encl.}} \qquad \text{joules} \end{aligned} \qquad (1.76)$$

Having removed the electric resistance from the system whose energy balance is stated in eq. 1.73, we need only move any mechanical friction to the external mechanical system to make the losses of the equivalent system equal to zero. Thus, we have

$$dW_{\text{loss}} = 0 \qquad (1.77)$$

The energy stored within the magnetic field of the plates may be found by considering that if the current is increased from zero to its value i while the plates are stationary, all the input to the lossless system will be in storage. Using eq. 1.76, we find

$$W_{\text{stored}} = \int_0^\phi i\,d\phi_{\text{encl.}} \qquad \text{joules} \qquad (1.78)$$

In this system, the enclosed magnetic flux is linearly proportional to the current, the constant of proportionality being the inductance L of the current loop.

$$\phi_{\text{encl.}} = Li \qquad \text{webers} \qquad (1.79)$$

The inductance is a function of the plate spacing x. Since we are presently considering a stationary system in order to find the stored energy expression, the inductance is a constant in the integration of eq. 1.78 and gives

$$\begin{aligned} W_{\text{stored}} &= \int_0^i i\,d(Li) \\ &= \tfrac{1}{2}Li^2 \\ &= \tfrac{1}{2}i\phi_{\text{encl.}} \qquad \text{joules} \end{aligned} \qquad (1.80)$$

The increase in energy stored during a displacement dx is found by differentiating eq. 1.80 with respect to x. By noting that both the current i and the enclosed flux ϕ may vary during this displacement, the differentiation gives

$$dW_{\text{stored}} = \tfrac{1}{2}i\,d\phi_{\text{encl.}} + \tfrac{1}{2}\phi_{\text{encl.}}\,di \qquad \text{joules} \qquad (1.81)$$

Substituting from eqs. 1.76, 1.77, and 1.81 into eq. 1.73 gives

$$dW_{\substack{\text{mech.} \\ \text{output}}} = i\,d\phi_{\text{encl.}} - \tfrac{1}{2}i\,d\phi_{\text{encl.}} - \tfrac{1}{2}\phi_{\text{encl.}}\,di \qquad (1.82)$$

From eq. 1.74, the force on the plate in the positive x direction is then given by

$$f_x = \frac{1}{2}\,i\,\frac{d\phi_{\text{encl.}}}{dx} - \frac{1}{2}\,\phi_{\text{encl.}}\,\frac{di}{dx} \qquad \text{newtons} \qquad (1.83)$$

If eq. 1.79 is substituted into eq. 1.83 to eliminate the flux term, the force may be expressed simply in terms of the current and the inductance.

$$
\begin{aligned}
f_x &= \frac{1}{2}\,i\left(L\frac{di}{dx} + i\,\frac{dL}{dX}\right) - \frac{1}{2}\,Li\,\frac{di}{dx} \\
&= \frac{1}{2}\,i^2\,\frac{dL}{dx} \qquad \text{newtons} \qquad (1.84)
\end{aligned}
$$

This expression states that if the inductance of a current-carrying loop is increased by displacing part of the loop, there is a force component acting on that part of the loop in the direction of the displacement. The analogy between this expression and the corresponding expression of eq. 1.29 for the electrostatic system should be noted.

The force may also be expressed in terms of the magnetic reluctance $\mathcal{R}$, which is defined as the magnetomotive force $\mathcal{F}$ per unit of magnetic flux ϕ produced.

$$\mathcal{F} = \mathcal{R}\phi \qquad \text{amperes} \qquad (1.85)$$

For the single-loop system of Fig. 1.21, the magnetomotive force is equal to the current i, and the flux is that enclosed by this current. Thus substituting

$$i = \mathcal{R}\phi \qquad (1.86)$$

into eq. 1.83 gives

$$
\begin{aligned}
f_x &= \frac{1}{2}\,\mathcal{R}\phi\,\frac{d\phi}{dx} - \frac{1}{2}\,\phi\left(\mathcal{R}\frac{d\phi}{dx} + \phi\,\frac{d\mathcal{R}}{dx}\right) \\
&= -\frac{1}{2}\,\phi^2\,\frac{d\mathcal{R}}{dx} \qquad \text{newtons} \qquad (1.87)
\end{aligned}
$$

Thus the force is always in such a direction as to reduce the reluctance of the magnetic system.

The expressions that have been developed for force apply generally to all magnetic systems that have a single current i and in which there is a linear relationship between magnetic flux and current at any position of the system.

If the plates in Fig. 1.21 are very large in comparison to the spacing x, it can be assumed that the magnetic field is reasonably uniform between the plates and has a negligible value outside the enclosed volume. From the circuital law of eq. 1.60, the magnetic field intensity H between the plates is obtained as

$$H = \frac{i}{y} \qquad \text{amperes/meter} \qquad (1.88)$$

By using eqs. 1.55 and 1.64, the magnetic flux enclosed by the plates is approximated by

$$\phi_{\text{encl.}} = Bzx$$
$$= \mu_0 \frac{izx}{y} \qquad \text{webers} \qquad (1.89)$$

The loop inductance is, from eq. 1.79,

$$L = \frac{\mu_0 zx}{y} \qquad \text{henrys} \qquad (1.90)$$

and the force on the plate is, from eq. 1.84,

$$f_x = \frac{1}{2} i^2 \frac{dL}{dx}$$
$$= \frac{i^2}{2} \frac{\mu_0 z}{y} \qquad \text{newtons} \qquad (1.91)$$

The force in the system of Fig. 1.21 can also be determined through the purely magnetic field approach discussed in Section 1.5.1. If the same assumptions are used, the same force expression as eq. 1.91 should result.

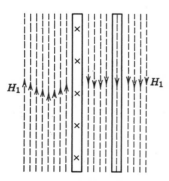

In this approach, the left-hand plate of Fig. 1.21 alone is considered to produce a magnetic field into which the right-hand plate is inserted, as shown in Fig. 1.22. For regions close to the left-hand plate, its magnetic field may be assumed to be constant and upward on one side, and to have an equal constant value and be directed downward on the other side. Applying the circuital law of eq. 1.60, the magnetic field intensity H_1 produced by the left-hand plate throughout the region occupied by the other plate is

Fig 1.22 Right-hand plate of Fig. 1.21 immersed in the assumed magnetic field of the left-hand plate.

$$H_1 = \frac{i}{2y} \qquad \text{amperes/meter} \qquad (1.92)$$

Using eqs. 1.55 and 1.92 in eq. 1.51, the force on the right-hand plate is given by

$$f = izB_1$$
$$= iz\mu_0 H_1$$
$$= \frac{i^2}{2}\frac{\mu_0 z}{y} \qquad \text{newtons} \qquad (1.93)$$

1.5.3 Linear Systems with Two or More Coils

For a single current-carrying coil in free space, the forces always act to distort the coil tó increase its inductance. With two or more current-carrying coils, forces of interaction are set up between the coils, and

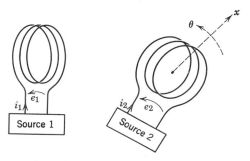

Fig. 1.23   System of two rigid coils.

energy conversion can result from the motion of one coil relative to another. Consider the system of two rigid coils shown in Fig. 1.23. Suppose we wish to find the component of force on coil 2 in some arbitrary direction x. Following the approach through conservation of energy, allow an incremental displacement dx of coil 2 to occur in a time dt, and evaluate the terms of the energy balance expression of eq. 1.73. If the electric resistances of the coils are associated with the sources, leaving resistanceless coils, the total electric energy input to the system of coils is

$$dW_{\substack{\text{elect.}\\ \text{input}}} = i_1 e_1\,dt + i_2 e_2\,dt$$
$$= i_1\,d\lambda_1 + i_2\,d\lambda_2 \qquad \text{joules} \qquad (1.94)$$

The flux linkage λ_1 of coil 1 is the total magnetic flux enclosed by the current i_1. While the symbol $\phi_{\text{encl.}}$ could continue to be used for flux linkage, the special symbol λ is introduced from this point on to signify only the total flux encircled by a coil, thus obviating the need to define the specific magnetic flux enclosed in each instance.

The flux linkages of the coils may be expressed in terms of their self-inductances L_{11} and L_{22} and their mutual inductance L_{12}.

$$\lambda_1 = L_{11}i_1 + L_{12}i_2 \quad \text{webers} \tag{1.95}$$

$$\lambda_2 = L_{12}i_1 + L_{22}i_2 \quad \text{webers} \tag{1.96}$$

Since the self-inductances of the rigid coils are constant, substitution from eqs. 1.95 and 1.96 into eq. 1.94 gives

$$dW_{\substack{\text{elec.} \\ \text{input}}} = i_1 L_{11}\, di_1 + i_1 L_{12}\, di_2 + i_1 i_2\, dL_{12}$$
$$+ i_2 L_{12}\, di_1 + i_2 i_1\, dL_{12} + i_2 L_{22}\, di_2 \tag{1.97}$$

The energy stored in a two-coil system may be stated in terms of the self- and mutual inductances as

$$W_{\text{stored}} = \tfrac{1}{2}L_{11}i_1{}^2 + \tfrac{1}{2}L_{22}i_2{}^2 + L_{12}i_1 i_2 \tag{1.98}$$

The increase in stored energy resulting from an incremental displacement, which may change the currents and the mutual inductance, is

$$dW_{\text{stored}} = L_{11}i_1\, di_1 + L_{22}i_2\, di_2 + L_{12}i_1\, di_2 + i_1 i_2\, dL_{12} + i_2 L_{12}\, di_1 \tag{1.99}$$

Thus, with no internal losses in the system, we have

$$dW_{\substack{\text{mech.} \\ \text{output}}} = dW_{\substack{\text{elec.} \\ \text{input}}} - dW_{\text{stored}}$$

$$= i_1 i_2\, dL_{12} \tag{1.100}$$

The component of force on coil 2 in the positive x direction is then given by

$$f_x = \frac{dW_{\substack{\text{mech.} \\ \text{output}}}}{dx}$$

$$= i_1 i_2 \frac{dL_{12}}{dx} \quad \text{newtons} \tag{1.101}$$

Hence, the force of interaction between two current-carrying coils is always such as to increase their mutual inductance, provided that the currents in the assigned direction of measurement in both coils are both positive or both negative. Generally, the force is directed in a way that tends to increase the magnitude of the flux linkage of each of the coils.

Instead of a lateral motion of coil 2 in Fig. 1.23, a rotational motion through an incremental angle $d\theta$ about some arbitrary axis may be made. The component of torque on the coil in the direction of positive θ is then, from eq. 1.100,

$$T_\theta = \frac{dW_{\substack{\text{mech.}\\ \text{output}}}}{d\theta}$$

$$= i_1 i_2 \frac{dL_{12}}{d\theta} \qquad \text{newton-meters} \qquad (1.102)$$

If there are more than two rigid coils, the force on any coil designated as number 1 may be expressed as

$$f_x = i_1 i_2 \frac{dL_{12}}{dx} + i_1 i_3 \frac{dL_{13}}{dx} + i_1 i_4 \frac{dL_{14}}{dx} + \cdots \qquad \text{newtons} \quad (1.103)$$

The forces and torques that depend on change of mutual inductance are inherently more useful than those that depend on a change in self-inductance as a result of the ability to control the direction of the force or torque. Examination of eq. 1.84 shows that the force in a single coil always acts to increase its self-inductance, regardless of the direction of its current. The direction of the force in eq. 1.101 or the torque in eq. 1.102 may, however, be reversed by reversing the sign of one of the currents.

Application of the force and torque expressions of eqs. 1.84, 1.101, and 1.102 requires that the self- and mutual inductances of the system be evaulated as functions of coil position. In a physical system, these inductances can be measured. In the prediction of the performance of a proposed system, they may be calculated using magnetic field concepts to evaluate individual flux linkages per unit of coil current.

1.6 PROPERTIES OF MAGNETIC MATERIALS

Very few practical electromechanical devices are built using only current-carrying conductors because of the relatively small forces or torques that can be obtained per unit of machine volume. While there is no limit on the intensity of the magnetic field that can exist in air or space, the value of the field intensity is limited practically by the current density permissible in the conductors producing the field. With copper or aluminum conductors at normal operating temperatures, current densities must generally be limited to about 10^6–10^7 amperes/meter^2.

With the introduction of superconducting materials, like niobium tin, which have zero resistance at low temperatures in the region of the boiling point of helium (4.2°K), much higher current densities are possible, and practical machines operating at these temperatures may be developed. Supercooled coils can produce flux densities of 10 webers/meter^2 or higher. In comparison, it is only with difficulty that a flux density greater than 0.1 weber/meter^2 can be produced using normal coils at room temperature.

At present, the easiest means of producing flux densities up to about 1.5–2.0 weber/meter² is by the use of ferromagnetic materials. The structure of most electromechanical devices is therefore mainly composed of ferromagnetic material and conductors, with the magnetic material often predominating in volume. An understanding of the properties and limitations of magnetic materials is therefore necessary for the analysis or design of these devices.

1.6.1 Magnetic Moments of Atoms

Magnetic effects in materials arise from the orbital motions of the electrons about the nuclei and the spin motion of each electron, as sug-

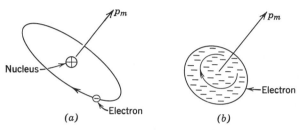

Fig. 1.24 (*a*) Orbital and (*b*) spin magnetic moments of electron.

gested by Fig. 1.24. Each electron produces a magnetic moment that is an integral multiple of the Bohr magneton, whose value is

$$p_{\text{Bohr}} = 9.27 \times 10^{-24} \quad \text{ampere-meter}^2 \quad (1.104)$$

Because of the symmetry of the electron arrangement, the net magnetic moment of most atoms is zero. It is only in atoms having incomplete inner shells of electrons that the atom has a significant magnetic moment. This net moment arises principally from the spins of electrons that are not paired with electrons of opposite spin direction.

Examination of a periodic table of the elements shows that an incomplete inner shell, and therefore a net magnetic moment, may be present in any element within the ranges of atomic numbers 21 to 28, 39 to 45, 57 to 78 and 89 and above. The most important range is the first, which includes vanadium, chromium, manganese, iron, cobalt, and nickel.

When visualizing the magnetic effects within materials, each atom may be regarded as equivalent to a small constant-current loop. The orientation of this loop may be altered by changing only the directions of the spin axes of the electrons.

1.6.2   Alignment of Magnetic Moments

In a solid material, the magnetic moments of adjacent atoms may be aligned as shown in Fig. 1.25a, producing a ferromagnetic material. Alternatively, the magnetic moments may be opposed, as shown in Fig. 1.25b, producing an antiferromagnetic material. In a ferromagnetic material, the magnetic flux is continuous along the alignment direction and is potentially useful. In an antiferromagnetic material, however, the flux paths merely link adjacent magnetic moments and cannot be made to link external current-carrying coils.

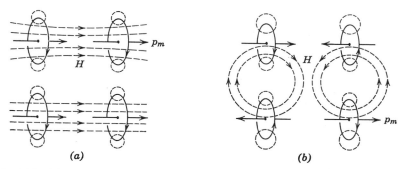

Fig. 1.25   (a) Ferromagnetic and (b) antiferromagnetic alignment of atoms together with the magnetic fields that each would produce.

While an application of the torque expression of eq. 1.102 might lead us to expect the two types of alignment shown in Fig. 1.25, the magnetic alignment torques between adjacent magnetic moments are found to be much smaller than the torques that actually occur. The type of alignment is determined by the exchange forces which operate only over short distances and are electrostatic rather than magnetic in nature.

It is only in a small group of the pure elements—iron, cobalt, and nickel—that the alignment torques cause ferromagnetism at normal temperatures. At somewhat below normal temperatures, some other elements, like gadolinium and dysprosium, are also ferromagnetic. Fortunately, this does not restrict ferromagnetic behavior to only these few materials. The exchange forces are critically dependent on the spacing between those electrons producing the magnetic moment in adjacent atoms. Antiferromagnetism occurs when this spacing is too small. The spacing between the atoms of an antiferromagnetic material may be increased by alloying it with a nonmagnetic material, for example, manganese with copper or tin. With the increased spacing, ferromagnetic alignment can occur. Alternatively, two groups of atoms or molecular groups having different magnetic moments may be arranged in anti-alignment, but, because of the difference in the moments, the result can be magnetic. This structure is called ferrimagnetic, and is characteristic of the group of magnetic materials known as ferrites.

Suppose a material has the magnetic moments of its atoms aligned as illustrated in Fig. 1.25a. To determine the net magnetic effect of such an alignment, let us consider each atom as equivalent to a current i circulating around the square perimeter of the volume d^3 occupied by the

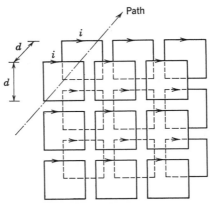

Fig. 1.26   Modeling the magnetic moments of atoms as circulating currents.

atom, as shown in Fig. 1.26. The current i is then related to the magnetic moment of the atom p_{ma} by

$$p_{ma} = id^2 \qquad \text{ampere-meter}^2 \qquad (1.105)$$

If we consider a path along the direction of alignment, we see that the currents i form an equivalent solenoid around this path and produce a magnetic field intensity H_m of

$$H_m = \frac{i}{d}$$

$$= \frac{p_{ma}}{d^3} \qquad \text{amperes/meter} \qquad (1.106)$$

Since d^3 is the volume occupied by one atom, the number n of atoms per meter^3 is $1/d^3$. The internally produced magnetic field intensity H_m is normally designated by the symbol $\mathscr{M}$, and is equal to the net aligned magnetic moment per unit volume.

$$\mathscr{M} = H_m$$

$$= np_{ma} \qquad \text{ampere-meter}^2/\text{meter or amperes/meter} \qquad (1.107)$$

To appreciate the magnitude of the field produced by this internal alignment of atomic moments, consider iron; on the average, it has a magnetic moment of 2.21 Bohr magnetons (eq. 1.104) per atom, and an atomic density of about 0.85×10^{29} atoms/meter^3. Thus if all the atoms have their magnetic moments aligned,

$$\mathcal{M} = np_{ma}$$
$$= 0.85 \times 10^{29} \times 2.21 \times 9.27 \times 10^{-24}$$
$$= 1.74 \times 10^6 \quad \text{amperes/meter} \tag{1.108}$$

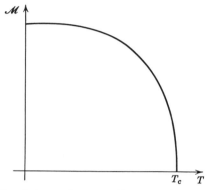

Fig. 1.27   The relation between the magnetic moment per unit volume $\mathcal{M}$ and the absolute temperature T (°K).

Because the magnetic moment $\mathcal{M}$ per unit volume is equivalent to a field intensity, the magnetic flux density which the alignment can produce in the material is

$$B = \mu_0 \mathcal{M}$$
$$= 4\pi \times 10^{-7} \times 1.74 \times 10^6$$
$$= 2.18 \quad \text{webers/meter}^2 \tag{1.109}$$

For cobalt and nickel, the numbers of Bohr magnetons per atom are 1.72 and 0.6, respectively. Their values of magnetic moment $\mathcal{M}$ per unit volume are correspondingly lower than that for iron.

The exchange forces that tend to hold the atomic magnetic moments in alignment are always in competition with the thermal forces in the material, which tend to make the electron axes—and therefore the magnetic moments—point in random directions. As a result the net magnetic moment per unit volume of a magnetic material decreases as the temperature of the material is increased, as shown in Fig. 1.27. At a temperature T_c, known as the Curie temperature, the randomization of atomic moments is complete, and the net magnetic moment per unit volume is zero. Typical values of Curie temperature are 770°C for iron, 1115°C for cobalt, and 348°C for nickel.

1.6.3 Magnetic Properties of Crystals

The direction of alignment of magnetic moments in a material is highly dependent on the structure of its crystals. Iron, which has a body-centered cubic lattice, tends to have its magnetic moments aligned parallel to one of the cube edges shown in Fig. 1.28. There are thus six normal or easy directions of alignment, two in each of three mutually perpendicular directions. For nickel, the easy alignment direction is along one of the

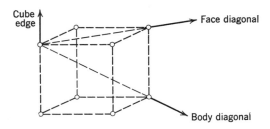

Fig. 1.28   Axes of a cubic crystal, such as iron.

four body diagonals. For cobalt, which has a hexagonal crystal, there are only two opposing easy directions.

The magnetic moments of crystals can be aligned in a direction other than the easy directions by applying to the crystal a sufficient magnetic field intensity H. The energy stored in the crystal in the process of rotating the magnetic moments away from their easy alignment directions is called magnetic anisotropy energy. Figure 1.29 shows the relationship between a magnetic field intensity H applied to an iron crystal in three different directions and the component of magnetic moment per unit volume $\mathcal{M}_H$ in the same direction. Consider a face diagonal which is 45° away from the easy direction of magnetization. With no external applied field, the magnetic moment component $\mathcal{M}_H$ along this face diagonal is cos 45° or $1/\sqrt{2}$ of the total magnetic moment. As a magnetic field of intensity H is applied along the face diagonal, the magnetic moments in the material are rotated away from the easy direction along the cube edge, and the component $\mathcal{M}_H$ of magnetic moment collinear with H increases. Note that a considerable value of magnetic field intensity is required to rotate the magnetic moments away from their easy direction. When the magnetic field intensity is decreased, the magnetic moments return to the nearest easy direction along a cube face. Figure 1.28 also shows the component $\mathcal{M}_H$ of magnetic moment collinear with the magnetic field intensity H when the field is applied along a body diagonal. At $H = 0$, the value of the component is $1/\sqrt{3}$ of the maximum value.

Let us now consider the crystal shown in Fig. 1.30a. All of the magnetic moments of this crystal could be aligned along one of the easy directions, as shown. This, however, would result in a magnetic field of density B

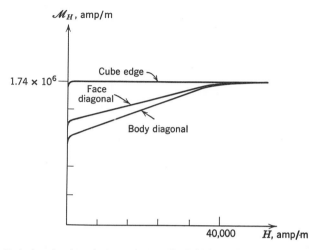

Fig. 1.29   Relation for iron between magnetic field intensity H and component $\mathcal{M}_H$ of magnetic moment per unit volume colinear with H, for field applied along (a) cube edge, (b) face diagonal, and (c) body diagonal of crystal.

being set up in the space around the crystal. The magnetostatic energy stored in this field external to the crystal is given by the expression

$$W = \int_{\substack{\text{over} \\ \text{volume V}}} \frac{B^2}{2\mu_0} \, dV \qquad \text{joules} \qquad (1.110)$$

Another possible alignment of magnetic moments within the crystal is shown in Fig. 1.30b. In this arrangement, there are two regions or domains with oppositely directed vectors of magnetic moment per unit volume $\mathcal{M}$ along easy magnetization directions of the crystal. Note that the external magnetic field is now confined to small regions around the ends of the crystal, resulting in a much lower value of the magnetostatic energy of eq. 1.110. On the other hand, there are atoms in the region of the wall between the two domains of opposite magnetization direction that have their magnetic moments turned away from the easy directions, and this

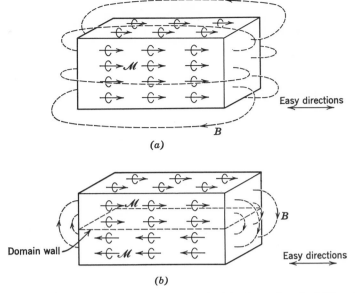

Fig. 1.30 The external magnetic field of a crystal with (a) no domain wall and (b) a central domain wall.

involves the storage of some magnetic anisotropy energy. Whether the alignment takes the form of Fig. 1.30a or Fig. 1.30b depends on which arrangement has the lower stored energy. In order to assess this, let us briefly examine the properties of a domain wall.

Figure 1.31 shows a section crossing a wall between two domains of oppositely directed magnetization. There are strong exchange forces tending to align the magnetic moment of each atom with that of its

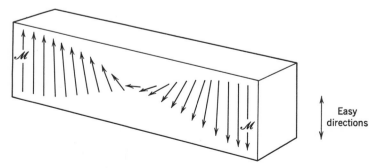

Fig. 1.31 A domain wall between oppositely directed domains.

nearest neighbors. The magnetic moments of the atoms arrange themselves so that there is a regular 180° twist in direction as the domain wall is crossed. All the magnetic moments within the domain wall, however, are aligned in a direction other than one of the easy directions of the crystal. There will therefore be anisotropy energy associated with these moments. The forces associated with anisotropy energy will tend to create a thin wall with the fewest possible atoms strained from the easy crystal directions. The exchange forces tend to widen the wall to minimize the angle between the magnetic alignment directions of adjacent atoms. The thickness of the domain wall makes the total energy associated with

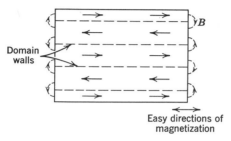

Fig. 1.32 The domain arrangement in a single cobalt crystal.

exchange and anisotropy in the wall a minimum. For iron, this wall thickness is of the order of 5×10^{-8} meter, that is, about 200 atomic diameters.

It has been noted previously that the choice between the two alignment arrangements of Fig. 1.30 depends on which has the lower total of wall energy plus magnetostatic energy. Because the wall energy depends on the cross-sectional area of the crystal, while the magnetostatic energy depends on the crystal volume, it can be seen that the alignment of Fig. 1.30a occurs only with very small crystals. For iron, the dimensions of a crystal of cubic shape must be less than about 10^{-8} meter for this arrangement to occur. If, however, the crystal is in the form of a long sliver, the alignment of Fig. 1.30a occurs up to much larger crystal volumes.

With larger crystals, a lower total of stored energy than that of Fig. 1.30b is obtained by having a larger number of walls and a smaller volume of external magnetic field, as shown in Fig. 1.32. The spacing between walls in crystals (such as cobalt) that have just two opposing directions of easy magnetization may only be about 10^{-5}–10^{-6} meter.

With magnetic crystals, like iron, that have mutually perpendicular directions of easy magnetization, a domain arrangement having a lower energy than that of either Figs. 1.30 or 1.32 is possible. The arrangement

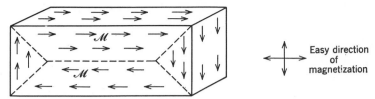

Fig. 1.33   A crystal with closure domains.

in Fig. 1.33 is similar to that of Fig. 1.30b, except that there are two smaller domains at the ends of the crystal that are aligned in directions perpendicular to those of the main domains. The magnetic flux closes on itself through these two closure domains and is entirely confined to the crystal. Although this arrangement has somewhat greater domain wall area than that of Fig. 1.30b, its magnetostatic energy is zero.

We might expect that any crystal having mutually perpendicular axes of easy magnetization, regardless of its size, would have the simple four-domain arrangement of Fig. 1.33, since this arrangement has a smaller wall area than would obtain with a larger number of domains. There is, however, one additional property that generally tends to limit the size of domains. Most magnetic materials are likely to change their dimensions along the direction of the magnetization. An iron crystal usually expands along its magnetization direction, while nickel and cobalt contract. The long horizontally directed domains in Fig. 1.33 are free to expand or contract along most of their length. But the vertically directed closure domains are constrained from motion in the direction of magnetization. If they expand, they will be in compression; if they contract, they will be in tension. These mechanical strains in the closure-domain region involve stored mechanical energy throughout this region. The overall energy stored in the crystal is therefore often lower in a domain arrangement such as the one shown in Fig. 1.34. In this figure, the volume of the strained closure domains at the ends of the crystal is reduced below that of Fig. 1.33 at the expense of a greater total domain wall area.

From the foregoing discussion, a mental picture of a normal ferromagnetic crystal emerges. Most of the magnetic moments of the crystal

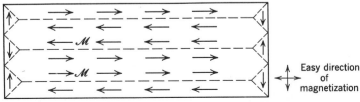

Fig. 1.34   Effect of strain energy on the number of domains in a crystal.

are aligned with their nearest neighbors along one of the easy directions of magnetization, the exceptions being the small number in the region of domain walls. For materials with mutually perpendicular easy directions of magnetization, there are generally closure domains providing closed paths for magnetic flux which are collinear with the magnetic moment vector $\mathcal{M}$ within the crystal. Application of the circuital law of eq. 1.60 around a closed path of flux, as in Figs. 1.33 or 1.34, results in the conclusion that all of the crystal, except a small portion in the region of domain walls, has a large and constant flux density B_s equal to

$$B_s = \mu_0 \mathcal{M} \qquad \text{webers/meter}^2 \qquad (1.111)$$

This is generally called the saturation flux density. Its value is approximately 2.2 webers/meter^2 for iron, 1.8 for cobalt, and 0.64 for nickel.

1.6.4   Domain Wall Motion and Coercive Force in Crystals

The discussion of Section 1.6.3 shows that the normal state of most ferromagnetic crystals is characterized by internally closed flux paths, all parts of which are at the saturation flux density of the material. Most of the uses of such magnetic materials depend on our ability to change their magnetic state by application of external forces. If we consider the relatively high values of saturation flux density in these materials, it is evident that a very high external magnetic field intensity H would have to be applied to produce any significant change in this flux density. Thus control of the magnetic state is affected, not by changing the magnitude of the flux density within the domains of a crystal, but rather by shifting the domain walls so that the orientation of this saturation flux density is changed.

Figure 1.35 shows a single ferromagnetic crystal, which has a window cut in its center. The sides of the window are parallel to the easy directions of magnetization. Domain walls are shown between regions that have different directions of the magnetic moment per unit volume $\mathcal{M}$. In the steady state shown in Fig. 1.35, there are two oppositely directed streams of magnetic flux within the crystal. Each of these streams closes on itself. The net magnetic flux ϕ through a cross section of the crystal in a clockwise direction is

$$\phi = B_s[zx - z(d - x)]$$
$$= B_s z(2x - d) \qquad \text{webers} \qquad (1.112)$$

where B_s is the saturation flux density of the material. Let us now enclose the crystal in a uniformly distributed coil of N turns carrying a current i. This coil produces a clockwise-directed magnetic field intensity H within the crystal. In the region of the main 180° domain wall, the magnetic

field intensity can be assumed to be uniform over the whole wall length
at the value

$$H = \frac{Ni}{2a + 2b + 8x} \qquad \text{amperes/meter} \qquad (1.113)$$

If this magnetic field intensity is sufficient to cause the domain wall in
Fig. 1.35 to move outward, the magnetic flux ϕ of eq. 1.112 will be increased. Let us therefore examine the effect of this externally applied field
on the wall.

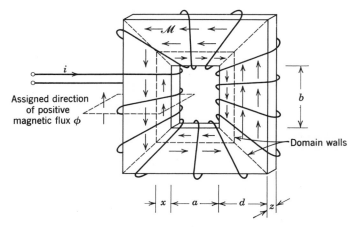

Fig. 1.35   Control of magnetization in a single-crystal core.

Figure 1.36a shows the magnetic moment vectors $\vec{p}_m$ of atoms in the
region of the domain wall along the left-hand side of the crystal. In an
applied magnetic field of intensity $\vec{H}$, the torque $\vec{T}$ acting on a magnetic
moment is given, from eqs. 1.54 and 1.55, by

$$\vec{T} = \vec{p}_m \times \vec{H} \qquad \text{newton-meters} \qquad (1.114)$$

This torque is zero on the magnetic moments on the right of Fig. 1.36a
because these are already aligned with $\vec{H}$; it is also zero on those on the
left, which are directed 180° away from the vector $\vec{H}$. It is only in the
region of the domain wall that the torque acts, the direction being that
shown in Fig. 1.36b. This torque causes the domain wall to move to the
left in Fig. 1.36a in the same way a twist can move along a paper strip.
    Suppose a domain wall moves across a unit volume of material causing
all the magnetic moments to turn from antiparallel to parallel with the
applied field intensity $\vec{H}$. The work done per unit volume in turning the

n magnetic moments, each of value p_m, through $180°$ is, using eq. 1.114,

$$w = n\int_0^\pi T \, d\theta$$

$$= 2np_m\mu_0 H \qquad \text{joules/meter}^3 \qquad (1.115)$$

From eqs. 1.108 and 1.111, this energy may also be expressed as

$$w = 2\mathcal{M}\mu_0 H$$

$$= 2B_s H \qquad \text{joules/meter}^3 \qquad (1.116)$$

The energy of eq. 1.116 is used in moving the domain wall past microscopic impurities, irregularities, or strain regions in the crystal. It all

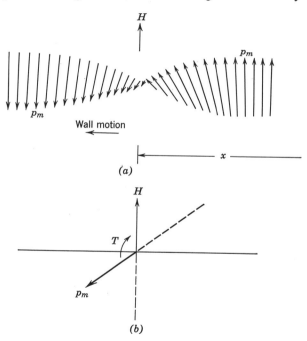

Fig. 1.36   Wall motion due to applied magnetic field of intensity $\vec{H}$.

eventually appears as heat within the crystal, and is called hysteresis loss. The value of the magnetic field intensity H_c required to move the domain wall across a material is known as the coercive force. In a very pure iron crystal this coercive force is of the order of 1–10 amperes/meter.

Let us now return to our discussion of the control of the magnetic state in the crystal of Fig. 1.35. When the current i in the coil is raised to a value that is sufficient to create a magnetic field intensity H in eq. 1.113

equal to the coercive force H_c at the domain wall, the wall moves outward, increasing x and increasing the net flux ϕ of eq. 1.112.

The flux linkage λ of the coil, given by

$$\lambda = N\phi \qquad \text{webers} \qquad (1.117)$$

is plotted as a function of the coil current i in Fig. 1.37. Before the current i is applied, the state of the core in Fig. 1.35 can be represented by the point 0 in Fig. 1.37. As the current i is increased, the flux linkage λ remains

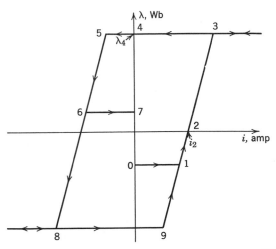

Fig. 1.37   Flux linkage λ versus current i characteristic for the single-crystal core of Fig. 1.35.

essentially constant until the point 1, where coercive force H_c is produced (eq. 1.113) for the position x of the domain wall shown in Fig. 1.35. Although this process starts the outward displacement of the domain wall, an increase in current i is required to produce coercive force for larger values of x in order to keep the wall moving. At point 2, the coil current is

$$i_2 = (2a + 2b + 4d)\frac{H_c}{N} \qquad \text{amperes} \qquad (1.118)$$

and the wall has moved to midposition, resulting in zero flux linkage. At point 3, the wall has moved to the outside of the crystal, that is, $x = d$, and further increase of the coil current produces an increase in flux linkage of only the small amount which the magnetic field intensity H would create in free space.

As the current is decreased to zero, the domain wall position remains fixed and the coil flux linkage remains essentially constant along the locus 3-4. Application of a negative current i of a value indicated by the state point 5 causes a new set of domain walls to start from the inner periphery of the crystal. These domain walls move outward as the negative value of the current i is increased. If this current is removed at a point 6 in Fig. 1.37 before it rises to a magnitude sufficient to move the wall across the crystal, the wall is left in some intermediate position, and the flux linkage λ of the coil remains constant at point 7.

If the coil current is cycled, first in a positive direction then in a negative direction so that the λ–i characteristic of Fig. 1.37 moves once around the path 9-3-5-8, the wall will have swept twice across the complete volume V of the crystal. The energy W dissipated in this operation is found by inserting the value of coercive force H_c in eq. 1.116 to give

$$W_{\text{loss}} = 2Vw \qquad \text{joules} \qquad (1.119)$$

By substituting from eqs. 1.118, 1.112, and 1.117 into 1.119, it can be shown that this dissipated energy can be expressed as

$$W_{\text{loss}} = 4(NB_s z d)\left[\frac{H_c}{N}(2a + 2b + 4d)\right]$$

$$= 4\lambda_4 i_2 \qquad \text{joules} \qquad (1.120)$$

From Fig. 1.37, it can be seen that this energy is equal to the area enclosed by the closed path 9-3-5-8 followed by λ and i during this operation. This conclusion may also be reached by determining the net electrical energy input to the coil, exclusive of its resistance loss, during one cycle of λ and i, and assuming that all this energy is lost within the material. Then the energy loss for one cycle of operation following the locus 4-5-8-9-3-4 is

$$W_{\text{loss}} = \int_{\substack{\text{complete} \\ \text{cycle}}} i\, d\lambda$$

$$= 4\lambda_4 i_2 \qquad \text{joules}$$

For a material having a saturation flux density of 2 webers/meter² and a coercive force of 10 amperes/meter, this hysteresis energy loss would be 80 joules/meter³ for one cycle.

The slope of the sides of the flux-linkage–current characteristic of Fig. 1.37 is determined by the shape of the crystal core in Fig. 1.35. If the width d of the material is made small in comparison with the length of the inner periphery, this slope is correspondingly large.

Although the discussion in this section has been limited to the rather impractical case of a single crystal, the properties described are the basis for understanding the behavior of practical polycrystalline magnetic materials.

1.6.5 Polycrystalline Magnetic Materials

Most practical ferromagnetic materials are polycrystalline in nature, the volume of each crystal being generally less than 1 millimeter^3. A closed toroidal core made of such a material is shown in Fig. 1.38a. In closely packed polycrystalline materials, it is not necessary that there be flux closure of the type shown in Fig. 1.33 within each crystal. Suppose

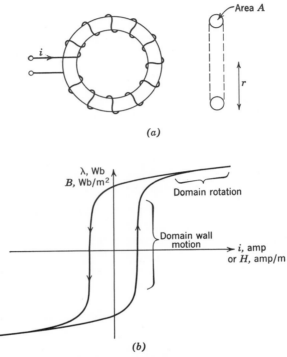

(a)

(b)

Fig. 1.38 A polycrystalline magnetic core and its flux linkage λ versus current i characteristic.

each crystal of the material has three mutually perpendicular easy directions of magnetization, as in iron. Even if the crystals are randomly oriented with respect to each other, the difference in angle between an easy direction of one crystal and the nearest easy direction of its neighbor is always between 0 and 55°. Magnetic flux can therefore continue easily from one crystal to another, as shown in Fig. 1.39a.

In a core like that of Fig. 1.38a, there will be many microscopic streams of magnetic flux proceeding through the material in complex paths following easy directions of magnetization in each crystal. Except in permanent magnetic materials, or other magnetic materials exposed to high external fields, these streams of flux close on themselves within the material. In the core of Fig. 1.38*a*, the flux streams may pass completely around the core or they may close locally.

If a magnetic field intensity $\vec{H}$ is now applied to the core of Fig. 1.38*a*, its effect is to move domain walls so that domains whose orientation direction is near that of the vector $\vec{H}$ grow at the expense of those which are oppositely directed. This process of domain growth, shown in Fig.

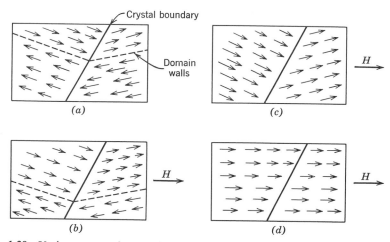

(a)

(b)

(c)

(d)

Fig. 1.39 Various stages of magnetization in a section of a polycrystalline material as the magnetic field intensity $\vec{H}$ is increased.

1.39*b*, continues until all crystals are eventually magnetized in their easy direction nearest the direction of the vector $\vec{H}$, as is suggested by Fig. 1.39*c*. At this stage, the total magnetic flux ϕ through the cross-sectional area A of the randomly oriented polycrystalline core of Fig. 1.38*a* consists of streams passing through this area at angles between 0 and 55° to the normal to this area, and is, as a result, generally less than 85% of the value which would have occurred if all crystals had been oriented along the axis of the core.

If the magnetic field intensity is further increased, the torque on the magnetic moments not aligned with the magnetic field intensity $\vec{H}$ tends to rotate these moments into line against the anistropy forces in each crystal. At very high values of $\vec{H}$, the moments approach alignment with $\vec{H}$, as shown in Fig. 1.39*d*.

The coil flux linkage λ is shown as a function of the coil current i in Fig. 1.38*b*. The steeply rising side of the characteristic is caused predominantly by domain wall motion at essentially constant coil current. For high currents, the dominant process is domain rotation. When the current is reduced from a high value, the domains rotate back to their nearest easy axis of magnetization, leaving a residual flux linkage. The characteristic is similar to that of a single crystal (Fig. 1.37), except that the corners are rounded and the condition of saturation is approached at a gradually decreasing slope rather than abruptly.

If the cross-sectional area of the core in Fig. 1.38a is small, the coil may be considered to produce a uniform magnetic field intensity $\bar{H}$ over the whole volume of the core material.

$$H = \frac{Ni}{2\pi r} \qquad \text{amperes/meter} \qquad (1.121)$$

The average magnetic flux density B directed normal to the cross-sectional area A of the core will then be

$$B = \frac{\phi}{A}$$
$$= \frac{\lambda}{NA} \qquad \text{webers/meter}^2 \qquad (1.122)$$

Thus the flux linkage–current characteristic of Fig. 1.38b may be rescaled to present the relationship between the average flux density B and the magnetic field intensity H for the material.

By the use of special rolling techniques, it is possible to produce sheets of magnetic material in which the crystals are oriented along the direction of desired magnetization. In these grain-oriented materials, domain rotation is essentially eliminated. The B–H characteristic of a typical grain-oriented material (50% Ni, 50% Fe) is shown in Fig. 1.40. This alloy has a saturation flux density B_s, which is approximately the mean of the values of saturation flux density for iron and for nickel.

The fact that the residual flux density B_r is greater than 95% of the saturation flux density B_s indicates that essentially complete crystal orientation is achieved. The B–H characteristic of Fig. 1.40 very closely approaches the ideal properties of a single crystal, the main difference being a slight rounding at the transitions between regions of high and low slope. The coercive force H_c has a value comparable to that of a single crystal. Materials having a similar low coercive force are generally termed "soft," in contrast to "hard" or permanent magnet materials.

Magnetic materials used with time-varying fluxes have an electric field induced in them. Since these materials are normally conducting, the electric field produces circulating currents known as eddy currents (see Section 2.2). The eddy currents and their resultant power loss can be reduced by increasing the resistivity of the material. The magnetic material most commonly used in machines and transformers is iron alloyed with a small addition of silicon (approximately 3.5%) to increase its electrical resistivity. This material has a saturation flux density of about 2 webers/meter^2 and a coercive force in the range 15–100 amperes/meter. The value

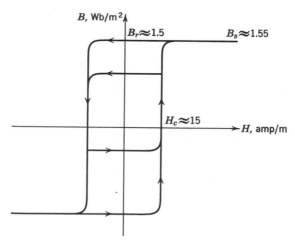

Fig. 1.40 Flux density B versus field intensity H for 50% nickel–50% iron core.

of the coercive force is dependent on the impurity content of the material and on the mechanical strains in the material, whether internally or externally produced. Where very high resistivity is required for high-frequency applications, cores are made of powdered iron in an insulating binding material.

The group of magnetic materials known as ferrites have the ferri-magnetic property referred to in Section 1.6.2. These are compounds having two sublattices XO and Fe_2O_3, where X may be any of the elements Mn, Zn, Ba, Mg, Ni, Co, or Cu. These materials are not metallic, and thus have very high electrical resistivity. The two sublattices have different magnetic moments, which are directed antiparallel to each other, as shown in Fig. 1.25b. As we might expect, the saturation flux density in ferrimagnetic materials is much lower than in pure iron, and is generally less than 0.4 weber/meter^2. Ferrite cores are produced by sintering the oxide mixture at high temperature. The coercive force depends both on the composition and on the process of preparation.

1.6.6 Permanent-Magnet Materials

The materials we have discussed are those whose magnetic state can be easily controlled by an externally applied magnetic field intensity. Permanent-magnet materials are those which can produce a magnetic field outside the material and maintain it in spite of a large externally applied field intensity. These materials are therefore characterized by very high values of coercive force.

Section 1.6.3 discussed the fact that very small crystals would not have domain walls and, therefore, flux closure, within themselves. It was also

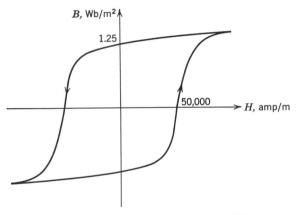

Fig. 1.41   Flux density B versus magnetic field intensity H for permanent-magnet material (Alnico, V).

noted that mechanical strain has a marked effect on the preferred direction of magnetic orientation. Most permanent-magnet materials achieve high coercive force by a combination of the following features: (1) high crystal anisotropy energy, as in cobalt; (2) very small crystals, often in the form of long slivers to increase the directional effect; and (3) high internal strain. The metallic permanent magnets are generally alloys of several of the elements Fe, Ni, Co, Cu, Cr, Al, V, and Mo. The small particles and the high strain are produced by heating and quenching the material, and also by cold rolling for some materials. It is possible to produce some preferred orientation by cooling the materials from the Curie temperature in a strong magnetic field or by directional cooling.

A typical B–H characteristic for a common metallic permanent magnet (Alnico V: 51% Fe; 24% Co, 14% Ni, 8% Al, 3% Cu) is shown in Fig. 1.41. Although the general shape of this characteristic is similar to that of soft magnetic materials, the coercive force is of the order of 1000 times as great. The residual flux density is of the same order of magnitude as soft metallic magnetic materials.

Permanent-magnet materials may also be made of ferrites such as barium ferrite. While the residual flux density of ferrite magnets is only about 0.2 to 0.4 weber/meter², exceptionally high coercive forces of the order of 200,000 amperes/meter can be obtained. When residual flux density has been established in such a material, an energy of the order of 60,000 joules/meter³ of material is required to remove it. Magnets of these materials are therefore particularly stable.

1.6.7 Magnetostriction

Magnetostriction is the elastic deformation of a magnetic material when its magnetic state is changed. Some materials, like nickel and cobalt,

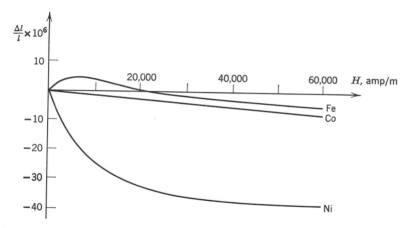

Fig. 1.42   Magnetostriction in iron, cobalt, and nickel as a function of magnetic field intensity H.

contract in the direction of magnetization, while others expand. If a ferromagnetic bar is subjected to an applied magnetic field (Fig. 1.5), the per unit change in dimension along the field direction is as shown in Fig. 1.42, for iron, cobalt, and nickel. Note that large values of magnetic field intensity H are required to produce the largest magnetostriction effect. The reason for this is that most of the change in dimension results from domain rotation near the saturation condition rather than from domain wall motion; the effect of wall motion is usually to reverse the magnetic moments, leaving them similarly oriented with respect to the length axis of the material.

The magnetostrictive effect is also reversible. If tension is applied to a material such as nickel, which normally contracts under magnetization, a much larger magnetic field intensity is required to produce a given flux density in the material, as shown in Fig. 1.43. Since magnetostriction is an elastic effect, the additional energy that must be applied to magnetize the material is recoverable when the magnetic field is removed.

Magnetostriction is important in many a-c devices because of the noise which is produced by the small but rapid changes in the dimensions

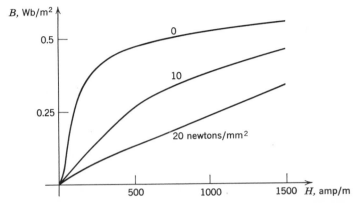

Fig. 1.43   Influence of tension on magnetic flux density B versus magnetic field intensity H for nickel.

of the device. The dimensional change shown in Fig. 1.42 is unchanged if the direction of the magnetic field is reversed. With an alternating field, the same dimensional change occurs during each half cycle. Thus the basic frequency of the noise produced by magnetostriction is normally twice that of the frequency of the electrical supply.

The applications of magnetostrictive materials as electromechanical energy converters are similar to those of piezoelectric materials, because both combine small motion and large force. The major uses of these material are in the production of ultrasonic waves, in electrical filters, and as strain gauges.

1.7 USE OF MAGNETIC MATERIALS TO PRODUCE FIELDS AND FORCES

In the preceding section we saw that the magnetic flux in a closed path of soft magnetic material can be controlled by the application of a relatively small external magnetic field. While closed magnetic paths are possible in transformers and other stationary magnetic devices, energy conversion devices normally require an air gap between the stationary and moving parts of the system. One of the major uses of magnetic materials is to produce intense concentrated magnetic fields in air gaps.

In this section we discuss the magnetization properties of a magnetic path with an air gap. We also examine and determine the forces that are exerted on the magnetic materials on each side of an air gap.

1.7.1 Magnetic Field in an Air Gap

Figure 1.44 shows a core of soft magnetic material which has an air gap of length x and area yz. The core is encircled by a concentrated coil of N turns. Typical magnetization characteristics of the core material are

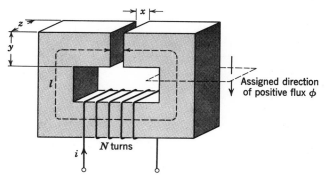

Fig. 1.44   Magnetic system with air gap.

shown in Fig. 1.45a. As the air gap length x is small in comparison to the dimensions y and z, let us assume that the magnetic flux ϕ is confined to the core and to the air gap volume. The average flux density B in the core and in the air gap is therefore given by

$$B = \frac{\phi}{yz} \qquad \text{webers/meter}^2 \qquad (1.123)$$

To support a magnetic flux density B in the air gap, a magnetic field intensity H_a is required, where

$$H_a = \frac{B}{\mu_0} \qquad \text{amperes/meter} \qquad (1.124)$$

The same flux density can be produced in the magnetic material with the magnetic field intensity H_m given in the B–H characteristic of Fig. 1.45a. According to the circuital law of eq. 1.60, the summation of the magnetic field intensity around the closed path of the magnetic flux equals the current encircling this path. Thus we have

$$Ni = H_m l + H_a x \qquad \text{amperes} \qquad (1.125)$$

For a particular value of flux density B, the values of H_a and H_m (found from eq. 1.124 and Fig. 1.45a) may be inserted into eq. 1.125 to find the required coil current. Fig. 1.45b shows the relationship between the magnetic flux ϕ and the coil current i.

For most soft magnetic materials, the magnetic field intensity H_m in the core is several orders of magnitude less than H_a. For example, for $B = 1.0$ weber/meter^2, a field intensity of $H_a = 800{,}000$ amperes/meter is required in the air, while in an iron core the field intensity H_m may be

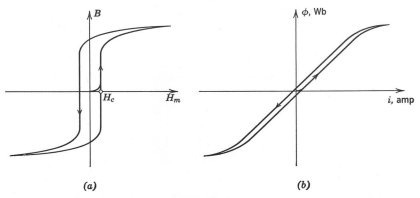

(a)   (b)

Fig. 1.45   (a) Flux density B versus field intensity H for the core material. (b) Relation between flux ϕ and coil current i for core of Fig. 1.44.

of the order of 20 amperes/meter. Unless the gap length x in Fig. 1.44 is very small, the term $H_m l$ in eq. 1.125 may often be neglected in analysis, provided the flux density in the core is well below its saturation value. Thus by combining eqs. 1.123, 1.124, and 1.125, the air gap flux can be approximated by

$$\phi = \frac{yz\mu_0 N}{x}\, i \qquad \text{webers} \qquad (1.126)$$

The effect of the magnetic material is therefore to concentrate the magneto-motive force Ni of the coil on the reluctance of the air gap.

An alternative approach to the analysis of this system follows from a consideration of the energy input to the coil to produce a magnetic field in the air gap. The magnetic energy stored in the air gap at a flux density B is

$$W_a = \frac{B^2}{2\mu_0}\, xyz \qquad \text{joules} \qquad (1.127)$$

The energy required to change the flux density in the core from zero to a value B is

$$W_m = lyz \int_0^B H_m \, dB \qquad \text{joules} \qquad (1.128)$$

For $B = 1$ weber/meter^2, the energy density in the gap will be about 400,000 joules/meter^3, while the energy density required by an iron core may be only about 20 joules/meter^3. Thus W_m may often be neglected, and the whole of the electric energy input to the coil may be assumed to be stored in the concentrated magnetic field in the air gap.

The means by which the magnetic material concentrates the effect of the coil to produce an air gap field may be appreciated by considering the behavior of the microscopic streams of magnetic flux that exist in the domains of the material. When the air gap flux density is zero, essentially all these streams of flux may be considered to close on themselves within the material. Figure 1.46a suggests, in very simplified form, the condition

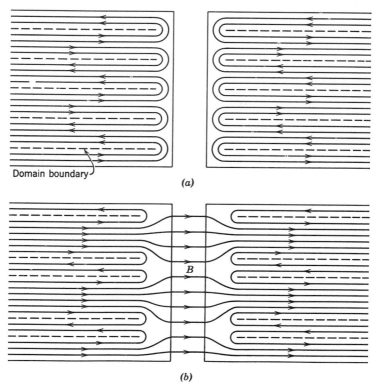

Fig. 1.46 Simplified model of the magnetic domains in the region of the air gap of Fig. 1.44. (a) With no air-gap flux. (b) Shifted domain boundaries, oriented domain streams terminating on air-gap surface, and air-gap flux.

of the material around the air gap of Fig. 1.44 with no air gap flux. As the coil current i is increased from zero, a magnetic field is applied to the material in the region of the coil only. The forces produced by this local applied field tend to move domain walls so as to increase the size of the domains aligned with the applied field. Since adjacent atoms are bound together by the exchange forces, the forces produced on the wall by the coil field are transferred along the whole length of the domain walls bounding the individual flux streams. The condition of the core material near the air gap after some domain walls have moved in response to these forces is suggested by Fig. 1.46b. Some streams of aligned magnetic moments now close on themselves within the material, but others terminate at the air gap surface, the flux stream continuing across the air gap. If the coil current is reduced to zero, the domain arrangement returns to the state suggested by Fig. 1.46a, unless the material has significant permanent magnetism.

1.7.2 Force on Magnetic Material—Energy Conservation Approach

Figure 1.47 shows a magnetic system, part of which can move to provide an air gap of variable length x. We wish to find the force on this movable part in relation to the dimensions of the system, the properties of the magnetic material, and the source characteristics. By following the conservation of energy approach, let us increase the gap length x by an increment dx. The mechanical energy output associated with this displacement is

$$dW_{\substack{\text{mech.} \\ \text{output}}} = f_x\, dx \qquad \text{joules} \qquad (1.129)$$

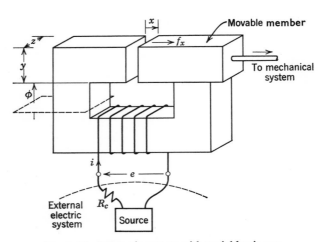

Fig. 1.47   Magnetic system with variable air gap.

where f_x is the component of force produced by the magnetic system in the positive x direction. The increment of mechanical output energy will be negative if the force component f_x is negative in sign. The energy increments of the system are related by

$$dW_{\substack{\text{elec.} \\ \text{input}}} = dW_{\text{loss}} + dW_{\text{stored}} + dW_{\substack{\text{mech.} \\ \text{output}}} \tag{1.130}$$

Our problem is therefore to find the input, loss, and stored energy increments accompanying this incremental displacement.

A simple approach that is reasonably accurate for most situations is based on the assumption that the magnetic material requires only a negligible amount of energy to change from one magnetic state to another. The loss term in eq. 1.130 then has no contribution from loss within the magnetic material; it can be made zero by associating the coil resistance R_c with the external electric circuit and the mechanical friction with the external mechanical system. The energy stored within the magnetic material is considered to be negligible. The stored energy of the system is therefore only that stored in the magnetic field of the air gap.

If we assume the magnetic field to be uniform within the air gap and zero in the space outside the gap, the magnetic flux ϕ in the system is given, from eq. 1.126, as

$$\phi = \frac{yz\mu_0 Ni}{x} \quad \text{webers} \tag{1.131}$$

The energy input increment to the system is equal to the current i times the change in flux linkage λ of the coil during the incremental displacement as shown in Section 1.5.2. Using eq. 1.131, we have

$$dW_{\substack{\text{elec.} \\ \text{input}}} = i\,d\lambda$$
$$= i\,dN\phi$$
$$= Ni\,d\phi$$
$$= \frac{\phi x}{yz\mu_0}\,d\phi \quad \text{joules} \tag{1.132}$$

The energy stored in the air gap, from eqs. 1.123 and 1.127, is

$$W_{\text{stored}} = \frac{B^2 xyz}{2\mu_0}$$
$$= \frac{\phi^2 x}{2\mu_0 yz} \quad \text{joules} \tag{1.133}$$

Thus the incremental increase in the stored energy during the displacement is

$$dW_{\text{stored}} = \frac{\phi^2\, dx}{2\mu_0 yz} + \frac{\phi x}{\mu_0 yz}\, d\phi \qquad \text{joules} \qquad (1.134)$$

Substituting from eqs. 1.132 and 1.134 into the energy balance expression of 1.130 gives

$$dW_{\substack{\text{mech.}\\ \text{output}}} = -\frac{\phi^2\, dx}{2\mu_0 yz} \qquad \text{joules} \qquad (1.135)$$

Thus, from eq. 1.129, we have

$$f_x = \frac{dW_{\substack{\text{mech.}\\ \text{output}}}}{dx}$$

$$= -\frac{\phi^2}{2\mu_0 yz} \qquad \text{newtons} \qquad (1.136)$$

Note that the force component in the positive x direction has a negative sign. The force is therefore in such a direction as to close the gap. The force per unit of air gap area A is seen, from eq. 1.136, to be

$$\frac{f_x}{A} = -\frac{B^2}{2\mu_0} \qquad \text{newtons/meter}^2 \qquad (1.137)$$

If the source in the system of Fig. 1.47 is adjusted so as to keep the magnetic flux ϕ and the flux density B constant during the displacement, the force is independent of the gap length x. The force may also be expressed as a function of coil current i and gap length x by substituting from eq. 1.131 into eq. 1.136 giving

$$f_x = -\frac{\mu_0 yz N^2 i^2}{2x^2} \qquad \text{newtons} \qquad (1.138)$$

The simplifying assumptions made in the previous analysis result in a linear relationship between the magnetic flux ϕ and the coil current i, as expressed in eq. 1.131. The reluctance $\mathscr{R}$ of the path of the magnetic flux is that of the air gap only and is independent of the value of ϕ.

$$\mathscr{R} = \frac{x}{\mu_0 yz} \qquad \text{amperes/weber} \qquad (1.139)$$

The force may therefore be found by use of the expression of eq. 1.87 developed for linear systems.

$$f_x = -\frac{1}{2}\phi^2\frac{d\mathscr{R}}{dx}$$

$$= -\frac{1}{2}\frac{\phi^2}{\mu_0 yz} \qquad \text{newtons} \qquad (1.140)$$

The force on the movable member of the magnetic system is in such a direction as to reduce the reluctance of the magnetic path of the flux. Alternately, the inductance L of the coil may be derived using eq. 1.131.

$$L = \frac{\lambda}{i} = \frac{N\phi}{i}$$

$$= \frac{N^2\mu_0 yz}{x} \quad \text{henrys} \tag{1.141}$$

Equation 1.84, which is also applicable to linear systems only, may then be used to derive the force expression of eq. 1.138.

$$f_x = \frac{1}{2} i^2 \frac{dL}{dx}$$

$$= -\frac{N^2\mu_0 yz i^2}{2x^2} \quad \text{newtons} \tag{1.142}$$

A coil that is in free space can change its self-inductance only by a change in its shape. The inductance of a rigid coil can be changed by changing the geometrical configuration of the magnetic material that forms part of its flux path. The direction of the force on the magnetic material is such as to tend to increase the inductance of the coil.

The assumption that the energy required to change the magnetic state of the material is negligible is not valid if the flux density in the material is in the saturation region or if the energy required for hysteresis is appreciable. Let us first consider how the force may be found in systems having magnetic saturation. The effects of hysteresis are considered later in this section.

Suppose the magnetic material in the system of Fig. 1.47 has a B–H relationship of the form shown in Fig. 1.45a. With an air gap, the flux-current relation for the system of Fig. 1.47 would have the form shown in Fig. 1.45b. To eliminate the hysteresis effect, let us approximate the relation of Fig. 1.45b by a single-valued curve following the mean value of the hysteresis loop. Figure 1.48a shows the relationship between the flux linkage λ and the current i for a gap length of $x = x_0$. Suppose the current is initially increased to the value i_1 with $x = x_0$. Now suppose that the air gap length is decreased very slowly by a finite displacement Δx. Since the resulting rate of change of flux linkage is very small, the induced voltage e in the coil may be ignored, and the current may be considered to remain constant at $i = i_1$. During the displacement, the flux linkage–current relation for the coil moves along the locus from 1 on the λ–i curve for $x = x_0$ to 2 on the λ–i curve for $x = x_0 - \Delta x$.

With a finite displacement Δx, the energy balance expression of eq.

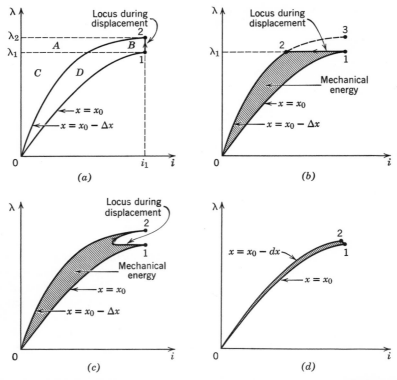

Fig. 1.48 Determination of force in a nonlinear magnetic system. (*a*) Displacement with constant current. (*b*) Displacement with constant flux linkage. (*c*) General λ–i locus during displacement. (*d*) Infinitesimal displacement.

1.130 must be stated as

$$\Delta W_{\text{elec.}\atop\text{input}} = \Delta W_{\text{loss}} + \Delta W_{\text{stored}} + \Delta W_{\text{mech.}\atop\text{output}} \tag{1.143}$$

The electrical energy input to the system during the displacement Δx is

$$\Delta W_{\text{elec.}\atop\text{input}} = \int_{\lambda_1}^{\lambda_2} i_1\, d\lambda = \text{Area}\,(A + B) \qquad \text{in Fig. 1.48}a \tag{1.144}$$

The loss energy is assumed to be zero because hysteresis has been neglected, and the resistance and friction losses have been moved to the external electric and mechanical systems. The increase in stored energy is equal to the stored energy W_2 at state 2, minus the stored energy W_1 at state 1. The energy W_1 is equal to the electric energy input to the system to increase the current from zero to i_1 at a constant gap spacing x_0. Thus we have

$$W_1 = \int_0^{\lambda_1} i \, d\lambda = \text{Area } (C + D) \qquad \text{in Fig. 1.48}a \qquad (1.145)$$

The stored energy W_2 is equal to the energy input to increase the current from zero to i_1 at gap spacing $x_0 - \Delta x$ along the λ–i locus 0-2. Thus, we have

$$W_2 = \int_0^{\lambda_2} i \, d\lambda = \text{Area } (A + C) \qquad \text{in Fig. 1.48}a \qquad (1.146)$$

The increase in stored energy during the displacement is

$$\Delta W_{\text{stored}} = W_2 - W_1 = \text{Area } (A - D) \qquad (1.147)$$

Substituting these energy components into eq. 1.143 gives

$$\Delta W_{\substack{\text{mech.} \\ \text{output}}} = \text{Area } (A + B) - \text{Area } (A - D)$$

$$= \text{Area } (B + D) \qquad \text{joules} \qquad (1.148)$$

Note that the mechanical output energy is represented in Fig. 1.48a by the area bounded by the locus 0-1-2-0.

An alternative method of determining the mechanical output energy of eq. 1.148 involves comparison of two ways of arriving at state 2 in Fig. 1.48a. Suppose the gap length is set at $x = x_0$ while the current is increased from zero to i_1, and is then reduced to $x = x_0 - \Delta x$ with $i = i$. For this sequence, the total electric input energy is the area $(A + B + C + D)$ to the left of the locus 0-1-2 in Fig. 1.48a. Now consider a second sequence of operations in which the gap is initially reduced to $x = x_0 - \Delta x$ with the current equal to zero, and the current is then increased to i_1. The electric input for this sequence is the area $(A + C)$ in Fig. 1.48a to the left of the 0-2 locus. It is assumed that neither sequence involves any loss of energy. The mechanical energy in the second sequence is zero, because the displacement is made at zero current. Both sequences arrive at the same final magnetic state for the system. Because the electric input energy for the first sequence exceeds that for the second sequence by an amount represented by the area $(B + D)$, it is concluded that this must be the mechanical output energy.

Let us now consider a reduction of gap length from $x = x_0$ to $x = x_0 - \Delta x$, which is made so rapidly that the flux linkage λ of the coil remains substantially constant during the displacement. While the flux linkage may not change appreciably, its rate of change is large. The resultant induced voltage e causes the current i to be reduced during the displacement, as shown in the locus 1-2 of Fig. 1.48b. After the displacement is completed, the coil current may rise along the locus 2-3 toward its original value i_1, all of the input energy going into storage in the magnetic field. As the flux linkage λ remains constant at λ_1 during the displacement, the electric input energy associated with the locus 1-2 is equal to zero. The losses in the system are assumed to be zero. Thus (from eq. 1.143) the mechanical output energy must be obtained from the stored energy of the system

$$\Delta W_{\substack{\text{mech.} \\ \text{output}}} = -\Delta W_{\text{stored}}$$

$$= -\left[\int_{\substack{0 \\ \text{along} \\ \text{locus} \\ 0-2}}^{\lambda_1} i \, d\lambda - \int_{\substack{0 \\ \text{along} \\ \text{locus} \\ 0-1}}^{\lambda_1} i \, d\lambda \right] \tag{1.149}$$

Note that the mechanical output energy is represented in Fig. 1.48b by the area bounded by the locus 0-1-2-0.

Figure 1.48c shows a general locus 1-2 of the flux linkage–current relation, which might be followed during a displacement Δx. The shape of this locus depends on the dynamic characteristics of both the electrical source system and the external mechanical system. The mechanical output energy is equal to the electric input energy required to arrive at state 2 along the locus 0-1-2, minus the electrical input required to arrive at the same state 2 along the locus 0-2. This mechanical output energy is represented in Fig. 1.48c as the area bounded by the static λ–i relations for the initial and final states and the locus followed in transition from the initial to the final state.

The average force during the displacement can be determined by dividing the mechanical output energy in eqs. 1.148 or 1.149 by Δx. To find the force at a particular value of spacing x, the displacement Δx may be contracted to an infinitesimal displacement dx. Figure 1.48d shows that as the locus 0-2 for $x = x_0 - dx$ becomes coincident with locus 0-1 for $x = x_0$, the shape of the locus 1-2 ceases to be significant in determining the area bounded by the locus 0-1-2-0. The force component f_x acting in the positive x direction is equal to the differential mechanical energy (represented by the area within locus 0-1-2-0) divided by the differential displacement dx. If the flux linkage is considered constant during the infinitesimal displacement, a general expression for the force component f_x can be deduced from eq. 1.149.

$$f_x = \frac{d}{dx} W_{\substack{\text{mech.} \\ \text{output}}}$$

$$= -\frac{\partial}{\partial x} W_{\text{stored}}\bigg|_{\lambda=\text{constant}} \qquad \text{newtons} \tag{1.150}$$

where

$$W_{\text{stored}} = \int_0^\lambda i \, d\lambda \qquad \text{joules} \tag{1.151}$$

The expression of eq. 1.150 is convenient for analytical determination of the force when the current i is expressed as a function of the flux linkage λ and the distance x.

An alternative expression for force can be derived by considering the current to be constant during the infinitesimal displacement. From eq. 1.148 and Fig. 1.48a, the force is equal to the rate of increase with displacement of the area under the λ–i curve. Let

$$W' = \int_0^i \lambda \, di \qquad \text{joules} \tag{1.152}$$

where W' is generally called the coenergy. Then

$$f_x = \frac{d}{dx} W_{\substack{\text{mech.} \\ \text{output}}}$$

$$= \left. \frac{\partial}{\partial x} W' \right|_{i=\text{const.}} \tag{1.153}$$

This expression is convenient when the flux linkage λ is expressed as a function of the current i and the distance x.

The expressions for force in eqs. 1.148, 1.149, 1.150, and 1.153 in general do not apply if losses occur in the magnetic material as a result of a displacement. Suppose the material has significant hysteresis. The flux linkage–current relation for a given spacing is then no longer single valued but depends on the previous magnetic history of the material. The methods for determining force developed earlier in this section may still be applied in some special circumstances. Suppose the magnetic material of Fig. 1.47 has a B–H relation of the form shown in Fig. 1.45a. If the air gap is held constant at $x = x_0$, while the coil current is increased from 0 to i_1, the λ–i relation for the coil follows a locus such as 0-1 in Fig. 1.49. The energy input during the operation is represented by the area $(C + D)$. Part of this input energy is stored and part is hysteresis loss. Now let us suppose the air gap length is decreased to $x_0 - \Delta x$, while the coil current is held constant. The energy input during this operation is represented by the area $(A + B)$. Part of this energy is stored, part is lost as hysteresis, and part is mechanical output energy. Because the initial magnetization at $x = x_0$ along locus 0-1 increased the flux density in the material, and the displacement increased the flux density still further, the net effect on the material should be essentially the same as would be obtained if the current were increased from 0 to i_1 as spacing $x_0 - \Delta x$. This would not be true if the flux density decreased as a result of the displacement. In that case, the material would be operating along some minor hysteresis loop. The effect also would not be the same if the distribution of the flux in the material were significantly different at the two values of gap spacing. Let us assume that the magnetization characteristic for spacing $x_0 - \Delta x$ with increasing current is the locus 0-2 in Fig. 1.49. The energy input to reach state 2 with spacing $x_0 - \Delta x$ is represented by the area $(A + C)$, part being stored and part being hysteresis loss. The total input energy required to reach state 2 along the locus 0-1-2 is represented by the area $(C + D + A + B)$. Assuming that the energy stored in state 2 is the same for either sequence of operations, and assuming that the same hysteresis loss occurs for either sequence of operations, the mechanical

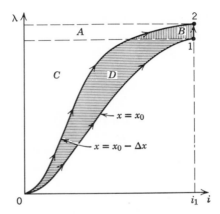

Fig. 1.49 Determination of mechanical energy in a system with magnetic hysteresis.

output energy is represented by the difference area $(B + D)$, that is, the area enclosed by the locus 0-1-2-0.

Analysis is more complicated for displacements that cause a decrease in the flux linkage. The average force during an increase in gap length is not equal to that obtained for an equivalent decrease in gap length when the material has hysteresis. The mechanical energy input required to increase the gap length must exceed the mechanical energy output obtained during the decrease of the gap length by the total hysteresis loss involved in the operation.

Another situation in which the force can be found in spite of the presence of hysteresis loss occurs when the displacement is made at essentially constant flux. If we suppose that the flux density does not change at any point in the material as a result of the displacement, it follows that the hysteresis loss is zero and that the energy stored in the material is unchanged. For this condition, the mechanical output energy must be obtained from a reduction in the energy stored in the air gap.

Equation 1.150 may therefore be used, the energy stored being equal to the gap energy plus a constant stored energy in the material.

While the hysteresis loss may be zero for the situation just described, the eddy current losses in the material may be significant. These losses depend on the rate of change of the flux in the material and on the resistivity of the material (see Section 2.2). Because of eddy current losses, the force produced by a magnetic actuator at a given gap length x and current i is not the same if x and i are varying rapidly with time as it is for the same set of values of constant length x and current i.

1.7.3 Physical Origin of Force on Magnetic Materials

The energy conservation approach of Section 1.7.2 leads to a number of very useful expressions by which the force in a magnetic system may be determined. But, by its nature, this approach is incapable of explaining the physical origin of the force. A similar situation was met in the analysis

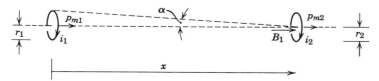

Fig. 1.50 Force between two aligned magnetic moments.

of electrostatic systems (section 1.3.3), where it was found that the most useful expressions arose from the energy conservation approach, while Coulomb's law was most useful in obtaining a physical understanding. Therefore, it would be helpful if we could develop an approach to forces between magnetic materials which would be analogous to the use of Coulomb's law in assessing forces between charged conductors.

The significant properties of ferromagnetic materials arise from the magnetic moments of the individual atoms. Thus, it should be possible to determine the force between two pieces of ferromagnetic material as the summation of the forces produced by the magnetic moments of one on the magnetic moments of the other.

Let us first determine the force between two small circular coils carrying currents i_1 and i_2 that are aligned as shown in Fig. 1.50. From Section 1.5.3 we know that the force between the coils may be found from the expression

$$f_x = i_1 i_2 \frac{dL_{12}}{dx} \qquad \text{newtons} \qquad (1.154)$$

Using the current element law of eq. 1.57, the magnetic flux density B_1 produced by coil 1 at the center of coil 2 is

$$B_1 = \mu_0 H_1$$

$$= \mu_0 \frac{i_1}{4\pi x^2} 2\pi r_1 \sin \alpha \qquad (1.155)$$

Since $r_1 \ll x$, $\sin \alpha$ may be approximated by r_1/x. The mutual inductance L_{12} of the coils is the flux linkage λ_2 of coil 2 per unit of current i_1 in coil 1. If $r_2 \ll x$, the flux density produced by i_1 over the area enclosed by coil 2 may be considered to be uniform at the value B_1 of eq. 1.155. Thus

$$L_{12} = \frac{\lambda_2}{i_1}$$

$$= \frac{\pi r_2{}^2 B_1}{i_1}$$

$$= \frac{\mu_0(\pi r_1{}^2)(\pi r_2{}^2)}{2\pi x^3} \quad \text{henrys} \qquad (1.156)$$

Substitution from this expression into eq. 1.154 gives the force in the positive x direction on coil 2 as

$$f_x = -\frac{3\mu_0(\pi r_1{}^2 i_1)(\pi r_2{}^2 i_2)}{2\pi x^4}$$

$$= -\frac{3\mu_0 p_{m1} p_{m2}}{2\pi x^4} \quad \text{newtons} \qquad (1.157)$$

In this expression, the coils are represented by their respective magnetic moments p_{m1} and p_{m2}. It may be seen that there is a force of attraction between two aligned magnetic moments that is proportional to the product of the moments and inversely proportional to the fourth power of the separation distance.

Inside a ferromagnetic material, the magnetic moments of the atoms align with their near neighbors. A chain of aligned moments may be regarded as equivalent to a long thin solenoid. The magnetic moment per unit of the volume within the solenoid is $\mathcal{M}$, as defined by eq. 1.107. As an intermediate step in finding the force between such solenoids, let us determine the force between a magnetic moment p_{m1} and a long solenoid, aligned as shown in Fig. 1.51. If the cross-sectional area of the solenoid

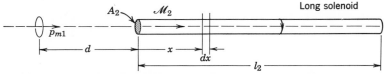

Fig. 1.51   Force between a magnetic moment and a long thin solenoid.

is A_2, and the magnetic moment per unit volume is $\mathscr{M}_2$, the magnetic moment of a length element dx of the solenoid is $\mathscr{M}_2 A_2\, dx$. Integrating eq. 1.157 over the length of the solenoid gives the force as

$$f_x = \int_{x=0}^{x=l_2} \left(-\frac{3\mu_0 p_{m1} \mathscr{M}_2 A_2}{2\pi(d+x)^4} \right) dx$$

$$= \frac{\mu_0 p_{m1} \mathscr{M}_2 A_2}{2\pi} \left(\frac{1}{(d+l_2)^3} - \frac{1}{d^3} \right) \qquad (1.158)$$

If the solenoid length l_2 is large in comparison with the distance d, the force may be approximated by

$$f_x = -\frac{\mu_0 p_{m1}(\mathscr{M}_2 A_2)}{2\pi d^3} \qquad \text{newtons} \qquad (1.159)$$

Figure 1.52 shows two long thin solenoids having a common axis. Assuming that the lengths of both solenoids are large in comparison with

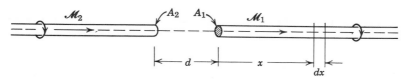

Fig. 1.52   Force between two aligned solenoids.

the distance d, the total force between the solenoids can be found by substituting $\mathscr{M}_1 A_1\, dx$ for p_{m1} in eq. 1.159 and integrating over the length of solenoid 1. Thus the force on solenoid 1, in the positive x direction, is

$$f_x = \int_{x=0}^{x=\infty} \left[-\frac{\mu_0(\mathscr{M}_1 A_1)(\mathscr{M}_2 A_2)}{2\pi(d+x)^3} \right] dx$$

$$= -\frac{\mu_0(\mathscr{M}_1 A_1)(\mathscr{M}_2 A_2)}{4\pi d^2} \qquad \text{newtons} \qquad (1.160)$$

The magnetic flux that is established within a long solenoid, by its aligned magnetic moments only, is (from eq. 1.109)

$$\phi = BA$$
$$= \mu_0 \mathscr{M} A \qquad \text{webers} \qquad (1.161)$$

Thus eq. 1.160 can be rewritten as

$$f_x = -\frac{\phi_1 \phi_2}{4\pi \mu_0 d^2} \qquad \text{newtons} \qquad (1.162)$$

where ϕ_1 is the flux in solenoid 1 and ϕ_2 the flux in solenoid 2.

The analogy between eq. 1.162 and Coulomb's law of eq. 1.1 suggests that the ends of long thin solenoids may be considered as point sources or point sinks of magnetic flux, the force of attraction between a point source and a point sink being proportional to the product of their magnitudes and inversely proportional to the square of their separation distance. A force of repulsion also would be expected between two point sources or between two point sinks.

The analogy in force properties between electric charges and magnetic flux sources, or sinks, provides a basis for a qualitative understanding of the forces between bodies of ferromagnetic material. The direct use of the inverse-square-law expression of eq. 1.162 for numerical calculation of force is limited, however, by the same considerations of arithmetic complexity that were discussed in relation to Coulomb's law in Section 1.3.

Consider, for example, the magnetic system of Fig. 1.47. When there is no magnetic flux across the air gap, the elementary solenoids of aligned magnetic moments close upon themselves within the material, as suggested by Fig. 1.46a. For each solenoid with $\mathscr{M}$ directed toward the gap, there is a similar solenoid with $\mathscr{M}$ directed away from the gap. There are no flux sources or sinks. Thus no net force is produced across the air gap. But when a magnetomotive force is applied to the system, a proportion of these solenoids terminate at or near the surfaces of the air gap. In Fig. 1.47b, the left-hand air gap surface may be considered to have a reasonably uniform distribution of magnetic flux source of total value ϕ. The right-hand air gap surface has an equal, uniformly distributed flux sink. The analogy between this situation and the oppositely charged parallel plates of Fig. 1.8 shows that the expression for the force on the magnetic material should be analogous to that of eq. 1.9, that is,

$$f = \frac{\phi^2}{2\mu_0 yz} \qquad \text{newtons} \qquad (1.163)$$

where yz is the cross-sectional area of the material and the gap. This is the same as the force expression of eq. 1.136 developed from the energy conversion approach.

It should be noted that the force expression of eq. 1.163 is valid only if the flux ϕ results from the magnetic moments within the magnetic material. If a large magnetic field intensity H is applied in the region of the air gap, the flux ϕ may be increased significantly above the value contributed by aligned magnetic moments (eq. 1.161). This increased flux caused by an external field does not increase the force on the magnetic material. In this situation, the force on the magnetic material should be derived from eq. 1.160 rather than from eq. 1.162.

1.7.4 A Rotating Machine Using Magnetic Materials

Figure 1.53a shows the magnetic structure of a rotating machine. The rotor is free to rotate on a horizontal shaft. Before attempting a quantitative analysis of the torque produced in this machine, let us examine it qualitatively using the flux source and sink concepts developed in the preceding section. Figure 1.53b shows the pattern of the magnetic flux

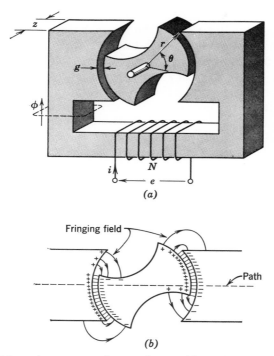

(a)

(b)

Fig. 1.53 (a) Magnetic structure of a rotating machine. (b) Magnetic field pattern showing flux sources (+) and sinks (−).

as it crosses the air paths between the stator and rotor. Within the air gaps of length g, the magnetic field intensity can be easily estimated if we assume that the magnetic field intensity in the iron is negligible. Applying the circuital law of eq. 1.60 to a path that passes through the coil and crosses the two air gaps in turn gives the average magnetic field intensity in the gaps as

$$H_{\text{gap}} = \frac{Ni}{2g} \qquad \text{amperes/meter} \qquad (1.164)$$

Throughout the whole of the two overlap regions of air gap length g, the magnetic field intensity can be considered as reasonably constant in

magnitude and radially directed. There are, however, fringing fields
beyond the regions of overlap, as shown in Fig. 1.53*b*. As the air path
lengths become longer, the average magnetic field intensity in these
fringing areas becomes proportionately smaller.

As was already discussed in Section 1.7.3, the magnetic flux enters the
air gap from the ends of elementary solenoids of the magnetic moments
of the ferromagnetic atoms. These solenoid ends may be considered as a
distributed flux source over the region where the flux emerges from the
material. Where the flux reenters the material there is a distributed flux
sink. The density of the flux source on a surface is numerically equal to
the magnetic flux density *B* out of the surface.

Let us now use eq. 1.162 in a qualitative manner to examine the forces
and torques in this system. There will be radially directed forces of
attraction between the uniformly distributed flux sources on one side of
the gap, and the flux sinks on the other side in the regions of overlap.
Since the motion of the rotor has been restricted to rotation about its
axis, these radial forces are not useful in producing mechanical output.
The useful forces in this system arise from the attraction between flux
sources and sinks bounding the fringing portion of the air gap field.
These forces are in such a direction as to rotate the rotor increasing
the angle of overlap θ between rotor and stator.

To a first approximation, the pattern and the intensity of the field in the
fringing areas are independent of the position θ of the rotor if the coil
current is held constant. Increasing the angle θ increases the flux in the
overlap region, but leaves the total fringing flux substantially constant.
This ceases to be true as the angle of overlap approaches its maximum
value. We could therefore expect that with constant coil current *i*,
the rotor torque tending to increase the overlap angle θ would be
independent of θ except in the range where θ approaches its maximum
value.

In the analysis of a machine such as the one illustrated in Fig. 1.53*a*
the physical concept of flux sources and sinks indicates the nature of the
forces, the region of their action, and some of their relationships. But
as we have already noted, this approach is seldom useful in numerical
calculation. For this type of calculation we revert to the energy conservation approach of Section 1.7.2. If the ferromagnetic material is assumed
to be lossless and to require negligible magnetic field intensity, there will
be a linear relation between the magnetic flux in the magnetic structure
and the coil current. For a linear system, the torque may be expressed
as a variant of eq. 1.84.

$$T_\theta = \frac{1}{2} i^2 \frac{dL}{d\theta} \quad \text{newton-meters} \tag{1.165}$$

where L is the inductance of the coil. This inductance may be approximated by assuming a uniform field in each of the air gaps of length g, as given in eq. 1.164 and considering the total flux ϕ to be the sum of this uniformly distributed flux plus a fringing flux ϕ_f proportional to the current i.

Then
$$L = \frac{N\phi}{i}$$

$$= \frac{N}{i}\left(\mu_0 \frac{Ni}{2g} zr\theta + \phi_f\right)$$

$$= N^2\left(\frac{\mu_0 zr\theta}{2g} + L_f\right) \quad \text{henrys} \tag{1.166}$$

where
$$L_f = \frac{N\phi_f}{i} \quad \text{henrys} \tag{1.167}$$

Substitution from this inductance expression into eq. 1.165 gives

$$T_\theta = \frac{N^2\mu_0 zri^2}{4g} \quad \text{newton-meters} \tag{1.168}$$

Note that this expression shows the torque to be independent of the angle θ, to be in such a direction as to increase the overlap angle θ, and to be proportional to the square of the current i. All these properties are as expected from the previous qualitative analysis.

If the coil current in Fig. 1.53a is held constant, the torque always acts to increase the angle of overlap θ. To obtain continuous rotation with a useful average torque, it is necessary to control the current i or the flux ϕ in such a way that the torque will be greater while the overlap angle θ is increasing than while it is decreasing. This can be done by using an a-c supply in a manner similar to that discussed in relation to the electrostatic machine in Section 1.3.4.

Suppose we apply to the coil terminals a source voltage of

$$e = \hat{E}\cos \omega t \quad \text{volts} \tag{1.169}$$

If the coil resistance is negligibly small, the magnetic flux in the system must change at a rate sufficient to produce an induced voltage equal to e, and is therefore given by

$$\phi = \frac{1}{N}\int e\,dt$$

$$= \frac{\hat{E}}{N\omega}\sin \omega t \quad \text{webers} \tag{1.170}$$

The torque on the rotor can be expressed as a variant of eq. 1.87.

$$T_\theta = -\frac{1}{2}\phi^2\frac{d\mathscr{R}}{d\theta} \qquad \text{newton-meters} \tag{1.171}$$

The variation of the reluctance $\mathscr{R}$ of the magnetic system with angle θ is of the form shown in Fig. 1.54, where θ is the angle of the rotor axis. This reluctance may be approximated by the first two terms of its Fourier series expansion.

$$\mathscr{R} = \mathscr{R}_0 + \mathscr{R}_2 \cos 2\theta \qquad \text{amperes/weber} \tag{1.172}$$

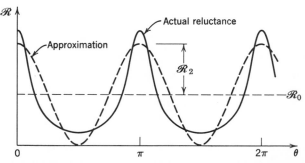

Fig. 1.54   Variation of reluctance $\mathscr{R}$ with angle θ for the machine of Fig. 1.53a.

If the angular velocity of the rotor is ν radians/second, and the angular position of the rotor at $t = 0$ is $\theta = -\delta$,

$$\theta = \nu t - \delta \qquad \text{radians} \tag{1.173}$$

If we now substitute from eqs. 1.170, 1.172, and 1.173 into eq. 1.171, the instantaneous torque is obtained as

$$T_\theta = -\frac{\hat{E}^2}{2N^2\omega^2}\sin^2\omega t\,\frac{d}{d\theta}\,[\mathscr{R}_0 + \mathscr{R}_2 \cos(2\nu t - 2\delta)]$$

$$= \frac{\hat{E}^2 \mathscr{R}_2}{2N^2\omega^2}\,[\sin(2\nu t - 2\delta) - \tfrac{1}{2}\sin(2\nu t - 2\omega t - 2\delta)$$

$$- \tfrac{1}{2}\sin(2\nu t + 2\omega t - 2\delta)] \tag{1.174}$$

All terms in this expression will be of sine form with zero average value unless $\nu = \pm\omega$ and $\delta \neq 0$. Setting the rotational velocity ν equal to the angular frequency ω of the supply gives an average torque of

$$\bar{T} = \frac{1}{4}\frac{\hat{E}^2 \mathscr{R}_2}{N^2\omega^2}\sin 2\delta \qquad \text{newton-meters} \tag{1.175}$$

This torque characteristic is of the same form as that developed in eq. 1.44 and shown in Fig. 1.15 for an electrostatic machine. The maximum torque occurs when the angle of lag δ is equal to $\pi/4$ or $45°$.

The maximum torque obtainable from this type of synchronous reluctance machine is limited by the maximum permissible flux ϕ and the value of the reluctance variation $\mathcal{R}_2$. These quantities are interrelated, because with the maximum value of reluctance $\mathcal{R}$, the overlap between rotor and stator is zero, and all the flux is in a highly concentrated fringing field near the tips of the rotor and stator poles. If this leads to saturation in the ferromagnetic material, the maximum value of the reluctance $\mathcal{R}$ of the system is reduced.

Problems

1.1 As an exercise in the application of Coulomb's law, consider the system of four small spheres shown in Fig. P1.1. The charges on the spheres are:

$$Q_1 = Q_3 = 2 \times 10^{-11} \qquad \text{coulomb}$$
$$Q_2 = Q_4 = -10^{-11} \qquad \text{coulomb}$$

The charge Q_4 is free to move along the x axis. The other charges are fixed in position.

(a) Find the force on the charge Q_4 as a function of the distance x.

(b) At what value of x will the force on the charge Q_4 be zero?

Ans.: 0.81 cm.

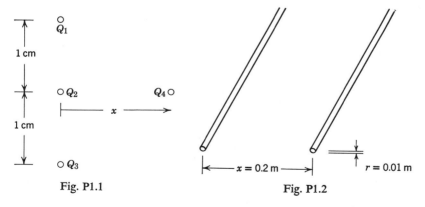

Fig. P1.1   Fig. P1.2

1.2 In Section 1.3 three methods are described for determining the electrostatic forces between oppositely charged bodies. To compare these methods, let us apply each of them to the pair of long, parallel, cylindrical conductors shown in Fig. P1.2. The conductors are oppositely charged and each carries a charge of 1.5 microcoulombs per meter of length. The problem is to find the force acting on each meter length of conductor.

(a) First, let us use Coulomb's law in solving the problem. Since the conductor radius r is small in comparison with the spacing x, the conductor may be considered as two filaments of charge, essentially infinite in length. Write a general expression for the force between the charges on increments of length on each of the conductors. Satisfy yourself that the components of force parallel to the conductor on any length increment will sum to zero because of symmetry. Determine the force produced by one conductor on an incremental length of the other.   *Ans.:* 0.202 newton/m.

(b) Next, let us use the electric field approach on the same problem. Using Gauss's theorem, find the electric field intensity produced by one conductor in the space occupied by the other conductor, and from this find the force per unit length on the conductor.

(c) Let us now approach the problem using the principle of conservation of energy. Derive an expression for the capacitance per unit length of the conductors as a function of the spacing x, and use this to find the force.

(d) Which of the preceding methods appears to give the solution most simply?

(e) Determine the force between the conductors in Fig. P1.2 when the potential difference between them is 250,000 V.

1.3   Two parallel plates (as in Fig. 1.11) are maintained at a potential difference e of 10^4 V. Each plate has an area of 0.02 m².

(a) Find the force between the plates as a function of their spacing x.

(b) Find the energy converted to mechanical form as the plate spacing x is reduced from 1 cm to 0.5 cm.   *Ans.:* 8.85×10^{-4} joule.

1.4   The force between charged plates is exploited in the electrostatic loudspeaker shown in Fig. P1.4. Two circular metallic plates are separated by a compressible ring of insulating material. When a voltage e_t is applied between the plates, the resulting force causes a change in the plate spacing x, which in turn results in an acoustic wave from the plate surfaces.

For accurate sound reproduction, the variation in spacing x should be proportional to the output voltage e of the audio amplifier. Unfortunately, the electrostatic force is proportional to the square of the terminal voltage e_t. To overcome this difficulty, a terminal voltage $e_t = E + e$ is applied, where E is a constant voltage much larger than the audio frequency signal voltage e.

(a) Suppose the voltage E is 1000 V. Assume the spacing x between the plates does not vary appreciably from a value of 0.5 mm. If the relative permittivity of the insulating ring is assumed to be 1.0, show that the force between the plates is given approximately by

$$f = 0.139 + 2.78 \times 10^{-4}\, e \text{ newtons}$$

(b) Suppose the ring provides a spring constant of 300 newtons/meter. If $e = 100 \sin \omega t$, determine the peak-to-peak oscillation in the plate spacing. *Ans.: 0.185 mm.*

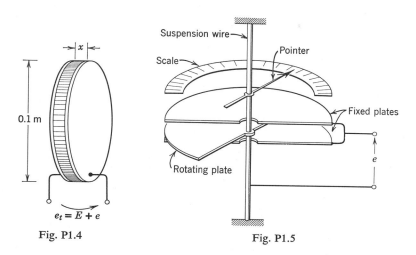

Fig. P1.4   Fig. P1.5

1.5 The electrostatic voltmeter movement shown in Fig. P1.5 consists of three semicircular metal plates. The middle plate is attached to a taut suspension wire which acts as a torsional spring. The rest position of the middle plate is at $\theta = 0$, where it is just about to enter the space between the outer plates. Suppose the plates have a radius of 4 cm and an air spacing of 1 mm between the center plate and the outer plates.

(a) Determine the capacitance of the system as a function of the angle θ.

(b) Determine the torque on the center plate as a function of the applied voltage e.

(c) Suppose the voltmeter is to have a full-scale deflection of $\theta = 3$ rad with an applied voltage of 1000 V. What should be the spring constant of the suspension system? *Ans.: 2.36 $\times$ 10^{-6} newton-m/rad.*

(d) When used on alternating voltage, does this instrument measure average, rms or peak values?

(e) Suppose an alternating voltage of 600 V rms at a frequency of 2000 c/s is applied to the meter. Determine the deflection and also determine the input impedance of the instrument. *Ans.: 5.2 $\times$ 10^6 Ω.*

(f) How could the plates be redesigned to make the scale of the instrument linear over a significant part of the voltage range?

1.6 The rotating electrostatic machine shown in Fig. P1.6 has N stationary plates and N rotating plates, each plate consisting of two quarter-circular sections of radius r. To assess the energy conversion capability of this type of machine let us idealize it by assuming that the thickness of each plate is negligible in comparison with the spacing between the plates.

(a) Derive an approximate expression for the capacitance between the stationary and rotating plates as a function of angular displacement. Express this capacitance as a Fourier series.

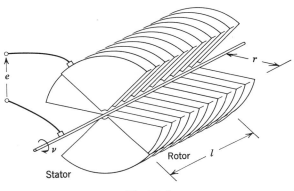

Fig. P1.6

(b) Suppose the supply voltage e varies sinusoidally with an angular frequency of ω rad/sec and that its peak value produces a maximum electric field intensity $\hat{\mathscr{e}}$ between adjacent plates. Show that the maximum value of average power output from the machine can be expressed as

$$P = \frac{\epsilon_0 \hat{\mathscr{e}}^2 \omega}{2\pi^2} V \quad \text{W}$$

where V is the volume of the machine (neglecting the volume of the plates and shaft).

(c) In air, the maximum electric field intensity is limited to about 3×10^6 V/m. If the machine is operated from a 60-c/s supply, what is the maximum power which can be converted per unit of machine volume?

(d) If the machine is operated at high vacuum, a maximum electric field intensity of about 10^8 V/m might be achieved. The velocity of the tips of the rotor plates is limited to about 200 m/sec by mechanical considerations. If the radius of the machine is 0.1 m, determine the length l required in this idealized machine to produce 500 kW.   *Ans.:* 1.77 m.

1.7 You have a choice of two materials to make a capacitor. One is a wax-impregnated paper having a dielectric constant of 2.5 and a breakdown strength of 20 kV/mm. The second is a glass with a dielectric constant of 9 and a breakdown strength of 10 kV/mm. Which material will produce the greater capacitance per unit volume for a given voltage rating?

1.8 Let us compare the energy that can be stored in the electrostatic field in a dielectric material with the energy that can be stored in a rotating flywheel of equivalent volume. Suppose the flywheel is a solid cylinder of steel having a density of 7800 kg/m³ and that its peripheral velocity is limited to 250 m/sec. Determine its stored energy per unit volume, and compare it with that of the waxpaper capacitor material of Prob. 1.7.

1.9 In a piezoelectric crystal the most useful parameters are d, the strain per unit of applied electric field, and g, the electric field per unit of applied stress. For quartz, $d = 2.5 \times 10^{-12}$ m/m per V/m and $g = 0.06$ V/m per newton/m².

(a) Consider the use of a quartz crystal in a microphone. Ordinary speech produces pressure waves up to about 0.1 newton/m². What will be the maximum open-circuit output voltage from a crystal that is 1.0 mm thick? *Ans.: 6 μV.*

(b) Consider the use of a quartz crystal to produce ultrasonic waves. If a voltage of 2500 V rms is applied across a crystal of 1-mm thickness, what will be the peak-to-peak amplitude of the mechanical vibration? *Ans.: 0.0177 μm.*

1.10 Figure P1.10 shows a rectangular loop carrying a current i in a region having a uniform flux density B.

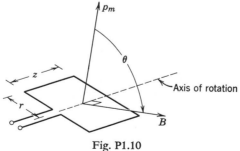

Fig. P1.10

(a) Using eq. 1.51, determine the force on each of the sides of the loop.

(b) Show that the net translational force on the loop is zero.

(c) Determine the torque on the loop and show that it can be expressed as

$$\vec{T} = \vec{p}_m \times \vec{B} \qquad \text{newton-m}$$

1.11 A 13.2-kV, single-phase transmission line carries a normal load current of 800 amp rms. The conductors are 2 cm in diameter and are spaced 1.5 m apart. The span between supporting poles is 200 m.

(a) Determine the average force acting on the conductors over one span during normal load conditions.

(b) Suppose that under short-circuit conditions, the line current is twelve times normal. Determine the average force per span.

Ans.: 246 newtons.

1.12 Figure P1.12 shows the essential components of a dynamometer wattmeter. The outer pair of circular coils, each of 50 turns, creates an

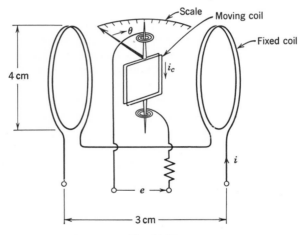

Fig. P1.12

essentially uniform magnetic flux density in the region between them. A second coil of 1000 turns is supported on pivots. The electrical connections for this coil are brought out on helical metallic springs, which together exert a torque of 2×10^{-5} newton-m/rad of deflection from the rest position. When used as a wattmeter, the outer coils carry the current i of the circuit being measured, while the central coil carries a current i_c proportional to the circuit voltage e.

(a) Using the current element law (eq. 1.57), determine the flux density at the center of the central coil as a function of the current i.

Ans.: $B = 1.61 \times 10^{-3}i$ Wb/m^2.

(b) Let us assume that the flux density found in part (a) is uniform over the region occupied by the central coil. The coil has a height of 1.5 cm and a width of 1.5 cm. In its rest position, its axis is at an angle of 60° to the axis of the outer coils. Derive an expression for the torque on the coil as a function of its current i_c and its deflection angle θ.

(c) Suppose the wattmeter is to produce its maximum deflection of $\theta = 60°$ when its current $i = 5$ amp and its potential e is 100 V. What should be the total resistance of the potential circuit?

Ans.: 7500 Ω.

(d) Will the scale of the wattmeter be linearly calibrated?

1.13 A pair of parallel busbars (as in Fig. 1.21) have a height y of 15 cm and a spacing x of 5 mm. The potential difference between the bars is 5000 V. The busbars supply a current i to a load. Note that there will be both electrostatic and magnetostatic forces acting on the conductors; at what value of load current i will the net force on the bars be equal to zero?

Ans.: 398 amp.

Show that this condition occurs when the load resistance R_L is equal to $\sqrt{L/C}$ where L is the inductance and C is the capacitance of the bars. Show also that the forces will be equal at each instant if the voltage and current are varying sinusoidally and have rms values equal to those given above.

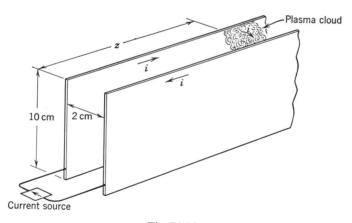

Fig. P1.14

1.14 Figure P1.14 shows a pair of parallel plates enclosing a cloud of ionized gas (plasma). A current source forces a current i of 1000 amp a distance z down one plate at which point it is conducted to the other plate by the plasma.

(a) Determine the inductance of the system.
(b) Determine the total force acting on the plasma cloud.
(c) Determine the pressure being applied to the plasma cloud.
Ans.: 62.8 newtons/m².

1.15 A fuse is made of wire having a radius r of 0.25 mm bent into a circular loop with its ends connected to adjacent terminals. The radius R of the loop is 1 cm. The problem is to determine the stress in the wire when a current of 5 amp is passed through the fuse. The inductance of a circular loop can be expressed approximately by

$$L = \mu_0 R \ln \left(1.083 \frac{R}{r} \right) \qquad \text{henrys}$$

(If you have difficulty relating the force on the wire to the stress in it, consider finding the force on each of six equal sectors of the loop and solving the force system for the tension on one of the sectors.)
Ans.: 60.6 newtons/m².

1.16 The long solenoidal coil shown in Fig. P1.16 has 200 turns. Since its length is much greater than its diameter, the field inside the coil may be considered uniform.

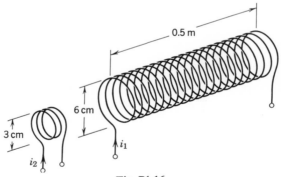

Fig. P1.16

(a) Derive an approximate expression for the inductance of this coil.
(b) If the current i_1 is 100 amp, determine the force tending to change the length of this solenoid.   *Ans.*: 2.84 newtons.
(c) A smaller coil of 500 turns and diameter 3 cm is placed inside the solenoid. The axes of the two coils are aligned. Derive an expression for the mutual inductance between the two coils.
(d) If $i_2 = 0.5$ amp and $i_1 = 100$ amp, what will be the force tending to move the smaller coil along the axis of the solenoid?

(e) Suppose the smaller coil is free to rotate so that its axis is at an angle θ to that of the solenoid. With $i_1 = 100$ amp and $i_2 = 0.5$ amp, what will be the maximum torque on the smaller coil?

Ans.: 8.9×10^{-3} newton-m.

(f) Suppose that the coils are initially aligned and carry currents $i_1 = 100$ amp and $i_2 = 0.5$ amp. How much mechanical energy is required to withdraw the smaller coil from the solenoid?   *Ans.:* 8.9×10^{-3} joule.

1.17   A dynamometer ammeter has one stationary coil and one moving coil. The self and mutual inductances of the two coils are $L_{11} = 0.01$ henry, $L_{22} = 0.004$ henry, and $L_{12} = 0.003 \cos \theta$ henry, where θ is the angle between the axes of the two coils. The coils are connected in series and carry a current of $i = \hat{\imath} \sin \omega t$.

(a) Derive an expression for the instantaneous torque on the moving coil as a function of the angle θ and the current i.

(b) Determine the average torque as a function of θ and $\hat{\imath}$.

(c) The helical restraining spring on the moving coil is adjusted to give a rest position of $\theta = 90°$. What should the spring constant be if the scale arc is to be $60°$ and full-scale deflection is to occur at 0.5 amp rms?

Ans.: 3.58×10^{-4} newton-m/rad.

(d) What is the current required to produce half-scale deflection?

Ans.: 0.269 amp.

(e) Suppose coil 2 is short circuited and an alternating current is passed through coil 1. What rms value of current will be required to produce full-scale deflection? The resistances of the coils may be assumed negligible.   *Ans.:* 0.621 amp.

1.18   Nickel has a magnetic moment of 0.6 Bohr magneton per atom. The density of nickel is 8850 kg/m³ and its atomic weight is 58.7. If all the magnetic moments are aligned, what will be the flux density in the material?   *Ans.:* 0.63 Wb/m².

1.19   Equation 1.102 states that there is a torque tending to align the axes of two current-carrying coils. It might be thought that this would be

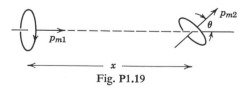

Fig. P1.19

the mechanism that causes alignment of magnetic moments in a ferromagnetic material. Let us examine this mechanism by considering the two magnetic moments of Fig. P1.19.

(a) Using the current element law (eq. 1.57), determine the flux density produced by moment p_{m1} at the center of moment p_{m2}. In doing this, the moment p_{m1} may be considered as a circular loop of any radius r_1 for which $r_1 \ll x$. *Ans.:* $\mu_0 p_{m1}/2\pi x^3$ Wb/m².

(b) Show that the magnitude of the torque acting on each of the moments is

$$T = \frac{\mu_0 p_{m1} p_{m2} \sin \theta}{2\pi x^3} \qquad \text{newton-m}$$

(c) For iron, each atom has a magnetic moment of 2.2 Bohr magnetons. The interatomic spacing can be derived from the atom density of 0.85×10^{29} atoms/m³. Determine the torque tending to align two adjacent moments.

(d) Determine the energy required to turn one moment from its aligned position of $\theta = 0$ to the unaligned condition of $\theta = \pi/2$.
Ans.: 7.09×10^{-24} joule.

(e) Iron remains ferromagnetic up to the Curie temperature of $T_c = 1043°$K. The average thermal energy per atom tending to randomize the alignments of the moments is kT, where $k = 1.38 \times 10^{-23}$ joule/deg (Boltzmann's constant). Compare this thermal energy with the energy of magnetic origin in part (d).

1.20 A crystal of iron has a magnetic moment per unit volume of $\mathcal{M} = 1.74 \times 10^6$ amp/m. If a magnetic field intensity of 8 amp/m is required to move a domain wall across the crystal, determine the hysteresis loss per unit volume when the crystal is magnetized to saturation flux density at a frequency of 100 c/s. *Ans.:* 6970 W/m³.

1.21 To a first approximation the fractional change in length $\Delta l/l$, due to magnetostriction in iron is given by the expression

$$\frac{\Delta l}{l} = 1.5 \times 10^{-6} B^2$$

Consider an iron bar, 0.1 m in length and 10^{-4} m² in cross-sectional area. Suppose the bar is surrounded by a uniformly distributed winding having 100 turns and negligible resistance.

(a) If a supply of 200 V rms at a frequency of 10 Kc/s is connected to the coil, determine the peak-to-peak variation in the length of the bar.
Ans.: 3.04×10^{-8} m.

(b) What is the frequency of the length oscillation in part (a)?

(c) Suppose a transducer is required in which the change in length will be proportional to an applied voltage. By analogy with Prob. 1.4, suggest a means by which this could be accomplished.

1.22 A toroidal magnetic core has a magnetization characteristic that can be approximated by the idealized B–H relation of Fig. P1.22. The core has a cross-sectional area of 1 cm² and a mean diameter of 6 cm. The flux density may be assumed uniform across the core.

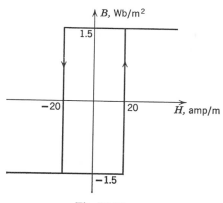

Fig. P1.22

(a) If the core has an initial flux density of $B = 1.5$ Wb/m², how much energy must be delivered to the core to create a flux density B of -1.5 Wb/m². *Ans.: 1.13 × 10⁻³ joule.*

(b) Suppose a coil of 400 turns is wound around the core. What current is required in this coil to change the flux density from $B = +1.5$ to $B = -1.5$ Wb/m²?

(c) Suppose a source of 1 V is connected to the coil. If the coil resistance is 25 Ω, what time will be required for the flux density to change from $+1.5$ to -1.5 Wb/m²? *Ans.: 0.157 sec.*

1.23 An air gap of 0.05 mm is cut in the toroidal core described in Prob. 1.22. Fringing of magnetic flux around this air gap may be neglected.

(a) What current is required in the coil to produce a flux density of 1.5 Wb/m² in the air gap? *Ans.: 0.159 amp.*

(b) When the current of part (a) is reduced to zero, what will be the flux density in the air gap? *Ans.: 0.0945 Wb/m².*

(c) Draw a flux-linkage–current characteristic for the coil. What is the approximate value of the inductance of the coil? *Ans.: 0.377 henry.*

1.24 A magnetic field of 1.2 Wb/m² is required in a space 4 cm by 10 cm by 0.6 cm. An electromagnet of the form shown in Fig. P1.24 is proposed. Our task is to design a suitable coil and core arrangement.

(a) Assuming that up to a flux density of 1.2 Wb/m², the magnetic field intensity required by the core is negligible, determine the magneto-motive force required of the coil.

(b) The temperature of the coil probably will be reasonably low if the current density in the copper conductors does not exceed 2 amp/mm². About 0.6 of the area of the window in the core can be occupied by the copper conductors, the rest being required for insulation and mechanical clearance. Determine appropriate values for the height and width of the core window.

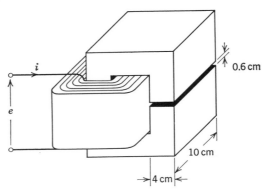

Fig. P1.24

(c) Suppose the coil is to operate from a 100 V d-c supply. The resistivity of the copper at the operating temperature is about 2×10^{-8} Ω-m. Determine the required number of turns and the cross-sectional area of the wire in the coil.

(c) Determine the power that must be dissipated as heat per unit of outside surface area of the coil. With organic insulating materials this should not exceed about 0.2 W/cm². If it does, the current density should be appropriately reduced.

1.25 A phonograph pickup shown in Fig. P1.25 consists of a 5-turn cylindrical coil of 1-cm diameter that is attached to the stylus. The coil is situated in the air gap of a cylindrical permanent magnet. The flux density is 0.3 Wb/m². The stylus-coil assembly is attached to the magnet by a flexible mounting, and the horizontal motion of the coil is approximately equal to that of the stylus. If the tip of the stylus oscillates sinusoidally with a peak-to-peak amplitude of 0.1 mm at 600 c/s, determine the rms output voltage of the pickup coil.   *Ans.: 6.26 mV.*

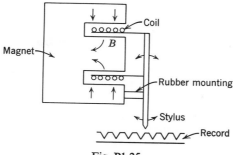

Fig. P1.25

1.26   Figure P1.26 shows the essential components of a loudspeaker. The permanent magnet produces a uniform radial magnetic flux density of 0.8 Wb/m² across a cylindrical air gap. The coil of 30 turns is wound on a fiber cylinder of diameter $d = 2$ cm. When assembled, the coil is inserted into the air gap of the magnet.

(a) Determine the force on the cone as a function of the current i. *Ans.*: 1.51 newtons/amp.

(b) Determine the induced voltage in the coil per unit of coil velocity.

(c) Neglecting coil resistance, show that the electrical power input to the coil is equal to the mechanical power delivered to the cone.

(d) Over most of the audio frequency range, the force is absorbed by the damping action of the air being driven by motion of the cone. Suppose the damping coefficient of the cone is 0.3 newton per m/sec of velocity. If the current in the coil is $i \sin \omega t$, determine the velocity of the coil and the voltage induced in the coil. Show that the impedance looking into the coil terminals is resistive and has a value of 7.6 Ω.

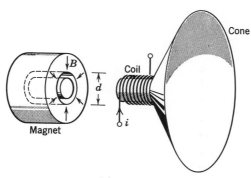

Fig. P1.26

(e) If the average power input to the speaker is 15 W, what is the peak-to-peak deflection of the coil at a frequency of 1000 c/s? *Ans.:* 3.17 mm.

(f) For very high audio frequencies, most of the force is used to accelerate the effective mass m of the coil-cone assembly. Neglecting the damping force, write a differential equation for the coil displacement as a function of the coil current for high-frequency operation. If the current is sinusoidal, show that the displacement is also sinusoidal. Show that the average power into the speaker becomes zero under this condition.

(g) For very low audio frequencies, most of the force is absorbed by the spring action of the flexible cone. Suppose the cone has a spring constant of k newtons/m. Neglecting damping and inertial forces, write a differential equation for the coil displacement as a function of current. If the current varies sinusoidally, show that the displacement is sinusoidal and that the average power input is zero.

(h) Write a differential equation relating the coil displacement to the coil current at any value of the frequency.

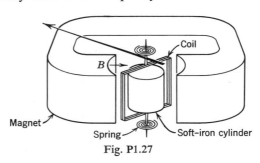

Fig. P1.27

1.27 Figure P1.27 shows the movement of a d-c instrument. The magnetic field is produced by a permanent magnet. The magnet poles and the central cylinder of soft iron are shaped so as to produce an essentially radial flux density of 0.4 Wb/m² in the air gaps. The coil is 1.5 cm high, 2 cm in width, and has 2000 turns of very fine wire. The electrical connections to the coil are brought out through helical springs, which together exert a restoring torque of 10^{-5} newton-m/rad.

(a) Determine the coil current required to produce the 70° rotation that corresponds to full-scale deflection.   *Ans.:* 51 μamp.

(b) Suppose the polar moment of inertia of the coil and pointer is 10^{-9} kg-m². Write a differential equation describing the angular position θ as a function of time and coil current. What is the natural frequency of oscillation of the coil?

Ans.: 100 rad/sec. Note the need for some form of damping and consider how this might be provided.

1.28 Figure P1.28 shows a pump used to move liquid metal along a rectangular channel. The channel is made of insulating material, except in the region of the two electrodes, which pass a current i through the metal. A uniform flux density of $B = 1.0 \text{ Wb/m}^2$ is produced across the channel by the use of a ferromagnetic core with an appropriate winding.

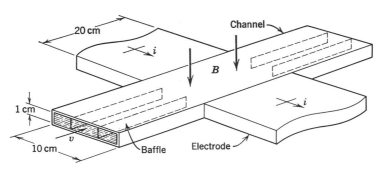

Fig. P1.28

(a) Suppose the metal flows with a uniform velocity of $v = 10$ m/sec. If the current i is zero, what is the potential difference between the electrodes?
Ans.: 1 V.

(b) Suppose the velocity in part (a) is not uniform but has an average value of 10 m/sec. What effect will this have on the potential difference between the electrodes?

(c) The metal has a resistivity of 10^{-6} Ω-m. Insulating baffles are provided in the entrance and exit portions of the channel to prevent the current from spreading out along the channel. Determine approximately the resistance between the two electrodes.

(d) Suppose a current of 2000 amp is passed through the electrodes when the velocity of the metal is 10 m/sec. What will be the potential difference between the electrodes?
Ans.: 1.1 V.

(e) Assuming that the metal encounters no friction as it passes through the pump, what will be the pressure difference between the entrance and exit of the pump?
Ans.: 2×10^5 newtons/m^2.

(f) Show that the electrical power input is equal to the sum of the mechanical power output and the loss in the resistance of the metal.

(g) The flux density B can be produced by using the electrode current i in a winding on the ferromagnetic core that bounds the top and bottom of the channel. How many turns should be used in this winding to produce $B = 1.0 \text{ Wb/m}^2$ with a current of $i = 2000$ amp?
Ans.: 4 turns.

1.29 Let us consider the possibility of measuring the blood flow in a vein. A permanent magnet is used to produce a flux density of 0.6 Wb/m² across the vein. Then needle contacts are made to points on opposite sides of the vein. The vein may be considered as a cylinder 3 mm in diameter. If the open-circuit voltage between the contacts is 1 mV, what is the flow in the vein?   *Ans.:* 3.93 cm³/sec.

1.30 A circular metal disk of radius r_0 is rotated with an angular velocity of ν rad/sec, as shown in Fig. P1.30. A uniform magnetic field of flux density B is directed perpendicularly to the plane of the disk.

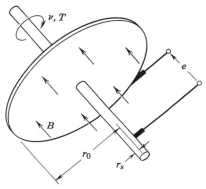

Fig. P1.30

(a) Make a sketch showing the magnetic forces on the free electrons in the disk, the charge distribution on the disk, and the electrostatic forces on the free electrons.

(b) Derive an expression for the potential difference e between brushes on the outside rim and on the surface of the shaft of radius r_s.

(c) Suppose sliding contacts are placed uniformly around the outside rim of the disk and that a current i is passed from them to the brush on the shaft. Assuming that the current density in the disk is directed radially, derive an expression for the torque T acting on the shaft.

(d) Assuming the disk to be perfectly conducting, show that the electrical power input equals the mechanical power output.

(e) The torque in part (c) arises from the circumferential forces on the free electrons, whose flow produces the current i. In a perfectly conducting material, these electrons would be absolutely free to move in response to forces. Through what mechanism is the force on these free electrons transferred to the body of the disk to produce torque? Is the current density directed radially?

(f) Let us examine some of the practical features and limitations of this machine. The magnetic flux density B is limited to about 1.5 Wb/m^2 by saturation in the ferromagnetic materials available. The peripheral velocity of the disk is limited to about 200 m/sec to prevent mechanical overstressing. If the disk has an outer radius of $r_0 = 0.2$ m and a shaft of radius $r_s = 2$ cm, determine the maximum terminal voltage e that can be obtained on no load. *Ans.: 29.7 V.*

(g) Suppose the disk has a thickness of 1 cm. If the current density is not to exceed 10^7 amp/m^2 at any point, what is the maximum current i which the machine can carry? What is its maximum power output?
Ans.: 373 kW.

(h) If the disk is made of copper having a resistivity of 2×10^{-8} Ω-m at the operating temperature of the machine, determine the resistance of the disk and show that its effect on the terminal voltage is negligible up to maximum load determined in part (g).

1.31 Figure P1.31 shows a cross section of a low-voltage, high-current generator, known as a homopolar machine. A thin metal cylinder of

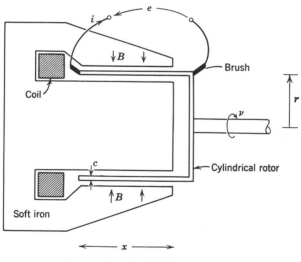

Fig. P1.31

radius r and length x is rotated at angular velocity v in a radial magnetic field of density B. In this problem, let us examine some of the features of this type of machine and attempt a preliminary design.

(a) The speed v of the cylinder is limited by the mechanical stress in the material. It can be shown that the stress around the cylinder is equal to $\rho_m v^2$ newtons/m², where ρ_m is the density of the material and v is the peripheral velocity. Suppose we use a copper alloy having a density of 8800 kg/m³ and a maximum working stress of 2.8×10^8 newtons/m². Determine the maximum peripheral velocity $\hat{v}$. Write an expression for the induced voltage between the ends of the cylinder.

Ans. $\hat{v} = 178$ m/sec.

(b) Current is passed through the cylinder by means of stationary brushes, which are distributed around both the inside and the outside rims. In high-current machines, the electrical contacts may take the form of a liquid metal channel. The current i that can be carried by the cylinder is limited by the heat that can be extracted from its surfaces. Let h denote the heat in W/m² that can be removed by air flow from the curved cylindrical surfaces (inside and outside) of the cylinder. If the thickness of the material is c and the resistivity is ρ, derive expressions for the current density J and the current i in the material.

(c) Show that the power P converted in the machine can be expressed as

$$P = 2\pi r x B \hat{v} \left(\frac{2hc}{\rho} \right)^{1/2} \quad \text{W}$$

(d) With forced air cooling, h might be about 5000 W/m². The copper alloy would have a resistivity of about 2×10^{-8} Ω-m at the operating temperature. The flux density B in the air gap would probably not exceed 1.0 Wb/m². The iron core cannot support a flux density in excess of about 1.6 Wb/m². Determine the required relation between the dimensions x and r to provide adequate magnetic material in the central cylindrical core of the machine. If the thickness c of the metal cylinder is made 1 cm, determine the radius r and the length x for a 1-MW machine.

Ans.: $r = x = 0.125$ m.

(e) Determine the resistance of the metal cylinder. Find the fraction of the converted power that will be dissipated as heat in the cylinder.

Ans.: 0.0008.

(f) If the current i were brought out from the inside brushes through holes in the magnetic structure, as shown in Fig. P1.31, what effect would this current have on the magnetic material? Show that this effect can be substantially eliminated by bringing out the current i along a stationary metal cylinder placed outside the revolving cylinder in the air gap.

(g) If the air gap length is 2.5 cm, estimate the magnetomotive force required in the coil.   *Ans.:* >20,000 amp.

(h) Determine approximately the required dimensions of the magnetic path around the coil and air gap.

1.32 The magnetic core shown in Fig. P1.32 has a square cross section 3 cm by 3 cm. When the two sections of the core are fitted together, air gaps, each of length $x = 1$ mm, separate them. The coil has 250 turns and a resistance of 7.5 Ω. The magnetic field intensity required by the magnetic material is negligible.

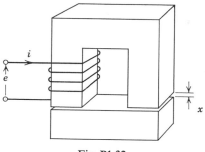

Fig. P1.32

(a) Suppose a d-c source of 40 V is connected to the coil. Determine the total force holding the two sections of the core together.

Ans.: 503 newtons.

(b) Suppose an a-c source of 100 V rms at 60 c/s is connected to the coil. Determine the force holding the sections together. What is its average value?   *Ans.:* 757 newtons.

(c) The magnetic field is not entirely confined to the air gap volume. It actually extends out into the space around the gap with diminishing density. This effect may be included in approximate calculations by assuming that the magnetic flux density is uniform for a distance equal to half the gap length x out from each side of the air gap. Consider the effect of this correction for fringing on the results of parts (a) and (b).

1.33 A toroidal core has a cross-sectional area of 10^{-3} m² and a mean length of 0.4 m. The material of the core has a maximum magnetic moment per unit volume of $\hat{\mathscr{M}} = 1.5 \times 10^6$ amp/m. For $\hat{\mathscr{M}} > \mathscr{M} > -\hat{\mathscr{M}}$, the required field intensity is negligible. The core is uniformly wound with a coil of 400 turns.

(a) Draw a *B–H* characteristic for the core material.

(b) Determine the flux density in the core if the coil current is 50 amp.

Ans.: 1.95 Wb/m².

(c) Now suppose an air gap of 1-mm length is cut across the core. What minimum value of coil current is required to make $\mathscr{M} = \hat{\mathscr{M}}$ in the core?   *Ans.:* 3.75 amp.

(d) What is the air gap flux density with a coil current of 50 amp?
Ans.: 1.94 Wb/m².

(e) What is the force acting on the core material to close the air gap for the condition of part (d)?   *Ans.:* 1415 newtons.

(f) If the coil of 400 turns had been concentrated around the side of the torus opposite to the air gapped side, would the air gap flux density reach the value given in part (d)? Would the force found in part (e) have changed?

1.34 The magnetic actuator shown in Fig. P1.34 is to be used to raise a mass m through a distance y. The coil has 5000 turns and can carry a

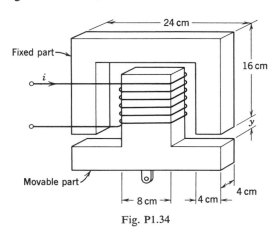

Fig. P1.34

current of 2 amp without overheating. The magnetic material can support a flux density of 1.5 Wb/m² with negligible field intensity. Fringing of flux at the air gaps may be neglected.

(a) Determine the maximum air gap y for which a flux density of 1.5 Wb/m² can be established with a current of 2.0 amp.   *Ans.:* 4.18 mm.

(b) With the air gap determined in part (a), what is the force exerted by the actuator?

(c) The mass density of the material is 7800 kg/m³. Determine the approximate value of the net mass m of the load which can be lifted against the force of gravity (at sea level) by the actuator.   *Ans.:* 578 kg.

(d) What current is required in the coil to lift the unloaded actuator?

(e) What is the initial acceleration of the unloaded actuator if it is released when the coil current i is 0.3 amp?   *Ans.:* 11.7 m/sec².

1.35 Figure P1.35 shows a cross section of a cylindrical magnetic actuator. The plunger, of cross-sectional area 15 cm², is free to slide vertically through a circular hole in the outer magnetic casing, the air gap between the two being negligible. The coil has 3000 turns and a resistance of 8 ohms. It is connected to a 12 V d-c source. The magnetic material may be assumed perfect up to its saturation flux density of 1.6 Wb/m².

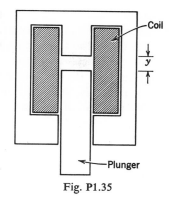

Fig. P1.35

(a) Determine the static force on the plunger as a function of the gap length y.

(b) Over what range of gap length y will the force on the plunger be essentially constant because saturation flux density has been reached? *Ans.: $y \leq 3.53$ mm.*

(c) Suppose the plunger is constrained to move slowly from a gap of 1 cm to the fully closed position. What will be the mechanical energy produced? *Ans.: 8.9 joules.*

(d) Suppose that the plunger is allowed to close so quickly from an initial gap of 1 cm that the flux linkage of the coil does not change appreciably during the motion. How much mechanical energy will be produced? *Ans.: 1.9 joules.*

1.36 The magnetic actuators discussed in the two preceding problems produce a large force over a relatively short displacement. Figure P1.36 shows a type of actuator that is capable of exerting a smaller force over a larger displacement. The central cylindrical plunger is separated from the outer cylindrical casing by a uniform air gap of 0.5 mm. The coil has 500 turns. The magnetic material of the plunger and casing can be considered perfect up to 1.6 Wb/m².

(a) One of the limitations of this actuator is the magnetic flux that can be supported by the plunger. If the flux density in this member is not to exceed 1.6 Wb/m², what is the maximum permissible current in the coil? *Ans.: 0.255 amp.*

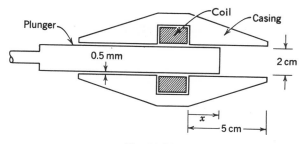

Fig. P1.36

(b) With the current held constant at the value found in part (a), derive an expression for the force as a function of the displacement x. Determine the maximum and minimum values of this force.

Ans.: 1.28 newtons (max).

(c) Suppose the coil current is increased to five times the value given in (a). This will cause the plunger to be magnetically saturated at $B = 1.6$ Wb/m² for most of the displacement x. Determine the force as a function of x for this condition. Is the force at $x = 5$ cm increased above the value found in (b)?

1.37 Figure P1.37 shows a moving-iron ammeter in which a curved ferromagnetic rod is drawn into a curved solenoidal coil against the

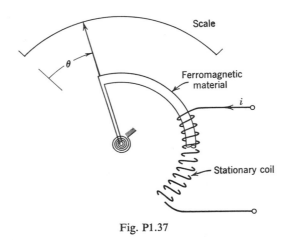

Fig. P1.37

torque of a restraining spring. The inductance of the coil is $L = 5 + 20\theta$ μH, where θ is the deflection angle in radians. The spring constant is 7×10^{-4} newton-m/rad.

(a) Show that the instrument measures the root-mean-square value of the current.

(b) What will be the full-scale deflection if the rated current is 10 amp?
Ans.: 1.43 rad.

(c) What will be the potential difference across the coil when the current is 5 amp rms at a frequency of 180 c/s? The coil resistance is 0.01 Ω.
Ans.: 85 mv.

1.38 A rotating actuator of the form shown in Fig. 1.53a has the following dimensions: $g = 1$ mm, $r = 2$ cm, $z = 4$ cm. The coil has 400 turns. The magnetic material may be considered perfect up to 1.2 Wb/m².

(a) Determine the maximum coil current if the flux density is to be limited to 1.2 Wb/m² in the material bounding the air gap.

(b) With the current found in part (a), determine the torque produced. What work will be done as the shaft moves from $\theta = \pi/2$ to $\theta = 0$?
Ans.: 1.44 joules.

1.39 In some control applications a rotating actuator with reversible torque is required. Figure P1.39 shows a device that has this feature.

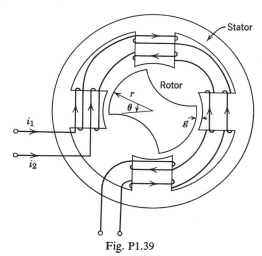

Fig. P1.39

In addition, it provides a torque that is linearly proportional to the product of its two coil currents. Each of the four stator poles has an angular width of 45° and a length z. The rotor faces each have an angular width of 90° and a radius r. The air gap length is g, and the flux outside the air gaps may be neglected. Each stator pole has two N-turn coils, one carrying a current i_1 and the other carrying a current i_2. The coils are connected so that the magnetomotive force on each of the horizontal poles is $N(i_1 + i_2)$, while that on each of the vertical poles is $N(i_1 - i_2)$.

(a) Note that because of the symmetry of the magnetic system, magnetomotive forces on the horizontal poles do not produce flux in the vertical poles. Derive an expression for the torque due to the magnetomotive forces on the horizontal poles. Derive a similar expression for the torque due to the magnetomotive forces on the vertical poles. Combine these two expressions and show that

$$T = \frac{4N^2\mu_0 z r i_1 i_2}{g} \qquad \text{newton-m}$$

over the range $0 < \theta < \pi/4$.

(b) Let $r = 2.5$ cm, $z = 5$ cm, $g = 1$ mm, and $N = 1000$ turns. If the air gap flux density is not to exceed 1.5 Wb/m² and the currents i_1 and i_2 are equal, what is the maximum permissible value of each of these currents? If the current i_1 is maintained constant at this value, show that the torque is given by $T = 3.75i_2$ newton-m.

1.40 A reluctance motor having the form shown in Fig. 1.53a has an axial length z of 20 cm, a rotor radius r of 10 cm, and an air gap g of 1 mm. The stator and rotor poles have angular widths of 90°.

(a) Using any reasonable assumptions, determine the reluctance of the magnetic system as a function of the angle θ. What is the minimum value of this reluctance?   *Ans.:* 5.06×10^4 amp/Wb.

(b) If fringing flux is neglected in part (a), the value obtained for the reluctance is infinite at $\theta = 0$. Suppose the fringing is such as to limit the maximum value of reluctance to four times the minimum value. Show that the reluctance can be represented approximately by the expression

$$\mathscr{R} = 5.06 \times 10^4 \, (2.5 + 1.5 \cos 2\theta) \qquad \text{amp/Wb}$$

(c) Suppose a voltage of 110 V rms at 60 c/s is applied to the 15-turn winding. If the winding resistance is negligible, determine the magnetic flux in the machine.

(d) At what angular velocity must the rotor rotate to produce an average torque?

(e) What is the maximum value of average torque this machine can produce when connected to a 110-V, 60-c/s supply? What is the maximum mechanical power?   *Ans.:* 5420 W.

1.41 A rotating machine of the form shown in Fig. 1.53a has a coil inductance which can be expressed approximately by

$$L = 0.01 - 0.03 \cos 2\theta - 0.02 \cos 4\theta \qquad \text{henry}$$

A current of 5 amp rms at 50 c/s is passed through the coil, and the rotor is driven at a variable speed of ν rad/sec.

(a) At what values of speed will the machine develop useful torque? *Ans.:* 157 and 314 rad/sec.

(b) Which value of speed will give the larger value of maximum torque? At that speed, what will be the maximum value of average torque developed by the machine?   *Ans.:* 0.5 newton-m.

REFERENCES

Chang, S. S. L., *Energy Conversion*. Prentice-Hall, Englewood Cliffs, N.J., 1963.

Dekker, A. J., *Electrical Engineering Materials*. Prentice-Hall, Englewood Cliffs, N.J., 1959.

Hadfield, D., *Permanent Magnets and Magnetism*. Swift Levick and Sons, London and John Wiley and Sons, New York, 1962.

Halliday, D. and R. Resnick, *Physics for Students of Science and Engineering*, Part II. John Wiley and Sons, New York, 1962.

Ham, J. M. and G. R. Slemon, *Scientific Basis of Electrical Engineering*. John Wiley and Sons, New York, 1961.

Jackson, W., *The Insulation of Electrical Equipment*. Chapman and Hall, London, 1954.

Messerle, H. K., "Dynamic Circuit Theory." *Transactions, American Institute of Electrical Engineers*, **59**, 1960, 567.

Morrish, A. H., *The Physical Principles of Magnetism*. John Wiley and Sons, New York, 1965.

Newhouse, V. L., *Applied Superconductivity*. John Wiley and Sons, New York, 1964.

Roters, H. C., *Electromagnetic Devices*. John Wiley and Sons, New York, 1941.

Skilling, H. H., *Electromechanics: A First Course in Electromechanical Energy Conversion*. John Wiley and Sons, New York, 1962.

Sproull, R. L., *Modern Physics* (second edition). John Wiley and Sons, New York, 1963.

Whitehead, S., *Dielectric Breakdown of Solids*. Oxford University Press, London, 1953.

Chapter 2
ANALYSIS OF MAGNETIC SYSTEMS

Ferromagnetic materials are used in essentially all electrical machines and transformers. There are several interrelated reasons for this widespread use. In a closed magnetic path, a large magnetic flux can be established and controlled by the application of a very small magnetomotive force from an encircling coil. In a magnetic path with an air gap, the effect of the magnetomotive force of the coil is concentrated at the gap, allowing the production of an intense magnetic field in a restricted volume of space. In addition, the forces between sections of magnetic material in a magnetic path with an air gap are several orders of magnitude greater than could be obtained with a similar volume of conductor material only.

In Section 1.6 we considered the physical basis of the relationship between the flux density B and the magnetic field intensity H in a ferromagnetic material. The saturation and hysteresis properties of this relationship can be exploited to produce a variety of useful devices. The relationship between B and H is nonlinear, multivalued, history dependent, and often time dependent. Formidable difficulties may therefore be expected in analysis. This chapter begins with a consideration of various approximate models for the B–H characteristic which may lead to useful prediction of performance with a minimum of analytical effort.

In addition to the complexity in the B–H relationship of the material, there is also complexity in the shapes of magnetic structures in electric apparatus. The latter part of the chapter considers means by which the complex magnetic field of the structure may be reduced, for analytical purposes, to a simple magnetic or electric equivalent circuit.

2.1 APPROXIMATE MODELS FOR B–H CHARACTERISTICS

Consider the uniformly wound torus of magnetic material shown in Fig. 2.1. The potential difference e across the coil terminals is

$$e = Ri + \frac{d\lambda}{dt} \qquad \text{volts} \qquad (2.1)$$

106

where R is the coil resistance and λ is the flux linkage of the coil. If the voltage e is to be expressed as a function of current and time only, the relation between the flux linkage λ and the current i must be known.

The magnetic field intensity H in the torus may be related to the current i by use of the circuital law of eq. 1.60. If the ratio of the inner radius r_1 to the outer radius r_2 of the torus is near unity, the magnetic field within the torus may be assumed to be uniform in intensity, its average magnitude being related to the coil current by

$$i = \frac{\bar{l}H}{N} \qquad \text{amperes} \qquad (2.2)$$

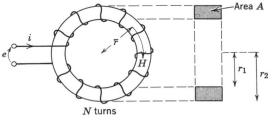

N turns

Fig. 2.1   A uniformly wound torus.

where $\bar{l}$, the mean length of the flux path, is equal to $2\pi\bar{r}$. Using the same assumption of uniformity of the magnetic field over the cross-sectional area A, the flux linkage λ is related to the magnetic flux density B by

$$\lambda = NAB \text{ webers} \qquad (2.3)$$

Combining eqs. 2.2 and 2.3 gives

$$\frac{\lambda}{i} = \left(\frac{N^2 A}{\bar{l}}\right)\left(\frac{B}{H}\right) \qquad \text{webers/ampere} \qquad (2.4)$$

This shows that the flux linkage–current relationship for the coil has the same shape as the *B–H* characteristic of the material. If the ordinate of the *B–H* characteristic is multiplied by NA and the abscissa by $\bar{l}/N$, the λ–i characteristic is obtained. It must be stressed that this applies only in situations where uniformity of the magnetic field can be assumed.

Since the magnetic flux ϕ in the core is equal to the product BA, and the magnetomotive force $\mathscr{F}$ of the winding is equal to $H\bar{l}$, the *B–H* relationship may also be rescaled to produce the relation between magnetic flux and magnetomotive force for the magnetic element.

The complexity of attempting an accurate representation of the *B–H* relationship is demonstrated in Fig. 2.2. This figure shows the *B–H* locus that may be followed as the magnetic field intensity H alternates through

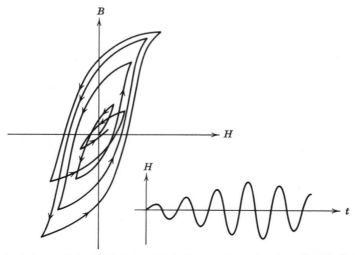

Fig. 2.2   A locus of the *B–H* characteristic for an alternating intensity *H* of variable magnitude.

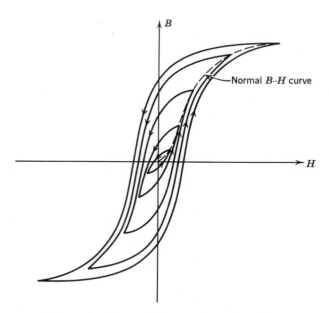

Fig. 2.3   A set of hysteresis loops and the normal magnetization curve for a ferromagnetic material.

a number of cycles with variable peak magnitude. Note that at a given value of magnetic field intensity, the flux density may have any value within a wide range. To determine the appropriate value, it is necessary to know the past history of the *B–H* locus. It is obviously impossible to record the loci for all possible past histories; thus actual *B–H* loci are seldom used in analysis. Simplified approximations generally give results of adequate accuracy.

For alternating current of constant peak magnitude, the set of closed, symmetrical *B–H* loops shown in Fig. 2.3 represent the behavior of the material. The analytical difficulty in using such loops is that it is necessary to know, in advance, the peak amplitude of either *B* or *H* to decide which loop is applicable.

2.1.1 Normal Magnetization Curve

Several simple and useful approximations can be obtained if the hysteresis effect in the material is neglected. Without its memory, the *B–H* relationship becomes single valued. The most commonly used approximation, known as the normal magnetization curve, is shown in Fig. 2.3. This curve is the locus of the tips of a set of symmetrical hysteresis loops. This is the curve that is most readily available in the descriptive literature on most types of soft magnetic material. It is obtained by use of a flux meter, which measures the total change in the flux of a sample when its exciting current is reversed.

Numerical techniques are applicable to analyses which involve the normal magnetization curve. As a simple example, consider the circuit of Fig. 2.4*a* in which a constant voltage *E* is applied to a coil at time $t = 0$ by closing the switch. The coil is represented by its resistance *R* and by the flux linkage λ versus current *i* curve of Fig. 2.4*b*. This curve is derived from the normal magnetization curve of Fig. 2.3 by rescaling the *B–H* curve using eqs. 2.2 and 2.3. At $t = 0$, the current *i* is zero. We want to find the current *i* as a function of time *t*. From eq. 2.1, we have

$$\left(\frac{d\lambda}{dt}\right)_{t=0} = E \tag{2.5}$$

Assuming that this rate of change of flux linkage remains approximately constant for a short interval of time Δt, the flux linkage λ_1 at time Δt can be approximated by

$$\lambda_1 = E\,\Delta t \tag{2.6}$$

Referring to the λ–*i* curve, the corresponding current is i_1. The slope of the λ–*t* curve at $t = \Delta t$ can now be determined as

$$\left(\frac{d\lambda}{dt}\right)_{t=\Delta t} = E - Ri_1 \tag{2.7}$$

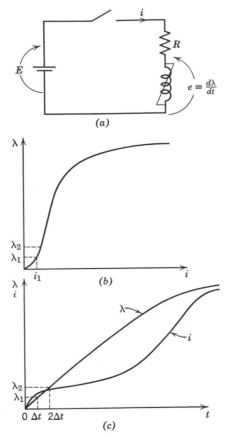

Fig. 2.4   (*a*) Circuit. (*b*) Flux linkage λ–i characteristic. (*c*) Flux linkage λ and current *i* as functions of time *t*.

and the flux linkage at time $2 \Delta t$ can be approximated by

$$\lambda_2 = \lambda_1 + \Delta t \left(\frac{d\lambda}{dt} \right)_{t=\Delta t} \tag{2.8}$$

Continued repetition of this calculation results in the data for the curves of flux linkage and current as functions of time, plotted in Fig. 2.4*c*.

This simple numerical method of solution is adequate for many non-linear systems. Reference should be made to books on numerical analysis for more elaborate techniques that provide either a greater accuracy or fewer steps in the computation, or both.

2.1.2   Piecewise Linearization of the Normal Magnetization Curve

In many analyses the normal magnetization curve (Fig. 2.3) may be adequately represented by the *B–H* characteristic of Fig. 2.5. This consists of a linear portion in the range $-B_k < B < B_k$ having an unsaturated relative permeability μ_n and two linear portions for the ranges $|B| > B_k$, each having a slope $\mu_s \mu_0$ where μ_s is termed the saturated relative permeability. Within the unsaturated range, the flux linkage–current relationship

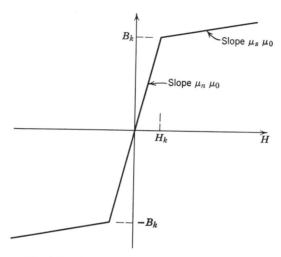

Fig. 2.5   Piecewise linearization of *B–H* curve.

of a coil (such as that of Fig. 2.1) may be expressed as the unsaturated value of inductance L_n where, from eq. 2.4,

$$L_n = \frac{\lambda}{i} = \frac{N^2 A}{l} \mu_n \mu_0 \qquad \text{henrys} \qquad (2.9)$$

In this expression, A is the core area, l the mean length of the flux path, and N the number of turns. If the magnitude of the coil current i is less than $i_k = H_k l / N$, the voltage-current relationship of the coil may be expressed by the linear differential equation

$$e = Ri + L_n \frac{di}{dt} \qquad \text{volts} \qquad (2.10)$$

If the magnitude of the current exceeds i_k, the voltage-current relationship becomes

$$e = Ri + L_s \frac{di}{dt} \qquad \text{volts} \qquad (2.11)$$

where

$$L_s = \frac{N^2 A}{l} \mu_s \mu_0 \qquad \text{henrys} \qquad (2.12)$$

Figure 2.6 shows the current versus time curve for the circuit of Fig. 2.4a for two values of applied voltage E. In the lower curve the current does not reach the value i_k; in the upper curve this value is exceeded. Since eqs. 2.10 and 2.11 are of the first order and have constant coefficients, all terms of the solutions are simple exponentials. To arrive at the solution for case 2 in Fig. 2.6, eq. 2.10 is used until $i = i_k$. The final conditions

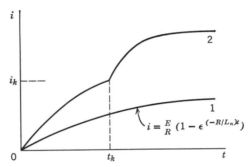

Fig. 2.6 Current-time curves for circuit of Fig. 2.4a. (1) $E/R < i_k$. Current insufficient to reach saturated region. (2) With increased applied voltage. $E/R > i_k$.

(i_k, t_k) of eq. 2.10 are then used as the initial conditions in the solution of eq. 2.11, which applies for $i > i_k$.

The process of simplifying the $B\text{–}H$ relation may be carried further for those situations where the magnetic field intensity H is negligible as long as the flux density B does not approach its saturation value. The unsaturated relative permeability μ_n of Fig. 2.5 may then be set at infinity. This approximation, shown in Fig. 2.7a, proves to be very useful in the analysis of devices, such as saturable reactors, which operate far into the saturated region of the $B\text{–}H$ curve.

Sometimes the further simplification of making the saturated relative permeability μ_s equal to zero is justified. Physically, we know that even a perfectly grain-oriented material cannot have a value of μ_s less than unity. This approximation, shown in Fig. 2.7b, is applicable in those situations where the saturated inductance L_s of eq. 2.12 is negligible in relation to the other parameters of the system under analysis.

To demonstrate the use of these simple linearized models, consider the circuit of Fig. 2.8a in which a voltage $e = \hat{E} \cos \omega t$ is applied to a coil at $t = 0$. Suppose the $\lambda\text{–}i$ characteristic of the coil is represented by the

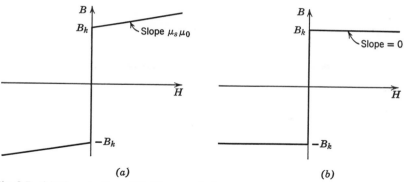

Fig. 2.7   (a) Linearization of *B–H* curve, similar to Fig. 2.6, with $\mu_n = \infty$. (b) $\mu_n = \infty$ and $\mu_s = 0$.

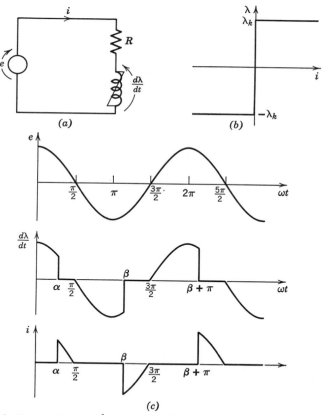

Fig. 2.8   (a) Circuit with $e = \hat{E} \cos \omega t$. (b) Idealized relation between flux linkage λ and current i. (c) Waveforms of e, $d\lambda/dt$, and i.

idealized model of Fig. 2.8b. The voltage-current relationship is given by
the equation

$$Ri + \frac{d\lambda}{dt} = e$$

$$= \hat{E} \cos \omega t \qquad \text{volts} \qquad (2.13)$$

For $\lambda_k > \lambda > -\lambda_k$, the current i is zero and all the applied voltage in
eq. 2.13 is absorbed as a rate of change of flux linkage. If $\lambda = 0$ at $t = 0$,
the flux linkage can be expressed initially as

$$\lambda = \int_0^t \hat{E} \cos \omega t \, dt$$

$$= \frac{\hat{E}}{\omega} \sin \omega t \qquad \text{webers} \qquad (2.14)$$

Equation 2.14 describes the flux linkage λ until $\omega t = \alpha$ where λ reaches
its critical value λ_k. Thus

$$\alpha = \sin^{-1} \frac{\omega \lambda_k}{\hat{E}} \qquad (2.15)$$

Since no further increase in flux linkage can occur, $d\lambda/dt$ is zero for the
rest of the interval during which e is positive. Thus, for $\alpha < \omega t < \pi/2$

$$i = \frac{\hat{E}}{R} \cos \omega t \qquad (2.16)$$

After $\omega t = \pi/2$, the flux linkage is given by

$$\lambda = \lambda_k + \int_{\pi/2\omega}^t e \, dt \qquad (2.17)$$

until λ reaches its negative value of $-\lambda_k$ at $\omega t = \beta$. From this point until
the end of the period of negative applied voltage, the current is again
given by eq. 2.16. The waveforms of the applied voltage e, the voltage
$d\lambda/dt$, and the current i are shown in Fig. 2.8b.

This example demonstrates one of the useful properties of a saturable
magnetic core. If the core can be represented by the idealized B–H relationship of Fig. 2.7b, and the coil resistance is negligible, all the applied
voltage is absorbed by the coil until the core reaches saturation. The coil
then becomes a short circuit, switching all the applied voltage to the
element connected in series. This property is exploited in saturable
reactors, magnetic amplifiers, and magnetic frequency multipliers.

2.1.3   Linear Models that Preserve the Hysteresis Effect

Operation of many devices such as permanent-magnet machines, hysteresis machines, and magnetic amplifiers is dependent on the hysteresis property of the magnetic material. Analysis of these devices can also be expedited by the use of piecewise linear models.

Figure 2.9 shows hysteresis loops that might apply for either a permanent-magnetic or a soft-magnetic material. As shown, the outer loop

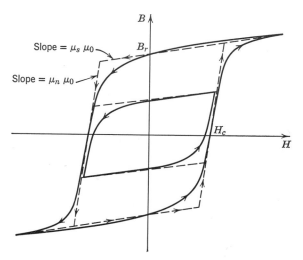

Fig. 2.9   Hysteresis loops and an approximate linearized model of the loops.

can be approximated by four straight lines, two of which have a slope $\mu_n\mu_0$, the other two of which have a slope $\mu_s\mu_0$. It may be seen that the approximation can be reasonably accurate, except at the corners of the loop. The enclosed areas of the actual loop and its linearized model can be made approximately equal by a judicious choice of the model, resulting in a model having the same hysteresis loss as the actual loop.

As the maximum flux density is decreased, the width of the hysteresis loop often decreases only slightly. In such circumstances a linearized model having lines of the same slopes as for the major loop may be used to represent the smaller loops. One of these smaller loops with its linearized model is shown in Fig. 2.9.

With good grain-oriented magnetic materials, the sides of the hysteresis loop are essentially vertical, and the saturated portions approach an incremental slope of μ_0. An example is shown in Fig. 1.40. It is often possible to represent such a loop with acceptable accuracy by the simple linearized model of Fig. 2.10. This model is similar to that of Fig. 2.7b, except that the hysteresis property has been retained. Any excursion in magnetic field intensity in the range $-H_c < H < H_c$ is assumed to occur along a horizontal locus of constant flux density, while a change of flux density is assumed to occur only at $H = \pm H_c$.

To demonstrate the use of this model, let us consider the system of Fig. 2.11a, which acts as a pulse counter. Suppose a number of irregularly

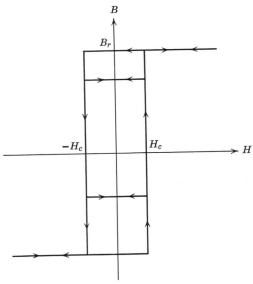

Fig. 2.10 Idealized model for the B–H loops of a grain-oriented material, including the hysteresis effect.

spaced rectangular pulses of amplitude E and time duration τ are applied to a load resistance R_L in series with a coil having a rectangular-loop core. The coil resistance is considered to be negligible in comparison with R_L. Suppose the core is initially set to have negative residual flux density B_r by use of a negative coil current. When a pulse of voltage is applied, the current i rises to the value

$$i_c = \frac{H_c l}{N} \qquad \text{amperes} \qquad (2.18)$$

where l is the mean path length of the core and N the number of coil turns. The rate of change of coil flux linkage λ is given by

$$\frac{d\lambda}{dt} = E - R_L i_c \qquad (2.19)$$

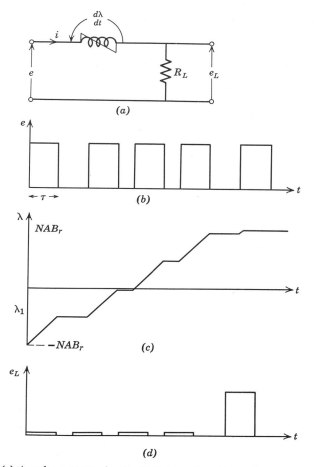

Fig. 2.11 (*a*) A pulse-counter circuit. (*b*) Pulses of applied voltage. (*c*) Flux linkage. (*d*) Output voltage.

Integrating eq. 2.19 yields the flux linkage λ_1 at the end of the first pulse as

$$\lambda_1 = -NAB_r + (E - R_L i_c)\tau \qquad \text{webers} \qquad (2.20)$$

At the cessation of the pulse the current and the magnetic field intensity return to zero. Subsequent pulses cause the flux linkage λ to increase by an amount $(E - R_L i_c)\tau$ for each pulse. When λ reaches its positive saturation value NAB_r, all of the applied voltage appears across the load resistance R_L, as shown in Fig. 2.11*d*. By judicious choice of core dimensions and turns, this system gives an output pulse following the application of any number (such as ten) of input pulses.

2.1.4 Impedance Model

Most a-c apparatus operates with a voltage that is approximately sinusoidal. It would therefore be useful to have a simple representation for a nonlinear inductor operating under this condition. Suppose a sinusoidal voltage of

$$e = \hat{E} \sin \omega t \qquad \text{volts} \qquad (2.21)$$

is applied to a coil whose resistance is negligible and whose core has the

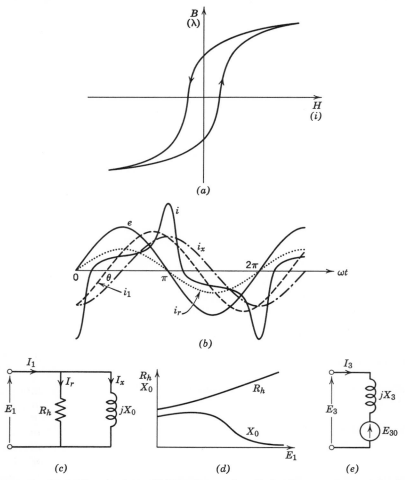

Fig. 2.12 (a) B–H or λ–i loop. (b) Waveforms of applied voltage e, current i, fundamental component i_1, in-phase component i_r, and quadrature component i_x. (c) Fundamental-frequency equivalent circuit. (d) Variation of equivalent circuit parameters with applied voltage E_1. (e) Third harmonic equivalent circuit.

flux linkage–current characteristic of Fig. 2.12*a*. This characteristic is obtained by rescaling a *B–H* loop of the material using eqs. 2.2 and 2.3. The flux linkage of the coil is

$$\lambda = \int e\, dt$$

$$= \frac{\hat{E}}{\omega} \sin\left(\omega t - \frac{\pi}{2}\right) \qquad \text{webers} \qquad (2.22)$$

The current *i* in the coil has the periodic but nonsinusoidal form shown in Fig. 2.12*b*. This current may be expressed as a Fourier series.

$$i = \hat{I}_1 \sin(\omega t - \theta) + \text{odd harmonic terms}$$

$$= \hat{I}_r \sin \omega t + \hat{I}_x \sin\left(\omega t - \frac{\pi}{2}\right) + \text{odd harmonic terms} \qquad (2.23)$$

In many analyses the harmonic components of the current can be ignored and only the fundamental-frequency component preserved. One reason is that if the voltage is sinusoidal, the harmonic currents deliver no net power. If necessary, the behavior of the harmonics may be studied separately after a first approximation to the solution has been obtained using fundamental-frequency quantities only.

In eq. 2.23 the fundamental component i_1 of the current *i* has been separated into a component i_r in phase with the voltage *e* and a component i_x lagging the voltage *e* by $\pi/2$ radians. The relation between the fundamental-frequency components of voltage and current can be represented by the equivalent circuit of Fig. 2.12*c*. In this figure E_1, I_1, I_r, and I_x are the phasors corresponding to *e*, i_1, i_r, and i_x, respectively. The hysteresis losses in the core are equal to the loss in the resistance R_h where

$$R_h = \frac{E_1}{I_r} = \frac{\hat{E}}{\hat{I}_r} \qquad \text{ohms} \qquad (2.24)$$

The magnetizing reactance X_0 is given by

$$X_0 = \frac{E_1}{I_x} = \frac{\hat{E}}{\hat{I}_x} \qquad \text{ohms} \qquad (2.25)$$

The hysteresis loop and waveforms of Fig. 2.12*a* and *b* apply for only one value of applied voltage. As the voltage is varied in magnitude, the equivalent circuit parameters R_h and X_0 also change. The reactance X_0 drops rapidly in value as the core enters its saturated region. The resistance

R_h generally tends to rise with increasing applied voltage, indicating that the hysteresis losses are proportional to a power of the applied voltage which is less than 2. It may be shown that in a core having the idealized $B-H$ loop of Fig. 2.10, the hysteresis losses at a given frequency are directly proportional to the applied voltage until saturation is reached. For this condition, R_h is directly proportional to E_1.

The values of the parameters R_h and X_0 could be derived from the $B-H$ loops of the material as described in relation to Fig. 2.12. This process is very tedious. The parameters can usually be derived directly from published data of the power loss and reactive volt-amperes per unit of volume of the material when tested at constant frequency and variable sinusoidal flux density.

When using the equivalent circuit of Fig. 2.12c to represent a nonlinear magnetic element, the parameters R_h and X_0 should be adjusted to the values appropriate for the applied voltage E_1. If this voltage E_1 varies over only a small range of magnitude, it is often possible to assume R_h and X_0 to be constant at appropriate average values.

The equivalent circuit of Fig. 2.12c represents only the fundamental-frequency behavior of the element. Examination of Fig. 2.12b shows that if the applied voltage e is sinusoidal, the current i consists of a fundamental frequency term plus a series of odd harmonic terms. The most important of these is the *third harmonic*, the magnitude of which may be as high as 70% of the fundamental component.

Since the third harmonic is the most important one, it is useful to have some circuit model which permits at least a qualitative analysis of the third-harmonic behavior under steady-state a-c operation. Suppose we regard the nonlinear magnetic element as a source of third harmonics. When the voltage applied to the nonlinear element is sinusoidal, this third-harmonic source can be considered as short circuited. When the current in the nonlinear element is sinusoidal, the third-harmonic source is open circuited. Fig. 2.12e shows a simple third-harmonic equivalent circuit that can be used to represent approximately the third-harmonic behavior of the nonlinear element. It consists of a source voltage E_{30} equal to the third-harmonic voltage with sinusoidal current in the element, in series with an inductive impedance jX_3, where X_3 is the ratio of E_{30} to the third-harmonic current with sinusoidal voltage applied to the element.

This third-harmonic equivalent circuit is very useful in qualitative analysis and also may be used to a limited extent for quantitative analysis. The value of E_{30} is normally in the range of 0.3–0.7 E_1, depending on the degree of saturation in the magnetic element. The value of X_3 is generally of the same order as X_0 in Fig. 2.12c.

2.2 EDDY CURRENTS

When a magnetic flux changes with time, an induced electric field is produced around the region of changing flux. Normally, we are most interested in the electromotive force which this electric field establishes in the windings encircling the magnetic paths. But this electric field is also produced within the magnetic material, and, if the material is a conductor, currents known as eddy currents are established.

Consider the long cylindrical solenoid of Fig. 2.13. Suppose the coil current i is positive and increasing. We would expect a positive and

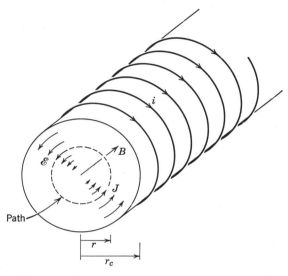

Fig. 2.13   The eddy currents in a magnetic core. (The current i is increasing with time.)

increasing flux density B in the material directed along its axis. The circular path shown encircles a magnetic flux ϕ of

$$\phi_{\text{encl.}} = \int \vec{B} \cdot d\vec{A} \qquad \text{webers} \tag{2.26}$$

By Faraday's law, the integral of the electric field intensity $\vec{\mathscr{E}}$ in a counter-clockwise direction around this path is equal to the rate of change of this flux. Because of the circular symmetry,

$$\mathscr{E} = \frac{1}{2\pi r} \frac{d\phi_{\text{encl.}}}{dt} \qquad \text{volts/meter} \tag{2.27}$$

If the material has a resistivity ρ, this electric field intensity sets up a collinear current density

$$\vec{J} = \frac{\vec{\mathscr{E}}}{\rho} \qquad \text{amperes/meter}^2 \qquad (2.28)$$

This eddy current density is in a direction that causes it to oppose the change in the enclosed magnetic flux. The opposition to the change in flux is greatest along the axis of the solenoid ($r = 0$), since all the eddy current encircles this axis. The effect becomes zero at the periphery of the solenoid where $r = r_c$.

Therefore one effect of eddy currents is to cause the time-varying magnetic flux density to be nonuniform within the material. An alternating magnetic flux tends to be concentrated toward the outside surface of the material, since the effect of eddy currents in preventing variation of magnetic flux is greatest near the central axis. This is known as the *magnetic skin effect*. If a magnetic material is to be used to best advantage, the magnetic flux density should be reasonably uniform over its cross-sectional area. Thus, there is a practical limit to the thickness of a solid conducting magnetic material which should be used at any given frequency of operation.

A second effect of the eddy currents is to produce power loss in the material. The eddy current loss per unit of volume of material is

$$p = \rho J^2 \qquad \text{watts/meter}^3 \qquad (2.29)$$

One means of controlling eddy current effects is the use of high-resistivity materials. Pure iron has a resistivity of about 10^{-7} ohm-meter. The addition of about 4% silicon to the iron increases its resistivity to about 6×10^{-7} ohm-meter. The ferrite materials described in Section 1.6.5 are oxides rather than metals and have very high resistivities. For example, nickel-zinc ferrite has a resistivity of about 10^{-4} ohm-meter.

With metallic magnetic materials, the principal means of controlling eddy currents is the use of thin sheets of laminations. Figure 2.14 shows

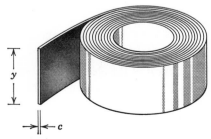

Fig. 2.14   Toroidal core made from a long, thin strip of material.

how a toroidal core can be made from a long, thin strip of magnetic material. The surfaces of the material are covered with a thin insulating coating. When the magnetic flux in the core changes, an electric field is set up in the material, as in Fig. 2.13. But the resultant eddy currents cannot flow from layer to layer and are restricted to paths within the cross section of the strip.

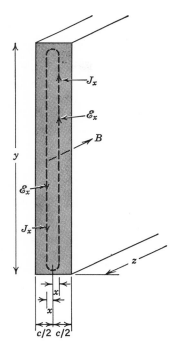

We now derive an approximate expression for the eddy current losses within a laminated magnetic material. Figure 2.15 shows an enlarged cross section of the strip used in the toroidal core of Fig. 2.14. We assume that the eddy currents are not large enough to influence significantly the magnetic field within the lamination. The flux density is considered to be uniform. Consider the closed path shown within the lamination in Fig. 2.15. The sides of this path are at distance x from the centerline of the lamination. This path encloses a magnetic flux of

Fig. 2.15 The determination of eddy-current loss in a lamination.

$$\phi_x = 2xyB \qquad \text{webers} \qquad (2.30)$$

Since $y \gg x$, the change of this magnetic flux may be assumed to produce an electric field of constant magnitude down one side of the path and up the other. By Faraday's law,

$$\mathscr{E}_x 2y = \frac{d\phi_x}{dt} \qquad \text{volts} \qquad (2.31)$$

Combining eqs. 2.30 and 2.31 gives

$$\mathscr{E}_x = x\frac{dB}{dt} \qquad \text{volts/meter} \qquad (2.32)$$

The current density at a distance x from the center plane of the lamination is therefore

$$J_x = \frac{\mathscr{E}_x}{\rho}$$

$$= \frac{x}{\rho}\frac{dB}{dt} \qquad \text{amperes/meter}^2 \qquad (2.33)$$

The total power loss in the lamination of thickness c, height y, and length z is found by integrating the loss density of eq. 2.29 over the volume V of the lamination.

$$P = \int \rho J^2 \, dV$$

$$= \int_{-c/2}^{c/2} \rho \left(\frac{x}{\rho} \frac{dB}{dt} \right)^2 yz \, dx$$

$$= \frac{c^3 yz}{12\rho} \left(\frac{dB}{d\tau} \right)^2 \quad \text{watts} \quad\quad (2.34)$$

Averaged over the volume cyz of the lamination, the instantaneous eddy current power loss per unit volume is

$$p = \frac{c^2}{12\rho} \left(\frac{dB}{dT} \right)^2 \quad \text{watts/meter}^3 \quad\quad (2.35)$$

If the flux density B is alternating at angular frequency ω as given by

$$B = \hat{B} \sin \omega t \quad\quad (2.36)$$

the average eddy current power loss per unit volume is

$$\bar{p} = \frac{1}{2\pi} \int_0^{2\pi} \frac{c^2 \omega^2 \hat{B}^2}{12\rho} \cos^2 \omega t \, d\omega t$$

$$= \frac{c^2 \omega^2 \hat{B}^2}{24\rho} \quad \text{watts/meter}^3 \quad\quad (2.37)$$

It is noted that this loss is proportional to the square of the lamination thickness, the square of the frequency, and the square of the maximum flux density. At power frequencies, laminations having a thickness of about 0.3–0.6 millimeter are often used. As the operating frequency is increased, the lamination thickness is generally reduced. For audio frequency apparatus, a lamination thickness of about 0.02–0.05 millimeter is used. For still higher frequencies, cores are often made of powdered iron and nickel molded to shape with an insulating adhesive.

In Section 2.14 an impedance model was developed to represent the a-c properties of a coil with a ferromagnetic core. It is convenient to include the eddy current properties within this model. For a core of cross-sectional area A, mean length of flux path $\bar{l}$, lamination thickness c, and turns N, the total eddy current power loss is, from eq. 2.35,

$$P = \frac{c^2}{12\rho} \left(\frac{dB}{dt}\right)^2 A \bar{l} \quad \text{watts} \tag{2.38}$$

The induced voltage in the coil is

$$e = \frac{d\lambda}{dt}$$

$$= NA \frac{dB}{dt} \quad \text{volts} \tag{2.39}$$

By substituting from eq. 2.39 into 2.38, the power loss can be expressed in terms of the induced voltage as

$$P = \frac{c^2}{12\rho} \frac{\bar{l}}{N^2 A} e^2$$

$$= \frac{e^2}{R_e} \quad \text{watts} \tag{2.40}$$

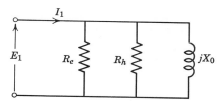

Fig. 2.16 Equivalent circuit for magnetic element similar to that of Fig. 2.12c, but with resistance R_e to represent eddy-current effect.

Thus, as shown in Fig. 2.16, the eddy current effect can be included in the model as a resistance

$$R_e = \frac{N^2 A}{\bar{l}} \frac{12\rho}{c^2} \quad \text{ohms} \tag{2.41}$$

This resistance applies for any value of frequency for which the assumption of uniform flux density in the material is valid.

The resistances R_e and R_h in Fig. 2.16 representing eddy and hysteresis losses are normally combined into one loss element R_0. This resistance is normally determined from published values of total power loss per unit of volume or weight of material at a given frequency and flux density.

The foregoing analysis of eddy currents is based on an assumption of uniform flux density over the cross section of the material. This assumption may be reasonably valid from a macroscopic point of view. But a change in the average value of flux density actually results from a complex displacement of microscopic domain walls (Section 1.6). The predictions of eq. 2.37—that eddy current losses vary as the square of the lamination thickness, the square of the frequency, and the square of the flux density—are often found to be inaccurate when compared with measured values of loss.

2.3 IDEAL TRANSFORMERS

Consider the magnetic core with two windings shown in Fig. 2.17. Let us determine the relationships between the voltages e_1 and e_2 and the

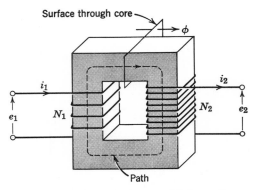

Fig. 2.17 A magnetic core with two coils.

currents i_1 and i_2 of the two coils having numbers of turns N_1 and N_2 under the following idealized conditions:

1. The coil resistances are ignored.
2. All the magnetic flux is considered to be in the core, linking all turns of both windings.
3. The B–H relationship of the core is represented by the idealized relation of Fig. 2.7.
4. The flux density is not to exceed the value B_k in Fig. 2.7.

Suppose a source having an instantaneous voltage e_1 is connected to the terminals of winding 1. A magnetizing current of negligible magnitude flows, establishing a magnetic flux ϕ in the core. The rate of change of the flux linkage $\lambda_1 = N_1\phi$ of winding 1 must equal the applied voltage e_1.

Thus

$$e_1 = \frac{d\lambda_1}{dt}$$

$$= N_1 \frac{d\phi}{dt} \qquad \text{volts} \qquad (2.42)$$

there being no voltage drop in the winding resistance. The flux linkage of winding 2 is

$$\lambda_2 = N_2 \phi$$

$$= \frac{N_2}{N_1} \lambda_1 \qquad \text{webers} \qquad (2.43)$$

The voltage across the terminals of winding 2 is

$$e_2 = \frac{d\lambda_2}{dt}$$

$$= \frac{N_2}{N_1} \frac{d\lambda_1}{dt}$$

$$= \frac{N_2}{N_1} e_1 \qquad \text{volts} \qquad (2.44)$$

Thus, under the idealizing assumptions made, the ratio of the terminal voltages of the two windings is equal to the ratio of their numbers of turns.

Suppose a load of resistance R_L is connected to winding 2. Then

$$i_2 = \frac{e_2}{R_L} \qquad \text{amperes} \qquad (2.45)$$

Since the magnetic field intensity in the core is assumed to be negligible, application of the circuital law to the path shown in Fig. 2.17 results in

$$N_1 i_1 - N_2 i_2 = \oint \vec{H} \cdot d\vec{l} \qquad (2.46)$$

$$= 0$$

from which we obtain the relation

$$i_2 = \frac{N_1}{N_2} i_1 \qquad \text{amperes} \qquad (2.47)$$

Thus, the ratio of the currents in the windings of this idealized transformer is equal to the inverse of the turns ratio. Combining eqs. 2.44 and 2.47

shows that the instantaneous power p_1 entering winding 1 is equal to the instantaneous power p_2 leaving winding 2.

$$p_1 = e_1 i_1$$
$$= \left(\frac{N_1}{N_2} e_2\right)\left(\frac{N_2}{N_1} i_2\right)$$
$$= e_2 i_2 = p_2 \qquad \text{watts} \qquad (2.48)$$

This power invariance of the idealized transformer follows from the assumption that it has no power loss and no energy storage.

In approximate analyses, transformers can often be considered ideal. Where the idealizing assumptions are not valid, a transformer can be considered as an ideal transformer in combination with other parameters representing its imperfections. It is therefore convenient to have a symbolic circuit element to represent an ideal transformer, as shown in Fig. 2.18. Its terminal variables are related by eqs. 2.44 and 2.47. Where necessary, for clarity, the starting ends of both windings are identified by a dot. The polarity of the potential difference between the dotted end and the undotted end is the same for each winding.

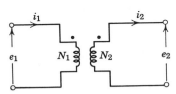

Fig. 2.18 Equivalent circuit symbol for an ideal transformer.

Consider the circuit shown in Fig. 2.19a in which a resistance R_L is connected to winding 2 and a source to winding 1 of an ideal transformer. The voltage-current relationship at the source is

$$\frac{e_1}{i_1} = \frac{(N_1/N_2)e_2}{(N_2/N_1)i_2}$$

or

$$R_L' = \left(\frac{N_1}{N_2}\right)^2 R_L \qquad \text{ohms} \qquad (2.49)$$

Thus the source sees an equivalent resistance R_L', as shown in Fig. 2.19b. A shunt resistance on one side of an ideal transformer may therefore be moved across the transformer, the value of the equivalent shunt resistance being equal to the original resistance, multiplied by the square of the turns ratio. Similarly, a resistance that is in series on one side of an ideal transformer may be moved to a series position on the other side, using the same multiplier. This ability to transfer elements across ideal transformers is not restricted to resistances but applies equally to inductances, capacitances, sources, and impedances. For example, Fig. 2.19d shows a circuit that is equivalent to the circuit of Fig. 2.19c. It is noted that

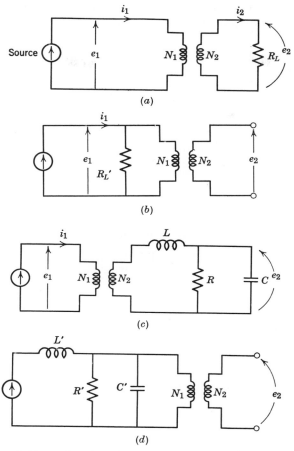

Fig. 2.19   (a) and (b) transfer of a resistance element across an ideal transformer. (c) and (d) the transfer of a network of elements across an ideal transformer.

$$R' = \left(\frac{N_1}{N_2}\right)^2 R; \; L' = \left(\frac{N_1}{N_2}\right)^2 L; \; C' = \left(\frac{N_2}{N_1}\right)^2 C.$$

inductances and resistances are multiplied by the square of the turns ratio, whereas capacitances are divided by the square of the turns ratio.

2.4   EQUIVALENT CIRCUITS FOR COMPLEX MAGNETIC SYSTEMS

When we encounter a complex system of electrical elements and wish to analyze its performance, our normal approach is to develop an electric equivalent circuit for the system. We put into the equivalent circuit only those parameters that are considered to be significant in influencing the performance. The equivalent circuit is thus a simplified mathematical model of the real system. Having developed an adequate equivalent circuit, we employ the well-known techniques of electric circuit analysis to determine its behavior. The accuracy with which the solution of the electric circuit behavior represents the performance of the real system is limited only by the adequacy of the equivalent circuit model.

In electrical machines, transformers and other electrical devices, ferromagnetic material is used in a wide variety of shapes. Various parts of multilimbed magnetic structures are encircled by coils. In this section we show how such complex magnetic systems may be represented approximately by equivalent circuits. The system is first represented by a magnetic equivalent circuit, which is then transformed into an equivalent electric circuit. The methods of electric circuit analysis may then be used.

2.4.1 Derivation of Magnetic Equivalent Circuits

Let us first derive a magnetic equivalent circuit for a simple magnetic system. Figure 2.20a shows a torus of magnetic material with a winding

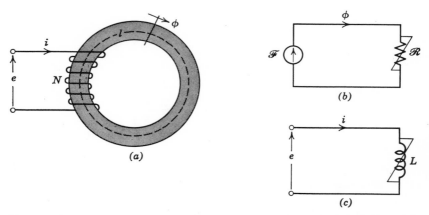

Fig. 2.20 (a) A simple magnetic element. (b) A magnetic equivalent circuit for the element. (c) An electric equivalent circuit for the element.

of N turns. The magnetomotive force around the magnetic path is

$$\mathscr{F} = Ni \qquad \text{amperes} \qquad (2.50)$$

This magnetomotive force establishes a magnetic field intensity H, which in turn produces a magnetic flux density B in the material. Integration of this flux density over the cross-sectional area A of the core gives the **magnetic flux** ϕ. The cause-effect relationship between the magnetomotive force $\mathscr{F}$ and the magnetic flux ϕ may be expressed symbolically by the equivalent magnetic circuit of Fig. 2.20b. The magnetic properties of the material and the dimensions of the core determine its reluctance $\mathscr{R}$. Under the idealized condition where the relative permeability can be regarded as constant, that is,

$$B = \mu_r \mu_0 H \tag{2.51}$$

the reluctance can be expressed as

$$\mathscr{R} = \frac{\mathscr{F}}{\phi}$$

$$= \frac{l}{\mu_r \mu_0 A} \qquad \text{amperes/weber} \tag{2.52}$$

In general, the reluctance of a ferromagnetic core is nonlinear. The reluctance symbol is then used in a magnetic equivalent circuit merely to denote a magnetic element for which a $\mathscr{F}$–ϕ relation exists. This relation may be obtained by rescaling the B–H characteristic for the material using the expressions

$$\phi = BA \qquad \text{webers} \tag{2.53}$$

and
$$\mathscr{F} = H\bar{l} \qquad \text{amperes} \tag{2.54}$$

For purposes of analysis, any of the approximate models for the B–H characteristic developed in Section 2.1 may be used.

Let us now consider, as an example, the magnetic system of Fig. 2.21a. This system consists of a three-legged magnetic core, two of the legs having windings and the third leg having an air gap. Basically, this is a complex three-dimensional magnetic field problem. But by the use of simplifying assumptions, the magnetic field can be reduced to a magnetic circuit of lumped reluctances. Let us assume that except in the air gap, all magnetic flux is confined to the magnetic material. The leakage flux in the air paths around the windings is considered negligible.

The magnetic system may now be divided into four sections, each of which has a uniform flux over its length. Three of these sections represent magnetic paths in the material, and the fourth represents the air-gap path. Each section may be represented by a reluctance which relates the flux to the magnetomotive force required to establish that flux along the length of the section.

Figure 2.21b shows the magnetic equivalent circuit that results from the foregoing assumptions. Reluctances $\mathscr{R}_1$, $\mathscr{R}_2$, and $\mathscr{R}_3$ represent the three paths in the magnetic material carrying magnetic fluxes ϕ_1, ϕ_2, and ϕ_3, respectively. The air gap is represented by the linear reluctance $\mathscr{R}_4$, and its magnetic flux is ϕ_3. The circuital law of eq. 1.60 applies to any closed

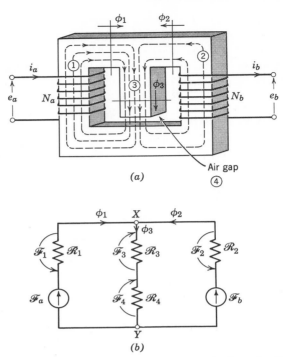

Fig. 2.21 (a) A magnetic system. (b) A magnetic equivalent circuit for the system.

path in a magnetic field system. In a magnetic equivalent circuit this law is represented by the following relation: Around any closed path, the total magnetomotive force of the windings is equal to the sum of the products of reluctance and flux.

$$\sum \mathscr{F} = \sum \mathscr{R}\phi \qquad \text{around closed path} \qquad (2.55)$$

The continuity of magnetic flux in the magnetic field is represented by equating the sum of the fluxes entering any junction of magnetic paths in the equivalent circuit to zero

$$\sum \phi_{\substack{\text{into} \\ \text{junction}}} = 0 \qquad (2.56)$$

Normal methods of circuit analysis may now be employed to determine the fluxes in Fig. 2.21b for a given set of magnetomotive forces. If the relative permeability of the magnetic material can be considered constant, the reluctance of the sections may be determined by use of eq. 2.52, in which l is the mean length of the flux path in each section and A is the cross-sectional area. If the permeability cannot be considered constant, each reluctance element may be represented by a graph of the relation between its flux and its magnetomotive force. Graphical or trial-and-error methods may then be used for analysis of the equivalent circuit.

It should be noted that all the assumptions are introduced in the process of deriving the magnetic equivalent circuit from the magnetic system. With different assumptions, a different equivalent circuit is obtained. For example, if the leakage fluxes in the air paths around the windings in Fig. 2.21a had not been neglected, the reluctances of these air leakage paths would have been connected across the respective magnetomotive forces in Fig. 2.21b. There is therefore no unique equivalent magnetic circuit for a magnetic system. The chosen circuit should contain just the information required for the problem to be solved.

2.4.2 Derivation of Electric Equivalent Circuits

A magnetic equivalent circuit, such as that shown in Fig. 2.21b, is most useful in the analysis and design of a device. However, if the device is connected to other electric elements, it is desirable to have an equivalent circuit for the device from which the relationships between the terminal voltages and currents can be obtained directly. In this section it is shown that the electric equivalent circuit can be derived directly and uniquely from the magnetic equivalent circuit.

First, let us consider the simple magnetic circuit of Fig. 2.20b, which relates two variables—the coil magnetomotive force $\mathscr{F}$ and the flux ϕ—by the reluctance parameter $\mathscr{R}$.

$$\mathscr{F} = \mathscr{R}\phi \quad \text{amperes} \tag{2.57}$$

In the equivalent electric circuit, the variables are the voltage e between the coil terminals and the current i in the coil. Let us assume that the core reluctance is constant and that the coil resistance is negligible. The electric circuit variables are related to the magnetic circuit variables by the two relations

$$i = \frac{\mathscr{F}}{N} \quad \text{amperes} \tag{2.58}$$

and

$$e = N\frac{d\phi}{dt} \quad \text{volts} \tag{2.59}$$

By substituting from eqs. 2.57 and 2.58 into eq. 2.59, the relation between the two electric circuit variables is

$$\begin{aligned}
e &= N\frac{d}{dt}\left(\frac{\mathscr{F}}{\mathscr{R}}\right) \\
&= \frac{N}{\mathscr{R}}\frac{d\mathscr{F}}{dt} = \frac{N^2}{\mathscr{R}}\frac{di}{dt} \\
&= L\frac{di}{dt} \quad \text{volts} \tag{2.60}
\end{aligned}$$

Thus, the reluctance parameter $\mathscr{R}$ in the magnetic circuit is replaced by an inductance parameter L in the electric equivalent circuit of Fig. 2.20c. The value of the inductance is inversely proportional to the value of the reluctance.

If the reluctance parameter is not constant, it can be represented by a curve relating magnetomotive force and flux. The corresponding non-linear inductance can be represented by a curve relating the core flux linkage $\lambda = N\phi$ to the current i. Approximations such as those shown in Figs. 2.4b, 2.7, 2.8b, 2.9, and 2.10 may be used for this relation where appropriate.

Let us now consider the more complex magnetic circuit of Fig. 2.21b. Suppose, for the present, that each of the fluxes ϕ_1, ϕ_2, and ϕ_3 links an N-turn coil. The corresponding voltages e_1, e_2, and e_3 produced in these coils are given by

$$e_1 = N\frac{d\phi_1}{dt} ; \quad e_2 = N\frac{d\phi_2}{dt} ; \quad e_3 = N\frac{d\phi_3}{dt} \tag{2.61}$$

At node X in Fig. 2.21b, the flux variables are related, from eq. 2.56, by

$$\sum_{\substack{\text{into} \\ \text{node}}} \phi = \phi_1 + \phi_2 - \phi_3 = 0 \tag{2.62}$$

The flux variables at node Y are related by the same equation. From eq. 2.61, the corresponding voltage variables must be related by the expression

$$e_1 + e_2 - e_3 = 0 \tag{2.63}$$

Now consider the left-hand mesh of the magnetic circuit of Fig. 2.21b. From eq. 2.55, the magnetomotive force variables are related by

$$\mathscr{F}_a = \mathscr{F}_1 + \mathscr{F}_3 + \mathscr{F}_4 \tag{2.64}$$

Let us consider each of these magnetomotive force components to be produced by corresponding components of current in N-turn coils. These current components are then related by the expression

$$i_a' = i_1 + i_3 + i_4 \tag{2.65}$$

Around the right-hand mesh of Fig. 2.21b, the magnetomotive force relation is

$$\mathscr{F}_b = \mathscr{F}_2 + \mathscr{F}_3 + \mathscr{F}_4 \tag{2.66}$$

The relation between the corresponding current variables is

$$i_b' = i_2 + i_3 + i_4 \tag{2.67}$$

The primes symbols are added to i_a' and i_b' to distinguish them from i_a and i_b in Fig. 2.21a.

Each reluctance in the magnetic circuit relates a magnetic flux variable ϕ and a magnetomotive force variable $\mathscr{F}$. From eqs. 2.58, 2.59, and 2.60, the corresponding voltage variable e and current variable i can be related by an inductance parameter. For example, the relation $\mathscr{F}_1 = \mathscr{R}_1\phi_1$ in the magnetic circuit corresponds to the relation

$$e_1 = L_1\frac{di_1}{dt} \tag{2.68}$$

Equations 2.63, 2.65, 2.67, and 2.68 describe the electric equivalent circuit shown in Fig. 2.22a. For each of the two independent meshes in the magnetic circuit, there is an independent node in the electric circuit. The branch currents entering these two nodes (designated as A and B) are related by eqs. 2.65 and 2.67. For each independent node in the magnetic circuit there is a corresponding mesh in the electric circuit. The branch voltages around the one independent mesh in the electric circuit are related by eq. 2.63. For each reluctance branch in the magnetic circuit, there is a corresponding inductance branch in the electric circuit. For each magnetomotive force source in the magnetic circuit, there is a corresponding coil current in the electric circuit.

The form of the electric circuit of Fig. 2.22a may be derived directly from the magnetic circuit of Fig. 2.21b by use of the topological principle of duality. This topological technique is demonstrated in Fig. 2.22b. A node is marked within each mesh of the magnetic circuit, and a reference node is marked outside the circuit. These nodes are then joined by branches, one of which passes through each element of the magnetic circuit. It is observed that the form of the resulting network of branches is identical to the form of the electric circuit of Fig. 2.22a. For each reluctance in a mesh of the magnetic circuit, there is an inductance connected to the corresponding node of the electric circuit. Where a reluctance is common to two meshes in the magnetic circuit, the corresponding inductance interconnects the corresponding nodes of the electric circuit. For each magnetomotive force, there is a corresponding driving current; for each flux, there is a corresponding voltage between nodes.

The reluctances corresponding to ferromagnetic parts of the magnetic system may represent nonlinear relationships between their fluxes and magnetomotive forces. Each reluctance element in the magnetic circuit has a corresponding inductance element in the electric circuit. Thus each inductance element may represent a similar nonlinear relationship between the flux linkage λ in a coil of N turns encircling the particular branch of the magnetic system and the current i in an N-turn coil that produces the magnetomotive force for the branch. The rate of change of the flux linkage produces the voltage variable in the electric circuit. The nonlinearities in

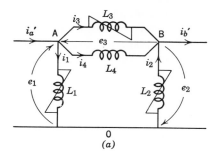

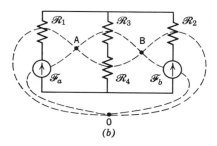

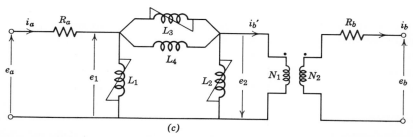

Fig. 2.22   Equivalent electric circuit for the magnetic circuit of Fig. 2.21. (a) Elementary form of circuit. (b) Topological technique of derivation. (c) Circuit including ideal transformer and winding resistances.

the magnetic circuit are therefore preserved in the electric equivalent circuit.

Any of the nonlinear models suggested by Figs. 2.4b, 2.7, 2.8b, 2.9, and 2.10 may be used to represent these nonlinear inductance elements. The choice depends on the problem under study. For use with alternating voltages, each nonlinear inductance element can be represented by a circuit model of the form shown in Fig. 2.16. This consists of an inductive reactance in parallel with a resistance representing the hysteresis and eddy current losses of the element. Both the reactance and the resistance are generally nonlinear functions of the voltage across the branch.

The electric equivalent circuit of Fig. 2.22a was developed with the assumption that all windings had N turns. Since the numbers of turns are generally different in the various windings, it is necessary to add ideal transformers at the terminals of the equivalent electric circuit to obtain the actual induced voltages and the actual currents in the windings. The reference number of turns N is normally made equal to the number of turns in one of the windings; no ideal transformer is then required for this winding. In Fig. 2.22c, N has been made equal to N_a.

The resistances R_a and R_b of the two windings have also been added to the equivalent circuit in Fig. 2.22c. The terminal voltages of the two windings are e_a and e_b; the induced voltages in the windings are e_1 and $-e_2(N_2/N_1)$.

When an appropriate equivalent circuit has been developed for a magnetic device, the performance of the device may be predicted by use of the techniques normally employed in circuit analysis. When convenient, elements may be transformed across the ideal transformers, as described in Section 2.3.

2.5 ANALYSIS OF PERMANENT-MAGNET SYSTEMS

A permanent-magnet material is one which can maintain a constant magnetic orientation of its domains in spite of a substantial externally applied field. Figure 2.23 shows the B–H locus that might be followed by a closed path of permanent-magnet material which is magnetized from an initially unmagnetized state. A large pulse of magnetic field intensity H is applied to the path, and on its removal the flux density remains at the

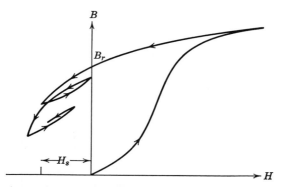

Fig. 2.23 B–H locus of permanent-magnet material during initial magnetization and subsequent application of demagnetization field intensity.

residual value B_r. Suppose a reversed magnetic field intensity of magnitude H_s is now applied to the path. On its removal and reapplication, the B–H locus follows a minor loop, as shown. In most analyses this minor loop may be considered as a single straight line. Application of a reversed magnetic field intensity of magnitude less than H_s causes an excursion along this line. If the reversed magnetic field intensity has a magnitude greater than H_s, the locus of operation moves down to a lower and more or less parallel line. The incremental slope of these lines representing minor loops is known as the *recoil permeability*. For Alnico magnets it is in the range of 3–5 μ_0, whereas for ferrite magnets it may be as low as 1.1 μ_0.

After a magnet has been initially magnetized, usual practice is to stabilize it by subjecting it to a demagnetizing magnetic field intensity H_s that is somewhat larger than the magnet is expected to encounter in service. As long as this demagnetizing intensity is not subsequently exceeded, the magnet should operate along an essentially straight-line minor loop.

2.5.1 Permanent-Magnet Systems with Air Gaps

Figure 2.24*a* shows a permanent magnet with an air gap. Suppose this magnet has been magnetized with a soft iron keeper in its air gap leaving

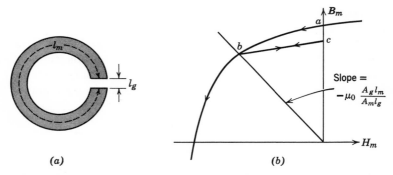

(a)   *(b)*

Fig. 2.24   (*a*) A permanent magnet with an air gap. (*b*) Graphical analysis of air-gap magnet.

it in the residually magnetized state denoted as *a* in Fig. 2.24*b*. What will be the flux density in the magnet and in the air gap if the keeper is now withdrawn from the air gap?

Let us assume that the magnetic flux is confined to the area A_m of the magnet and to an effective area A_g of the air gap (making allowance for some fringing of flux around the gap). Application of the circuital law around the system gives $H_m l_m + H_g l_g = 0$, or

$$H_m = -H_g \frac{l_g}{l_m} \qquad \text{amperes/meter} \qquad (2.69)$$

The continuity of flux around the path requires that $B_m A_m = B_g A_g$, or

$$B_m = B_g \frac{A_g}{A_m} \qquad \text{webers/meter}^2 \qquad (2.70)$$

By substituting from eq. 2.69 into 2.70 and noting that $B_g = \mu_0 H_g$, we arrive at the following relation between the flux density and the field intensity in the material.

$$B_m = -\mu_0 \frac{A_g}{A_m} \frac{l_m}{l_g} H_m \qquad \text{webers/meter}^2 \qquad (2.71)$$

The second relation between B_m and H_m is the B–H curve of Fig. 2.24b. As shown, the operating point of the material is at the intersection of the B–H curve and the straight line representing eq. 2.71. As the magnet keeper is removed, the operating point of the material moves along the locus a-b. If the keeper is reinserted, the operating point of the material moves along the essentially straight-line recoil locus b-c.

The foregoing analysis shows that the operating point of an air-gap magnet is determined by the demagnetization portion of its B–H loop and by the dimensions of the magnet. The corresponding design problem is to choose the operating point and dimensions of the material so that a given air-gap field may be produced with a minimum of magnet material. Suppose we wish to obtain a flux density B_g in an air gap of length l_g and cross-sectional area A_g. By using eqs. 2.69 and 2.70, the required volume of magnet material is

$$\begin{aligned} V_m &= A_m l_m \\ &= \left(\frac{B_g A_g}{B_m}\right)\left(\frac{-H_g l_g}{H_m}\right) \\ &= \frac{B_g^2 V_g}{\mu_0 |B_m H_m|} \qquad \text{meter}^3 \qquad (2.72) \end{aligned}$$

Thus, to produce a flux density B_g in an air gap of volume V_g, a minimum volume of magnet material is required if the material is operated where the magnitude of the product $B_m H_m$ is greatest. This product is a measure of the energy that can be supplied per unit volume of material to an air-gap field. It is known as the energy product of the material and its value is in the range of 5000–50,000 joules/meter^3 in the better permanent-magnet materials.

When an operating point such as b in Fig. 2.24b has been chosen, the length l_m and area A_m of the magnet material may be chosen to make the intersection of lines occur at that point. In the simple magnet of Fig. 2.24a the areas A_g of the air gap and A_m of the material are nearly equal. The air-gap flux density must then be essentially the same as the flux density in the material. If these flux densities are to be different, the magnet may be fitted with pole shoes of soft magnetic material to increase or decrease the gap area as required.

2.5.2 Linear Models for Permanent Magnets

The fact that the operating locus of a permanent magnet is an essentially straight line, as shown in locus b-c of Fig. 2.24b, suggests that the magnet might be represented by a linear model. Such a model would facilitate calculations, particularly in complex systems that include permanent magnets.

Figure 2.25a shows a permanent magnet of area A_m and length l_m, which forms part of a closed magnetic path encircled by a coil. Let us assume that the soft magnetic material requires negligible magnetic field intensity. Figure 2.25b shows the relation between the magnetic flux ϕ_m and the magnetomotive force $\mathscr{F}_m$ of the block of permanent-magnet material. This curve may be obtained by rescaling the demagnetizing portion of the B–H curve of the material using

$$\phi_m = B_m A_m \qquad \text{webers} \qquad (2.73)$$

and

$$\mathscr{F}_m = H_m l_m \qquad \text{amperes} \qquad (2.74)$$

Suppose that the magnet is initially magnetized using a positive current i and then stabilized by application of a negative current sufficient to make $\mathscr{F}_m = Ni = -\hat{\mathscr{F}}$. This brings the operating point on the ϕ_m-$\mathscr{F}_m$ locus to point a, where the magnet flux is ϕ_a. If, in the subsequent operation of this magnet, the magnitude of the magnetomotive force applied in the negative direction does not exceed $\hat{\mathscr{F}}$, the magnet operates along the locus a–b–c. This locus may be closely approximated by a straight line of slope $1/\mathscr{R}_0$ denoted by the expression

$$\mathscr{F}_m = -\mathscr{F}_0 + \mathscr{R}_0 \phi_m \qquad \text{amperes (for } \mathscr{F}_m > -\hat{\mathscr{F}}) \qquad (2.75)$$

This equation describes the equivalent magnetic circuit of Fig. 2.25c. The magnet is represented as a source of magnetomotive force $\mathscr{F}_0$ in series with a reluctance $\mathscr{R}_0$. The part of the system external to the magnet is simply a magnetomotive force $\mathscr{F}_m = Ni$ in this case.

Equation 2.75 may be divided through by $\mathscr{R}_0$ and rewritten in the form

$$\phi_m = \phi_0 + \frac{\mathscr{F}_m}{\mathscr{R}_0} \qquad \text{webers (for } \phi_m > \phi_a) \qquad (2.76)$$

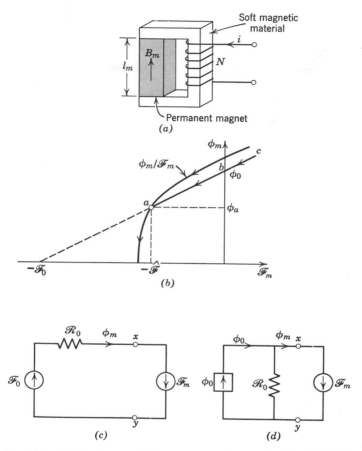

Fig. 2.25 (a) A closed system containing a permanent magnet and a coil. (b) Graphical analysis. (c) Equivalent circuit with magnetomotive force source. (d) Equivalent circuit with magnetic flux source.

This equation describes the alternative form of equivalent magnetic circuit of Fig. 2.25d. In this circuit the magnet is represented as a flux source ϕ_0 in parallel with a reluctance $\mathcal{R}_0$. This form of equivalent circuit is preferable to that of Fig. 2.25c for magnets that approach the ideal behavior of constant flux and very high equivalent reluctance $\mathcal{R}_0$.

The two equivalent circuits of Fig. 2.25c and d may be considered as analogous to the Thévenin and Norton forms of electric equivalent circuit. When the magnet is closed by a zero reluctance path, its "short-circuit" flux is ϕ_0. The incremental reluctance encountered by a magnetomotive force applied to the magnet is $\mathcal{R}_0$. The magnet cannot, of course, be "open circuited," since the air path between the ends of the magnet always has a finite reluctance. In addition, the model applies only for $\mathscr{F}_m > -\hat{\mathscr{F}}$.

As an example of the use of these linear models, let us determine the magnetic flux in the air-gapped magnet of Fig. 2.24a. Suppose that the magnet has been stabilized so as to operate along the locus b-c in Fig.

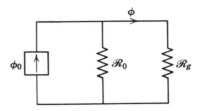

Fig. 2.26 Equivalent magnetic circuit for the air-gapped magnet of Fig. 2.24a.

2.24b. The magnet may be represented by a flux source ϕ_0 in parallel with a reluctance $\mathscr{R}_0$. If B_0 is the flux density at point c in Fig. 2.24b, and if the slope of the line b-c is the recoil permeability $\mu_r\mu_0$,

$$\phi_0 = B_0 A_m \qquad \text{webers} \qquad (2.77)$$

and

$$\mathscr{R}_0 = \frac{l_m}{\mu_r\mu_0 A} \qquad \text{amperes/weber} \qquad (2.78)$$

The magnetic system external to the magnet consists of the reluctance $\mathscr{R}_g$ of the air gap, where

$$\mathscr{R}_g = \frac{l_g}{\mu_0 A_g} \qquad \text{amperes/weber} \qquad (2.79)$$

The system may therefore be represented by the equivalent circuit of Fig. 2.26. The magnetic flux ϕ in the air gap is given by

$$\phi = \frac{\mathscr{R}_0}{\mathscr{R}_0 + \mathscr{R}_g} \phi_0 \qquad \text{webers} \qquad (2.80)$$

Problems

2.1 A toroidal magnetic core (as shown in Fig. 2.1) has a cross-sectional area of 1 cm² and an average radius of 2.5 cm. The material has the set of cyclic hysteresis loops shown in Fig. P2.1. The coil on the core has 200 turns and negligible resistance.

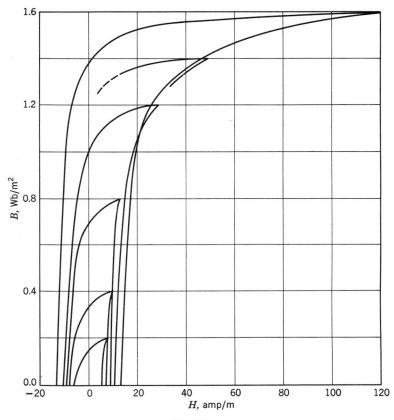

Fig. P2.1

(a) Suppose a square-wave voltage having a peak-to-peak value of 12 V is applied to the coil. What value of the period of this voltage wave will produce a peak flux density of 1.6 Wb/m^2? *Ans.: 21.4 msec.*

(b) Sketch the current waveform for the condition of part (a). Determine the peak value of the current in the coil. *Ans.: 0.0942 amp.*

(c) What rms value of a sine-wave voltage at 50 c/s would produce a peak flux density of 1.2 Wb/m^2? *Ans.: 5.34 V.*

(d) Sketch the current waveform for the condition of part (c). Determine the value of the current at the instant of maximum voltage.
Ans.: 8.64 × 10^{-3} amp.

2.2 (a) Using the *B–H* loops of Fig. P2.1, plot a normal magnetization curve for the magnetic material.

(b) Suppose a core of the material has a sinusoidal flux density of peak value 1.2 Wb/m². Plot B and H as functions of time for a complete cycle using the normal magnetization curve. Compare the H waveform with that obtained in Prob. 2.1(d) using the actual B–H loop. Over what parts of the cycle are the two waveforms approximately equal?

2.3 Suppose we wish to measure the normal magnetization curve for a core made of the material of Fig. P2.1. The core is toroidal with a cross-sectional area of 5 cm² and average circumference 20 cm. A coil of 500

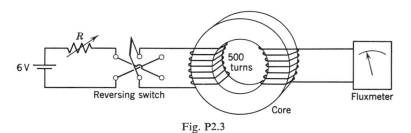

Fig. P2.3

turns is connected to a 6-V source in series with a variable resistance R through a reversing switch, as shown in Fig. P2.3. A second coil is to be wound on the core and connected to a fluxmeter. The deflection of the fluxmeter is proportional to the integral with time of the voltage applied to its terminals.

(a) If the resistances of the coils are negligible, what should be the minimum value of the variable resistance R to test the material up to $B = 1.6$ Wb/m². *Ans.: 125 Ω.*

(b) The fluxmeter has a full-scale deflection when the flux linkage of the coil connected to it changes by 0.01 Wb. In operation, the fluxmeter is set to zero, and then the switch on the first coil is reversed. How many turns should be used in the second coil to make best use of the range of the fluxmeter? *Ans.: 6.*

(c) What operating procedure should be adopted to measure a point on the normal magnetization curve?

2.4 The normal magnetization curve of a sample of grain-oriented silicon steel has the following points:

B(webers/m²): 0.01 0.05 0.1 0.2 0.5 0.75 1.0 1.2 1.3 1.4 1.5 1.6
H(amp/m):   1.1   2.9   4.5 6.4 9.6 12.4 16   22   27.6 37   55   116

A toroidal core of this material has a cross-sectional area of 0.2 cm² and an average diameter of 1.5 cm. The coil has 1500 turns and a resistance of 50 Ω. At time $t = 0$, a source having a constant internal voltage of 2 V and an internal resistance of 500 Ω is connected to the coil.

(a) Determine the final value of the coil current.

(b) Calculate approximately the coil current as a function of time. At approximately what time will the coil current reach one-third of its final value? *Ans.:* At about 24 msec.

2.5 The coil in Prob. 2.4 has been connected to its source for a long time. Suppose the terminals of this coil are now short circuited. There is a second 1500-turn coil on the core, which is open circuited.

(a) What will be the voltage across the terminals of the second coil when the flux density in the core has dropped to 1.0 Wb/m²? *Ans.:* 0.0252 V.

2.6 Data for a normal magnetization curve for silicon steel are given in Prob. 2.4.

(a) Develop a piecewise linear approximation of the form shown in Fig. 2.5 for this normal magnetization curve for the range $-1.6 < B < 1.6$.

(b) Determine the values of the unsaturated and saturated relative permeabilities for this approximation. *Ans.:* Approximately 44,000 and 1330.

2.7 A toroidal core having a cross-sectional area of 0.2 cm² and an average diameter of 1.5 cm is wound with a coil having 1500 turns and a resistance of 50 Ω. The linearized magnetization curve has an unsaturated relative permeability of 44,000 up to $B = 1.45$ Wb/m², and a saturated relative permeability of 1330 for $B > 1.45$ Wb/m².

(a) Determine the unsaturated inductance of the coil.

(b) Determine the time constant of the coil when in the unsaturated region. *Ans.:* 1.06 sec.

(c) Suppose the coil is connected, at $t = 0$, to a 2-V source having an internal resistance of 500 Ω. Write the differential equations describing the current during the unsaturated and saturated periods of operation. Sketch the current-time curve and compare it with the results of Prob. 2.4(b). At what time does the current reach one third of its final value? *Ans.:* 25.2 msec.

2.8 In previous problems we have assumed that the flux density was uniform over the cross section of the core. Figure P2.8a shows a toroidal core that has a ratio of its outside diameter to its inside diameter of 1.5. The material may be represented by the linearized magnetization curve of Fig. P2.8b. Suppose the core has a coil of 400 turns.

(a) Determine the unsaturated relative permeability of the core.

(b) Determine the inductance of the system when no part of the core has a flux density greater than 1.5 Wb/m². *Ans.:* 15.6 H.

(c) Up to what value of coil current does the inductance of part (b) apply?

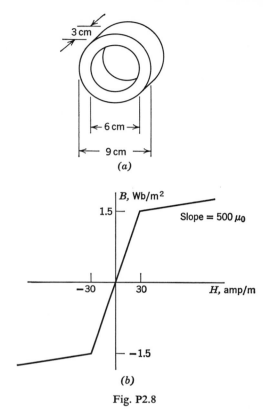

Fig. P2.8

(d) What is the minimum value of current for which the complete **core** has a flux density of 1.5 Wb/m² or greater?   *Ans.:* 0.0211 amp.

(e) Show that the flux linkage–current relationship can be expressed as

$$\lambda = 15.6i \qquad\qquad \text{for } i \le 0.0141 \text{ amp}$$
$$= 0.266 + 0.195i \qquad \text{for } i \ge 0.0211 \text{ amp}$$

(f) Let us calculate one point in the interval between these two expressions for flux linkage. For simplicity, consider the condition where $B = 1.5$ Wb/m² exists at the average core diameter of 7.5 cm. Determine the flux linkage and current for this condition.   *Ans.:* 0.259, 0.0177.

(g) Sketch the flux linkage–current curve for this inductor. Note that the rounded knee of this curve results from the geometrical configuration rather than from the *B–H* characteristic.

(h) Compare the curve of part (g) with that which would result from assuming a uniform flux density over the cross section of the core.

2.9 The B–H characteristic of a magnetic core can be approximated by Fig. 2.7a for many situations in which the core is driven far into saturation. Suppose the core has a cross-sectional area A, and a magnetic path length l. Suppose the coil has N turns and negligible resistance.

(a) Derive an expression for the incremental inductance L_s of the coil in the saturated region.

(b) Let us determine the steady-state current in the coil when a sinusoidal voltage $e = \hat{e}\sin\omega t$ is impressed on its terminals. Suppose the core absorbs the applied voltage with no current flowing until $\omega t = \pi - \alpha$, where the flux density reaches B_k. Write a differential equation for the coil current i and show that

$$i = \frac{-\hat{e}}{\omega L_s}(\cos\omega t + \cos\alpha)$$

for the interval $(\pi - \alpha) < \omega t < (\pi + \alpha)$.

(c) The results of part (b) show that in the steady state the core is in its unsaturated state over the interval $\alpha < \omega t < \pi - \alpha$. Show that

$$\alpha = \cos^{-1}\frac{\omega B_k NA}{\hat{e}}$$

(d) In most circumstances the fundamental-frequency component of the coil current will be of primary importance. Show that its peak value can be expressed as

$$i_1 = \frac{4\hat{e}}{\pi\omega L_s}\left[\frac{\alpha}{2} - \frac{1}{4}\sin 2\alpha\right] \qquad \text{amp}$$

(e) Suppose $A = 40$ cm², $l = 0.8$ m, $B_k = 1.7$, $\mu_s = 15$, $N = 100$, and the supply frequency is 60 c/s. Determine the rms value of the fundamental component of current if the supply voltage is 240 V rms.   *Ans.: 96 amp.*

2.10 A 350-turn coil is wound on a closed core having a cross-sectional area of 10^{-4} m² and a mean path length of 0.15 m. The core material can be represented by an idealized B–H characteristic of the form shown in Fig. 2.7b, with $B_k = 1.5$ Wb/m². The coil resistance is 1.5 Ω. Suppose the coil is connected in series with a load resistance of 20 Ω, and a sinusoidal source of 120 V rms, at 400 c/s, is applied to the circuit.

(a) Determine the waveform of the periodic voltage across the load resistance.

(b) Determine the rms value of the load voltage.   *Ans.: 45.6 V.*

2.11 A protective system is required that will close a relay when the 60-c/s sinusoidal voltage supply in a laboratory exceeds 125 V rms. The proposed system consists of a relay with a coil resistance of 1000 Ω and negligible inductance, connected in series with a nonlinear inductor to the supply voltage. The relay will close when its half-cycle average current (disregarding polarity) reaches 10 m amp. The inductor is to have a toroidal core made of 50% nickel, 50% iron. The B–H characteristic of this material may be idealized as shown in Fig. 2.7b with $B_k = 1.5$ Wb/m². To insure mechanical reliability, the cross-sectional area of the wire should not be less than about 0.1 mm². Design a suitable inductor, specifying the core dimensions and the number of turns on the coil.

2.12 Figure P2.12 shows a proposed system for measuring the frequency of an alternating-voltage signal. A nonlinear inductor in series with a

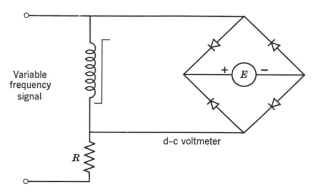

Fig. P2.12

resistor R is connected to the signal source. The voltage across the inductor is applied to a full-wave bridge rectifier and measured using a high-resistance d-c voltmeter.

(a) Suppose the signal voltage is of sufficient amplitude to saturate the inductor core before the end of each half cycle of the signal. The inductor may be assumed to have an idealized B–H characteristic, as in Fig. 2.7b, with a saturation flux density B_k. Let the cross-sectional area of the core be A, and let N be the number of turns. Assuming the coil resistance to be negligible in comparison with R, show that the voltmeter reading will be $E = 4NAB_kf$ V, where f is the signal frequency.

(b) The meter is to measure frequency over the range of 25–500 c/s. Let $B_k = 0.7$ Wb/m², $A = 0.2$ cm², and $N = 500$. What minimum rms values of sinusoidal voltage at 25 c/s and at 500 c/s must be applied to give correct measurement of frequency?   *Ans.* 15.6 V for 500 c/s.

(c) Show that the voltmeter reading will be 0.028 V per c/s for any waveform of adequate amplitude, provided that the voltage changes sign only once in each half cycle.

2.13 An iron-cored inductor, commonly known as a choke, is often used to smooth out the ripples on the current from a rectifier. To be effective, the choke must have an appreciable inductance when carrying the direct current of the rectifier. Saturation of the magnetic path is prevented by the use of an appropriate air gap.

Design a choke to have an inductance of 10 H when carrying a direct current of 0.5 amp. The magnetic material may be assumed to require no appreciable magnetic field intensity up to a flux density of 1.4 Wb/m². A current density of 2 amp/mm² may be used in the coil.

To start the design, the volume of the air gap required to store the magnetic field energy may be found. A reasonably shaped air gap may then be chosen. Next, the number of turns may be found; allowing adequate space for these turns and their insulation, the dimensions of the magnetic core may be chosen.

2.14 A magnetic core of the form shown in Fig. P2.14 is made of a material for which the *B–H* loops can be represented by the linearized

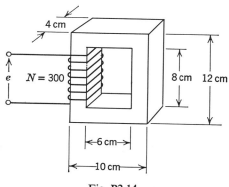

Fig. P2.14

model shown in Fig. 2.9, with $H_c = 10$ amp/m, $B_k = 1.2$ Wb/m², $\mu_n = 10^5$, and $\mu_s = 10^4$.

(a) Find the peak value of sinusoidal voltage *e* at 50 c/s that will drive the core around a *B–H* loop passing through B_k and H_c. The coil resistance is negligible.

(b) Sketch the magnetizing current for the applied voltage determined in part (a). What is its peak value? *Ans.:* 0.026 amp.

(c) Determine the hysteresis loss in the core for the operating condition of part (a). *Ans.:* 0.76 W.

2.15 The toroidal magnetic core shown in Fig. P2.15*a* has a uniformly distributed winding of 200 turns. The magnetization characteristic of the magnetic material can be approximated by the idealized form shown in Fig. P2.15b. Since the outside diameter of the core is considerably greater than the inside diameter, the magnetic field intensity cannot be considered uniform over the cross-sectional area of the core.

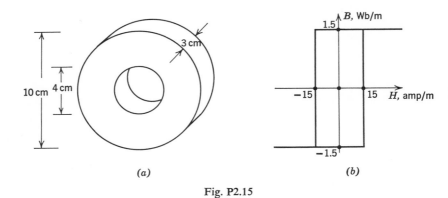

(a)   (b)

Fig. P2.15

(a) Sketch the relationship between the flux linkage and the current of the coil.

(b) Suppose a sinusoidal voltage at a frequency of 400 c/s is applied to the coil and increased in amplitude until core is operating between its saturation limits. The coil resistance may be ignored. Sketch the waveform of the magnetizing current, and determine its peak value.

Ans.: 0.0236 amp.

(c) Determine the in-phase and quadrature fundamental-frequency components of the magnetizing current.

(d) Compare the magnetizing current of this core with that of another core having the same cross-sectional area and volume, but having a near-unity ratio of outside to inside diameter. Show that the quadrature component of fundamental-frequency magnetizing current arises from the shape of the core and not from its B–H characteristic.

(e) Show that the hysteresis loss obtained from the in-phase component of fundamental-frequency magnetizing current and the applied voltage is equal to the area of the B–H loop multiplied by the core volume and the frequency.

2.16 A relay is to be energized 0.25 sec after a switch is closed. The proposed scheme, shown in Fig. P2.16a, consists of a nonlinear inductor having two identical windings, one of which is connected in series with the relay coil. This winding is intended to absorb most of the battery voltage for the 0.25-sec interval after the switch is set to position *a*. At the end of this interval the core saturates, and most of the battery voltage is applied to the relay coil. The second winding is required to reset the core flux density to negative saturation when the switch is operated to position *b*.

The relay will operate with a current of 0.01 amp. This current may be increased to 0.02 amp without overheating. The relay coil may be con-

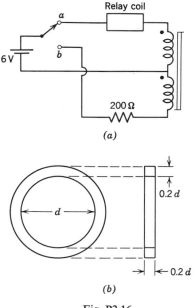

Fig. P2.16

sidered to have negligible inductance and to have a resistance of 200 Ω.

Toroidal cores having the shape shown in Fig. P2.16*b* are available with inside diameters of 2.5 cm, 4 cm, 5 cm, and 6 cm. Figure P2.15*b* is a reasonable idealization of the *B–H* characteristics of the magnetic material. The current density in the inductor coils should not exceed 2 amp/mm². The same wire size may be used for both coils. Design a suitable inductor for this application.

2.17 Rectangular voltage pulses of the form shown in Fig. 2.11*b* are produced each time a package on a conveyor belt passes a detector. The pulses have a height of 3 V and a duration of 1 msec. A magnetic counter, which will give a 3-V output pulse across a 20-Ω load for each tenth package is required. An available toroidal core has a cross-sectional area of 0.5 cm² and a mean diameter of 3 cm. Its *B–H* characteristic is shown in Fig. P2.15*b*. Determine the approximate number of turns required on the core.   *Ans.:* 172.

2.18 Figure P2.18 shows typical ferrite cores in the memory system of a digital computer. Each core has a rectangular hysteresis loop of the form shown in Fig. 2.10, with $B_r = 0.3$ Wb/m² and $H_c = 25$ amp/m. Each core has a mean diameter of 2 mm and a cross-sectional area of 10^{-7} m².

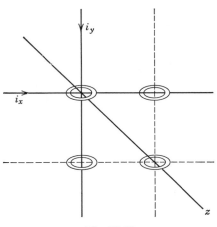

Fig. P2.18

(a) Determine the magnitude of a current pulse i_x that will provide a magnetic field intensity equal to $0.7 H_c$ in the core.

Ans.: 0.11 amp. Note that this pulse will not change the core flux.

(b) To change the magnetic state of a core from negative to positive saturation, simultaneous current pulses i_x and i_y are applied, each having the amplitude found in part (a). Simultaneous pulses of reversed polarity return the core to the state of negative saturation.

A winding, denoted as z, passes through all the cores. The appearance of a voltage pulse e_z on this winding indicates that flux switching is taking place in the core linked by the simultaneously applied currents i_x and i_y. If the core flux switches at a uniform rate between saturation limits in 1.0 μsec, determine the amplitude of the pulse e_z.   *Ans.:* 0.06 V.

(c) If the core is already at positive saturation, will any voltage e_z be produced when the core is pulsed with currents i_x and i_y?

2.19 When a 115-V rms, 60-c/s source is connected to a nonlinear inductor, the current is 0.23 amp rms and the input power is 14.1 W. The coil resistance is negligible. Observation of the current waveform on an oscilloscope indicates that the third-harmonic component of the magnetizing current is about 0.3 of the fundamental component and that higher harmonics are negligible.

Determine the values of the two parameters in an equivalent circuit of the form shown in Fig. 2.12c. *Ans.: 940 Ω; 630 Ω.*

2.20 The magnetizing current of an iron-cored inductor can be expressed approximately as

$$i = 0.28 \sin(\omega t + 30°) - 0.12 \sin 3\omega t + 0.05 \sin 5\omega t$$

The applied voltage is 160 cos ωt V.

(a) Sketch the waveform of the magnetizing current.

(b) Determine the rms value of the magnetizing current. *Ans.: 0.218 amp.*

(c) Determine the average power entering the inductor. *Ans.: 11.2 W.*

2.21 A sinusoidal voltage of 200 V rms at 500 c/s is applied to an 80-turn coil on a toroidal core of cross-sectional area 10^{-3} m² and mean diameter 0.1 m. The core material can be represented by the idealized model of Fig. 2.10 with $B_r = 1.6$ Wb/m² and $H_c = 20$ amp/m. The coil resistance may be ignored.

(a) Determine the amplitude and waveform of the magnetizing current.

(b) Derive a Fourier series representation for the magnetizing current, and evaluate the rms value of the third-harmonic component. *Ans.: 0.0235 amp.*

(c) Determine the ratio of the rms value of the fundamental-frequency component to the rms value of the total magnetizing current. *Ans.: 0.9.*

2.22 A manufacturer lists a grain-oriented magnetic material in sheets which are 0.3 mm thick. The resistivity of the material is given as 5×10^{-7} Ω-m. The published static B–H loop for the material is essentially rectangular in form, with a coercive force of 12 amp/m for all values of peak flux density in the range 0.8 to 1.6 Wb/m². The quoted value for the total loss in the material is 1.2 W/kg, with a sinusoidal flux density of 1.0 Wb/m² (peak) at 100 c/s. The mass density of the material is 7650 kg/m³.

Calculate the loss in the material from its properties, and compare the value obtained with the quoted value. Suggest possible reasons for the errors in predicting the loss.

2.23 The magnetic core shown in Fig. P2.14 is made of laminations of thickness 0.35 mm and resistivity 6×10^{-7} Ω-m. The static B–H characteristic of the material may be approximated by the idealized form shown in Fig. 2.7, where $B_k = 1.2$ Wb/m². The coil resistance is negligible.

(a) Show that the inductor can be represented as a resistance connected across the voltage e, providing the magnitude of the flux density B in the core does not exceed the value B_k.

   (b) Determine the value of this resistance.   *Ans.: 11,750 Ω.*

   (c) Estimate the eddy current loss in the core when it is operated with a sinusoidal, 400-c/s voltage that produces a peak flux density of 1.2 Wb/m².
   Ans.: 22.2 W.

2.24   A power of 1 kW is to be supplied to a load having a resistance of 3 Ω. A source of 115 V at 60 c/s is available. Specify the turns ratio of a 2-winding transformer suitable for this purpose. The transformer may be considered to be ideal. Also specify the minimum voltage and current ratings for each of the windings.

2.25   An audio amplifier is to be connected to a loudspeaker by means of a 2-winding transformer. The loudspeaker can be considered as a resistive load of 8.0 Ω (see Prob. 1.26). The source can be represented as an audio frequency voltage in series with a resistance of 1000 Ω. Assuming the transformer to be ideal, determine the turns ratio that will provide maximum power into the loudspeaker.   *Ans.: 11.2:1.*

2.26   In Fig. P2.26 an alternating, square-wave voltage e of peak value 20 V and period 0.0025 sec is applied to a 200-Ω resistor in series with one

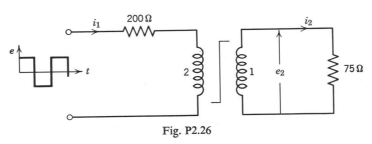

Fig. P2.26

winding of a 2:1-ratio transformer. The core material of the transformer may be represented by an idealized model of the form shown in Fig. 2.7b. Saturation occurs when the flux linkage of the winding connected to the 75-Ω load reaches a magnitude of 0.005 Wb. The resistances of the coils are negligible.

   (a) Determine the waveform of the current i_1.

   (b) Sketch the waveform of the voltage e_2 across the 75-Ω load, and determine its rms value.   *Ans.: 4.91 V.*

2.27   Suppose that in the system of Fig. P2.26, the 75-Ω resistance is replaced by a capacitance of 50 μf. Initially, the capacitor voltage is zero, and the core is at negative saturation. At $t = 0$, a constant voltage e of 10 V is connected to the system.

(a) Derive expressions for the current i_1 and the voltage e_2 as functions of time t.

(b) At what time will the core reach positive saturation?
Ans.: 0.004 sec.

(c) When the core reaches saturation, will the capacitor voltage remain constant, decay exponentially to zero, or fall immediately to zero?

2.28 Figure P.2.28 shows a toroidal magnetic core with a winding of $N = 250$ turns. The *B–H* characteristic for the core material can be approximated by a linear relation with a relative permeability of 15,000 if the flux density is less than 1.5 Wb/m² in magnitude.

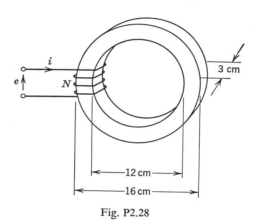

Fig. P2.28

(a) Represent the system by a magnetic equivalent circuit, and determine the value of the reluctance.   *Ans.:* 3.88 × 10⁴ Wb/amp.

(b) Suppose an air gap of length 0.2 mm is cut across the core in Fig. P2.28. Draw a magnetic equivalent circuit for the system, and use it to determine the coil current i required to produce a magnetic flux in the core of 5 × 10⁻⁴ Wb.   *Ans.:* 0.61 amp.

(c) For the conditions of part (b) find the energy stored in the magnetic material and in the air gap.

(d) For values of flux density greater than 1.5 Wb/m² in magnitude, the incremental saturated permeability of the core material is 1000. Develop a graph showing the relationship between the core flux and the magnetomotive force required to produce the flux in the core material only. Determine the coil current required to produce a magnetic flux of 10⁻³ Wb in the air-gapped core.

(e) For the air-gapped core, determine the magnetic flux produced by a coil current of 2.0 amp.   *Ans.:* 1.7×10^{-3} Wb.

2.29 The magnetic system of Fig. P2.29 has a coil of 50 turns on its middle leg. The magnetic material may be assumed to have a constant relative permeability of 4000. Leakage flux may be neglected.

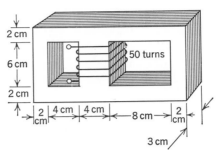

Fig. P2.29

  (a) Derive a magnetic equivalent circuit for this system inserting the values of all parameters.

  (b) Determine the magnetic flux in the right-hand leg when the coil current is 2 amp.   *Ans.:* 7.65×10^{-4} Wb.

2.30 The toroidal core of Fig. P2.28 has a relative permeability of 15000. The coil has 250 turns and a resistance of 1.5 Ω.

  (a) Develop an electric equivalent circuit relating the terminal voltage *e* and the coil current *i*.

  (b) Determine the value of the coil inductance.   *Ans.:* 1.61 H.

  (c) Suppose an air gap, whose length is 0.2 mm, is cut across the core. Use the magnetic equivalent circuit developed in Prob. 2.28(b) to obtain an electric equivalent circuit for the air-gapped system. What is the value of the inductance representing the air gap?   *Ans.:* 0.236 H.

  (d) Determine the time constant of the coil with the air-gapped core. *Ans.:* 0.137 sec.

2.31 In Prob. 2.29 a magnetic equivalent circuit was developed for the magnetic system of Fig. P2.29.

  (a) Derive an electric equivalent circuit for this system inserting the value of all inductances.

  (b) Determine the total inductance as seen from the terminals of the 50-turn coil.   *Ans.:* 0.0452 H.

(c) Suppose a 100-turn winding is now placed on the right-hand leg. Insert an appropriate ideal transformer into the equivalent electric circuit. If a 10-V alternating voltage is applied to the 50-turn winding, what will be the open-circuit voltage across the 100-turnwinding?   *Ans.:* 8.45 V.

(d) Suppose the 100-turn winding is short circuited. Determine the impedance at 400 c/s as seen from the terminals of the 50-turn coil. The coil resistances may be considered negligible.   *Ans.:* 72.9 Ω.

2.32 A magnetic system having two coils is shown in Fig. P2.32. The reluctance of the ferromagnetic material may be ignored. At each air gap

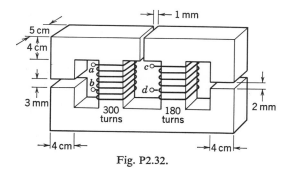

Fig. P2.32.

the magnetic field is not entirely confined to the gap volume. The fringing flux around the gap edges may be taken into account in the calculation of reluctance by an appropriate increase in the cross-sectional area of the gap. A useful approximation is obtained if the region of uniform flux density is assumed to extend outward by a distance equal to half the gap length from each of the gap edges.

(a) Develop an electric equivalent circuit for the system including the values of all parameters. The coil resistances may be neglected.

(b) If the frequency is 180 c/s, what is the reactance of the system with the two coils connected in series, terminal *b* being connected to terminal *d*? *Ans.:* 830 Ω

(c) Repeat part (b) with terminal *b* connected to terminal *c*.

2.33 Figure P2.33 shows the structure of an impulse transformer used to produce firing pulses for controlled rectifiers. A sinusoidal voltage of 28 V rms at 400 c/s is applied to the 120-turn winding. The output pulses are obtained from the 35-turn winding. A *B–H* characteristic of the form shown in Fig. 2.7*b* with $B_k = 1.6$ Wb/m² may be assumed for the magnetic material. All ferromagnetic parts of the system may therefore be assumed to have zero reluctance until the magnitude of the flux density reaches B_k, when the reluctance then may be assumed to be infinite.

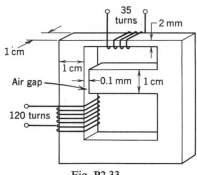

Fig. P2.33

(a) Develop an equivalent electric circuit for the system describing each inductive element either by its inductance value or by its flux linkage–current relationship.

(b) Neglecting the resistance of the 120-turn coil and assuming the 35-turn coil to be open circuited, determine the peak amplitude and the width of the output pulse.   *Ans.:* 11.56 V; 0.196 msec.

(c) Using the equivalent circuit of part (a), devise a system having similar terminal properties to those of the system of Fig. P2.33 and using a saturable toroidal core with 120-turn and 35-turn windings. If the toroidal core is made of the same material as that used in the system of Fig. P2.33, specify the required cross-sectional area.

2.34 A rectangular block of permanent-magnet material is to be magnetized using an arrangement similar to the one shown in Fig. 2.25a.

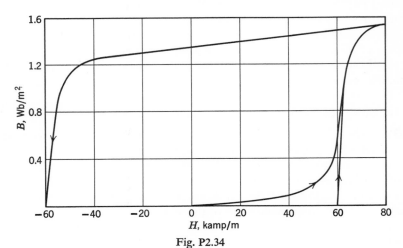

Fig. P2.34

The block has a length of $l_m = 5$ cm and a cross-sectional area of 10 cm². The soft magnetic material may be assumed to have infinite permeability. The coil has 100 turns. Figure P2.34 shows the B–H characteristic published by the manufacturer of the material.

(a) Suppose that the material has an initial flux density of zero. Determine the peak value of the coil current i required to magnetize the magnet so it will have a residual flux density of 1.35 Wb/m².

Ans.: About 40 amp.

(b) Determine approximately the energy required to magnetize the magnet under the conditions of part (a). Coil resistance may be neglected.

(c) One simple method of magnetizing a magnet consists of connecting a charged capacitor to the winding in the system shown in Fig. 2.25a. If the capacitance is 100 μf, to what voltage should the capacitor be charged to provide the necessary magnetization current? Coil resistance may be neglected. *Ans.: 290 V.*

(d) The method of magnetization discussed in part (c) produces an oscillatory current, which might tend to demagnetize the magnet. Show that this demagnetization can be prevented by placing a rectifier in series with the capacitor.

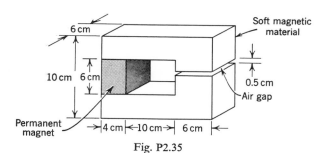

Fig. P2.35

2.35 In the system shown in Fig. P2.35, the permanent-magnet material has the B–H characteristics shown in Fig. P2.34. The soft magnetic material may be assumed to have infinite permeability. Initially, a keeper made of soft magnetic material is inserted into the air gap, and the permanent magnet is magnetized to a residual flux density of 1.35 Wb/m² by means of a coil.

(a) Determine the flux density in the air gap when the keeper is removed. Fringing flux around the air gap may be ignored. *Ans.: 0.745 Wb/m².*

(b) The permanent-magnet material has a recoil permeability of about 2.0 μ_0. Suppose the keeper is reinserted into the air gap. What is the new value of residual flux density in the permanent-magnet material? *Ans.: About 1.25 Wb/m².*

2.36 In Prob. 2.35 the air flux was assumed to be confined within the air gap. There is, however, some fringing flux around the gap edges. This may be included by the method discussed in relation to Prob. 2.32. In addition, there is a leakage flux between the upper and lower horizontal sections of soft magnetic material. Let us assume that this leakage flux density is uniform throughout the volume of the air space between the two horizontal members and is zero outside this volume.

(a) Initially, the permanent magnet has a residual flux density of 1.35 Wb/m^2 with the keeper inserted in the air gap. Determine the flux density in the permanent magnet when the keeper is removed.   *Ans.:* 1.23 Wb/m^2.

(b) Determine the air-gap flux density and compare it with the value found in Prob. 2.35(a).

(c) The leakage flux of the arrangement in Fig. P2.35 may be reduced considerably by placing the permanent-magnet material closer to the air gap. Sketch an improved rearrangement of the system using the same volume of permanent-magnet material and the same air-gap dimensions.

2.37 A magnetic flux density of 0.8 Wb/m^2 is required in an air gap having a length of 2 cm and a circular cross section of radius 10 cm. Permanent-magnet material having the *B–H* characteristic of Fig. P2.34 is available in cylinders of any length and radius. Soft magnetic material is also available in any shape; it can be regarded as perfect up to a flux density of 1.4 Wb/m^2. Since the permanent-magnet material is relatively costly, its volume should be minimized.

(a) At what value of flux density should the permanent-magnet material be operated?

(b) Design a permanent-magnet assembly that will have reasonably low leakage.

(c) What volume of permanent magnet material is required?
Ans.: 5670 cm^3, approximately.

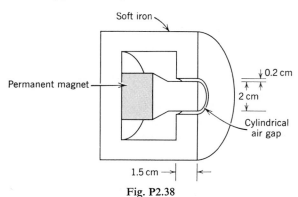

Fig. P2.38

2.38 Figure P2.38 shows a half-sectional view of the permanent-magnet assembly of a loudspeaker (see Prob. 1.26). A magnetic flux density of 1.2 Wb/m^2 is required in the cylindrical air gap. Permanent-magnetic material having the characteristics shown in Fig. P2.34 may be used.

(a) Neglecting leakage and fringing fluxes, determine the appropriate dimensions for the various parts of the magnet assembly. The flux density in the soft iron should not exceed 1.2 Wb/m^2.

(b) Determine the mass of the permanent magnet if the material has a mass density of 7330 kg/m^3. *Ans.: 0.31 kg.*

2.39 Suppose the permanent magnet in Fig. P2.35 has been stabilized so that its residual flux density is 1.2 Wb/m^2 (with the keeper in the air gap). The recoil permeability of the material is $2.0 \ \mu_0$.

(a) Represent the system by a linearized magnetic circuit. Include a reluctance element to represent, approximately, the leakage flux path between the upper and lower horizontal members. For simplicity, the field may be assumed to be uniform within the space between those members. Make the usual allowance for fringing flux in calculating the reluctance of the air gap.

(b) Use the equivalent circuit to determine the air-gap flux.

Ans.: 2.46×10^{-3} Wb, including the fringing flux.

2.40 Figure P2.40*a* shows a small magnet assembly intended for use as a door holder. The keeper is to be attached to the door, while the remainder of the assembly is to be attached to the door frame. The permanent magnet is made of a ferrite ceramic material. The *B–H* characteristic for this material is shown, in somewhat idealized form,

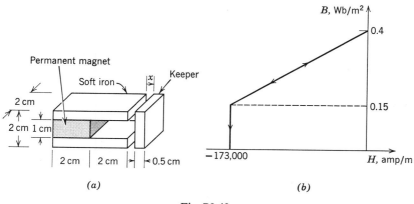

Fig. P2.40

in Fig. P2.40b. The soft iron may be assumed to have infinite permeability.

(a) The recoil permeability of the permanent-magnet material is 1.15 μ_0. Show that the sloped part of the demagnetization characteristic may be used as the recoil characteristic for this material.

(b) Derive a linearized magnetic circuit for the magnet assembly, neglecting leakage and fringing flux components. Determine the maximum value of air-gap length x for which this magnetic circuit is valid. *Ans.:* 1.81 mm.

(c) In one of its possible forms, the equivalent magnetic circuit consists of a constant magnetomotive force in series with three reluctance elements, two of which represent the air gaps. Use the analogy suggested by this equivalent circuit to derive an expression for the force acting on the keeper at any value of gap spacing x. Evaluate the expression for $x = 1$ mm. *Ans.:* 55 newtons.

(d) The linear model derived in part (b) predicts that the magnet will be demagnetized if the air gap exceeds a length of 1.81 mm. Show that the leakage reluctance between the upper and lower soft-iron members is low enough to prevent demagnetization from occurring.

2.41 A meter movement of the type shown in Fig. P1.27 has a magnetic flux density of 1.1 Wb/m² in the spaces between the pole faces and the central core. The total volume of this magnetic field is 1.5 cm³.

(a) If Fig. P2.40b represents the *B–H* characteristic of the material, determine the minimum volume of permanent-magnet material required to establish the magnetic field.   *Ans.:* 52.1 cm³.

(b) If the material whose characteristics are shown in Fig. P2.34 were used, what would be the required volume of the magnet?

2.42 Figure P2.42 shows a magnetic reluctance type of phonograph pickup. As the stylus moves from side to side in the groove of the recording, the central magnetic member rotates about its pivot. A displacement of the stylus causes a proportional increase δ in the lengths of two of the air gaps while the lengths of the other two air gaps are decreased by δ. The rubber mountings restrain the deflections δ to small values so that δ is much less than the average gap spacing l. Each gap has a cross-sectional area A.

(a) Develop a magnetic equivalent circuit for this device. The magnet may be represented as a flux source ϕ_0 in parallel with a reluctance $\mathcal{R}_0$. Denote the flux ϕ linking each turn of the pickup coil.

(b) Show that, if $\delta \ll l$, the reluctance seen by the magnet is essentially constant.

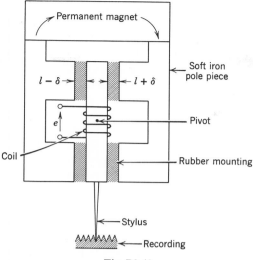

Fig. P2.42

(c) Show that the induced voltage e in the coil may be expressed as

$$e = \frac{N\phi_0}{l}\left(\frac{\mathscr{R}_0}{\mathscr{R}_0 + \dfrac{l}{\mu_0 A}}\right)\frac{d\delta}{dt}$$

(d) Design a reluctance pickup assigning any reasonable set of dimensions to the various parts. A ferrite magnet having the demagnetization characteristic of Fig. P2.40b may be used.

2.43 A magnetic field of density B is required in the rectangular channel of width x, height y, and length z of a magnetohydrodynamic machine (see Prob. 1.28). The proposed design, shown in Fig. P2.43, consists of a

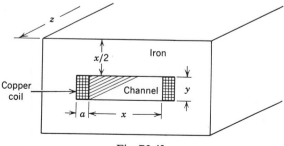

Fig. P2.43

soft iron frame enclosing the channel and a coil, whose turns go down one side of the channel and back on the other. The soft iron may be assumed to have infinite permeability. The copper conductors are to be operated at a current density J. Let k_s be the space factor of the coil, that is, the ratio of the copper area to the total cross-sectional area of the coil. The resistivity of the copper is ρ.

(a) Show that the required width of the coil is $a = B/\mu_0 k_s J$ m.

(b) Show that the power loss in the coil is given approximately by the expression $P = 2\rho JByz/\mu_0$ W, providing the channel length z is considerably greater than the channel width x.

(c) Show that the magnetic field energy stored in the channel per watt of power dissipation in the coil is given approximately by $Bx/4\rho J$.

(d) A proposed magnetohydrodynamic generator requires a channel with $x = 3$ m, $y = 0.6$ m, and $z = 26$ m, with a flux density of 1.6 Wb/m². The water-cooled coil can be operated at a current density of 10^7 amp/m². Its space factor might be about 0.4. The average temperature of the copper may be taken as 40°C. Estimate the power required by the coil, the mass of the copper (density = 8890 kg/m³), and the mass of the iron frame (density = 7870 kg/m³). *Ans.:* 7.38 MW; 35,200 kg; 4.46 × 10⁶ kg.

(e) Suggest an alternative design using Alnico permanent magnets to produce the magnetic field. Figure P2.34 may be used as a representative *B–H* characteristic. What minimum mass of permanent-magnet material (density = 7350 kg/m²) would be required? Compare this with the mass of the iron found in part (d).

2.44 Figure P2.44 shows the essential elements of a magnetic earphone. For faithful reproduction of speech it is necessary to exert a force on the

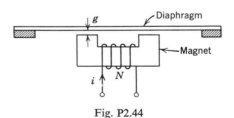

Fig. P2.44

diaphragm that is directly proportional to the coil current i. If the whole assembly were made of soft magnetic material, the force would be proportional to the square of the current (eq. 1.84). To overcome this difficulty, the coil is wound on a permanent magnet of area A and length l. The diaphragm is sufficiently stiff that the gap spacings g do not change appreciably, and they may be regarded as essentially constant in the preliminary analysis. The permanent-magnet material has a stabilized residual flux density B_r and a relative recoil permeability of μ_r. Fringing flux may be neglected, and the diaphragm permeability may be assumed infinite.

(a) Develop an equivalent magnetic circuit for the system.

(b) Develop an expression for the force on the diaphragm as a function of the current i.

(c) Show that if $i \ll B_r l / \mu_r \mu_0 N$, the force on the diaphragm is a constant term plus a term

$$f = \frac{2AB_r \mu_r l N}{(l + 2\mu_r g)^2} i \qquad \text{newtons}$$

REFERENCES

Boast, W. B., *Principles of Electric and Magnetic Fields*. Harper and Row, New York, 1948. (Includes chapters on flux plotting and estimation of reluctances.)

Cunningham, W. J., *Introduction to Nonlinear Analysis*. McGraw-Hill, New York, 1958.

Katz, H. W., *Solid State Magnetic and Dielectric Devices*. John Wiley and Sons, New York, 1959.

Parker, R. J. and R. J. Studders, *Permanent Magnets and Their Applications*. John Wiley and Sons, New York, 1962.

Slemon, G. R., "A Method of Approximate Steady-State Analysis for Nonlinear Networks." *Proceedings, Institution of Electrical Engineers*, **100**, Part 1, 1953, 275.

Stanton, R. G., *Numerical Methods for Science and Engineering*. Prentice-Hall, Englewood Cliffs, N.J., 1961.

Chapter 3

TRANSFORMATION OF ELECTRIC ENERGY

Various static magnetic devices are used to transform electric energy from one form to another. Most of these are known as transformers. In elementary terms, they consist of two or more closely coupled coils. To achieve this close coupling, the coils are generally wound on a closed ferromagnetic core.

The properties of a perfect or ideal two-winding transformer have already been discussed, in Section 2.3. It was shown that the voltages e_1 and e_2 of the windings are related to the numbers of turns N_1 and N_2 by

$$\frac{e_1}{e_2} = \frac{N_1}{N_2} \tag{3.1}$$

and the winding currents i_1 and i_2 are related by

$$\frac{i_1}{i_2} = \frac{N_2}{N_1} \tag{3.2}$$

Most applications of transformers can be appreciated by a consideration of these idealized properties. In electric power systems, transformers are used to transform electric energy at a voltage of about 10–25 kilovolts (which is most economical for large generators) to a voltage of 50–750 kilovolts (which is suitable for long-distance transmission). When this energy arrives in bulk quantity at the load area, it is generally transformed to a voltage in the range of 2–20 kilovolts, because this level is most economical for distribution of smaller quantities over short distances. At a point near the premises of most customers, the energy is further transformed to one of the standard utilization voltages such as 115, 230, 440, or 575 volts. Transformers, large and small, are included in many kinds of electric and electronic apparatus to produce energy at a voltage suitable for particular load devices.

Most power transformers operate at a frequency of 50 or 60 cycles per second. Other frequencies, such as 400 or 2000 cycles per second, may be used for control systems and for power supply in aircraft. In electronic or communication apparatus, transformers are required to operate over a wide range of audio and radio frequencies.

Further applications of transformers arise from their ability to couple two electric systems without requiring a conductive connection between them. This isolation feature is of particular importance in the transformers designed for measurement purposes.

In analyzing many transformer applications, eqs. 3.1 and 3.2 are obeyed to within a few per cent, and ideal behavior can be assumed. There is probably no other electrical device that approximates its ideal behavior so closely, but there are many situations in which even small imperfections are important. For example, an efficiency of 98 % may be considered as essentially ideal. The heat arising from the remaining 2 % loss, however, must be withdrawn from the transformer; it is thus of major concern to the designer. Even a 2 % loss in a large transformer is economically important. In some transformers, significant imperfections are intentionally introduced to achieve a desired operating characteristic. In the following sections, the imperfections of transformers are discussed, and means of analyzing their effects are developed.

3.1 EQUIVALENT CIRCUITS FOR TRANSFORMERS

In this section we develop some equivalent circuits that are useful in predicting the behavior of transformers. In each instance the equivalent circuit consists of one or more ideal transformers and elements to represent the physical properties that cause a departure from ideal behavior.

Some of the imperfections in the transformer are readily appreciated. There is resistance in each of the windings, and this produces both a loss of power and a drop in voltage. The ferromagnetic core requires finite magnetic field intensity to produce its magnetic flux. The ideal current relation of eq. 3.2 does not apply exactly, because the sum of the magnetomotive forces of the coils must be sufficient to supply this field intensity.

Perhaps the most important imperfection in a transformer arises from magnetic flux that fails to link all the windings. As this leakage flux varies with time it produces an induced voltage in some of the windings, but not in others; it thus causes a departure from the ideal voltage relation of eq. 3.1. To minimize leakage flux, the windings are arranged close to each other. Figure 3.1 shows several common arrangements of cores and coils. In the shell-type construction of Fig. 3.1a the windings are concentric, winding 2 being placed outside winding 1. The core consists of laminations that are stacked so that the windings encircle the central leg. The core-type construction of Fig. 3.1b has two identical sets of concentric coils placed on the two legs of a single-path laminated core. Figures 3.1c and d show similar shell- and core-type arrangements using cores that are wound

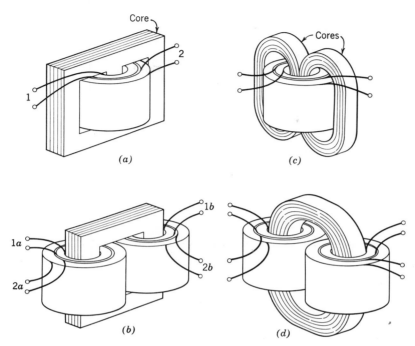

Fig. 3.1   Winding and core arrangements. (*a*) Shell-type with core of laminated sheets. (*b*) Core-type with core of laminated sheets. (*c*) Shell-type with wound core. (*d*) Core-type with wound core.

from a long strip of magnetic material. This wound-core arrangement is particularly advantageous when grain-oriented magnetic material is used.

3.1.1   Equivalent Circuit for Two-Winding Shell-Type Transformer

Methods for developing an equivalent electric circuit to represent a magnetic system approximately were discussed in Section 2.4. Let us now apply these methods to the two-winding shell-type transformer, a cross section of which is shown in Fig. 3.2*a*. The first step in producing an equivalent electric circuit is to reduce the significant features of the magnetic system to a magnetic equivalent circuit. The pertinent assumptions are introduced at this stage.

The flux pattern in Fig. 3.2*a* occurs when the magnetomotive force $\mathscr{F}_1$ of the inner winding 1 is slightly greater than the magnetomotive force $\mathscr{F}_2$ of the outer winding 2. A magnetic flux ϕ_1 passes upward through the central leg and divides into two equal parts that proceed outward along the yokes. A part ϕ_L of this flux takes the path down

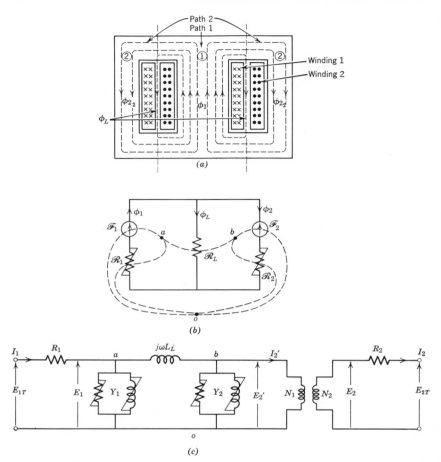

Fig. 3.2 (a) A two-winding, shell-type transformer. (b) Magnetic circuit. (c) Equivalent electric circuit.

through the air space between the windings to avoid the oppositely directed magnetomotive force of winding 2. The remainder ϕ_2 passes down the outer legs and thereby links winding 2. This flux pattern suggests that the ferromagnetic core consists of two significant paths, each of which carries a distinctive magnetic flux. Path 1, carrying the flux ϕ_1, includes the central leg and about half of each of the yoke sections. Path 2, carrying the total flux ϕ_2, consists of the outer legs and the remainder of the yoke sections. This second path consists of two physically separate parts, but, because of the symmetry, they may be regarded as being in parallel magnetically.

Figure 3.2b shows a magnetic equivalent circuit in which the assumed paths of flux are represented by their reluctances. In this circuit, winding 1 (represented by its magnetomotive force $\mathscr{F}_1$) is linked by the flux ϕ_1, which exists in the reluctance $\mathscr{R}_1$ of path 1. This reluctance may be dependent on the value of the flux ϕ_1 and is therefore indicated as nonlinear in the equivalent magnetic circuit. The magnetic flux ϕ_L is established in the air space between the windings. Methods for determining the reluctance $\mathscr{R}_L$ of this leakage path are discussed later in Section 3.1.4. As this path is assumed to be entirely in the air space, its reluctance is constant. The flux $\phi_2 = \phi_1 - \phi_L$ is established in the reluctance $\mathscr{R}_2$ of the combined parts of path 2. This flux ϕ_2 links winding 2 which is represented by its magnetomotive force $\mathscr{F}_2$. Since path 2 is ferromagnetic, its reluctance is regarded as nonlinear.

In developing an electric circuit that is equivalent to the magnetic circuit of Fig. 3.2b, let us use the number N_1 of the turns of winding 1 as a reference number. The form of the electric circuit may be derived by use of the simple topological technique described in Section 2.4.2. The result is the set of dashed lines joining the nodes a, b, and o in Fig. 3.2b.

Suppose the transformer is to operate at an angular frequency of ω radians per second. The equivalent electric circuit of Fig. 3.2c includes an inductive impedance $j\omega L_L$ connected between nodes a and b. The value of the leakage inductance L_L is related to the leakage reluctance by

$$L_L = \frac{N_1^2}{\mathscr{R}_L} \qquad \text{henrys} \qquad (3.3)$$

as the reference winding has N_1 turns. The equivalent circuit includes two magnetizing branches representing the reluctances $\mathscr{R}_1$ and $\mathscr{R}_2$ of the magnetic circuit. If these reluctances could be considered constant, the corresponding magnetizing branches would consist of constant inductive impedances. To include the effects of nonlinearity, hysteresis, and eddy current losses in paths 1 and 2, each branch of the electric circuit corresponding to a nonlinear reluctance is represented by parallel nonlinear resistive and inductive impedances. This model is similar to that developed for simple nonlinear inductors in Figs. 2.12c and 2.16. For convenience in notation, these nonlinear branches are identified by their admittances Y_1 and Y_2.

The induced voltage phasor E_1 in winding 1 is given by

$$E_1 = j\omega N_1\Phi_1 \qquad \text{volts} \qquad (3.4)$$

where Φ_1 is the phasor representing the magnetic flux ϕ_1. The terminal voltage E_{1T} differs from the induced voltage by the drop across the winding

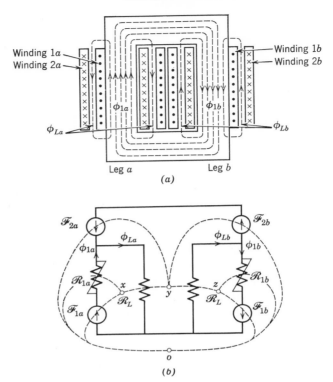

Fig. 3.3 (a) A core-type transformer. (b) Magnetic circuit. (c) Equivalent electric circuit as four-winding transformer. (d) Equivalent electric circuit with windings 1a and 1b in parallel, windings 2a and 2b in series.

resistance R_1. The voltage E_2' is given by

$$E_2' = j\omega N_1 \Phi_2 \qquad \text{volts} \qquad (3.5)$$

This is the induced voltage which would apply for winding 2 if $N_2 = N_1$. The actual induced voltage in winding 2 is E_2, which appears on the other side of the ideal transformer of ratio $N_1 : N_2$. Thus

$$E_2 = \frac{N_2}{N_1} E_2'$$
$$= j\omega N_2 \Phi_2 \qquad \text{volts} \qquad (3.6)$$

Winding 2 has a resistance R_2 and a current phasor I_2. If winding 2 were replaced by a winding of N_1 turns, its current would have the value noted on the other side of the ideal transformer, that is,

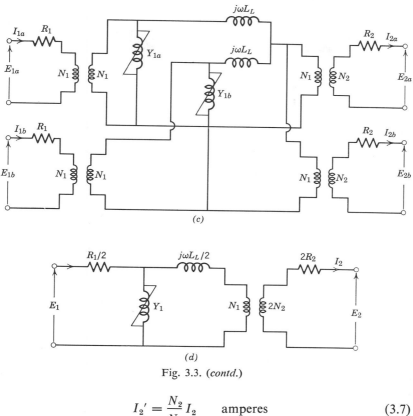

Fig. 3.3. (contd.)

$$I_2' = \frac{N_2}{N_1} I_2 \qquad \text{amperes} \qquad (3.7)$$

The voltage E_{ab} in Fig. 3.2c is equal to the induced voltage in a winding of N_1 turns caused by the rate of change of the leakage flux ϕ_L.

Note that the equivalent circuit of Fig. 3.2c is not the only one which could have been developed for this transformer. In fact, the leakage paths are not as simple as indicated in Fig. 3.2a. Some of the leakage flux links only a part of each of the windings and passes through parts of the core legs. To represent the increased complexity in flux paths, more complex equivalent magnetic and electric circuits are required. Fortunately, such complex models are seldom needed. The circuit may, in fact, be simplified by assuming that the difference between the fluxes ϕ_1 and ϕ_2 is so small that single reluctance $\mathcal{R}_1 + \mathcal{R}_2$ may be used to represent the whole magnetic core. In the electric equivalent circuit, this has the effect of paralleling the admittances Y_1 and Y_2. This resultant admittance may be connected between nodes a and o if the whole core is assumed to carry the flux ϕ_1. In some studies, the core reluctances are so small that the corresponding admittances Y_1 and Y_2 may be considered zero. This leaves an equivalent circuit which consists only if the winding resistances, the leakage impedance, and the ideal transformer.

3.1.2 Equivalent Circuit for Core-Type Transformer

As a further example of the development of equivalent circuits, let us consider the core-type transformer of Fig. 3.3a. This unit has four windings, two of which are placed concentrically on each leg of the core. Windings 1a and 1b each have N_1 turns; windings 2a and 2b each have N_2 turns.

The flux pattern of Fig. 3.3a indicates, to some extent, the assumptions we shall make in deriving an equivalent magnetic circuit of Fig. 3.3b. A leakage path is shown between the inner and outer windings on each leg, and its reluctance is $\mathscr{R}_L$. For simplicity, it is assumed that the flux in each yoke section is the same as in the adjacent leg. Leakage paths around the outside of the outer windings have been neglected for simplicity, but they could have been included as reluctances shunted across $\mathscr{F}_{2a}$ and $\mathscr{F}_{2b}$.

By use of the topological technique, the equivalent electric circuit of Fig. 3.3c is obtained, using N_1 as a reference number of turns. Its admittances Y_{1a} and Y_{1b} represent the reluctances of legs a and b and their associated yoke sections. The leakage inductance of the pair of windings on each leg is L_L. The apparent complexity of the circuit of Fig. 3.3c arises from the fact that it represents a four-winding transformer with no conductive connection between any of its windings. Although this transformer could be operated with four independent windings, it is usual to connect the two pairs of identical windings either in series or in parallel. Figure 3.3d shows the equivalent circuit that applies with windings 1a and 1b connected in parallel and windings 2a and 2b connected in series. In comparing Figs. 3.3c and d, note that $I_1 = I_{1a} + I_{1b}$; $E_1 = E_{1a} = E_{1b}$; $I_2 = I_{2a} = I_{2b}$; $E_2 = E_{2a} + E_{2b}$; and $Y_1 = Y_{1a} + Y_{1b}$.

3.1.3 Measurement of Equivalent-Circuit Parameters

It is often desirable to determine the parameters of the equivalent circuit of an existing transformer so that its performance in service may be predicted. The methods developed in the preceding sections may be used to determine the form of an adequate equivalent circuit. Measurements may then be made on the transformer to determine the values of the parameters.

Suppose the transformer is to be represented by the equivalent circuit of Fig. 3.4a. A source of variable voltage E_1 is applied to winding 1 with winding 2 open circuited. Arrangements are made to measure the magnitudes of E_1, I_1, the input power P_1, and E_2. Then, since R_1 is generally negligible in comparison with the magnetizing impedance,

$$R_{1m} = \frac{E_1^{\,2}}{P_1} \quad \text{ohms} \tag{3.8}$$

$$X_{1m} = \left[\left(\frac{I_1}{E_1}\right)^2 - \frac{1}{R_{1m}^{\,2}}\right]^{-\frac{1}{2}} \quad \text{ohms} \tag{3.9}$$

and

$$\frac{N_2}{N_1} = \frac{E_2}{E_1} \tag{3.10}$$

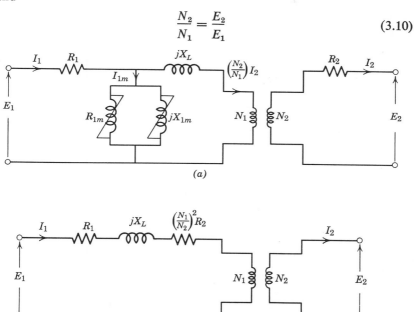

(a)

(b)

Fig. 3.4   (a) Equivalent circuit for a transformer. (b) Circuit with negligible magnetizing current.

Since impedances in the equivalent circuit relate the fundamental-frequency components of voltage and current, the measurement of I_1 should be of this component only. There are, however, odd harmonics in the magnetizing current, the third harmonic being the most significant. If the rms value of these harmonics is 50% of the fundamental component, the rms value of the input current is $(1 + 0.5^2)^{\frac{1}{2}} = 1.12$ times the fundamental-component value. In spite of the error involved, it is the rms value of the input current that is normally measured because of the ease in instrumentation. Fortunately, an accurate knowledge of the magnetizing reactance X_{1m} is not required in most analyses of performance.

The results of the open-circuit test leave R_1, X_L, and R_2 still to be measured. To determine these, winding 2 may be short circuited, possibly through an ammeter, and a low voltage E_1 may be applied to winding 1. Measurements are made of E_1, I_1, P_1, and I_2. To calculate the required parameters, let us first shift the resistance R_2 across the ideal transformer, as shown in Fig. 3.4b, multiplying its value by the square of the turns ratio. The magnetizing branch in Fig. 3.4a is seen to be connected in parallel with the impedance $R_2(N_1/N_2)^2 + jX_L$ when winding 2 is short circuited. Since the test is made with a low applied voltage, the magnetizing current I_{1m} is generally negligible in comparison with the current $(N_2/N_1)I_2$, and the circuit of Fig. 3.4b may be considered to apply for the short-circuit test. The parameters are then derived from the measurements as follows:

$$R_{1e} = R_1 + \left(\frac{N_1}{N_2}\right)^2 R_2 = \frac{P_1}{I_1^2} \qquad \text{ohms} \qquad (3.11)$$

$$X_L = \left[\left(\frac{E_1}{I_1}\right)^2 - R_{1e}^2\right]^{\frac{1}{2}} \qquad \text{ohms} \qquad (3.12)$$

and

$$\frac{N_1}{N_2} = \frac{I_2}{I_1} \qquad (3.13)$$

If the turn ratios as determined by eqs. 3.10 and 3.13 are significantly different, this is an indication that the assumptions made in determining the parameters are not valid.

The resistances of the windings are not obtained separately in eq. 3.11, nor are separate values needed for performance calculations. These resistances may be measured using direct current. The values obtained however, may be significantly less than obtained from eq. 3.11 for transformers with large conductors or for operation at high frequencies, because of skin effect in the conductors.

3.1.4 Determination of Leakage Inductance from Dimensions

In the shell- and core-type transformers shown in Figs. 3.2a and 3.3a, the windings are placed concentrically and are of the same height. A section through the sides of a pair of such windings is shown in Fig. 3.5. For simplicity, suppose each winding has N turns and carries a current i. The directions of the currents are opposite in the two windings. The resultant magnetomotive forces create a magnetic field. If the energy stored in this magnetic field can be determined, the value of the leakage inductance can be found.

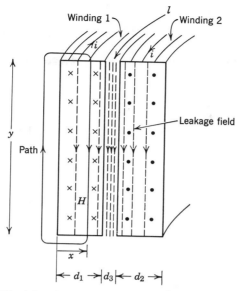

Fig. 3.5 The calculation of leakage inductance.

Let us assume that the leakage flux follows a vertical path through and between the windings and that the return path between the top and bottom of the windings has zero reluctance. Then, if we apply the circuital law to the path shown in Fig. 3.5, we have

$$Hy = Ni \frac{x}{d_1}$$

or

$$H = \frac{Nix}{yd_1} \quad \text{amperes/meter} \quad (0 < x < d_1) \quad (3.14)$$

within winding 1. Between the windings

$$H = \frac{Ni}{y} \quad \text{amperes/meter} \quad [d_1 < x < (d_1 + d_3)] \quad (3.15)$$

and within winding 2,

$$H = \frac{Ni}{yd_2}(d_1 + d_2 + d_3 - x) \quad \text{amperes/meter}$$

$$[(d_1 + d_3) < x < (d_1 + d_2 + d_3)] \quad (3.16)$$

Let l be the mean circumferential length of the windings. Then the energy stored in the volume V of the magnetic field is

$$W = \int \frac{1}{2} \mu_0 H^2 \, dV$$

$$= \int_0^{d_1+d_2+d_3} \frac{1}{2} \mu_0 H^2 y l \, dx$$

$$= \frac{1}{2} \mu_0 \frac{N^2 i^2 l}{y} \left(\frac{d_1}{3} + d_3 + \frac{d_2}{3} \right) \qquad \text{joules} \qquad (3.17)$$

Since $W = \frac{1}{2} L i^2$, the leakage inductance of the pair of N-turn windings is

$$L = \mu_0 \frac{N^2 l}{y} \left(\frac{d_1}{3} + d_3 + \frac{d_2}{3} \right) \qquad \text{henrys} \qquad (3.18)$$

The actual leakage inductance is somewhat less than the value calculated in eq. 3.18, because the return path outside the windings has some reluctance, and because some of the leakage flux leaves the sides of the windings.

The expression of eq. 3.18 indicates how the transformer designer can vary the leakage inductance by varying the dimensions and turns of the windings. To achieve a low value of leakage inductance, the winding height y should be large, the widths of the windings and the spacing between them should be small, and a minimum number of turns should be used. A further reduction of inductance may be achieved by interleaving layers of the two windings. In general, high-voltage transformers have relatively high values of leakage inductance because the insulation requirements prevent close proximity of the windings.

3.2 OPERATING CHARACTERISTICS OF TRANSFORMERS

We have now represented a transformer by an equivalent circuit, which includes an ideal transformer element and other elements to model the imperfections of the transformer. In this section we use this information to predict some of the operating characteristics of transformers.

Let us first examine how much the voltage and current ratios depart from ideal when the transformer is loaded. Figure 3.6a shows an approximate equivalent circuit that is applicable for most transformer studies. The winding resistances R_1 and R_2 have been combined into one equivalent resistance R_{1e} on the winding "1" side of the ideal transformer, where

$$R_{1e} = R_1 + \left(\frac{N_1}{N_2} \right)^2 R_2 \qquad \text{ohms} \qquad (3.19)$$

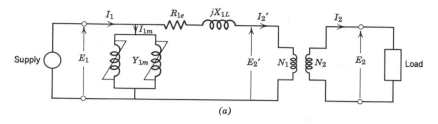

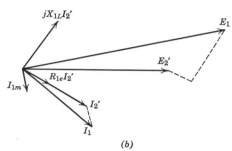

Fig. 3.6   (a) Equivalent circuit of transformer with supply and load. (b) Phasor diagram on load.

The leakage reactance X_{1L} and the magnetizing admittance Y_{1m} are the values as seen from winding 1, which has N_1 turns.

Let us suppose that the phasor voltage E_2 and current I_2 of a load are known and that we wish to determine the corresponding quantities E_1 and I_1. The voltage E_2' and current I_2' on the winding 1 side of the ideal transformer are

$$E_2' = \frac{N_1}{N_2} E_2 \qquad \text{volts} \tag{3.20}$$

and

$$I_2' = \frac{N_2}{N_1} I_2 \qquad \text{amperes} \tag{3.21}$$

The supply voltage E_1 is then given by

$$E_1 = E_2' + (R_{1e} + jX_{1L})I_2' \tag{3.22}$$

and the supply current is

$$I_1 = I_2' + Y_{1m}E_1 \tag{3.23}$$

The relations of eqs. 3.22 and 3.23 are shown in exaggerated form in the phasor diagram of Fig. 3.6b.

It is noted that the departure of the voltage ratio form its ideal value $N_1 : N_2$ not only depends on the resistance and leakage reactance of the windings but also on the magnitude and phase angle of the load impedance. In large transformers the leakage reactance X_{1L} is considerably greater than the resistance R_{1e}. For a resistive load, the voltage $jX_{1L}I_2'$ across the leakage reactance adds in quadrature to the voltage E_2' producing a phase shift between E_1 and E_2' but little difference in magnitude. For an inductive load in which I_2' lags E_2' by 90°, E_1 is equal to the sum of the magnitudes of E_2' and $X_{1L}I_2'$. It is this inductive type of load which gives the lowest voltage ratio E_2/E_1. On the other hand, E_2' may well be greater than E_1 in magnitude for capacitive loads.

Suppose we are given the resistance R_{1e} and reactance X_{1L} in ohms for the transformer of Fig. 3.6a. To assess the effects of these parameters on the voltage ratio, we might multiply each by the rated current of winding 1 and compare it with the rated voltage of winding 1. The resulting ratios are known as the *per-unit resistance* and *leakage reactance*, and are given by

$$R_{1e} = \frac{I_{1b}}{E_{1b}} R_{1e\text{(ohms)}} \qquad \text{per unit} \tag{3.24}$$

and

$$X_{1L} = \frac{I_{1b}}{E_{1b}} X_{1L\text{(ohms)}} \qquad \text{per unit} \tag{3.25}$$

where $E_{1b} = |E_1|_{\text{rated}}$ and $I_{1b} = |I_1|_{\text{rated}}$. These per-unit values are much easier to interpret than their ohmic counterparts. In large high-voltage power transformers the leakage reactance is generally between 0.1 and 0.15 per unit, whereas the resistance is usually less than 0.005 per unit. As the size of the transformer is reduced, the per-unit resistance increases, while the reactance remains in the range 0.03–0.15 in all but a few special transformers.

The departure of the current ratio from its ideal value is caused by the magnetizing current I_{1m}, as shown in Fig. 3.6b. It is again convenient to use a per-unit notation to describe the magnitude of this current relative to the rated current. Thus

$$I_{1m} = \frac{I_{1m\text{(amperes)}}}{I_{1b}} \qquad \text{per unit} \tag{3.26}$$

Magnetizing currents in transformers are normally less than 0.05 per unit. Using wound-core construction (Fig. 3.1) and grain-oriented materials, the magnetizing current can be reduced to less than 0.005 per unit.

Essentially all electric load devices are designed to operate well only over a narrow range of supply voltage. If the voltage is too high, heating appliances may overheat, insulation may be overstressed, and lighting devices may burn out prematurely. If the voltage is too low, motors may overheat or fail to start, and illumination levels are lowered. Even small transient changes in supply voltage result in an undesirable flicker in the illumination from lighting devices. The contribution of a transformer to this change of supply voltage with changing load may be expressed in terms of its *voltage regulation*. This is defined as the per-unit increase in magnitude of the output voltage when a specified load is removed, the input voltage being held constant. Using symbols from Fig. 3.6a, we have

$$\text{Regulation} = \frac{|E_2|_{\text{(open circuit)}} - |E_2|_{\text{(on load)}}}{|E_2|_{\text{(on load)}}} \quad \text{per unit} \quad (3.27)$$

The normally specified load is one requiring the rated output current and the rated output voltage. To make the regulation meaningful, the power factor of the load must be specified.

3.2.1 Efficiency

The efficiency η of an energy transformation device is a per-unit quantity indicating the ratio of the average output power to the average input power.

$$\eta = \frac{\text{output power}}{\text{input power}} \quad \text{per unit} \quad (3.28)$$

In general, transformers are highly efficient devices. In large units the efficiency is so close to unity that any attempt to measure this small difference from unity by measuring output and input power is frustrated by the small inaccuracies of instruments. An alternative approach is to express the efficiency as

$$\eta = \frac{\text{output power}}{\text{output power} + \text{losses}} \quad \text{per unit} \quad (3.29)$$

The power losses in the transformer may be calculated readily by reference to the equivalent circuit of Fig. 3.6a. The eddy current and hysteresis losses in the core are represented by the real part G_{1m} of the admittance Y_{1m} and are given by

$$P_c = G_{1m} |E_1|^2 \quad \text{watts} \quad (3.30)$$

Alternatively, P_c may be measured as the input power on open circuit as a function of E_1. The power losses in the windings are approximated by

$$P_w = R_{1e} |I_2'|^2$$
$$= R_{1e} |I_1|^2 \quad \text{watts} \quad (3.31)$$

since the magnetizing current is generally small and partially in quadrature with the load current.

If a transformer is operating at its rated voltage and current, its losses are essentially constant. But its power output at rated load depends on the power factor of the load. Thus the efficiency is greatest at unity power factor in the load and is, of course, zero for a zero power factor load. A quantity that is more meaningful than efficiency is the per-unit loss at rated load. If E_{1b} and I_{1b} are the rated voltage and current of winding 1 of a transformer, its voltampere rating is

$$U_b = E_{1b}I_{1b} \quad \text{voltamperes} \tag{3.32}$$

The per-unit loss is then given by

$$P_1 = \frac{P_c + P_w}{U_b}$$

$$= \frac{G_{1m}E_{1b}^2 + R_{1e}I_{1b}^2}{E_{1b}I_{1b}} \quad \text{per unit} \tag{3.33}$$

In large power transformers the per-unit loss is usually in the range of 0.01–0.04.

An important feature in the application of some transformers is the way in which the efficiency varies with load. The output power, using voltage and current magnitudes, is

$$P_2 = E_2I_2 \cos \theta$$

$$= E_2'I_2' \cos \theta \quad \text{watts}$$

where $\cos \theta$ is the load power factor. Let us neglect any change in the voltages E_1 and E_2 as the load current I_2 is varied at constant power factor. The core loss P_c is then constant. The efficiency may be stated, from eq. 3.29, as

$$\eta = \frac{E_2'I_2' \cos \theta}{E_2'I_2' \cos \theta + P_c + R_{1e}(I_2')^2} \quad \text{per unit} \tag{3.34}$$

To determine the condition for maximum efficiency, eq. 3.34 may be differentiated with respect to the variable I_2'.

$$\frac{d\eta}{dI_2'} = \frac{[E_2'I_2' \cos \theta + P_c + R_{1e}(I_2')^2] E_2 \cos \theta - E_2'I_2' \cos \theta(E_2' \cos \theta + 2I_2'R_{1e})}{[E_2'I_2' \cos \theta + P_c + R_{1e}(I_2')^2]^2}$$

$$= 0 \tag{3.35}$$

from which the maximum efficiency condition is found to be

$$P_c = R_{1e}(I_2')^2 = P_w \tag{3.36}$$

Thus the maximum efficiency at any load power factor occurs for that load at which the constant core losses are equal to the winding losses.

The transformer designer may vary the relative volumes of conductor material and magnetic material in the transformer to achieve maximum efficiency at some average value of load.

3.2.2 Variable-Frequency Operation

In electronic and communication systems, transformers are often used over a wide range of frequencies. An example is the transformer used in an audio amplifier to couple the output stage to the speaker. Ideally, this audio transformer should operate well over the audible frequency range of about 50–15000 cycles per second. Another example is a pulse transformer. A train of pulses may be represented as a Fourier series of frequency components.

The relationship between the voltage ratio of a transformer and frequency can be found by using a general equivalent circuit such as that of Fig. 3.4a. In certain frequency ranges several of the parameters are negligible and the analysis may be simplified. At high frequencies, the effects of interwinding capacitances may have to be included to obtain an adequate analysis.

Figure 3.7a shows an equivalent circuit that is applicable over the middle of the frequency range for which the transformer is designed. In this range, the leakage reactance and the magnetizing current generally can be neglected. In small transformers, the winding resistances may be significant. In Fig. 3.7, the source (for example, electronic amplifier) is represented as a variable-frequency source voltage E_s in series with an internal resistance R_s. The load (for example, speaker) is represented by its resistance R_L. In the midfrequency range, the ratio of the load voltage to the source voltage is given approximately by

$$\frac{E_L}{E_s} = \frac{nR_L}{R_{11} + R_{22}} \tag{3.37}$$

where $R_{11} = R_1 + R_s$, $R_{22} = n^2(R_2 + R_L)$, and n is the turns ratio N_1/N_2.

To obtain maximum power input to the load, the transformer parameters should be chosen so that the load resistance R_L is equal to the magnitude of the equivalent Thévenin impedance as seen from the load terminals. In the midfrequency range, the load resistance for maximum load power is given by

$$R_L = \frac{R_s + R_1}{n^2} + R_2 \tag{3.38}$$

Under this condition

$$\frac{E_L}{E_s} = \frac{1}{2n} \tag{3.39}$$

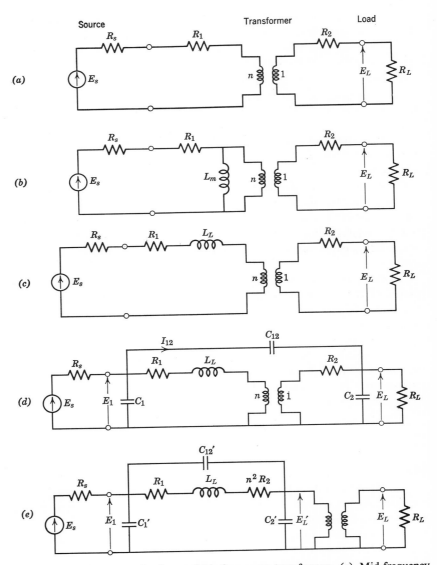

Fig. 3.7 Equivalent circuits for variable-frequency transformer. (*a*) Mid-frequency range. (*b*) Low-frequency range. (*c*) High-frequency range. (*d*) High-frequency range including interwinding capacitances. (*e*) Circuit equivalent to (*d*).

As the frequency decreases, the magnetizing current of the transformer becomes significant, and the circuit of Fig. 3.7b applies. At these low frequencies, core losses normally may be neglected. If the magnetizing inductance L_m is regarded as constant, the ratio of load to source voltage can be expressed approximately as

$$\frac{E_L}{E_s} = \frac{nR_L}{R_{11} + R_{22}} \left(\frac{1}{1 - jR_q/\omega L_m} \right) \tag{3.40}$$

where $R_q = R_{11}R_{22}/(R_{11} + R_{22})$. At the frequency $\omega_l = R_q/L_m$ radians/ second, the magnitude of the voltage ratio is $1/\sqrt{2}$ of its value in the mid-frequency range, and the load power for a given source voltage is reduced to one-half.

In using this low-frequency equivalent circuit, note that excessive magnetizing current drives the core of the transformer into saturation and thus reduces the effective value of the magnetizing inductance L_m. Equation 3.4 applies only if the source voltage is low enough to allow the magnetizing inductance to be regarded as constant.

In the high-frequency range the leakage inductance of the transformer becomes significant and the equivalent circuit of Fig. 3.7c is applicable. The load-to-source voltage ratio for this range may be expressed as

$$\frac{E_L}{E_s} = \frac{nR_L}{R_{11} + R_{22}} \left[\frac{1}{1 + j\omega L_L/(R_{11} + R_{22})} \right] \tag{3.41}$$

At the frequency $\omega_h = R_{11} + R_{22}/L_L$ radians/second, the magnitude of the voltage ratio is again $1/\sqrt{2}$ of its value in the midfrequency range, and the power is reduced to one-half.

Figure 3.8 shows the voltage ratio, relative to its value in the mid-frequency range (eq. 3.39), as a function of frequency plotted on a

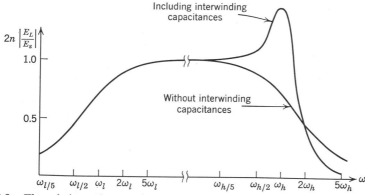

Fig. 3.8. The relative voltage ratio of a transformer as a function of frequency ω.

logarithmic scale. The bandwidth of the transformer is defined as the frequency range from ω_l to ω_h, that is, between the frequencies at which the load voltage is reduced to 0.707 and the load power is reduced to 0.5 of the values obtained in the midfrequency range.

In the high-frequency range, the effects of distributed capacitances across and between the windings may become significant. Figure 3.7d shows an equivalent circuit in which these distributed capacitances are represented approximately by capacitances C_1 and C_2 across the transformer terminals and a capacitance C_{12} between the primary and secondary terminals. The values of these capacitances depend on the arrangement of the windings. For example, if the primary and secondary windings are interleaved to reduce the leakage inductance, the capacitances are increased. The capacitances also depend on the connections made between the windings; their effects can be minimized by connecting primary and secondary terminals of like polarity.

Analysis of the equivalent circuit of Fig. 3.7d is facilitated if all parameters are referred to one side of the ideal transformer, as shown in Fig. 3.7e. As may be seen from the primary winding, the current I_{12} in the interwinding capacitance can be expressed as

$$I_{12} = j\omega C_{12}(E_1 - E_L) = j\omega C_{12}\left(E_1 - \frac{E_L{}'}{n}\right)$$

$$= j\omega \frac{C_{12}}{n}(E_1 - E_L{}') + j\omega C_{12}\left(\frac{n-1}{n}\right)E_1 \qquad (3.42)$$

If the interwinding capacitance current I_{12} entering the secondary terminal is referred to the other side of the ideal transformer, it can be expressed as

$$\frac{I_{12}}{n} = j\omega \frac{C_{12}}{n}(E_1 - E_L)$$

$$= j\omega \frac{C_{12}}{n}(E_1 - E_L{}') - j\omega C_{12}\left(\frac{1-n}{n}\right)E_L{}' \qquad (3.43)$$

From these equations, the equivalent capacitances of Fig. 3.7e are

$$C_{12}{}' = \frac{C_{12}}{n}$$

$$C_1{}' = C_1 + C_{12}\left(\frac{n-1}{n}\right)$$

$$C_2{}' = C_2 + C_{12}\left(\frac{1-n}{n}\right) \qquad (3.44)$$

The effects of the winding capacitances on the ratio of load to source voltage are most pronounced in a step-up transformer where $n < 1$. Figure 3.8 shows a typical effect of interwinding capacitance on the frequency response of a transformer. The load to source voltage ratio can be increased substantially above the midfrequency value if the capacitance C_2' in Fig. 3.7e is in series resonance with the parallel branches containing L_L and C_{12}'. The voltage ratio can be reduced substantially in the frequency range of parallel resonance between L_L and C_{12}'.

The equivalent circuit of Fig. 3.7e may be used in the analysis of some transient phenomena in transformers. For example, it may be used in an approximate analysis of pulse transformers. The analysis of transient surge voltages in high-voltage transformers generally requires a more elaborate circuit model in which the distributed nature of the leakage inductance and interwinding capacitances is represented.

3.2.3 Transient Inrush Current of a Transformer

Most power transformers are designed so that the magnetizing current under normal steady-state operation is a negligible fraction of the rated current. In the transient period, however, between the instant of applying voltage to the transformer and the eventual establishment of a steady-state condition, it is possible for the magnetizing current to be very high. It can sometimes be greater than the short-circuit current of the transformer. A knowledge of this transient current is therefore of importance in determining the maximum stresses that result from currents in the windings; it is also important in designing the protective system for the transformer.

Consider a winding of a transformer in which the resistance is R and the flux linkage–current relationship can be approximated by the idealization of Fig. 3.9a. Under steady-state conditions the flux linkage is designed to be in the range $\lambda_k > \lambda > -\lambda_k$, and the magnetizing current i is effectively zero. When the supply voltage is switched off, the flux linkage may remain at a value λ_r because of residual magnetism in the core material. Suppose that the voltage $e = \hat{E} \sin \omega t$ of Fig. 3.9b is applied to the winding. Starting at $\lambda = \lambda_r$, the flux linkage increases according to the relation

$$\lambda = \lambda_r + \int_0^t e \, dt \qquad \text{webers} \qquad (3.45)$$

Unless λ_r happens to be in the region of $-\lambda_k$, the flux linkage will reach $\lambda = \lambda_k$ sometime before the end of the first half cycle of voltage. Subsequently, the magnetizing current is given by the differential equation

$$L_s \frac{di}{dt} + Ri = e \qquad (3.46)$$

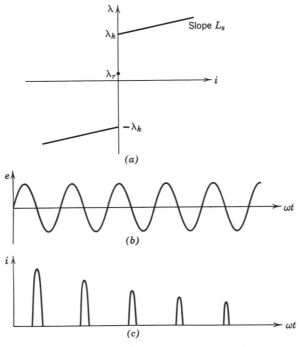

Fig. 3.9   The inrush current of a transformer. (*a*) Flux linkage-current model of core. (*b*) Applied voltage. (*c*) Magnetizing current transient.

which applies from the instant that λ reaches λ_k until it again returns to λ_k.

Figure 3.9*c* shows the resultant transient in the current *i*. It consists of a series of current pulses that occur around the region where the applied voltage *e* becomes negative. Because of the effect of the winding resistance *R*, the amplitudes of these pulses decrease with each succeeding cycle.

The value of the saturated inductance L_s of the winding depends on the saturated permeability and dimensions of the core; it also depends on the reluctance of the flux paths in air around the winding. Its value bears no direct relation to the leakage inductance of the transformer.

3.3   TRANSFORMERS FOR POLYPHASE SYSTEMS

Most electrical energy is generated and transmitted using a three-phase system. The three-phase power may be transformed either by use of suitably connected banks of single-phase transformers or by use of special polyphase transformers. In the following sections some of the features of transformers in polyphase systems are discussed.

3.3.1 Connections of Transformers for Three-Phase Systems

Star-star connection. There are several ways in which three single-phase transformers may be connected to transform three-phase power. Figure 3.10a shows a star or Y connection of three two-winding transformers to interconnect a four-wire, three-phase source to a three-phase load. In this connection, the voltage on each transformer is the line-to-neutral voltage of the system and the transformer current is the line current.

Suppose the source voltages e_{ao}, e_{bo}, and e_{co} form a balanced set, represented by the fundamental-frequency phasors E_a, $\alpha^2 E_a$, and αE_a, respectively, for the sequence *a-b-c*, where α is a phasor operator having

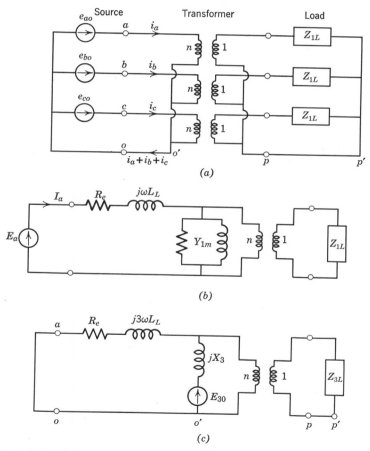

Fig. 3.10 (*a*) Y-Y connection of transformers. (*b*) Fundamental-frequency, single-phase equivalent circuit. (*c*) Third-harmonic, single-phase equivalent circuit.

unit magnitude and an angle of $2\pi/3$ radians or 120°, that is, $\alpha = 1 \underline{/120°}$. If the three transformers are identical and the load is balanced, the primary-phase currents i_a, i_b, and i_c also form a balanced set. The fundamental-frequency phasors of the currents are then I_a, $\alpha^2 I_a$, and αI_a, respectively. It may be noted that

$$I_a + \alpha^2 I_a + \alpha I_a = I_a(1 + \alpha^2 + \alpha)$$
$$= 0 \qquad (3.47)$$

Thus even if the link $o\text{-}o'$ in Fig. 3.10a contained an impedance, it would not have a fundamental-frequency voltage drop.

The fundamental-frequency behavior of the three-phase system of Fig. 3.10a may be analyzed by use of the single-phase equivalent circuit of Fig. 3.10b. In this circuit the transformer may be represented by an appropriate model as was developed in Section 3.1.

From eq. 3.47 it might be considered that the neutral connection $o\text{-}o'$ between the source and the transformer could be eliminated. There are several reasons why this is impractical. First, even slight differences in the load impedances or in the magnetizing characteristics of the three transformers cause a fundamental-frequency voltage to appear across the opened link $o\text{-}o'$, unbalancing the load voltages. The second reason arises from the harmonic components of the magnetizing currents in the transformers. With the Y connection of Fig. 3.10a, the voltage applied to each transformer is sinusoidal. The magnetizing currents contain fundamental and odd-harmonic components. The fundamental current components in the three transformers are displaced 120° with respect to each other and sum to zero. The kth harmonic components are displaced 120k° with respect to each other. If $k = 3, 9, 15, 21$ etc, this displacement is a multiple of 360° causing these harmonics to be in phase with each other. When the link $o\text{-}o'$ in Fig. 3.10a is closed, these triplen harmonics flow in this link.

The most important of the triplen harmonics is the third harmonic. In Section 2.14, an equivalent circuit (Fig. 2.12e) was developed to represent the third-harmonic behavior of a nonlinear magnetic element. Figure 3.10c shows how this may be used to assess the third-harmonic behavior of the three-phase system. The magnetizing branch is represented as a third-harmonic source E_{30} with internal impedance jX_3. If the links $o\text{-}o'$ and $p\text{-}p'$ are both closed, the third-harmonic current in each phase flows mainly through the resistance R_e and the third-harmonic leakage impedance $j3\omega L_L$. The fundamental-frequency source voltage may be regarded as a short circuit for third-harmonic current. Part of the third-harmonic magnetizing current may flow in the third-harmonic impedance Z_{3L} of the load.

If the neutral connections o-o' and p-p' in Fig. 3.10a are opened, triplen harmonic voltages appear across these open links. In the third-harmonic equivalent circuit of Fig. 3.10a, it is seen that opening these links open circuits the equivalent third-harmonic source.

Delta-star connection. The delta (Δ) connection of transformers overcomes several of the difficulties encountered with the star connection. In Fig. 3.11a the primary windings are connected in delta to the supply, whereas the star connection is retained on the load side. It is seen that the voltage applied to each of the delta-connected windings is equal to the line-to-line voltage of the supply. Suppose this voltage to be sinusoidal and constant; we would expect each of the secondary voltages to be essentially sinusoidal and constant, regardless of the loads placed on them.

If the system is balanced, it is convenient to analyze it by extracting a single-phase equivalent circuit. Let us first develop a relation between the line-to-neutral voltages on the primary and secondary sides of the transformer bank, assuming each transformer to be ideal. In the phasor diagram of Fig. 3.11b, the line-to-neutral voltages E_{ao}, E_{bo}, and E_{co} of the supply with phase sequence a-b-c may be combined to give the voltages E_{ab}, E_{bc}, and E_{ca}, which are applied to the primary windings of the transformers. The voltage E_{ab} divided by the turns ratio n then becomes one of the line-to-neutral voltages on the secondary side. To obtain a symmetry in notation, let us denote this secondary phase as C (a and b having already been used as subscripts of the primary voltage). Thus

$$E_{ab} = nE_{CN}$$
$$E_{bc} = nE_{AN} \tag{3.48}$$
$$E_{ca} = nE_{BN}$$

Examination of the resultant phasors shows that, assuming ideal transformers, the line-to-neutral voltage of phase a of the primary is related to the line-to-neutral voltage of phase A of the secondary by

$$E_{ao} = j\,\frac{n}{\sqrt{3}}\,E_{AN} \quad \text{(sequence } a\text{-}b\text{-}c\text{)} \tag{3.49}$$

With the notation used, the voltages E_{ao}, E_{bo}, and E_{co} of the primary lead the corresponding secondary voltages E_{AN}, E_{BN}, and E_{CN} by 90°. With another scheme of designation for the secondary phases, this phase shift could have been $90° - 120° = -30°$ or $90° + 120 = 210°$. It also may be shown that if the phase sequence had been a-c-b, the relation of eq. 3.49 would have been

$$E_{ao} = -j\,\frac{n}{\sqrt{3}}\,E_{AN} \quad \text{(sequence } a\text{-}c\text{-}b\text{)} \tag{3.50}$$

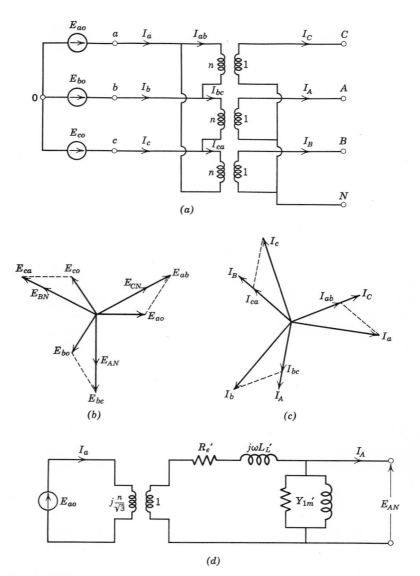

Fig. 3.11   (a) Δ-Y connection of transformers. (b) Voltage phasor diagram. (c) Current phasor diagram. (d) Single-phase equivalent circuit.

The relation between the primary and secondary currents is shown in the phasor diagram of Fig. 3.11c. Starting with a set of balanced load currents I_A, I_B, and I_C of phase sequence a-b-c, the currents in the primary windings of the transformers are

$$I_{ab} = \frac{I_C}{n}; \quad I_{bc} = \frac{I_A}{n}; \quad I_{ca} = \frac{I_B}{n} \tag{3.51}$$

These currents may be combined to give the supply currents. From the phasor diagram note that

$$I_a = j\frac{\sqrt{3}}{n} I_A \tag{3.52}$$

Taken together, eqs. 3.49 and 3.52 constitute a power-invariant transformation, that is,

$$
\begin{aligned}
U_{\substack{\text{primary} \\ \text{per phase}}} &= I_a E_{ao}{}^* \\
&= \left(j\frac{\sqrt{3}}{n} I_A\right)\left(-j\frac{n}{\sqrt{3}} E_{AN}{}^*\right) \\
&= I_A E_{AN}{}^* \\
&= U_{\substack{\text{secondary} \\ \text{per phase}}}
\end{aligned}
\tag{3.53}
$$

The asterisk denotes the conjugate of a phasor.

Figure 3.11d shows a single-phase equivalent circuit for the delta-star system. The transformer is represented by its resistance, leakage reactance, and magnetizing branch referred to the secondary winding. The ideal transformer incorporates the properties of eqs. 3.49 and 3.52. In many analyses, the phase shift between the two three-phase systems interconnected by this Δ-Y transformer is not significant. But where transformers or large parts of the systems are to be connected in parallel, due account must be kept of the phase shift.

Since each of the transformers in Fig. 3.11a has a sinusoidal voltage, its magnetizing current will include all odd harmonics. The triplen harmonics in the three transformers are normally equal in magnitude and are normally in phase with each other. When the primary currents of two transformers are subtracted to obtain the line current, the result contains no triplen harmonics. If a third-harmonic equivalent circuit of the type shown in Fig. 3.10c is developed for this Δ–Y transformer, it will be found that the connection constitutes a short circuit for third-harmonic currents.

In summary, the delta connection has the advantages of maintaining the balance and the waveform of the voltages in spite of unbalances and harmonics, and of providing a path in which the necessary triplen harmonics may flow. The star connection has the advantage that the neutral point can be connected to earth. In high-voltage transformers this feature is important for limiting the maximum voltage stresses on the insulation. In low-voltage transformers, it is important to the safety of personnel that one side of each single-phase supply be at earth potential. It is therefore understandable that the star-delta connection, combining the features of both, is the most commonly used connection. The star-star connection is normally restricted to use with four-wire systems.

Delta-delta connection. Transformers can be connected in delta on both the primary and secondary sides, where neutral connections are not required. One advantage of the Δ–Δ connection is that service can be continued with little unbalance when one of the three transformers is removed.

3.3.2   Polyphase Transformers

Instead of using a bank of three single-phase transformers, a polyphase transformer having three sets of primary and secondary windings on a common magnetic structure may be constructed, with resulting savings in material and space.

To visualize the development of a three-phase core-type transformer, let us start with three single-phase core-type units, as shown in Fig. 3.12a. Each of these is similar to the transformer of Fig. 3.1b, except that windings have been placed on one leg only. For simplicity, only the primary windings have been shown. If the induced voltages in these three transformers are sinusoidal and balanced, the fluxes Φ_a, Φ_b, and Φ_c also will be sinusoidal and balanced. Thus if the three legs carrying these fluxes are merged, the total flux in the combined leg is zero, and this leg can be omitted, as shown in Fig. 3.12b.

A magnetic system having the general shape of Fig. 3.12b can be produced using wound cores of the type shown in Fig. 3.1. For cores made of stacked laminations, the in-line structure of Fig. 3.12c is more convenient. This structure can be evolved from Fig. 3.12b by eliminating the yokes of section b and fitting the remainder between a and c. The result does not have complete symmetry, since the magnetic paths of legs a and c are somewhat longer than that of leg b. But the resultant unbalance in the magnetizing currents is seldom significant.

By using the methods of Section 2.4, an equivalent electric circuit can be produced for the three-phase, core-type transformer. It is found that this circuit has a form similar to that of three single-phase transformers connected in delta. Because of the removal of the path for the combined return flux, the phase voltages must sum to essentially zero. The harmonic behavior of this transformer is similar to that of a delta-connected bank in that essentially no triplen-harmonic magnetizing currents flow in the

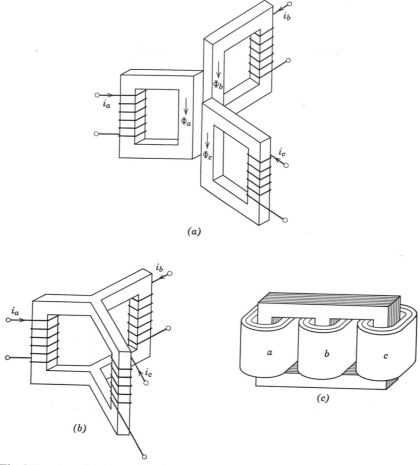

Fig. 3.12 Evolution of the three-phase, core-type transformer. (a) Three single-phase transformers. (b) Return path for $\Phi_a + \Phi_b + \Phi_c$ removed. (c) In-line construction.

windings under balanced operation, irrespective of the connections. This can be seen by regarding each leg as an equal, in-phase source of third harmonics. In the equivalent circuit, these sources are connected in delta and short circuit each other.

The shell-type, three-phase transformer is evolved by stacking three single-phase, shell-type units, as shown in Fig. 3.13a. The winding direction of the center unit b is made opposite to that of units a and c. If the system is balanced with phase sequence a-b-c, the fluxes are also balanced, that is, $\Phi_a = \alpha\Phi_b = \alpha^2\Phi_c$. The adjacent yoke sections of units a and b

carry a combined flux of

$$\frac{\Phi_a}{2} + \frac{\Phi_b}{2} = \frac{\Phi_a}{2}(1\underline{/0^\circ} + 1\underline{/240^\circ})$$

$$= \frac{\Phi_a}{2}\underline{/-60^\circ} \qquad\qquad (3.54)$$

Thus the magnitude of this combined flux is equal to the magnitude of each of its components. In this way, the cross-sectional area of the combined yoke sections may be reduced to the same value as that used in the outer legs and in the top and bottom yokes, as shown in Fig. 3.13b.

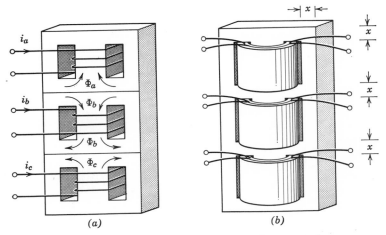

Fig. 3.13   Evolution of the three-phase, shell-type transformer.

The slight unbalance in the magnetic paths among the three phases has very little effect on the performance of the three-phase, shell-type transformer. Its behavior is essentially the same as that of a bank of three single-phase transformers.

The windings of either core or shell-type three-phase transformers may be connected in star or delta as desired.

3.3.3   Phase Transformation

Most electric apparatus is designed to operate from the generally available supplies of three-phase or single-phase power. There are, however, situations in which a different number of phases is desirable. For example, an increase in the number of phases in a polyphase rectifier results in lower harmonic content in the output voltage.

In transforming from one polyphase system to a system with a different number of phases, use is made of the fact that a voltage of any arbitrary magnitude and phase can be produced by adding or subtracting appropriate magnitudes of two voltages having different phases. The required magnitudes of voltages are obtained by use of transformers with appropriate turns ratios.

Suppose we have two equal voltage sources E_1 and E_2 at 90° to each other and wish to produce a three-phase source. Figure 3.14 shows a

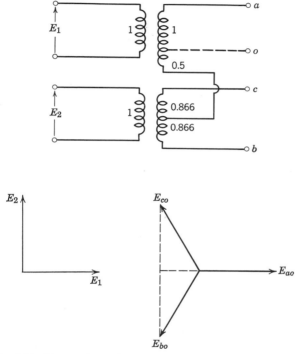

Fig. 3.14 Two-to-three phase transformation (Scott connection).

simple connection of two transformers to accomplish this. The voltage E_{ao} is produced directly from E_1 using a 1:1 transformer ratio. To produce E_{bo}, transformer ratios are arranged to give

$$E_{bo} = -0.5E_1 - 0.866E_2 \qquad (3.55)$$

Similarly,
$$E_{co} = -0.5E_1 + 0.866E_2 \qquad (3.56)$$

The system of Fig. 3.14 is commonly known as the *Scott connection*. It may be used with or without the neutral connection on the three-phase side. It can be used in reverse to convert from three-phase to two-phase. The transformer ratios are all multiplied by a common factor to produce any other level of output voltage.

The two-phase system of Fig. 3.14 is actually an asymmetrical half of a symmetrical four-phase system. Such a four-phase system may be produced by adding another identical primary winding to each of the transformers in Fig. 3.14 and connecting the four primary windings in star.

As an example of the general way in which a phase transformation may be made, Fig. 3.15 shows that a five-phase system can be produced from a

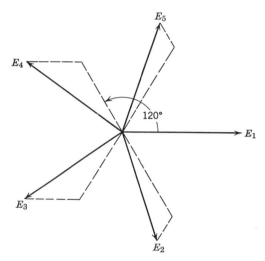

Fig. 3.15   Phasor relations for three-to-five phase transformation.

three-phase system by adding or subtracting appropriate magnitudes of voltages at the available angles $0°$, $120°$, and $240°$. This transformation requires three transformers, each with three secondary windings.

Transformation from three-to-six phase is accomplished simply by adding another identical winding to each transformer of a three-phase bank and connecting it with reversed polarity to the same star point. A similar connection may be used to double the number of phases if the original system has an odd number of phases. There are a number of specialized connections used in rectifier systems to obtain larger numbers of phases.

One feature of practical phase transformation arrangements is that a balanced load on one of the polyphase systems is reflected as an essentially balanced load on the other polyphase system. This property can be demonstrated for the systems shown in Figs. 3.14 and 3.15 by routine analysis. Any unbalance that does occur usually results from small differences in the leakage impedances of the transformer windings associated with the different phases.

3.4 SOME SPECIAL TRANSFORMATION DEVICES

The analytical methods discussed earlier in this chapter are sufficient to determine the operating characteristics of most types of transformers. There are, however, a few types, which—because of a special construction or application—may deserve further comment. Some special magnetic devices such as saturable reactors, magnetic amplifiers, and frequency multipliers are also considered briefly.

3.4.1 Autotransformers

A two-winding transformer provides for a change in voltage level and for isolation of its primary and secondary circuits. If this isolation feature is not required, the voltage transformation can be achieved with a single-tapped winding as shown in Fig. 3.16a. If this autotransformer is regarded

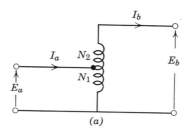

(a)

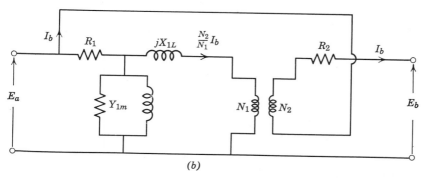

(b)

Fig. 3.16 (a) Autotransformer connection. (b) Equivalent circuit.

as ideal, its voltage ratio is

$$\frac{E_b}{E_a} = \frac{N_2 + N_1}{N_1} \qquad (3.57)$$

As power is invariant in an ideal transformer, its current ratio is

$$\frac{I_b}{I_a} = \frac{N_1}{N_2 + N_1} \qquad (3.58)$$

The current in the section of the winding having N_2 turns is I_b. Since the total magnetomotive force of the winding must be essentially zero, the current in the section of winding having N_1 turns is $N_2 I_b / N_1$.

For a more detailed analysis, it is preferable to consider an autotransformer as a two-winding transformer with its two windings connected in series. It may then be represented by an appropriate equivalent circuit of the form shown in Fig. 3.16b. In this equivalent circuit, R_1 and R_2 are the resistances of the winding sections of N_1 and N_2 turns, respectively, and X_{1L} is the leakage reactance referred to N_1 turns. To simplify the analysis, the magnetizing admittance Y_{1m} generally may be moved out to the left-hand terminals; the resistance R_1 and the impedance jX_{1L} may be moved across the ideal transformer to a position in series with the output terminals.

In general, as compared with two-winding transformers of equivalent rating, autotransformers are smaller, more efficient, and have lower internal impedance. They are used extensively in power systems where the voltages of the two systems coupled by the transformer do not differ by a factor greater than about 3.

Adjustable output voltage is obtainable from autotransformers that have a single-layer winding on a toroidal core and a sliding brush which makes direct contact with the winding.

3.4.2 Current Transformers

A-c measuring instruments and protective relays are normally made to operate near earth potential and at currents not exceeding a few amperes. Where current must be measured in a high-potential conductor, or where the current is greater than a few amperes, it is usual to use a current transformer.

Figure 3.17a shows a current transformer that consists of a toroidal core with a uniformly distributed winding of N_2 turns to which the load instrument is connected. The conductor carrying the current to be measured is passed through the aperture in the toroidal core one or more times and constitutes the primary winding of N_1 turns.

Ideally, the current ratio of the transformer is the inverse of the turns ratio

$$\frac{I_2}{I_1} = \frac{N_1}{N_2} \tag{3.59}$$

The departure from ideal ratio may be analyzed by use of an equivalent circuit, as shown in Fig. 3.17b. In this circuit, R_2 is the resistance of the secondary winding, and X_{2L} is the leakage reactance associated with the air paths in and around the conductors of the secondary winding. As

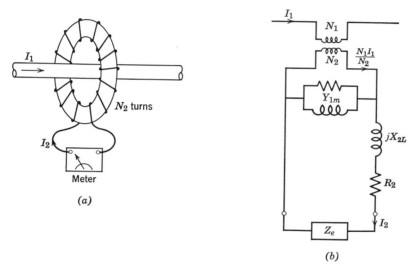

Fig. 3.17 (*a*) Current transformer. (*b*) Equivalent circuit.

the primary is a current source, its resistance and leakage reactance are not significant. The ratio of the secondary current to the primary current is given by

$$\frac{I_2}{I_1} = \frac{1}{1 + Y_{1m}(R_2 + jX_{2L} + Z_e)} \frac{N_1}{N_2} \tag{3.60}$$

where Z_e is the impedance of the external secondary circuit. To minimize the error it is necessary that the magnetizing admittance Y_{1m} be made as small as possible by the use of low coercive force materials operated at low flux density. In addition, the load impedance Z_e must be made small.

If the current transformer is used for current measurement, only the magnitude error is of importance. But if it is used to supply the current coil of a wattmeter, the phase-angle error is also important.

Opening the secondary circuit causes all the primary current to act as a magnetizing magnetomotive force on the core. The core flux is driven rapidly between negative and positive saturation, thus producing very high voltage pulses. For the protection of personnel and the transformer insulation, provision must be made to prevent any inadvertent break in this secondary circuit.

Measurement of large values of direct current is sometimes required. This may be accomplished by the system shown in Fig. 3.18a, which

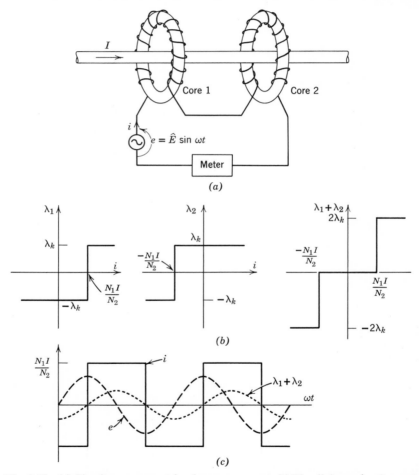

Fig. 3.18   (a) Circuit arrangement for d-c measurement. (b) Flux linkages λ_1 of core 1, λ_2 of core 2, and $\lambda_1 + \lambda_2$. (c) Waveforms of source voltage, total flux linkage, and current.

consists of two identical saturable cores with their primary windings of N_1 turns connected in series and carrying the current I to be measured. Their secondary windings are connected in series to an alternating-voltage source and a measuring instrument. Let us suppose that the B–H relationship of the core material has the ideal shape of Fig. 2.7b with infinite unsaturated permeability and zero saturated permeability. With a constant direct current I in the N_1 turns of each primary winding, core 1 is unsaturated only when its secondary current i is

$$i = \frac{N_1 I}{N_2} \qquad \text{amperes} \tag{3.61}$$

and core 2 is unsaturated only when

$$i = -\frac{N_1 I}{N_2} \qquad \text{amperes} \tag{3.62}$$

Figure 3.18b shows the idealized relations between the secondary current i and the flux linkage λ_1 of the secondary winding of core 1, the flux linkage λ_2 of core 2, and the total flux linkage $\lambda_1 + \lambda_2$ of the two windings in series. Note that the total flux linkage can change only when the current i has one of the values given by eqs. 3.61 and 3.62.

Suppose a sinusoidal voltage source $\hat{E}\sin \omega t$ is connected as shown. If we neglect the impedance of the meter and the windings, the total flux linkage of the circuit is given by

$$\lambda_1 + \lambda_2 = -\frac{\hat{E}}{\omega}\cos \omega t \qquad \text{webers} \tag{3.63}$$

Let us limit the applied voltage e so that

$$\frac{\hat{E}}{\omega} < 2\lambda_k \tag{3.64}$$

The current i is equal to $N_1 I/N_2$ when $\lambda_1 + \lambda_2$ is positive and is equal to $-N_1 I/N_2$ when $\lambda_1 + \lambda_2$ is negative. Thus it has the square waveform shown in Fig. 3.18c.

The current i may be measured by an a-c instrument, or it may be rectified in a bridge rectifier to produce a direct current that is related to the measured current I by the inverse of the turns ratio.

Inaccuracies in this measurement system arise principally from the finite coercive force required in the cores and from their finite saturated permeability. In contrast with a-c transformers, the inaccuracies in this system generally tend to result in too high a reading on the meter.

3.4.3 Saturable Reactors

A saturable reactor is a group of saturable magnetic elements connected in such a way as to permit control of the power supplied from a source to a load. Figure 3.19a shows two saturable magnetic cores, each with a primary winding of N_p turns and a control winding of N_c turns. The primary windings are connected in series with each other and with the load. A direct current I_c is supplied to the control windings that are connected in series opposition. A large inductance in the control winding insures that its current is essentially constant and free of ripple.

The operation of this system is based on the same principle as the a-c measurement system described in Section 3.4.2. If the control current is I_c, core 1 is unsaturated only when

$$i_L = \frac{N_c I_c}{N_p} \qquad (3.65)$$

and core 2 is unsaturated only when

$$i_L = -\frac{N_c}{N_p} I_c \qquad (3.66)$$

Let us follow a development similar to that used in Section 3.4.2; the total flux linkage $\lambda_1 + \lambda_2$ of the primary windings is related to the current i_L as shown in Fig. 3.19b.

When the alternating voltage of $e = \hat{E} \sin \omega t$ is connected, the current i_L in the load is a square wave having the amplitudes given in eqs. 3.65 and 3.66. Figure 3.19c shows the idealized waveforms of the supply voltage e and the load voltage $R_L i_L$. The saturable reactor acts as a source of constant square-wave current, the magnitude of which is directly proportional to the control current. Assuming ideal cores, this square waveform of the load current and voltage is retained over most of the usable range. It can be shown that the square waveform is maintained until the average value of a half wave of the load voltage equals 84% of the average value of a half wave of the supply voltage. In practice, the finite saturated permeability of the cores causes some departure from square waveform. In addition, when the control current is zero, the load still carries the small magnetizing current required by the cores.

The large inductance in the control circuit of the saturable reactor of Fig. 3.19a causes this circuit to have a large time constant. Following a change in control voltage, the control current and the load current change slowly. If the inductance is removed to overcome this sluggishness in response, the saturable reactor continues to control the load voltage, but its action is markedly different.

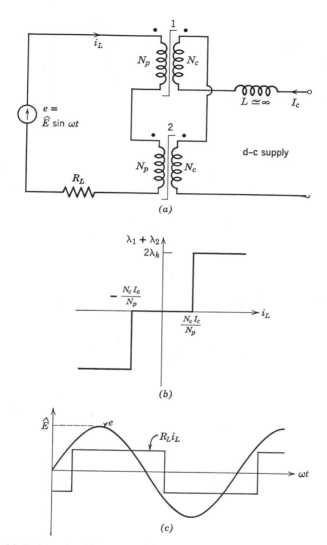

Fig. 3.19 (a) Series saturable reactor (high-impedance control). (b) Flux linkage in primary windings versus current. (v) Waveforms of supply voltage e and load voltage $R_L i_L$.

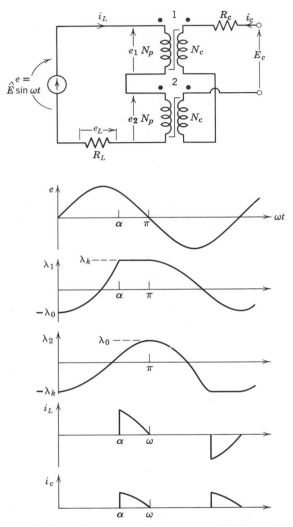

Fig. 3.20 Series saturable reactor with low-impedance control, together with its idealized waveforms.

Figure 3.20 shows a series saturable reactor without control circuit inductance, together with the waveforms of its variables. The total resistance of the control windings is R_c. Let the turns ratio be

$$\frac{N_c}{N_p} = n \tag{3.67}$$

The resistances of the primary windings are neglected, and the cores are assumed to be ideal saturable elements. Under all conditions

$$e = e_1 + e_2 + e_L \tag{3.68}$$

and

$$E_c = R_c i_c + n e_1 - n e_2 \tag{3.69}$$

At the beginning of a cycle of the applied voltage at $\omega t = 0$, let us assume that core 2 is at negative saturation, making its primary-winding flux linkage $\lambda_2 = -\lambda_k$, and that core 1 has a primary-winding flux linkage of $\lambda_1 = -\lambda_0$. With positive applied voltage, both flux linkages increase. Since both cores are unsaturated, the currents i_L and i_c must both be zero. As long as this condition obtains, solution of eqs. 3.68 and 3.69 gives

$$e_1 = \frac{e + E_c/n}{2} \tag{3.70}$$

and

$$e_2 = \frac{e - E_c/n}{2} \tag{3.71}$$

At some instant $\omega t = \alpha$, core 1 reaches positive saturation $(\lambda_1 = \lambda_k)$f and the core voltage e_1 becomes zero.

$$\lambda_{1(\alpha)} = -\lambda_0 + \frac{1}{\omega} \int_0^\alpha \left(\frac{e + E_c/n}{2} \right) d\omega t = \lambda_k \tag{3.72}$$

Since only core 2 now remains unsaturated, load and control currents may flow according to the relation

$$i_L = n i_c \tag{3.73}$$

Rearrangement of eq. 3.69 with $e_1 = 0$ gives

$$e_2 = \frac{1}{n}(R_c i_c - E_c)$$

$$= \frac{R_c}{n^2} i_L - \frac{E_c}{n} \tag{3.74}$$

Since core 1 started the cycle at flux linkage $-\lambda_0$, we would expect core 2 to finish the first half cycle at flux linkage λ_0 if the system is to repeat cyclically. Thus, using eqs. 3.71 and 3.74, we have

$$\lambda_{(2\pi)} = -\lambda_k + \frac{1}{\omega} \int_0^\alpha \left(\frac{e - E_c/n}{2} \right) d\omega t + \frac{1}{\omega} \int_\alpha^\pi \left(\frac{R_c}{n^2} i_L - \frac{E_c}{n} \right) d\omega t = \lambda_0$$

(3.75)

Solution of eq. 3.72 with eq. 3.75 gives

$$\frac{E_c \pi}{n} = \frac{R_c}{n^2} \int_\alpha^\pi i_L \, d\omega t$$

(3.76)

Since the half-cycle average value $\bar{i}_L$ of the load current is

$$\bar{i}_L = \frac{1}{\pi} \int_\alpha^\pi i_L \, d\omega t$$

(3.77)

eq. 3.76 can be rewritten as

$$\bar{i}_L = n \frac{E_c}{R_c}$$

(3.78)

Thus the average load current is directly proportional to the control voltage. This linear relation applies until the whole of the source voltage appears across the load, that is,

$$\bar{i}_{L(\text{max})} = \frac{2}{\pi} \frac{\hat{E}}{R_L}$$

(3.79)

As shown in Fig. 3.20, the control current consists of sections of waves, the average value of which is E_c/R_c.

An alternative saturable reactor arrangement is similar to that of Fig. 3.20, but with the primary windings connected in parallel. The control characteristics and load voltage waveform are similar to those for the series connection. Saturable reactors provide an efficient and reliable means of controlling the power delivered to a load from a constant alternating-voltage source.

3.4.4 Magnetic Amplifiers

Magnetic amplifiers are connections of saturable magnetic elements and rectifiers that are used to control the flow of power to a load. Although this purpose is similar to that of saturable reactors, magnetic amplifiers generally have the advantages of requiring much lower control power per unit of output and of responding more quickly to control signals.

Perhaps the simplest of the many types of magnetic amplifier is shown in Fig. 3.21a. An understanding of some of its principles provides a basis for appreciation of more complex types. This type of magnetic amplifier consists of a saturable core with its primary winding connected in series

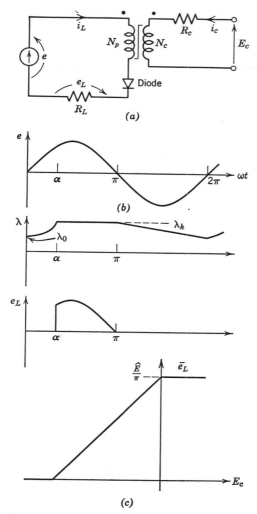

Fig. 3.21 (a) Elementary magnetic amplifier. (b) Idealized waveforms. (c) Control characteristics.

with a rectifier, a load, and an alternating-voltage source. The control winding of resistance R_c is connected to a direct-voltage control signal.

In the following analysis, the magnetic core is assumed to be ideal, having infinite unsaturated permeability and zero saturated permeability. The resistance of the primary winding is neglected. The rectifier is assumed to have zero resistance to positive load current i_L and infinite resistance in the opposite direction. As a starting point, let us assume that the flux linkage λ of the primary winding is λ_0 at the start of the sine wave of applied voltage $e = \hat{E} \sin \omega t$. This applied voltage is absorbed by the primary winding until the core saturates at $\omega t = \alpha$, giving $\lambda = \lambda_k$. The winding then acts as a short circuit, and the remainder of the half wave of applied voltage is applied through the rectifier to the load, as shown in the waveforms of Fig. 3.21*b*.

Up to this point, the action is similar to that of a saturable reactor. The difference in the magnetic amplifier operation is that during the negative half cycle of the supply, the primary winding is effectively disconnected from the supply by the rectifier. During this negative half cycle, a negative value of control voltage E_c acts alone to reset the flux linkage of the primary winding back to its initial value λ_0. If there were no control voltage, the flux linkage would remain at saturation value λ_k during the negative half cycle, and the whole of the next positive half cycle of supply voltage would be applied to the load. As a larger negative value of control voltage E_c is applied, the flux linkage is reset to a lower value of λ_0, and more supply voltage can be absorbed in the positive half cycle before switching occurs.

The relation between load voltage e_L and control voltage E_c may be expressed as follows. During the interval $0 < \omega t < \alpha$, the primary flux linkage moves from λ_0 to λ_k driven by the applied source voltage. Thus

$$\lambda_{(\alpha)} = \lambda_0 + \frac{1}{\omega} \int_0^\alpha \hat{E} \sin \omega t \, d\omega t = \lambda_k \qquad (3.80)$$

During the interval $\pi < \omega t < 2\pi$, the flux linkage λ is returned from λ_k to λ_0. The core is unsaturated during this latter period and the rectifier insures that the load current is zero. It follows that the control current i_c is also zero. Thus

$$\lambda_{(2\pi)} = \lambda_k + \frac{1}{\omega} \int_\pi^{2\pi} \frac{E_c}{n} \, d\omega t = \lambda_0 \qquad (3.81)$$

where $n = N_c/N_p$. If eqs. 3.80 and 3.81 are combined, the result is

$$\frac{\hat{E}}{\omega}(1 - \cos \alpha) = -\frac{E_c \pi}{n \omega} \qquad (3.82)$$

The average value $\bar{e}_L$ of the load voltage is

$$\bar{e}_L = \frac{1}{2\pi} \int_\alpha^\pi \hat{E} \sin \omega t \, d\omega t$$

$$= \frac{\hat{E}}{2\pi}(1 + \cos \alpha) \qquad (3.83)$$

Elimination of cos α from eqs. 3.82 and 3.83 gives the relation

$$\bar{e}_L = \frac{\hat{E}}{\pi}\left(1 + \frac{\pi}{2n}\frac{E_c}{\hat{E}}\right) \qquad \text{volts} \qquad (3.84)$$

This idealized relation is shown in Fig. 3.21c.

An interesting feature of this idealized analysis is that control current flows only during the positive half cycle, when the control action is ineffective. During the negative half cycle, the control current is ideally zero but in practice is equal to the small amount of magnetizing current required to change the flux. It is therefore desirable to apply the control voltage only during the negative half cycle of effective control action. Several different types of magnetic amplifier are based on ingenious methods of accomplishing this. The voltage E_c may be a pulse applied in the reset half cycle; it may be a half-wave rectified sine wave, or it may be a normal sine wave.

Since the control current in a practical magnetic amplifier is of the same order as the magnetizing current of the core, the previous idealized analysis is rarely adequate. The idealized rectangular loop model of Fig. 2.10 provides a better basis for analysis of magnetic amplifier performance.

The output voltage e_L in Fig. 3.21b is unidirectional. If an alternating output voltage is desired, two elementary units of the form of Fig. 3.21a may be combined as shown in Fig. 3.22. Other arrangements have been

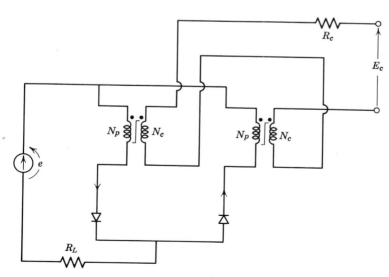

Fig. 3.22   Full-wave magnetic amplifier.

developed to provide for polyphase input and output. Magnetic amplifiers are built in a wide range of ratings and find their major uses in control systems.

3.4.5 Magnetic Frequency Multipliers

Electric power is normally available only at the standard supply frequencies of 50 or 60 cycles per second. For some applications such as

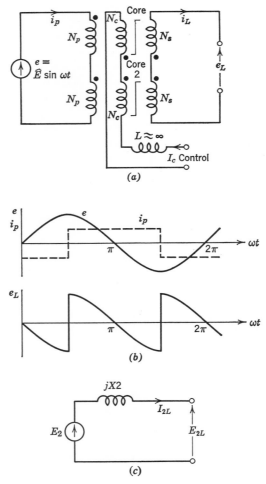

Fig. 3.23 (a) Frequency doubler. (b) Waveforms of supply voltage e, supply current i_p, and load voltage e_L on open circuit. (c) Equivalent second-harmonic circuit of output.

heat treating of metals, high-speed induction machines, and various control devices, a higher supply frequency is desirable. Integral multiples of the supply frequency can be obtained by the use of systems of saturable magnetic elements.

Figure 3.23a shows the circuit of a frequency doubler. This consists of two saturable magnetic cores each with primary, secondary, and control windings. A smoothed direct current I_c is passed through the control windings. Without the secondary windings, the system of Fig. 3.23a would be identical with the saturable reactor of Fig. 3.19a. Core 1 would be saturated for half of the applied voltage cycle, whereas core 2 would be saturated for the other half. Induced voltages in the unsaturated cores are subtracted in the secondary winding connection to give the open-circuit output voltage shown in Fig. 3.23b. Note that this output voltage contains only even harmonics of the supply voltage. In practice, the higher harmonics are considerably reduced by the imperfections in the cores, and the second harmonic is predominant.

If the output terminals are short circuited, an even-harmonic current i_L flows. The magnitude of this short-circuit current is directly proportional to the control current I_c. The load characteristics of a practical frequency doubler may be approximated by use of the equivalent circuit of Fig. 3.23c. The doubler acts as an essentially constant second-harmonic voltage E_2 in series with an inductive impedance jX_2, the value of which is inversely dependent on the control current I_c. The control current may therefore be used to control the flow of power to the load. One of the features of a frequency doubler is that if the control current I_c is reversed, the phase of the second-harmonic output voltage is also reversed.

Frequency triplers are based on the exploitation of one of the undesirable effects in three-phase star-connected transformers, namely, the triplen harmonics of the magnetizing currents which must flow in the neutral connection. Figure 3.24a shows a simple circuit arrangement for a frequency tripler. It consists of three, single-winding saturable cores connected in star to a three-phase, four-wire supply. Consider first the condition where the load is a short circuit and the supply voltage is sufficient to drive the cores well into the saturated region. The magnetizing current in each phase then contains a series of odd harmonics. The third harmonic is the largest of these harmonics; its value may be about 0.5 to 0.7 of the fundamental conponent. As we discussed in Section 3.3.1, the sum of the phase currents $i_a + i_b + i_c$ contains only the triplen harmonic components (3, 9, 15, etc.) that flow in the load. When the load is a short circuit, the third-harmonic component I_{3L} of the load current i_L is therefore about 1.5 to 2.1 times the fundamental component of one of the phase currents.

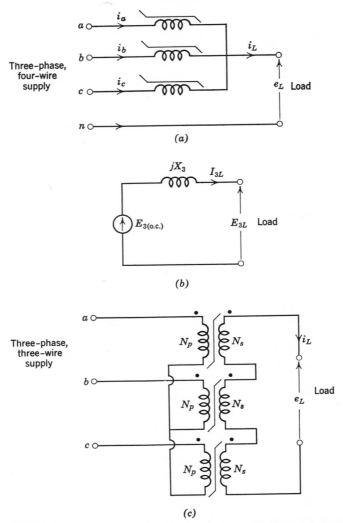

Fig. 3.24 (a) Elementary frequency tripler. (b) Equivalent circuit of output. (c) Alternative connection.

When the load is an open circuit, the triplen harmonic components of magnetizing current cannot flow. As a result, the induced voltage in each core winding contains triplen harmonic components, which appear across the open load terminals. The third-harmonic component E_{3L} of the load voltage e_L on open circuit may have a value of about 0.5 to 0.6 of the fundamental-frequency, line-to-neutral voltage E_{an}.

The load characteristics of a frequency tripler may be determined approximately by use of the equivalent source circuit of Fig. 3.24b. This is essentially a Thévenin equivalent circuit in which the third-harmonic source is represented by its open-circuit voltage $E_{3(o.c.)}$ in series with an inductive impedance jX_3 where X_3 is the ratio of the open-circuit voltage $E_{3(o.c.)}$ to the current I_{3L} on short circuit. Prediction of the parameters of a practical frequency tripler requires a rather more detailed analysis which may be based on the idealized B–H model of Fig. 2.7a.

An alternative arrangement for a frequency tripler is shown in Fig. 3.24c. The primary windings are connected in star, and only a three-wire supply is required. The secondary windings are connected in series (open Δ). In this arrangement, the turns ratio may be chosen to provide the desired level of output voltage.

Other odd multiples of the supply frequency may be obtained by use of a 5-, 7-, or 9-phase supply with core windings in each phase connected in star, the supplies being obtained by phase transformation, as described in Section 3.3.3. Higher even harmonics, such as the sixth, may be obtained with controlled output by cascading a frequency tripler and a frequency doubler.

Problems

3.1 When a transformer having two or more windings is represented symbolically as in Fig. P3.1, it is desirable to have some convenient means of relating the polarities of the voltages at the terminal of the windings. One simple convention is to place a dot near those ends of the windings that have, simultaneously, the same polarity of voltage with respect to the unmarked ends.

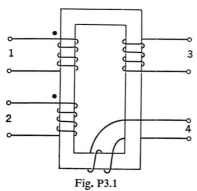

Fig. P3.1

(a) Place appropriate polarity markings on windings 3 and 4 in Fig. P3.1.
(b) How many turns has winding 4?

3.2 A 2-winding transformer that can be considered ideal has 200 turns on its primary winding and 500 turns on its secondary winding. The primary winding is connected to a 220-V sinusoidal supply and the secondary winding supplies 10 kVA (kilovolt-amperes) to a load.

(a) Determine the load voltage, the secondary current, and the primary current.

(b) Determine the magnitude of the impedance as seen from the supply. *Ans.: 4.84 Ω.*

3.3 An a-c, 5000-c/s generator can be modeled as a constant voltage of 250 V rms in series with an inductive reactance of 31 Ω. This generator is to be used to supply power to a resistive load of 0.65 Ω through a transformer that may be considered ideal.

(a) What should be the turns ratio of the transformer to achieve maximum power into the load?   *Ans.: 6.91.*

(b) Specify the required voltage and current ratings of the two windings of the transformer.

3.4 In electric welding a voltage of about 50–70 V is generally required to strike an arc. After the arc is struck, an essentially constant-current supply is desired. Figure P3.4 shows a 2-winding transformer designed for use in a

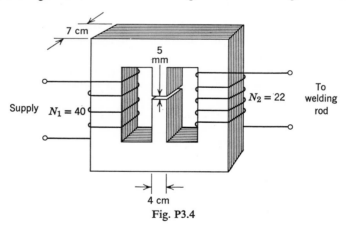

Fig. P3.4

welder. To limit the load current, a low reluctance path is provided for leakage flux between the primary and secondary windings.

(a) Derive an electric equivalent circuit for the transformer. As a first approximation, the core material may be regarded as perfect, the leakage paths around each of the windings may be ignored, and the winding resistances may be neglected. Fringing flux around the air gap may also be neglected.

(b) The supply is 115 V at 60 c/s. Determine the open-circuit secondary voltage and the short-circuit current in the secondary winding.

(c) If the arc can be regarded as a variable resistance dependent on the arc length, what is the maximum power that can be delivered to the arc? *Ans.:* 15.5 kW.

(d) Would the power determined in part (c) have been increased if the effects of the leakage paths around the windings had been included?

3.5 The output voltage of a rectifier can be expressed as $e = 200 + 35 \sin 2260t$ V. This rectifier is to supply a resistive load of 5 Ω. To prevent the 360-c/s ripple voltage from being applied to the load, it is suggested that a parallel inductance-capacitance filter tuned to the ripple frequency be placed in series with the rectifier. The difficulty with this suggestion is that the required capacitor operates at a low alternating voltage and is therefore relatively expensive. As an alternative, the system shown in Fig. P3.5 is proposed.

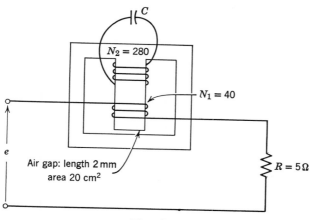

Fig. P3.5

(a) Derive an equivalent circuit for the 2-winding transformer with the air-gapped core. Leakage around each of the windings and fringing around the gap may be neglected. The core material may be regarded as perfect up to a flux density of 1.3 Wb/m².

(b) Neglecting the resistances of the 280-turn windings determines the required value of the capacitance C to produce resonance at 360 c/s. *Ans.:* 2.0 μf.

(c) If the resistance of the 280-turn coil is negligible, the impedance of the filter to the ripple voltage is essentially infinite. Determine the required voltage and voltampere ratings of the capacitor.

(d) Determine the peak value of the flux density in the core material bounding the air gap. *Ans.:* 1.198 Wb/m².

3.6 The transformer shown in Fig. P3.6 is to operate with 115 V rms at 60 c/s on its primary winding. The secondary winding is to produce an output at 500 V rms. All core dimensions are given in cm. The core material is to be operated at a maximum flux density of 1.4 Wb/m². The laminated core has a stacking factor of 0.95, that is, only 0.95 of the total core volume is magnetic material.

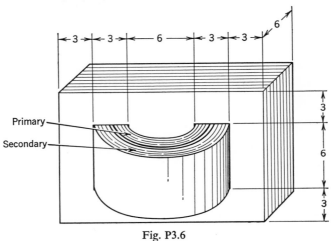

Fig. P3.6

(a) Determine the required numbers of turns on the primary and secondary windings. *Ans.:* 90; 392.

(b) The winding can be operated with a current density of 2 amp rms/mm² of copper cross-sectional area. The space factor (the ratio of copper area to the area of each window in the core) is estimated at 0.45. Determine the kVA rating of the transformer. *Ans.:* 1.035.

(c) At the operating temperature the resistivity of the copper is about 2×10^{-8} Ω-m. Estimate the power loss in the windings when operating at rated current. It may be assumed that the projecting ends of the coil are semicircular in shape. *Ans.:* 26.1 W.

3.7 A single-phase transformer is rated at 2300:115 V and 10 kVA. A short-circuit test on the transformer with the secondary winding short circuited gave the following measurements: primary voltage 162 V, primary current 4.0 amp, input power 93 W. An open-circuit test with the primary winding open circuited gave the following measurements: secondary voltage 115 V, secondary current 3.44 amp, input power 72 W.

(a) Determine the equivalent series resistance and series reactance of the transformer as seen from the primary terminals.

Ans.: $5.81 + j40 \, \Omega$.

(b) Determine the shunt admittance of the transformer as seen from the primary terminals. *Ans.:* $13.6 - j73.5 \, \mu$ mhos.

(c) Draw an equivalent circuit that is appropriate for finding the relation between the terminal voltages under various load conditions.

3.8 Suppose the transformer in Prob. 3.7 is of the core type shown in Fig. 3.3, with both primary windings and both secondary windings connected in parallel. The user of this transformer is informed that the power supply is to be changed to 4600 V.

(a) How should the transformer windings be reconnected?

(b) What will be the series resistance and series reactance of the reconnected transformer as seen from the primary terminals?

Ans.: $23.3 + j160 \, \Omega$.

(c) When reconnected, will the voltage regulation and the efficiency of the transformer be increased, decreased, or unchanged?

3.9 The 115:500-V, 60-c/s, 1-kVA transformer shown in Fig. P3.6 has 90 primary turns and 392 secondary turns. The projecting ends of the coil may be assumed to be semicircular in shape. The space between the primary and secondary windings is approximately 5 mm in width.

(a) Determine the approximate value of the leakage reactance of the transformer referred to the 115-V side. *Ans.:* $0.344 \, \Omega$.

(b) Determine the leakage reactance per unit of the rated impedance of the transformer.

(c) Suppose the window height in Fig. P3.6 is multiplied by a factor k and the window width is divided by the same factor. The numbers of turns and the core cross section remain unchanged. By approximately what factor is the leakage changed?

3.10 Figure P3.10 shows the coil of a 2-winding, unity-ratio, shell-type transformer. Each of the N-turn windings consists of a strip of aluminum foil the thickness c. The foil strips are separated by slightly wider strips of insulation of thickness d. Leads are brought out from the ends of each of the strips.

(a) If the windings carry oppositely directed currents i, derive approximate expressions for the magnetic field intensity at all points in the insulation and in the conductor.

(b) Show that the leakage inductance of the windings can be expressed approximately as

$$L = \frac{\mu_0 N \bar{l}(d + c/3)}{2y} \quad \text{H}$$

where $\bar{l}$ is the mean length of a turn.

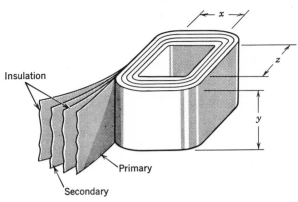

Fig. P3.10

(c) Derive an expression for the total capacitance between the two windings.

(d) If the core can be operated at a flux density of B Wb/m² rms, and the foil can be operated with a current density of J amp/m² rms, determine the V-amp rating of the transformer at a frequency of ω rad/sec.

Ans.: $U = \omega NBJxyzc$ voltamperes.

3.11 A 2-winding transformer has the following nameplate data: 200-kVA, 2300:230 V, 60-c/s. The impedance of the high-voltage winding when the low-voltage winding is short circuited is $0.24 + j1.6\ \Omega$. The admittance of the low-voltage winding with the high-voltage winding open circuited is 0.03-j0.075 mhos.

(a) The rated nameplate quantities are to be used as base values in determining per-unit values. Determine the base voltage, current, impedance and, voltamperes for both the high- and the low-voltage sides of the transformer.

(b) Determine the per-unit value of the total resistance and leakage reactance of the transformer.   *Ans.:* 0.00905 + j0.0604 per unit.

(c) Determine the per-unit value of the loss in the transformer when operated at rated voltage on open circuit.   *Ans.:* 0.00795 per unit.

(d) Determine the per-unit value of the magnetizing current when operated at rated voltage on open circuit.   *Ans.:* 0.0214 per unit.

(e) Determine the per-unit value of the total power loss in the transformer when operated at rated load.   *Ans.:* 0.017 per unit.

3.12 A transformer has an equivalent winding resistance of 0.01 per unit, a leakage reactance of 0.05 per unit, and a no-load power loss of 0.01 per unit, the base for all unit quantities being the rating of the transformer.

(a) Determine the efficiency of the transformer when supplying rated load at rated voltage and 0.8 lagging power factor. *Ans.:* 0.975.

(b) Determine the voltage regulation when supplying rated load at rated voltage and 0.8 lagging power factor. *Ans.:* 0.038.

3.13 When tested at rated frequency and rated secondary voltage of 240 V rms with the primary winding open circuited, a single-phase 10-kVA, 60-c/s, 2400:240-V distribution transformer requires a current of 0.55 amp and an input power of 55 W. When operated with rated frequency and rated current in its primary winding with its secondary winding short circuited, it requires an input power of 150 W at a primary voltage of 60 V.

(a) Determine the parameters of an equivalent circuit for this transformer with all impedances referred to the secondary side of the ideal transformer.

(b) Compute the voltage regulation of this transformer for a load of 10 kVA at rated secondary voltage and at 0.80 power factor lagging. *Ans.:* 0.0242 per unit.

(c) Compute the efficiency of the transformer when supplying the load specified in part (b). *Ans.:* 0.975 per unit.

(d) For what value of load per unit of rating is the transformer efficiency at its maximum value. *Ans.:* 0.607.

3.14 A 10-MVA transformer is required to supply a unity-power-factor industrial process. It is to be used at full load for 8 hours per day and at essentially no load for the remainder of the day. Supplier *A* offers a transformer having a full-load efficiency of 99% and a no-load loss of 0.5%. Supplier *B* offers a transformer at the same price having a full-load efficiency of 98.8% and a no-load loss of 0.3%.

(a) Which transformer should be chosen?

(b) If power costs 0.8 cents per kWh, what will be the daily differential in power cost between the two transformers? *Ans.:* $1.28.

3.15 Figure P3.15 shows, schematically, the coil and core arrangement of a 3-winding transformer. In developing an appropriate form of equivalent circuit for this type of transformer, let us assume that each winding has a separate leakage flux path, and that the leakage fluxes do not contribute to saturation of the core.

(a) Develop an electrical equivalent circuit for the transformer.

(b) Devise a test procedure to measure the parameters required for this equivalent circuit.

(c) Suppose the rated voltages of the windings are $E_1 = 11,000$ V, $E_2 = 550$ V and $E_3 = 115$ V. The impedance of winding 1 with winding 2 short circuited is 363 Ω; the impedance of winding 1 with winding

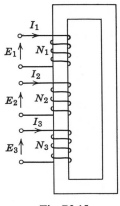

Fig. P3.15

3 short circuited is 605 Ω; the impedance of winding 2 with winding 3 short circuited is 0.121 Ω. When 115 V is applied to winding 3, with no load on the other two windings, the current is 125 amp. Assuming the losses in the transformer are negligible, determine the values of the equivalent circuit parameters.   *Ans.: $X_1 = 242$ Ω, etc.*

3.16 Two single-phase transformers designated as *A* and *B* have the same physical proportions. The linear dimensions of all parts of transformer *A* are *k* times the corresponding dimensions of transformer *B*. The magnetic material has the same lamination thickness in both transformers. The operating values of magnetic flux density, conductor-current density, and frequency are the same for the two transformers.

Determine the value of the following quantities for transformer *A* relative to the corresponding quantities for transformer *B*: rated voltage, rated current, rated voltamperes, mass, output per unit of mass, winding losses, winding resistances, core loss, heat loss per unit of surface area, total loss in per unit of rating, leakage reactance in ohms, and magnetizing reactance in per unit.

3.17 A transformer for use at audio frequencies can be represented by the equivalent circuit of Fig. P3.17. A source of variable frequency

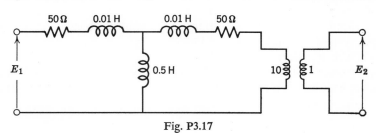

Fig. P3.17

supplies the input voltage E_1. The output voltage E_2 is applied to a resistive load of 10 Ω.

(a) Derive and sketch the ratio of the magnitude of E_2 to the magnitude of E_1 as a function of frequency over the reasonably useful frequency range.

(b) If the magnitude of the supply voltage is maintained constant, determine the values of frequency for which the load power is half the value obtained in the midfrequency range.   *Ans.: 15.2 and 8760 c/s.*

3.18 A 500,000:230,000-V, 100-MVA, 60-c/s transformer has 1500 turns on its primary winding. The core has a cross sectional area of 0.8 m² and a magnetic path of length 8 m. The magnetic material may be represented by the idealized model of Fig. 2.7a with $B_k = 1.6$ Wb/m² and $\mu_r = 10$.

(a) Determine the incremental magnetizing inductance as seen from the primary winding when the core is in saturation. *Ans.: 2.83 H.*

(b) Suppose a sinusoidal voltage of 500 kV rms is applied to the core at the instant that the voltage is zero. Determine the maximum value of the magnetizing inrush current. The secondary winding is unloaded. The initial flux density in the core may be taken as zero and coil resistance may be ignored. *Ans.: 649 amp.*

(c) Suppose this transformer has a leakage reactance of 0.15 per unit based on its rating. Determine the rms value of the steady-state current in the primary winding with the secondary short circuited and rated voltage applied to the primary winding.

(d) Suppose rated voltage is applied to the primary of the transformer at the instant of zero voltage with the secondary short circuited. Determine the peak value of the primary current. *Ans.: 3760 amp.*

3.19 Two single-phase, 10-MVA transformers are connected in parallel on both the primary and secondary sides. Their turns ratios are identical and their winding resistances are negligible. One transformer has a leakage reactance of 0.1 per unit while the other has a leakage reactance of 0.06 per unit.

(a) Suppose the transformers are used to supply a 20-MVA load. Determine the load carried by each of the transformers.

(b) What is the maximum total load that can be supplied without overloading either of the transformers? *Ans.: 16 MVA.*

(c) If each of the transformers has an equivalent winding resistance of 0.01 per unit, will the sum of the voltampere loads on the two transformers equal to the total load supplied by the transformers?

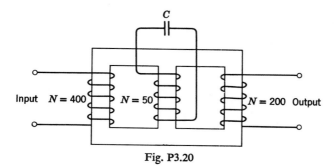

Fig. P3.20

3.20   Figure P3.20 shows the core and winding arrangement of a transformer that is supposed to maintain a constant ratio of its output voltage to its input voltage, regardless of load. The supply frequency is 400 c/s.

(a) Develop an equivalent electric circuit for the system. The winding resistances and the magnetizing current may be considered negligible. The leakage path around each winding may be assigned a reluctance of 10^7 amp/Wb. Mutual leakage fluxes may be ignored.

(b) Determine the value of capacitance C required to achieve the desired condition of zero voltage regulation.   *Ans.:* 212 μf.

(c) Show that the system of Fig. P3.20 is identical in operation to a normal 2-winding transformer with a capacitor connected in series with one of its windings.

3.21   A 3-phase, 60-c/s synchronous generator produces an output of 100 MVA at 15.8 kV line-to-line. This output is to be fed into a transmission line at 345 kV line-to-line. The transformer bank is to consist of three 2-winding transformers connected in Δ on the low-voltage side and in star on the high-voltage side.

(a) Specify the required rated values for the winding voltages and currents in each transformer.   *Ans.:* 2100:167 amp.

(b) Suppose each transformer has a leakage reactance of 0.15 per unit based on its rating. Determine the required generator voltage, line-to-line, to provide rated balanced output at 0.8 lagging power factor and 345 kV to the transmission line.   *Ans.:* 17.3 kV.

(c) Draw a single-phase equivalent circuit of the transformer bank.

3.22   Consider a load which is supplied from a source by means of two 3-phase transmission lines connected in parallel electrically but following different geographical routes. Suppose the shorter line is overloaded, while the longer line is underloaded. The current distribution in the two

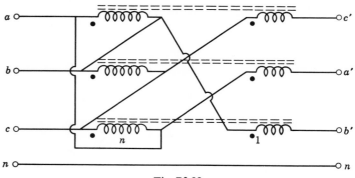

Fig. P3.22

lines can be altered by inserting a phase-shifting transformer into one of the lines. Figure P3.22 shows a simple means of obtaining a small phase shift.

(a) If each transformer has a turns ratio of $n:1$ and may be considered ideal, show that the phase shift θ of the output voltages with respect to the input voltages is given by $\theta = \tan^{-1}(\sqrt{3}/n)$.

(b) If the turns ratio of each transformer is 5:1, determine the ratio of the voltages phasors $E_{a'b'}$ and E_{ab}.   *Ans.:* $1.058 \underline{/-19°}$.

3.23   Suppose the 3-phase, core-type transformer shown in Fig. 3.12c has windings of N_1 and N_2 turns on each leg, the N_1-turn winding being on the inside.

(a) Develop a magnetic equivalent circuit for the transformer. Assume that the core material has infinite permeability. Include reluctance elements to represent the leakage paths between the pair of windings on each leg. Also include a reluctance element to represent the flux paths in air from the top yoke to the bottom yoke outside the windings.

(b) Derive an equivalent electric circuit for the transformer with all reactances referred to the N_1-turn windings.

(c) Suppose the three N_1-turn windings are connected in parallel. Show that the impedance of the resultant 2-terminal system is $R_1/3 + j(X_L/3 + X_0/9)$, where R_1 is the resistance of each winding, X_L is its leakage reactance, and X_0 is the reactance representing the yoke-to-yoke path.

(d) Is it possible to use the windings on one leg only as a single-phase transformer?

(e) Is it practical to connect the three N_1-turn windings in parallel and the three N_2-turn windings in parallel and use the resultant system as a single-phase transformer?

3.24   Figure 3.13b shows a 3-phase, shell-type transformer with windings of N_1 and N_2 turns on each coil.

(a) Develop a magnetic equivalent circuit for this transformer assuming the permeability of the core material to be infinite. Include reluctance elements to represent the leakage paths between the pair of windings in each coil.

(b) Derive an equivalent electric circuit for the transformer.

(c) Is it practical to connect the three N_1-turn windings in parallel and the three N_2-turn windings in series and use the resultant system as a single-phase transformer?

3.25   Figure P3.25 shows an arrangement of two transformers which may be used to connect a 3-phase load to a 3-phase supply. Suppose the transformers are each rated at 10 MVA. What total load may be supplied by this arrangement without overloading either of the transformers?

Ans.: 17.32 MVA.

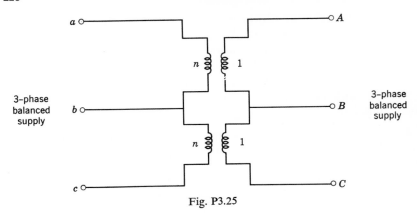

Fig. P3.25

3.26 A 400-c/s, 2-phase control motor requires a voltage of 115 V rms on each phase. The only 400-c/s supply available is a 3-wire, 3-phase system with a line-to-line voltage of 240 V rms. Magnetic cores having a cross-sectional area of 4 cm² and a peak operating flux density of 1.4 Wb/m² are available.

(a) Specify the required numbers of turns on the windings of the two transformers.   *Ans.:* 210:116. 242 (center-tapped):116.

3.27 A balanced 5-phase system of voltages can be provided from a 3-phase system using three 4-winding transformers. The required phase relationships are shown in Fig. 3.15.

(a) Sketch the connection diagram of the transformer windings with both the 3-phase and the 5-phase systems connected in star.

(b) Suppose the line-to-neutral voltage is to be the same for the 5-phase and the 3-phase systems. Determine the turns ratios required on each of the three transformers.

Ans.: 1.0:1.0:0.459:0.459;   1.0:0.859:068:0.24.

3.28 A 9-phase set of voltages is to be developed from a 3-phase supply. The line-to-neutral voltage is to be the same in both systems. It is not necessary that the two systems be conductively isolated.

(a) Show that the phase transformation can be accomplished using three identical transformers, each having a tapped primary winding and two identical secondary windings. Determine the required turns ratios.

3.29 An industrial process requires a single-phase supply of 500 kVA at 2400 V. The available utility supply is at a voltage of 4000 V. An autotransformer is to be used.

(a) Determine the required current ratings of the two sections of the transformer winding.

(b) Suppose the two sections of the autotransformer winding are disconnected. Determine the kVA rating of the resultant 2-winding transformer.

Ans.: 200 kVA.

3.30 Figure P3.30 shows a variable ratio autotransformer. A sliding brush makes contact with a bared part of the top of the single-layer winding.

Determine the required number of turns N and the dimension d for an autotransformer with an output of 0 to 115 V-rms at 60 c/s and an output

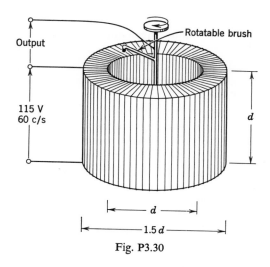

Fig. P3.30

current of 8.7 amp rms. Square wire having a 0.25-mm insulation thickness may be used with a current density of 1 amp rms/mm² in the copper. The toroidal core may be operated at a peak flux density of 1.5 Wb/m².

Ans.: 98; 10.8 cm.

3.31 A toroidal current transformer has a core with a mean diameter of 6 cm and a cross-sectional area of 10^{-4} Wb/m². The material has a relative permeability of 5000 for small values of flux density. The primary consists of a single bus bar passing through the aperture of the core and carrying a 60-c/s current.

(a) How many turns are required on the core to give a nominal current ratio of 800:5?

(b) Determine the magnetizing reactance as seen from the secondary side.

Ans.: 32.1 Ω.

(c) Suppose the secondary winding is connected by means of a 2-conductor cable to a 5-amp ammeter. If the combined impedance of the meter, the cable, the winding resistance, and leakage reactance is 0.07 + $j0.06\ \Omega$, determine the magnitude error of the current measuring system. *Ans.:* 0.187%.

(d) If the current transformer supplies the current coil of a wattmeter rather than an ammeter, the error in phase of the current is significant. For the combined impedance given in part (c), determine the phase error. *Ans.:* 0.124°.

(e) Would the phase error of part (d) cause the wattmeter to read too high or too low if the short-circuit loss of a transformer were being measured?

3.32 Figure 3.18*a* shows an arrangement of two cores that may be used for the measurement of the direct current in a bus bar. Suppose each core has a cross-sectional area of 1 cm², a mean diameter of 10 cm, and 4000 turns. The core material has a residual flux density of 1.5 Wb/m² and negligible coercive force.

(a) Determine the largest rms value of 60-c/s sinusoidal voltage which should be applied to the windings connected in series. *Ans.:* 319 V.

(b) If the meter indicates the full-wave rectified, average value, what will be the meter reading when the bus bar current is 2000 amp?

(c) If the coercive force of the material is 20 amp/m and the hysteresis loop is rectangular, what is the meter reading with no current in the bus bar?   *Ans.:* 1.59 mA.

(d) Does the magnetizing current produce an error in the meter reading? Assume that the core has an ideal rectangular hysteresis loop.

3.33 (a) Show that the output voltage in the idealized series saturable reactor with high-impedance control (shown in Fig. 3.19) maintains its rectangular waveform for all values of control current in the range

$$0 < I_c < 0.535\ \frac{\hat{E}N_p}{R_L N_c}$$

(b) If the source in Fig. 3.19 has a voltage of 220 V at 400 c/s, the control current I_c is 1.0 amp, and the turns ratio on each core is unity, determine the maximum value of load resistance R_L for which the output voltage waveform is rectangular.

3.34 A series saturable reactor is required to control the power supplied to a 25-Ω resistive load from a 220-V, 400-c/s sinusoidal source. Toroidal cores having a cross-sectional area of 2×10^{-4} m² and a mean diameter of 6 cm are available. The material has a rectangular hysteresis loop with a residual flux density of 1.6 Wb/m² and negligible coercive force.

(a) What is the minimum number of primary turns required on each of the cores to produce zero output voltages when the control current is zero?

Ans.: 194.

(b) If the control current is not to exceed 0.5 amp, how many control turns are required on each core to produce maximum load voltage?

Ans.: 3070 turns.

(c) When the control current is zero, what is the maximum value of the induced voltage in each of the control windings? *Ans.:* 4900 V.

3.35 Figure 3.21a shows an elementary type of magnetic amplifier. Suppose the supply voltage is a rectangular wave of peak value $\hat{e}$ volts and period T seconds. The core may be assumed ideal. The maximum primary-winding flux linkage is $\hat{\lambda}$, and the turns ratio is $n = N_c/N_p$.

(a) Assume that the resistance of the control circuit is very large. If a constant voltage E_c is applied to the control winding, show that the average value $\bar{e}_L$ of the load voltage is given by the expression

$$\bar{e}_L = \frac{\hat{e}}{2}\left(1 + \frac{E_c}{n\hat{e}}\right)$$

for the range $0 \geq E_c \geq -n\hat{e}$.

(b) What is the average load voltage $\bar{e}_L$ if the control voltage E_c has a positive value?

(c) Consider the situation with a finite value of control circuit resistance R_c. During the part of the positive half cycle of supply when the core is unsaturated, the 2-winding reactor may be considered as an ideal transformer. Show that the load voltage during this unsaturated period is

$$e_L = \frac{R_L}{R_L + R_c/n^2}\left(\hat{e} - \frac{E_c}{n}\right)$$

(d) Will the average control current be E_c/R_c for all values of constant control voltage?

3.36 A magnetic amplifier is required to control the power supplied to a 12-Ω resistive load from a 28-V, rectangular-wave, 400-c/s source. The connection of Fig. 3.21a is to be used.

(a) If the reactor is fully reset each negative half cycle, determine the saturation flux linkage required in the primary winding of the reactor to absorb all of the positive half cycle of the supply voltage.

(b) A core having a cross-sectional area of 1 cm² and a saturation flux density of 1.5 Wb/m² is available. How many primary turns are required?

Ans.: 116.

(c) During the negative half cycle of the supply, a rectangular pulse of -100 V amplitude and variable duration τ is to be applied to the control winding. During the remainder of the cycle, the control winding is open circuited. The core is to be reset to negative saturation when the pulse duration τ has a maximum value of 1.0 msec. The coercive field intensity of the core is negligible. Determine the required number of control-winding turns.   *Ans.:* 350.

3.37 A frequency doubler of the type shown in Fig. 3.23a has a supply voltage of 115 V rms at 60 c/s. Each reactor has a turns ratio N_s/N_p of 2.5.

(a) Determine the rms value of the 120-c/s component of the open-circuit output voltage.   *Ans.:* 244 V.

(b) If the turns ratio N_c/N_p is 5.0, determine the value of inductance which must be placed in the control circuit to limit the 120-c/s current in that circuit to 0.1 amp rms.   *Ans.:* 6.5 H.

REFERENCES

Blume, L. F., *Transformer Engineering* (second edition). John Wiley and Sons, New York, 1951.

Harris, F. K., *Electrical Measurements*. John Wiley and Sons, New York, 1952.

LaFuze, D. L., *Magnetic Amplifier Analysis*. John Wiley and Sons, New York, 1962.

Lee, R., *Electronic Transformers and Circuits*. John Wiley and Sons, New York, 1955.

Milnes, A. G., *Transductors and Magnetic Amplifiers*. Macmillan, London, 1957.

M. I. T. Electrical Engineering Staff, *Magnetic Circuits and Transformers*. M. I. T. Press, 1943.

Storm, H. F., *Magnetic Amplifiers*. John Wiley and Sons, New York, 1955.

Chapter 4
COMMUTATOR MACHINES

4.1 EVOLUTION OF ROTATING MACHINES

In Chapter 1 various processes for converting energy from electrical to mechanical form were discussed. In a variety of ways these processes exploit the forces on electric charges, as summarized in the expression

$$\vec{f} = Q(\vec{\mathscr{E}} + \vec{v} \times \vec{B}) \qquad \text{newtons} \qquad (4.1)$$

Electrostatic machines are dependent mainly on the forces produced on charges Q in an electrostatic field of intensity $\vec{\mathscr{E}}$, which is set up by other charges. It is also possible to set up an electric field intensity $\vec{\mathscr{E}}$ by means of a time-varying magnetic field. Although this property of induction is widely exploited in energy transformation devices, it is used directly to produce electromechanical energy conversion only in special situations such as in particle accelerators.

In most electromechanical devices the energy conversion process is dependent primarily on the forces on moving charges or currents in a magnetic field. This predominance of magnetic-type machines derives from several advantageous properties of magnetic materials. Intense magnetic fields of high flux density B may be set up in desired regions of space using relatively little energy in the bounding magnetic materials. Electric currents, which consist of large numbers of free charges Q moving at velocity v, experience forces when placed in these regions of intense field. In addition magnetic materials allow us to exploit not only the forces on free charges but also the forces on the bound charges whose motions create the magnetic moments of atoms. Because of this latter property, most electrical machines depend primarily upon the forces between sections of magnetic material rather than on the direct forces on current-carrying conductors. The conductors are used mainly to establish the magnitude and direction of the magnetic field, and thereby control the force between the stationary and moving parts of the magnetic structure.

In this chapter and in Chapter 5, we will examine a number of types of electrical machines. This discussion is arranged for convenience under two broad classifications—commutator and polyphase (induction and synchronous). All of these machines are based on the same energy conversion processes, and all can act as generators to convert mechanical energy to electric energy, or as motors to convert electric to mechanical energy. Their differences arise from the variety of needs of the electric and mechanical systems which they couple together. As generators, they must produce an electric output of the desired form using available prime movers. As motors, they must produce continuous mechanical output having the desired properties using available supplies of electric power.

4.1.1 Energy Flow in Machines

From the principle of conservation of energy, the energy flow through any machine may be stated as

$$\begin{array}{c}\text{Energy} \\ \text{input}\end{array} = \begin{array}{c}\text{Energy} \\ \text{output}\end{array} + \begin{array}{c}\text{Energy} \\ \text{lost}\end{array} + \begin{array}{c}\text{Increase in energy} \\ \text{stored}\end{array} \qquad (4.2)$$

When operating as a generator, the machine has a mechanical input and electrical output. For a motor the input is electrical, the output mechanical.

Energy is lost as heat because of the resistance of the electrical conductors. There are also hysteresis and eddy-current losses within the magnetic material. Finally, there are the losses due to friction between the moving parts and either their bearings or the surrounding air. Dielectric losses in the insulation of the conductors are generally negligible.

Energy is stored in the magnetic field of the machine. Most of this energy is in the air gap between the stationary and moving parts and in the air spaces around the conductors. An appreciable amount of magnetic energy may also be stored in magnetic material that is operated in the saturation region. Mechanical energy is also stored in the moving parts of the machine. In rotating machines, this is generally only in the form of kinetic energy. The energy stored in the electric field is generally negligible.

When the mechanical speed and the winding currents are constant, the stored energy is either constant or varying about some constant average value. The stored energy term in eq. 4.2 may therefore be neglected in many analyses of steady-state operation. But since the stored energies act to prevent a change in speed or current, they are of considerable importance in determining the performance during transient conditions such as starting or stopping. In machines that are used to produce accurately controlled output of mechanical or electric power, it is therefore desirable to minimize the stored energies.

4.1.2 Induced Voltage and Torque in Elementary Machines

Let us first examine some of the terminal properties of an idealized elementary machine. The practical imperfections of the machine are introduced later. Figure 4.1a shows a magnetic system arranged to produce a constant radially directed flux density of magnitude B across a

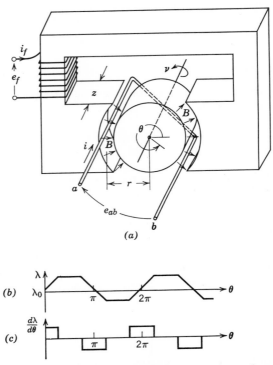

Fig. 4.1 (a) An elementary machine. (b) Coil flux linkage λ as a function of position θ. (c) Rate of change of flux linkage with position.

uniform air gap. A single-turn coil is free to rotate through the air gap. Suppose the coil rotates at an angular velocity $v = d\theta/dt$ radians per second. When the coil is in the air gap, it has a linear velocity $v = rv$, which is directed perpendicular to the flux density $\vec{B}$. A charge Q in the conductor therefore experiences a force

$$f = Q(\vec{v} \times \vec{B}) \qquad \text{newtons} \qquad (4.3)$$

For the coil position shown in Fig. 4.1a this force tends to move positive charge toward terminal a and away from terminal b. The summation of this force per unit of charge around the coil gives the electromotive force

$$e_{ab} = \int_b^a (\vec{v} \times \vec{B}) \cdot d\vec{l}$$

$$= 2zBrv \qquad \text{volts} \qquad (4.4)$$

Suppose we connect an electrical source to terminals a and b and cause a current i to flow in the coil against the electromotive force of eq. 4.4. A length element $d\vec{l}$ of the coil will experience a force

$$d\vec{f} = i(d\vec{l} \times \vec{B}) \qquad \text{newtons} \qquad (4.5)$$

Since all force increments acting on the coil of Fig. 4.1a are tangential and counterclockwise in direction, they act together to produce a torque

$$\vec{T} = r \int_b^a d\vec{f}$$

and

$$T = 2zBri \qquad \text{newton-meters} \qquad (4.6)$$

The current i in the coil produces its own magnetic field. Let us assume that the flux of this field linking the coil does not vary as the coil position is varied. Then, if the current i is constant, the flux it produces is also constant, and there is no additional contribution to the electromotive force in the coil. If, in addition, the current i encounters no coil resistance, the potential difference between the coil terminals is equal to the electromotive force of eq. 4.4. Under these idealizing assumptions, the electric power input to the coil is found to be equal to the mechanical power it produces.

$$P_{\substack{\text{elec.} \\ \text{input}}} = e_{ab}i = 2zBrvi$$

$$= Tv = P_{\substack{\text{mech.} \\ \text{input}}}. \qquad (4.7)$$

The electromotive force and torque of the coil can also be determined from the rate of change of its flux linkage λ. At $\theta = 0$ in Fig. 4.1a the coil has a constant flux linkage λ_0 as a result of the magnetic field of its own constant current i. As θ increases, the coil flux linkage increases linearly until the coil passes out of the air-gap region of constant uniform flux density B. Figure 4.1b shows the variation of the flux linkage with coil position, neglecting the fringing around the ends of the gap. Since the flux linkage is a function of position θ only, the electromotive force in the coil may be expressed as

$$e_{ab} = \frac{d\lambda}{dt} = \frac{d\lambda}{d\theta}\frac{d\theta}{dt}$$

$$= \frac{d\lambda}{d\theta}v \qquad \text{volts} \qquad (4.8)$$

where $d\lambda/d\theta$ is shown in Fig. 4.1c.

From eq. 1.66, the mechanical energy converted in moving a conductor carrying a current i across a flux ϕ is

$$W = i\phi_{\text{crossed}} \quad \text{joules} \tag{4.9}$$

Since the flux linkage λ of this one-turn coil is assumed to consist of a constant component λ_0 caused by its own current, plus the flux ϕ crossed by the coil, the torque on the coil may be expressed as

$$
\begin{aligned}
T &= \frac{dW}{d\theta} \\
&= i\frac{d\phi_{\text{crossed}}}{d\theta} \\
&= i\frac{d\lambda}{d\theta} \quad \text{newton-meters}
\end{aligned} \tag{4.10}
$$

With constant current i, the torque has the same form as $d\lambda/d\theta$, shown in Fig. 4.1c. It can easily be shown that the torque has the value given in eq. 4.6 while the coil is in the air gap.

Neglecting the resistance of the coil, and using eqs. 4.8 and 4.10, we find that the electric power input to the coil is

$$
\begin{aligned}
p_{\substack{\text{elec.}\\\text{input}}} &= ie_{ab} \\
&= i\frac{d\lambda}{d\theta}\,v \\
&= Tv = p_{\substack{\text{mech.}\\\text{input}}}
\end{aligned} \tag{4.11}
$$

The machine is therefore an ideal energy converter, provided all losses can be neglected and the stored energy in the magnetic field can be assumed constant.

The coil in Fig. 4.1a rotates about a cylindrical core of magnetic material. This arrangement is often used in instruments for the measurement of direct current. To provide greater mechanical rigidity, the coil could be attached to the surface of the cylindrical core and the combined core and coil could be rotated. Since the flux linkage of the coil is not altered appreciably by this change, the induced voltage and torque remain essentially as before. There may, however, be hysteresis and eddy-current losses in the core as the rotor revolves. To prevent excessive eddy-current loss, the rotor may be made of stacked circular laminations.

Let us now consider the possibility of fitting the conductor into a slot cut in the rotor surface, as shown in Fig. 4.2a. This arrangement provides

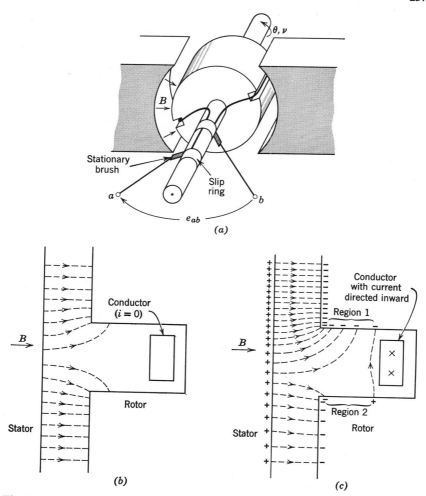

Fig. 4.2 (a) Elementary machine with coil in slots. (d) Magnetic field around slot with zero conductor current. (c) Magnetic field around slot with conductor current.

still greater mechanical support for the conductor. It also permits short-ening of the air gap between stator and rotor, thus reducing the magneto-motive force $N_f i_f$ required to produce a given flux density B in the gap, and reducing the stored magnetic energy. On first examination, it might appear that the machine would no longer operate as before. The conductor is now in a region of very low flux density because most of the flux takes the short path across the gap as shown in Fig. 4.2b and very little penetrates down into the slot. Equations 4.4 and 4.6 indicate that the induced voltage and torque are very small. On the other hand, the flux linkage λ of the coil still varies with the rotor position θ in essentially the same way as shown in Fig. 4.1*b*. Thus eqs. 4.8 and 4.10 indicate that the induced voltage and torque are the same as with the conductor on the core surface.

The explanation of this apparent anomaly is that eqs. 4.4 and 4.6 no longer represent the major parts of the induced voltage and torque on the rotor system. As the rotor position θ is changed, the flux paths in the rotor core change, particularly in the region of the slots. This time-varying magnetic flux sets up an electric field, which produces the induced voltage in the coil as given by eq. 4.8. The $\vec{v} \times \vec{B}$ contribution to the induced voltage as given in eq. 4.4 is a negligible part. The torque of eq. 4.6 still acts on the conductor, but it is of negligible magnitude because of the small flux density in the slot. The major part of the torque on the rotor acts on the magnetic material, particularly in the region of the slots. Figure 4.2*c* shows the pattern of the magnetic field in the region of the slot on the left-hand side of Fig. 4.2*a* with current entering at terminal *a*. It is noted that the conductor current increases the flux density above the slot and reduces it below the slot. Using the flux source concept of Section 1.7.3, we note that outside the region of the slot the forces are directed radially across the air gap. But in the region of the slot, the flux pattern is asymmetrical. The negative "flux sources" in region 1 experience a larger downward component of force than the upward component of force acting on region 2. Thus the rotor experiences a net force that is downward with respect to the stator.

One way of demonstrating that the force is on the magnetic material and not on the conductor is to consider the coil in Fig. 4.2*a* to be loosely fitted in its slot. With current flowing in the conductor and the rotor core held stationary, the coil experiences essentially no force. But with the coil held stationary, a large torque is experienced by the rotor core. Similarly, movement of the conductor alone produces essentially no induced voltage, but movement of the core with the coil stationary produces a large induced voltage.

4.1.3 Some Elementary Types of Machines

The machine of Fig. 4.2*a*, if operated at constant speed v, produces an open-circuit terminal voltage of the form shown in Fig. 4.3*a*. The flux linkage of the coil changes at an approximately constant rate while the slots are under the poles. When the slots are not under the poles, the coil flux linkage is essentially constant and the induced voltage is zero. One cycle of this alternating voltage is produced for each complete revolution of the rotor. If the machine is mechanically driven, alternating current can be supplied to a load connected to the terminals *a-b*. The frequency f

of alternation of this current is related to the angular velocity v of the rotor by

$$f = \frac{v}{2\pi} \quad \text{cycles/second} \quad (4.12)$$

The most readily useable form of alternating voltage is the sine wave, as shown in Fig. 4.3b. One way of obtaining this form approximately is by shaping the stator poles so that the magnitude of the flux density B varies sinusoidally with angle θ. Other methods of achieving sine form are developed in Chapter 5.

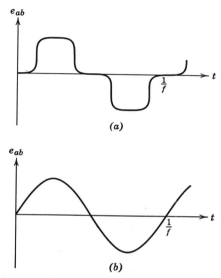

Fig. 4.3 (a) Induced voltage in machine of Fig. 4.2a. (b) Sine-wave voltage produced by pole shaping.

If the machine of Fig. 4.2a is to be operated as a motor, the current i supplied to the machine must have the same frequency as the induced voltage; otherwise, the average power entering the machine is equal to zero. Thus for a supply of a given frequency f, there is normally only one value of angular velocity v at which the motor can operate. Because of this synchronism between the electrical frequency and the mechanical speed of rotation, this type of machine is known as *synchronous*.

An alternative form of structure for a synchronous machine is shown in Fig. 4.4. In this structure the coil is placed in slots on the outer stationary member, whereas the poles that produce the magnetic field rotate. The field current i_f is supplied through brushes which are in contact with slip rings on the shaft.

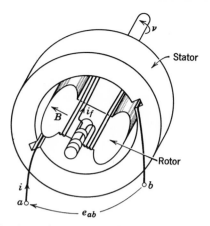

Fig. 4.4   Elementary synchronous machine.

A serious limitation of a synchronous machine used as a motor is its inability to operate at any speed other than the synchronous value. It is generally unable to start from standstill, and, unless an electrical source of variable frequency is available, its speed cannot be controlled over a range of values. To overcome this limitation, other types of machine are required. To introduce these types in elementary form, let us first examine the machine of Fig. 4.5, which acts as a brake rather than as a motor. When the rotor is rotated at an angular velocity v, a voltage e is generated in the rotor coil. If the coil is short circuited, a current i flows through its resistance R. This current i causes a torque T to act on the rotor in such a direction as to oppose rotation. The value of this braking torque is directly dependent upon the rotor speed v and on the pole magnetic flux ϕ

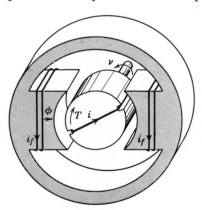

Fig. 4.5   Elementary machine operating as a brake.

because these two quantities determine the induced voltage. The angular frequency ω of the coil current is directly related to the rotor speed by

$$\omega = 2\pi f = \nu \qquad \text{radians/second} \qquad (4.13)$$

The machine can operate as a brake over a wide range of speeds, the braking torque being controlled by variation of the field current i_f.

The braking torque of the machine in Fig. 4.5 may be increased and made more uniform by using a number of coils placed in diametrically opposite slots, each coil being short circuited. Alternatively, a conducting cylinder may be rotated in the air gap.

As a further step in arriving at variable-speed motor action, let us consider the machine of Fig. 4.6. This machine acts as an electrically operated clutch linking two mechanical systems. The outer "stator" section carrying the magnetic poles is rotated at an angular velocity ν_s by a prime mover. The changing flux linkage of each rotor coil produces a generated voltage, which in turn causes a current i to flow through the conductor resistance. This current is in such a direction as to prevent the change in flux linkage of the coil. The torque T on the rotor is therefore in the same direction as the stator rotation and tends to accelerate the rotor to make its angular velocity ν_r approach the value ν_s. The torque is proportional to the mag-

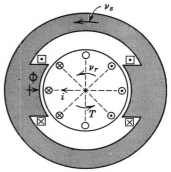

Fig. 4.6 Cross section of machine operating as a clutch.

netic flux ϕ because this determines the flux linkages of the coils; it is also proportional to the difference in the angular velocities $(\nu_s - \nu_r)$, since this determines the rate at which the flux linkages change with time. To drive a mechanical load requiring a torque T at a speed ν_r, the current in the stator coils is adjusted so that a torque T is developed at that rotor speed. If there is no mechanical load, the rotor speed ν_r tends to approach the value ν_s.

The polyphase induction motor to be discussed in Chapter 5 achieves the same drive characteristics as the clutch of Fig. 4.6. Instead of revolving the magnetic system of the stator, a similar revolving magnetic field is produced by symmetrically placed stator coils carrying appropriate alternating currents. An elementary form of this type of machine is shown in Fig. 4.7a. The stator coil a carries a current

$$i_a = \hat{I} \sin \left(\omega t + \frac{\pi}{2} \right) \qquad \text{amperes} \qquad (4.14)$$

while coil b carries a current of the same peak amplitude but delayed by $\pi/2$ radians.

$$i_b = \hat{I} \sin \omega t \qquad \text{amperes} \qquad (4.15)$$

At $\omega t = 0$, a flux density is produced in the air gap by the current i_a. This flux density is directed from stator to rotor on the left-hand side of the machine and from rotor to stator on the right-hand side. The axis of

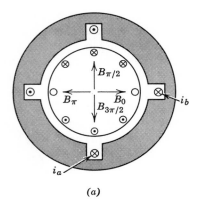

(a)

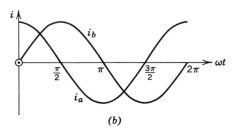

(b)

Fig. 4.7 Elementary polyphase induction machine.

symmetry of this magnetic field is indicated by B_0. As shown in Fig. 4.7b, the current i_a decreases, while the current i_b increases. At $\omega t = \pi/2$, the flux density distribution has rotated through $\pi/2$ radians so that its axis is in the direction of $B_{\pi/2}$. The current i_a then increases negatively to bring the field direction to B_{π}. Following this process through a complete cycle, we note that the direction of the field axis makes one complete revolution for one cycle of the supply currents. To the rotor, this revolving field appears much the same as that produced by the revolving stator of Fig. 4.6 with a speed $v_s = \omega$ radians per second. The driving properties of the rotor of an induction machine are therefore similar to those described previously for the clutch.

Although induction motors are capable of starting and of operating at any speed between $v_r = 0$ and $v_r = \omega$, they do not provide any simple means of controlling the speed v_r to any desired value, regardless of the load torque. Such motors are also inefficient unless the rotor speed v_r approaches the angular velocity ω of the rotating field.

To achieve simple control of speed, we must remove the limitations imposed by the fixed supply frequency ω. This is accomplished in the d-c

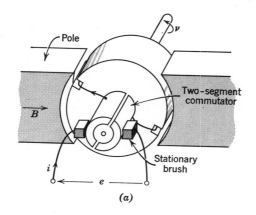

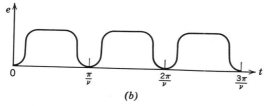

Fig. 4.8 An elementary commutator machine and its generated voltage e.

machine by the use of a switch or commutator that converts the direct current of the supply into current of the frequency required by the rotor coils.

The machine of Fig. 4.2a produces an alternating generated voltage of the form shown in Fig. 4.3a. The terminal voltage e may, however, be made unidirectional by using a switch attached to the rotor shaft, as shown in Fig. 4.8a. This switch, or commutator, consists of two insulated sectors to which the coil ends are attached. The stationary brushes are so placed that the polarity of the connections between the coil ends and the terminals is reversed each time the generated voltage in the coil passes through its zero value. Figure 4.8b shows the resultant unidirectional terminal voltage. If a direct current i is supplied to the machine, a uni-directional power flows in the machine.

A more nearly constant generated voltage and a more effective use of rotor space may be achieved by the use of a number of symmetrically placed rotor coils connected in series and parallel combination by a more complex commutator. Some of these coil arrangements are discussed in Section 4.3.

4.2 MAGNETIC SYSTEM OF MACHINE

Figure 4.9*a* shows the magnetic system of a simple two-pole machine. The system is magnetized by one or more field coils encircling each pole core. The magnetic flux passes along the pole core and is then distributed over an arc of the armature periphery by the pole shoe. It then crosses the air gap and passes along the teeth in the slotted armature to the armature core. After passing through the teeth, gap, and core of the other

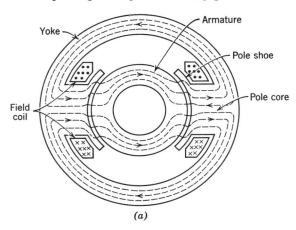

(a)

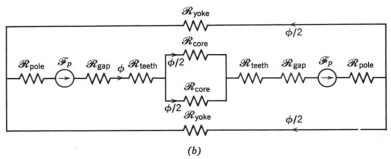

(b)

Fig. 4.9 (*a*) Magnetic system of two-pole machine. (*b*) Magnetic equivalent circuit.

pole, the magnetic flux returns along the two magnetically parallel yoke paths.

To determine the performance of the machine, it is necessary to know the relation between the magnetic flux ϕ, which crosses the air gap under each pole and the magnetomotive force $\mathscr{F}_p$ of the coils on each pole. Following the methods of Section 2.4, the equivalent magnetic circuit of Fig. 4.9b can be derived. In this circuit, a separate reluctance has been assigned to each section of the magnetic system that has a reasonably uniform flux density.

At low values of the flux ϕ, the magnetic material in the machine may be considered as essentially ideal. If we set all the corresponding reluctances to zero, the magnetic flux in each pole is approximated by

$$\phi = \frac{2\mathscr{F}_p}{2\mathscr{R}_g}$$

$$= \frac{\mathscr{F}_p}{\mathscr{R}_g} \quad \text{webers} \tag{4.16}$$

Since the reluctance $\mathscr{R}_g$ of the air gap is dominant, its calculation deserves first consideration. If the armature surface were smooth and the air-gap length constant, the reluctance could be approximated by

$$\mathscr{R}_g = \frac{g}{\mu_0 A_p} \quad \text{amperes/weber} \tag{4.17}$$

where A_p is the surface area of the pole face and g is the gap length. But with a slotted armature, the effective area of the flux path is substantially reduced. If the air-gap length g in Fig. 4.10a is very small, all of the flux can be considered to cross the gap sections above the teeth. The effective area A_g of the air-gap path is thus reduced to

$$A_g = A_p \frac{t}{t+d} \quad \text{meters} \tag{4.18}$$

There is, however, some fringing of flux around the teeth edges. This flux penetrates down the slot as is shown in the field pattern of Fig. 4.10b. The effective air-gap area is therefore between the value given in eq. 4.18 and the area A_p of the pole surface. The appropriate value may be found for any tooth and slot shape by field plotting. For certain idealized shapes, the value may be determined mathematically.*

---

* In an empirical approximation, which is adequate for most cases, the effective air-gap area may be expressed as $A_g = A_p (t + kd)/(t + d)$ where $k = 1/(1 + d/5g)$. Instead of applying the correction factor $(t + kd)/(t + d)$ to the area A_p in eq. 4.17, its inverse may be applied to the air-gap length g, giving an effective gap length $g' = g(t + d)/(t + kd)$.

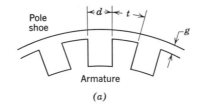

(a)

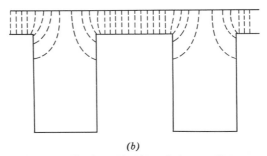

(b)

Fig. 4.10 The determination of air-gap reluctance.

As the flux in the machine is increased, the first region to experience magnetic saturation is generally the teeth. The slots are generally made with parallel sides to accommodate rectangular coils, and the teeth are therefore tapered, as shown in Fig. 4.10a. For a given value of flux ϕ, the magnetic potential across the tooth reluctance may be found by (1) determining the flux in one tooth, (2) determining the flux density B at various points along the tooth path, (3) obtaining corresponding values of field intensity H from an appropriate B–H curve for the material, and (4) integrating H numerically along the tooth path to obtain the magnetic potential difference.

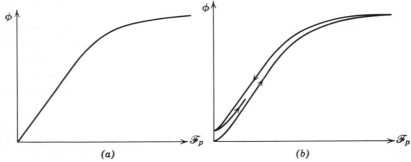

(a)   (b)

Fig. 4.11 Relation between air-gap flux ϕ and magnetomotive force $\mathscr{F}_p$ per pole. (a) Neglecting hysteresis. (b) Including hysteresis.

For a given value of flux ϕ, the calculation of the magnetic potentials across the remaining reluctances may be made using appropriate B–H curves for the materials used. The magnetic potentials across the reluctances of a closed path in Fig. 4.9b may then be summed to give the required magnetomotive force of the field windings. Figure 4.11a shows the resultant relation between the flux ϕ in each air gap and the magnetomotive force $\mathscr{F}_p$ per pole. This relation follows eq. 4.16 until saturation in some part of the magnetic system becomes significant. If the machine is so designed that all parts of the magnetic system enter the saturated region of their B–H curves more or less simultaneously, the $\phi/\mathscr{F}_p$ relation of Fig. 4.11a enters saturation rapidly. But if different parts enter saturation at different values of the flux ϕ, the change of slope of the $\phi/\mathscr{F}_p$ characteristic is gradual.

When normal magnetization curves (see Fig. 2.3) are used in calculating the $\phi/\mathscr{F}_p$ relation, hysteresis effects are neglected. Although this assumption is justified in many analyses, the effects of hysteresis are significant in certain types of machines. Figure 4.11b shows, in somewhat accentuated form, the multivalued relation between flux and magnetomotive force, which may be obtained experimentally.

In a two-pole machine, such as the one in Fig. 4.9a, it is difficult to make efficient use of the available armature surface and of the air space between the yokes and the armature. By the use of a larger number of poles, as shown in Fig. 4.12, a more compact design using less magnetic material per unit of output power may be achieved. The magnetomotive forces on adjacent poles have opposite directions. Because of the symmetry of the system, the relation between the flux ϕ in each air gap and the magnetomotive force $\mathscr{F}_p$ of each pole may be determined by considering only one flux path such as a-b-c in Fig. 4.12.

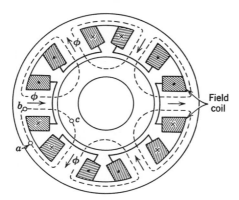

Fig. 4.12   Magnetic system of a six-pole machine.

There is a leakage flux across the air path between the tips of adjacent poles. As this flux does not enter the armature, it does not affect the induced voltage or torque. But it does increase the flux linkage of the field coil beyond the value that would be predicted by the magnetic circuit of Fig. 4.9b. It also contributes to the magnetic saturation of the pole cores and the yoke sections.

4.3   ARMATURE   COIL   ARRANGEMENTS

To produce a symmetrical armature and to make efficient use of its available surface, coils are distributed in slots over the complete circumference of the rotor. Each of these coils normally has a span of $1/p$ of the circumference for a p-pole machine. As each coil passes from under one pole to under the next, its flux linkage changes and voltage is generated. There are a number of ways in which these coils can be interconnected symmetrically so that the sum of the voltages of a group of coils is available at the armature terminals after commutation. One of these arrangements, known as a *lap winding*, is shown in Fig. 4.13. Starting

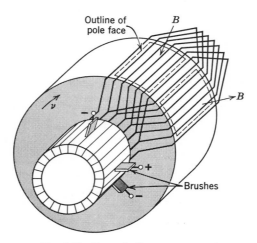

Fig. 4.13   Lap-winding arrangement.

from one end, which is connected to a first commutator bar, the coil passes along a slot to the back of the armature, through an end connection to a similar position under the next pole and has its other end connected to the commutator bar adjacent to the first. Subsequent coils are added in series with a connection to a commutator bar where the coil ends join. This pattern is continued around the armature until the last coil joins the first.

Figure 4.13 shows only $1/p$ of the coils of the winding. These are connected in series, and their total voltage may be obtained at the terminals by placing two stationary brushes on the commutator, as shown. The next group of $1/p$ of the coils has a voltage of equal magnitude but opposite polarity because these coils are in an oppositely directed magnetic field. This second group can be paralleled electrically with the first group by connecting the two negative-polarity brushes shown in Fig. 4.13. Continuing around the p-pole machine, there are p groups of coils connected in parallel by interconnection of the $p/2$ positive brushes and the $p/2$ negative brushes.

Each coil may have one or more turns. Since each coil has two ends and each commutator bar has two ends connected to it, the number of commutator bars is equal to the number of coils. Generally, one side of a coil is placed in the bottom of a slot and the other side in the top of a slot. Each slot may then contain any even number of coil sides.

One of the limitations of a lap winding is that increasing the number of poles does not increase the terminal voltage; rather, it increases the number of parallel connected groups of coils. For large machines, this type of winding is most useful in low-voltage, high-current applications.

Another arrangement, known as *wave winding*, is shown Fig. in 4.14. Starting at point a, a coil is placed so that it spans $1/p$ of the armature circumference. It is then connected in series with a coil, which is similarly placed under the next pair of poles. After $p/2$ coils have been series connected in this way (the winding has proceeded almost once around the

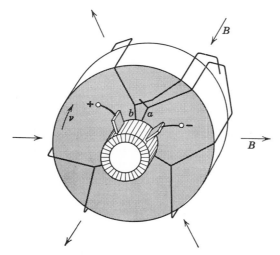

Fig. 4.14   Wave-winding arrangement (six-pole machine).

circumference), the connection is made at point *b* to the commutator bar adjacent to the starting point *a*. The winding proceeds in this pattern until it closes on itself. Between two adjacent commutator bars there is now the total voltage of $p/2$ coils in series, in contrast with the single-coil voltage of the lap winding. Between two adjacent brushes, spaced at $1/p$ of the commutator circumference, there now appears the total voltage of $(p/2)(1/p)$ or $\frac{1}{2}$ of all the coils. The major feature of this winding arrangement is that regardless of the number of poles, the coils are arranged in two parallel paths only.

It is possible to operate a wave-wound machine with only two brushes, as shown in Fig. 4.14. The commutator bars under these brushes are connected by coils to bars spaced $2/p$ of the circumference away. It is, however, preferable to use *p* brushes, half of which are connected in parallel to each of the positive and negative terminals, as this permits the required brush surface area to be accommodated on a shorter commutator.

4.4 ANALYSIS OF COMMUTATOR MACHINES

Having considered the general arrangement of the magnetic system and the armature coils, the next step is to develop a basis for the prediction of machine performance. For analysis, it is necessary to know the relations between the six terminal variables of the machine, that is, the terminal voltages and currents of the field and armature circuits, and the torque and speed of the shaft. In this section, these relations are developed and incorporated in an equivalent circuit model of the machine.

4.4.1 Generated Voltage

Suppose the field coils of a *p*-pole machine are supplied from a d-c source, thereby producing an air-gap flux ϕ in each pole. If the machine is now driven at an angular velocity of *v* radians per second, a voltage e_g is generated in the armature and appears across the open-circuited terminals of the armature. To determine this generated voltage e_g, let us first consider the generated voltage in a single turn of a winding. At the instant that this turn undergoes commutation, it encircles the flux ϕ from one pole. If the armature is now rotated through $1/p$ of a revolution, the turn is at its next point of commutation and encircles the flux ϕ of the next pole that is oppositely directed. Thus, in $1/p$ of a revolution, the change in flux linkage of a turn is

$$\Delta\lambda_{\text{turn}} = 2\phi \qquad \text{webers} \qquad (4.19)$$

The time required for $1/p$ of a revolution is

$$t_p = \frac{1}{p}\frac{2\pi}{v} \qquad \text{seconds} \qquad (4.20)$$

The average voltage generated in the turn is therefore

$$\bar{e}_{\text{turn}} = \frac{\Delta\lambda_{\text{turn}}}{t_p}$$

$$= \frac{p}{\pi}\phi\nu \qquad \text{volts} \tag{4.21}$$

Suppose the total number of turns in all the coils of the armature winding is N. At any instant the coils are arranged in a parallel groups where

$$a = p \qquad \text{for a lap winding} \tag{4.22}$$
$$= 2 \qquad \text{for a wave winding}$$

Within each group, there are N/a turns connected in series between the armature terminals. The average value of the generated voltage appearing at the armature terminals is therefore

$$\bar{e}_g = \frac{N}{a}\bar{e}_{\text{turn}}$$

$$= \frac{Np}{a\pi}\phi\nu$$

$$= K_a\phi\nu \qquad \text{volts} \tag{4.23}$$

As expected, the generated voltage is directly proportional to the flux and to the speed. The constant K_a is determined by the design of the armature winding.*

$$K_a = \frac{Np}{a\pi} \tag{4.24}$$

Each coil produces a generated voltage of the waveform shown in Fig. 4.8b. The total generated voltage is the sum of a group of similar voltage waves, which are displaced in time with respect to each other, as is shown in Fig. 4.15. Note that the total generated voltage contains a ripple component, the repetition period of which is the time t_p of eq. 4.20 divided by the number of coils in series. As the number of series coils in each of the parallel groups is increased, the amplitude of this ripple component decreases and its frequency increases. The effects of this ripple generally

* In many references, this constant is expressed in terms of the number of conductors Z in the armature winding. Since each turn has two conductors in slots, $Z = 2N$.

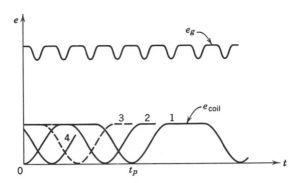

Fig. 4.15 Summation of coil voltages to produce the generated voltage e_g.

can be neglected. Only the average generated voltage as given in eq. 4.23 is normally used in analysis.

The air-gap flux ϕ is related to the magnetomotive force $\mathscr{F}_p$ on each pole by a magnetization curve such as the one shown in Fig. 4.11. If each pole has a single field winding of N_f turns and a current of i_f is passed through the field coils connected in series,

$$\mathscr{F}_p = N_f i_f \qquad \text{amperes} \qquad (4.25)$$

The quantity of $K_a\phi$ is therefore related to the field current i_f by a curve of the form shown in Fig. 4.16. This curve may be obtained by rescaling

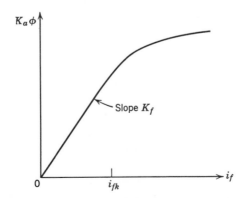

Fig. 4.16 Relation between quantity $K_a\phi$ (in volts generated per radian per second or newton-meters of torque produced per ampere of armature current) and the field current i_f.

the $\phi/\mathscr{F}_p$ relation of Fig. 4.11. Alternatively, the curve may be obtained experimentally for a given machine by measuring the open-circuit voltage of the armature at a fixed speed ν as the field current is varied. From eq. 4.23, the quantity $K_a\phi$ is the generated voltage divided by the rotational velocity.

If magnetic saturation and hysteresis can be neglected, the quantity $K_a\phi$ can be linearly related to the field current by use of eqs. 4.16 and 4.25.

$$K_a\phi = \frac{K_a N_f}{\mathscr{R}_g} i_f$$
$$= K_f i_f \qquad \text{volts/radian per second} \qquad (4.26)$$

From Fig. 4.16, this linear approximation might apply over a range of field current such as $i_{fk} > i_f > -i_{fk}$. The generated voltage is then given by

$$e_g = K_f i_f \nu \qquad \text{volts} \qquad (4.27)$$

Although this equation is based on an assumption of magnetic linearity, note that it is nonlinear mathematically, since it involves the product of two variables i_f and ν. Reversal of either the field current or the direction of rotation reverses the polarity of the generated voltage.

In applications that do not require control of the generated voltage, the flux ϕ may be obtained from permanent magnets in the poles. One example of a permanent-magnet commutator machine is the d-c tachometer in which the open-circuit terminal voltage is directly proportional to the speed. Permanent-magnet commutator machines may also be used as starting motors for automobiles.

4.4.2 Torque

Suppose a current i_a is supplied to the armature terminals. Let us assume for the present that this current does not change the magnetic flux ϕ produced by the magnetomotive force of the field windings. If the armature coils are arranged in a parallel groups, the current in each turn is

$$i_{\text{turn}} = \frac{i_a}{a} \qquad \text{amperes} \qquad (4.28)$$

where a is given by eq. 4.22.

The torque on a single turn is equal to its current multiplied by the rate of change of its flux linkage with angular motion (eq. 4.10). As one turn moves through $1/p$ of a revolution, or $2\pi/p$ radians between successive positions of commutation, its flux linkage changes by 2ϕ (eq. 4.19). Thus the average torque on one turn is

$$\bar{T}_{\text{turn}} = i_{\text{turn}} \frac{2\phi}{2\pi/p}$$

$$= \frac{p\phi}{a\pi} i_a \qquad \text{newton-meters} \qquad (4.29)$$

If there are N turns on the armature winding, each carrying the current i_{turn}, the average torque produced within the machine is

$$T = N\bar{T}$$

$$= \frac{Np}{a\pi} \phi i_a$$

$$= K_a \phi i_a \qquad \text{newton-meters} \qquad (4.30)$$

The quantity $K_a \phi$ is related to the field current i_f by a curve of the form shown in Fig. 4.16. A comparison of eqs. 4.23 and 4.30 shows that the quantity $K_a \phi$ is a measure of both the torque per ampere of armature current and the generated voltages per radian per second of rotational velocity.

If the magnetic system of the machine can be considered as linear, the torque may be expressed as

$$T = K_f i_f i_a \qquad \text{newton-meters} \qquad (4.31)$$

using eq. 4.26.

With constant armature and field currents, there are ripples in the torque-time curve similar to those in the generated voltage of Fig. 4.15. The repetition frequency of these ripples depends upon the speed and is the same as for the generated voltage. These ripples in torque generally can be neglected.

4.4.3 Effect of Armature Magnetomotive Force

It has so far been assumed that the magnetic flux ϕ in the air gap is dependent only on the magnetomotive force of the field coils; but the armature winding also produces magnetomotive force. A digression is therefore made at this stage to assess the magnetic effect of the armature current. Consider path 1 in Fig. 4.17a. Since armature coils undergo commutation when they are midway between the poles, all armature conductors under one pole carry current in one direction; under the adjacent pole, the currents are in the opposite direction. The net armature magnetomotive force of path 1 is zero. Thus, the flux density at the center of each pole is not affected by the armature current. For path 2, the net armature magnetomotive force enclosed is in such a direction as to oppose the field magnetomotive force. The flux density is therefore reduced on this side of the pole. For path 3, the magnetomotive forces of the armature and field coils assist, increasing the flux density.

If the magnetic system of the machine is linear, the reduction in flux density on one side of each pole is exactly balanced by the increase in flux density on the other side, as is shown in Fig. 4.17b. The net air-gap flux ϕ

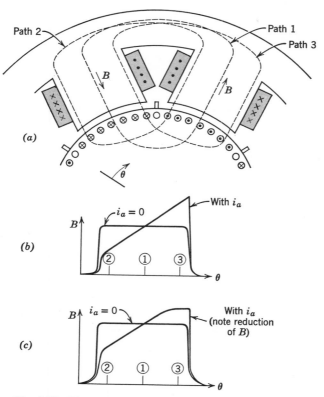

Fig. 4.17 The effect of the armature magnetomotive force.

is therefore not affected by the armature magnetomotive force. The shape of the voltage generated in each coil is changed, but the average value (eq. 4.21) is unaffected. If, however, either the field or the armature magnetomotive force is increased so that saturation occurs—such as along path 3 in Fig. 4.17a—the net flux per pole will be decreased, as shown by the flux density distribution curve of Fig. 4.17c.

The distortion of the flux density distribution under each pole depends upon the relative values of the field and armature magnetomotive forces.

If there are N turns on the armature winding (or $2N$ conductors), each carrying a current i_a/a, the fraction $1/2p$ of the armature conductors between the center of a pole and a brush produce a magnetomotive force of*

$$\mathscr{F}_a = \frac{Ni_a}{pa} \qquad \text{amperes} \qquad (4.32)$$

Suppose the poles cover a fraction α of the armature periphery. Then along path 3 on one pole edge in Fig. 4.17a, the total magnetomotive force is

$$\mathscr{F}_3 = 2(\mathscr{F}_p + \alpha\mathscr{F}_a) \qquad \text{amperes} \qquad (4.33)$$

while along path 2, the total magnetomotive force is

$$\mathscr{F}_2 = 2(\mathscr{F}_p - \alpha\mathscr{F}_a) \qquad \text{amperes} \qquad (4.34)$$

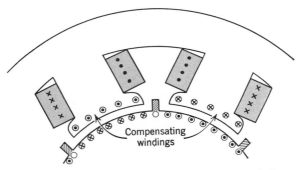

Fig. 4.18   Use of compensating windings in the pole faces.

Unless other means are used to counteract this effect of armature magnetomotive force, it is necessary to design the machine so that the pole magnetomotive force $\mathscr{F}_p$ is always significantly greater than $\alpha\mathscr{F}_a$. This constraint limits the minimum length of air gap that may be used in the machine.

The flux distortion caused by armature magnetomotive force may be substantially eliminated by feeding the armature current i_a through a compensating winding placed in holes or slots in the pole face, as shown in Fig. 4.18. The number of conductors N_c placed in each pole face is so chosen that the total current in the compensating conductors is equal to

* This quantity is generally known as the armature reaction or the armature magnetomotive force per pole, although a better description might be the magnetomotive force per interpolar space. If the conductors between a brush and a pole center on one side are paired with the conductors between the brush and pole center on the other side, the fraction $1/p$ of the armature winding can be visualized as a coil of N/p turns carrying current i_a/a and centered about the brush position.

the total current in the armature conductors beneath the pole, that is,

$$N_c i_a = \alpha \frac{2N}{p} \frac{i_a}{a}$$

or
$$N_c = \frac{2\alpha N}{pa} \quad \text{conductors} \tag{4.35}$$

Compensating windings are widely used in control machines that may have very large transient values of armature current.

4.4.4 Commutation

Let us now consider the action of the commutator. A particular coil in Fig. 4.19a has a current i_a/a, while its sides are under a pair of poles. When its sides are midway between poles, the coil is short circuited for a short time t_c by the brush. As soon as it passes the brush, its current becomes $-i_a/a$. It is important that the reversal of this coil current be accomplished without excessive sparking at the point of contact between the brush and the commutator bar.

One of the causes of sparking is the inductance L_c of the coil. From Fig. 4.19b it can be seen that the inductance arises from the flux linking the portions of the coil in the slots and around the end connections. This flux arises from the coil current. The inductance acts to prevent the coil current from changing.

Ideally, the coil current might change at a linear rate over the commutation period t_c arriving at the correct value at the instant it is open circuited, as is shown in Fig. 4.19c. This could be accomplished by generating the appropriate voltage e_c in the coil during commutation. The coil current during commutation is described by the expression $L_c(di/dt) + Ri = e_c$. Neglecting the resistance R of the coil and the brush, the required generated voltage is (from Fig. 4.19c)

$$e_c = L_c \frac{di}{dt}$$

$$= L_c \frac{2i_a}{at_c} \quad \text{volts} \tag{4.36}$$

Figure 4.19a shows how this voltage e_c may be produced by use of commutating poles, with windings carrying current i_a, which produce a magnetic flux in the region of the coils undergoing commutation. The magnetomotive force required on these commutating poles may be found by considering the path shown in Fig. 4.19a. This path encloses no net current from the main field windings. But it encloses the current of $1/p$ of the armature conductors, that is, a magnetomotive force of $2\mathcal{F}_a$,

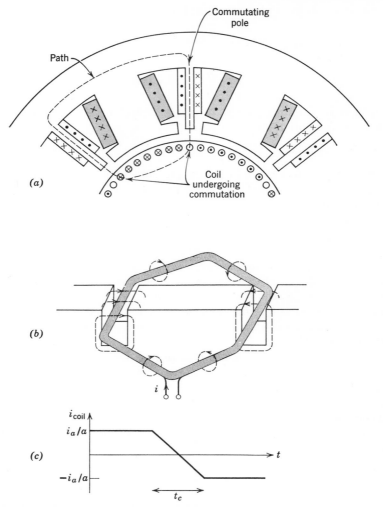

Fig. 4.19. (a) The arrangement of commutating poles. (b) The inductance of a coil. (c) Ideal commutation.

where $\mathscr{F}_a$ is given in eq. 4.32. The total magnetomotive force $2\mathscr{F}_c$ of the two commutating pole windings must therefore exceed $2\mathscr{F}_a$ by a sufficient amount to provide the required flux density B in the commutating pole air gap. The generated voltage in the commutated coil is then proportional to the flux density B, which in turn is proportional to the current i_a, as required by eq. 4.36. The generated voltage is also proportional to the speed on which the commutation time t_c depends inversely, as required by eq. 4.36.

Commutating poles are used in most large commutator machines. In small machines, the brush resistance is usually sufficient to provide adequate commutation.

4.4.5 Equivalent Circuit and General Equations

For purposes of analysis it is convenient to visualize a commutator machine as an ideal energy converter in combination with other parameters that represent its various imperfections. Let us first examine the properties of the ideal machine.

Suppose a machine is driven at a speed of v radians per second by a mechanical prime mover. The voltage generated in the armature will be (from eq. 4.23)

$$e_g = K_a \phi v \qquad \text{volts} \qquad (4.37)$$

If an electric load is connected to the armature terminals, a current i_a flows. The electric power generated in the machine is given by

$$P_{\text{elec.}} = e_g i_a$$
$$= K_a \phi v i_a \qquad \text{watts} \qquad (4.38)$$

From eq. 4.30, the armature current i_a reacts with the flux ϕ to produce a torque

$$T = K_a \phi i_a \qquad \text{newton-meters} \qquad (4.39)$$

in such a direction as to oppose the rotation. The mechanical power converted in the armature is then given by

$$P_{\text{mech.}} = T$$
$$= K_a \phi i_a v$$
$$= P_{\text{elec.}} \qquad \text{watts} \qquad (4.40)$$

Thus, internally, the machine behaves as an ideal energy converter. The properties of this ideal converter are given in eqs. 4.37 and 4.39.

Figure 4.20 shows an equivalent circuit for a commutator machine in which this ideal commutator machine is represented symbolically. The remainder of the equivalent circuit introduces the various imperfections of the machine.

When current flows in the armature circuit, there is a power loss in the armature coils. The resistance R_a of the a parallel groups of armature coils is

$$R_a = \rho \frac{Nl}{a^2 A} \qquad \text{ohms} \qquad (4.41)$$

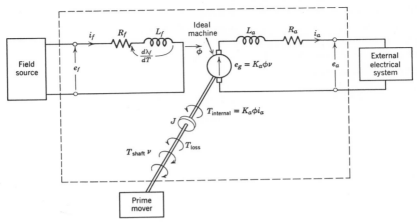

Fig. 4.20   Equivalent circuit of commutator machine.

where ρ is the conductor resistivity at the operating temperature, N is the total number of armature turns, and l is the length of conductor of area A in each turn. This resistance may be measured by passing a constant current i_a through the stationary armature winding and measuring the voltage on the commutator bars under adjacent brushes.

There is also an electrical power loss in the brushes that make contact with the commutator. These brushes are normally made of carbon in either hard or graphite form and sometimes contain metal such as copper in solution. The permissible current density in a brush varies from about 5 to 25 amperes per centimeter.[2] The voltage drop in a brush occurs mainly at the surface of contact with the commutator. It varies nonlinearly with current density, as shown for a typical brush in Fig. 4.21. Since the total voltage drop across the two sets of brushes by which the current

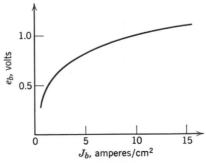

Fig. 4.21   Voltage drop e_o across a typical brush having a current density J_b.

enters and leaves may be as high as 2 volts, the brush loss is significant in low-voltage machines. In high-voltage machines, it may often be neglected in approximate analyses.

The armature circuit also has an inductance L_a representing the flux linkage of the armature circuit per unit of armature current i_a. This armature circuit includes not only the armature winding but also the interpole and compensating windings, if these exist. The armature inductance generally may be regarded as a constant.

With a constant field current i_f, all the power input to the field coils represents a power loss. The field circuit resistance R_f is p times the resistance of each coil if the coils are connected in series. Parallel and series-parallel connections of the field coils also may be made.

The inductance L_f of a field circuit of p field coils, each having N_f turns connected in series, may be expressed as

$$L_f = \frac{pN_f\phi_f}{i_f} \quad \text{henrys} \tag{4.42}$$

The pole flux ϕ_f consists of the air-gap flux ϕ plus a leakage flux, which crosses the air path between adjacent pole tips (Fig. 4.12). The relationship between the air-gap flux ϕ and the field current i_f has the form shown in Fig. 4.16. Within the linear range of this relationship, the air-gap flux is equal to the field magnetomotive force $N_f i_f$ divided by the air-gap reluctance $\mathscr{R}_g$ (eq. 4.16). The pole leakage flux ϕ_{L_f} is equal to the field magnetomotive force $N_f i_f$ divided by $\mathscr{R}_{L_f}$, where $\mathscr{R}_{L_f}$ is half the reluctance of the air path between two adjacent pole tips. In the linear range, the inductance of a series-connected field circuit may be expressed as

$$L_f = \frac{\lambda_f}{i_f}$$
$$= p\frac{N_f\phi_f}{i_f}$$
$$= \frac{pN_f^2}{\mathscr{R}_{Lf}} + \frac{pN_f^2}{\mathscr{R}_g}$$
$$= L_{Lf} + L_{fg} \quad \text{henrys} \tag{4.43}$$

If the p field coils are connected in parallel, the field circuit inductance is

$$L_f = \frac{N_f^2}{p\mathscr{R}_{Lf}} + \frac{N_f^2}{p\mathscr{R}_g} \quad \text{henrys} \tag{4.44}$$

In most machines the leakage reluctance $\mathscr{R}_{Lf}$ is 5–10 times the air-gap reluctance $\mathscr{R}_g$.

When the machine is operated in the nonlinear region of Fig. 4.16, the use of the inductance parameter L_f is not appropriate; rather, a graph showing the flux linkage λ_f of the field circuit as a function of the field current i_f should be used. The field flux linkage caused by air-gap flux may be obtained by rescaling the ordinate of the $K_a\phi - i_f$ relation of Fig. 4.16, the rescaling factor being L_{fg}/K_f. Since the pole-tip reluctance R_{Lf} is reasonably constant, the flux linkage caused by pole leakage flux is equal to $L_{Lf}i_f$. This leakage flux linkage may be added to the air-gap flux linkage to obtain the total flux linkage λ_f.

The shaft torque of the machine differs from the electromagnetic or internal torque (eq. 4.39) by the sum of the torque required to overcome the mechanical losses and the torque required by the inertia of the machine. Components of loss torque arise from bearing friction, brush friction, and friction with the air (windage). It is usually convenient to include with these components the torque that arises from eddy currents in the armature magnetic system as it rotates through the pole fluxes. The total loss torque is nonlinearly dependent on the speed v. But since the loss torque is generally a small fraction of the total torque, a linear relation with speed may often be assumed.

The kinetic energy stored in the rotor of the machine at speed v is

$$W_{\text{kin}} = \tfrac{1}{2}Jv^2 \qquad \text{joules} \qquad (4.45)$$

where J is the polar moment of inertia in kilogram-meters². A change in rotor speed therefore requires a change in the stored energy. The rate of change with time of the stored energy W_{kin} is equal to the accelerating torque multiplied by the speed. Thus

$$T_{\text{accel.}} = \frac{1}{v}\frac{d}{dt}W_{\text{kin}}$$

$$= J\frac{dv}{dt} \qquad \text{newton-meters} \qquad (4.46)$$

The equivalent circuit of Fig. 4.20 shows that the machine has six terminal variables; e_f and i_f for the field circuit, e_a and i_a for the armature circuit, v and T_{shaft} for the mechanical system. These variables are related by three equations (plus one or two graphs to define the nonlinear relations).

$$e_f = R_f i_f + \frac{d\lambda_f}{dt} \qquad \text{volts} \qquad (4.47)$$

$$e_a = K_a\phi v - L_a\frac{di_a}{dt} - R_a i_a \qquad \text{volts} \qquad (4.48)$$

$$T_{\text{shaft}} = K_a\phi i_a + J\frac{dv}{dt} + T_{\text{loss}} \qquad \text{newton-meters} \qquad (4.49)$$

$K_a\phi$ is related to the field current i_f by a graph such as the one in Fig. 4.16, and the field flux linkage λ_f is related to i_f by a similar graph.

If the machine is operated in the linear magnetic range, the three machine equations are

$$e_f = R_f i_f + L_f \frac{di_f}{dt} \quad \text{volts} \quad (4.50)$$

$$e_a = K_f i_f \nu - L_a \frac{di_a}{dt} - R_a i_a \quad \text{volts} \quad (4.51)$$

and

$$T_{\text{shaft}} = K_f i_f i_a + J \frac{d\nu}{dt} + T_{\text{loss}} \quad \text{newton-meters} \quad (4.52)$$

Note that the differential eqs. 4.51 and 4.52 are still mathematically nonlinear, since one term in each involves the product of two variables. If any of the variables i_f, i_a, or ν is constant, the term in the equations involving its derivative with time becomes zero. If all three variables are constant, the resultant equations describe the steady-state performance of the machine.

As there are six terminal variables in the system of Fig. 4.20, the three machine equations must be combined with three other equations to provide sufficient information for solution. These additional equations describe the terminal properties of the field source, the electrical system connected to the armature, and the mechanical system connected to the shaft. These equations depend upon the application of the machine. Specific examples are considered in Sections 4.5 and 4.6.

4.5 PERFORMANCE OF GENERATORS

Because of the wide variety of applications of d-c commutator machines, it is convenient to classify them as generators or motors, depending upon the dominant direction of energy flow.

Generators are further classified by the means used to provide excitation for the field windings. For a generator, the speed is determined by the characteristics of the prime mover. This speed may be essentially constant if the prime mover is a well-governed engine or a synchronous motor. Or the speed may be dependent on the shaft torque. In some situations it may be continuously variable.

The main analytical problems with generators are concerned with the determination and control of the armature terminal voltage for a specified electric load. When the speed, excitation, and load are all constant, the steady-state performance is of interest. But we are also concerned with the transient performance during the change from one steady state to another or when the excitation and load are continuously changing.

4.5.1 Separately Excited Generator

A separately excited generator system is one in which the source of the field current is external to the machine. This source may be another d-c generator, a rectifier, an electronic or magnetic amplifier, or it may be any d-c supply such as the battery shown in Fig. 4.22. This external field source is described by the equation

$$e_f = E_{fs} - R_e i_f \qquad \text{volts} \tag{4.53}$$

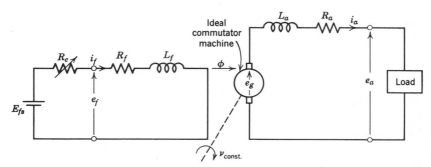

Fig. 4.22   Connections for separately excited generator.

whereas, in the steady state, the field circuit of the machine is described, from eq. 4.47, by

$$e_f = R_f i_f \tag{4.54}$$

Thus
$$i_f = \frac{E_{fs}}{R_e + R_f} \qquad \text{amperes} \tag{4.55}$$

The value of the steady-state field current in this system may be controlled by adjustment of either the source voltage E_{fs} or the series resistance R_e.

The generated voltage e_g is related to the field current and speed by a $K_a\phi/i_f$ curve, as shown in Fig. 4.23a. This curve may be obtained from an experimentally obtained characteristic of open-circuit armature voltage versus field current, by dividing the ordinate values by the speed v at which the test was made. Or the curve may be predicted from the dimensions and windings of the machine. The generated voltage is given by

$$e_g = K_a\phi v \qquad \text{volts} \tag{4.56}$$

Suppose the load on the armature circuit is a resistance described by

$$e_a = R_L i_a \tag{4.57}$$

In the steady state with i_f, v, and i_a all constant, the armature circuit is described (from eq. 4.48) by

$$e_a = K_a\phi v - R_a i_a \qquad (4.58)$$

Thus

$$i_a = \frac{K_a\phi v}{R_a + R_L} \quad \text{amperes} \qquad (4.59)$$

Instead of determining the load current for each value of load, the e_a/i_a relation of eq. 4.58 (with i_f and v held constant) may be displayed graphically. This is known as a terminal or external characteristic of the

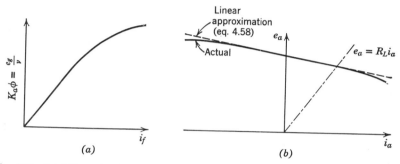

Fig. 4.23 (a) Magnetization characteristic giving generated voltage e_g per unit of speed v as function of field current i_f. (b) Terminal or external characteristic of separately excited generator with constant speed and field current.

generator. A typical characteristic is shown in Fig. 4.23b. If a load characteristic—such as the one in eq. 4.57—is drawn on the same graph, the point of its intersection with the terminal characteristic of the machine gives the operating values of e_a and i_a.

Equation 4.58 indicates that the terminal voltage of a separately excited generator drops linearly with increase in load current because of the armature circuit resistance. At high values of armature current, an additional drop in terminal voltage may occur, as shown in Fig. 4.23b. This results from a reduction in the flux ϕ caused by the saturating effect of the armature magnetomotive force (see Section 4.4.3). This effect can often be neglected for armature currents below the rated value.

Under certain circumstances, the load may become an electrical source causing the machine to operate as a motor. Figure 4.23b shows that the terminal characteristic with reversed armature current i_a is represented adequately by eq. 4.58 for the major part of the current range. With high values of armature current, the flux and the generated voltage may be reduced by the saturating effect of the armature magnetomotive force.

The analysis of the generator performance under transient conditions involves the solution of differential equations that may be nonlinear. As an example, consider the application of a source voltage E_{fs} to the field terminals of Fig. 4.22 at $t = 0$ with $R_e = 0$. The field circuit is described for $t \geq 0$ by

$$E_{fs} = R_f i_f + \frac{d\lambda_f}{dt} \qquad \text{volts} \qquad (4.60)$$

where the flux linkage λ_f is related to the field current i_f by a curve of the form shown in Fig. 4.24a. Numerical techniques, such as the one described

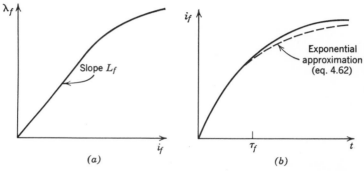

Fig. 4.24 (a) Flux linkage λ_f related to field current i_f. (b) Field current transient obtained by numerical analysis or experiment compared with linearized approximation.

in Section 2.1.1, may be used to determine the time variation of the field current i_f. If the final steady state is within the reasonably linear range of the λ_f / i_f characteristic, eq. 4.60 may be replaced by the linear equation

$$E_{fs} = R_f i_f + L_f \frac{di_f}{dt} \qquad (4.61)$$

from which the field current is

$$i_f = \frac{E_{fs}}{R_f} (1 - \epsilon^{-t/\tau_f}) \qquad \text{amperes} \qquad (4.62)$$

The field time constant is

$$\tau_f = \frac{L_f}{R_f} \qquad \text{seconds} \qquad (4.63)$$

This time constant ranges in value from several seconds for large machines to a few hundredths of a second for small machines.

If the linear approximation is used when the final steady state is beyond the linear range of Fig. 4.24a, the exponential solution of eq. 4.62 will be reasonably accurate for values of field current within the linear range only. Figure 4.24b shows a comparison of the results of a numerical analysis of eq. 4.60 with the solution of eq. 4.62 for such a case. It is noted that magnetic saturation causes the current to approach its final steady state more rapidly than would occur in the linear region.

Suppose a load R_L is connected to the armature terminals of a constant-speed machine and a variable voltage e_f is applied to the field terminals. Assuming magnetic linearity, we may describe the system by the equations

$$e_f = R_f i_f + L_f \frac{di_f}{dt} \tag{4.64}$$

$$e_a = K_f i_f v - L_a \frac{di_a}{dt} - R_a i_a \tag{4.65}$$

and

$$e_a = R_L i_a \tag{4.66}$$

Since these equations are linear, the relationship between the Laplace transformer $e_{a(s)}$ of the load voltage and $e_{f(s)}$ of the field voltage may be expressed simply in operational form using the complex frequency variable s. From eqs. 4.64, 4.65, and 4.66, we have

$$e_{a(s)} = \frac{R_L}{R_L + R_a} \frac{K_f v}{R_f} \frac{1}{(1 + s\tau_f)(1 + s\tau_a)} e_{f(s)} \tag{4.67}$$

where $\tau_a = L_a/(R_a + R_L)$ is the armature-circuit time constant. Figure 4.25a shows a block diagram representation of the relationship of eq. 4.67.

If a constant voltage $e_f = E_{fs}$ is applied to the field circuit at $t = 0$, the solution of eq. 4.67 for the terminal voltage is

$$e_a = \frac{R_L K_f v E_{fs}}{(R_L + R_a)R_f}\left(1 - \frac{\tau_f}{\tau_f - \tau_a}\epsilon^{-t/\tau_f} + \frac{\tau_a}{\tau_f - \tau_a}\epsilon^{-t/\tau_a}\right) \tag{4.68}$$

Figure 4.25b shows a typical curve of this terminal voltage transient. Because of the relatively large value of the load resistance R_L, the armature time constant τ_a is normally much smaller than the field constant τ_f. For comparison, the solution neglecting the armature time constant is also shown in Fig. 4.25b. Note that the effect of the armature time constant τ_a is to delay the buildup of the terminal voltage by a time of approximately τ_a.

In control systems it is often derirable for the output voltage of a generator to be proportional to the sum or difference of a number of voltages or currents. If the main poles of the generator are provided with several sets of field windings, the magnetomotive forces caused by the various signal currents in these windings are summed within the machine. An advantage of this method of summation is that no conductive connection is required between the sources of the field currents. In addition, a different number of turns can be chosen for each input current.

A separately excited generator can be considered as a power amplifier. Suppose a variable voltage e_f is applied to the field terminals in Fig. 4.22. The terminal voltage e_a is proportional to the input voltage e_f in the linear

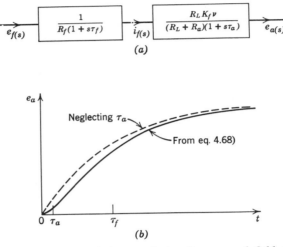

(a)

(b)

Fig. 4.25 (a) Block diagram relating terminal voltage e_a and field voltage e_f. (b) Terminal voltage buildup after a constant voltage is applied to the field.

steady state, the voltage amplication being $R_L K_f v / (R_L + R_a) R_f$, from eq. 4.67. In the transient state, the output variation is delayed with respect to the input variation by the effect of the time constants τ_f and τ_a. The power required by the field circuit of a d-c machine is generally about 0.5–5% of the rated output power, lower values applying for machines of higher rating. Thus the power amplification of the generator is generally in the range of 20–200. If a resistance is added to the field circuit, the field time constant is reduced and the generator responds more rapidly to changes in its field circuit voltage. The power amplification is also reduced. It can be shown that the ratio of the power amplification to the field circuit time constant is unchanged.

An alternating-voltage output can be provided by a separately excited generator if the voltage applied to the field circuit is alternating. The maximum frequency ω of operation is limited, however, mainly by the field time constant τ_f. Setting $s = j\omega$ in eq. 4.67 to obtain the sinusoidal response, and neglecting the armature time constant τ_a, we note that the voltage amplication is reduced to $1/\sqrt{2}$ of its maximum value at a frequency of $\omega = 1/\tau_f$ radians per second. Since field time constants range from about 0.02–2 seconds, the maximum useable frequency is normally about 0.1–10 cycles per second.

4.5.2 Separately Excited Generator with Series Field[•]

The terminal voltage of a separately excited generator decreases as the load current is increased, as shown in Fig. 4.23b. Suppose we wish to maintain the terminal voltage more or less constant as the load is changed.

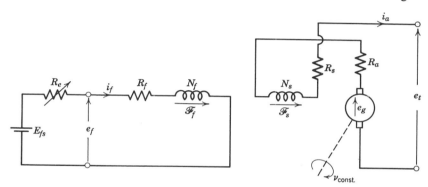

Fig. 4.26. Separately excited generator with series field.

This can be accomplished by increasing the flux ϕ in eq. 4.58 by an amount that is proportional to the current i_a. This may be achieved, as shown in Fig. 4.26, by passing the armature current i_a through series field windings placed on the main poles of the machine.

Suppose the flux ϕ per pole is related to the magnetomotive force on each pole by the curve of Fig. 4.27a. Let the number of turns per pole of the main and series field windings be N_f and N_s, respectively. The total magnetomotive force per pole is then given by

$$\mathscr{F}_p = \mathscr{F}_f + \mathscr{F}_s$$
$$= N_f i_f + N_s i_a \qquad \text{amperes} \qquad (4.69)$$

At any value of load current i_a, the appropriate value of the flux ϕ may be found from the curve.

Experimentally, the curve that can be measured most readily for a machine is the open-circuit voltage at a constant speed v as a function of

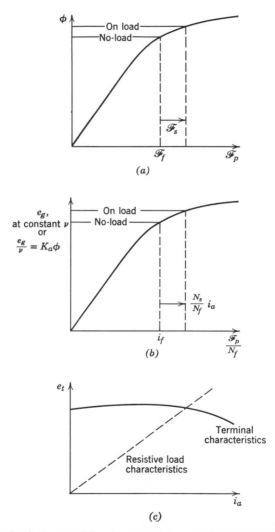

Fig. 4.27. The load characteristic of a separately excited generator with series field.

the main field current i_f, as shown in Fig. 4.27b. This curve may be used by dividing eq. 4.69 by N_f to give

$$\frac{\mathscr{F}_p}{N_f} = i_f + \frac{N_s}{N_f} i_a \qquad \text{amperes} \qquad (4.70)$$

The quantity $\mathscr{F}_p/N_f$ is the equivalent current in the main field that would produce as much magnetomotive force as the combined main and series fields. When the generated voltage e_g or the quantity $K_a\phi$ has been determined from the curve for a particular value of load current i_a, the terminal voltage in the steady state is

$$e_a = K_a\phi v - (R_a + R_s)i_a \qquad \text{volts} \qquad (4.71)$$

where R_s is the resistance of the series field circuit.

If the machine is operated in the range of magnetic linearity where, from eq. 4.26,

$$K_a\phi = K_f\left(i_f + \frac{N_s}{N_f} i_a\right) \qquad (4.72)$$

the terminal voltage may be made to rise or fall linearly as the load current is increased. If we have

$$\frac{N_s}{N_f} = \frac{R_a + R_s}{K_f v} \qquad (4.73)$$

the terminal voltage in the steady state is independent of the load current.

When the machine is operated in the magnetically nonlinear region, the number of series field turns can be chosen to produce the same terminal voltage at no load and one particular value of load. A typical terminal characteristic is shown in Fig. 4.27c.

The transient equations for a magnetically linear, separately excited generator with a series field are

$$e_f = R_f i_f + L_f \frac{di_f}{dt} + L_{fs} \frac{di_a}{dt} \qquad (4.74)$$

and, from eqs. 4.71 and 4.72,

$$e_t = K_f i_f v + \left(K_f \frac{N_s}{N_f} v - R_a - R_s\right)i_a - (L_a + L_s)\frac{di_a}{dt} - L_{fs}\frac{di_f}{dt} \qquad (4.75)$$

where L_s is the self-inductance of the series field winding and L_{fs} is the mutual inductance between the main and series field windings. Since the coupling between these two windings is essentially perfect,

$$L_s \approx \left(\frac{N_s}{N_f}\right)^2 L_f \qquad \text{henrys} \qquad (4.76)$$

and

$$L_{fs} \approx (L_s L_f)^{\frac{1}{2}} \qquad \text{henrys} \qquad (4.77)$$

If a generator has a terminal voltage that rises as the terminal current is increased, there are certain types of loads it cannot supply stably. Suppose the generator of Fig. 4.26 is supplying power to a storage battery which can be represented by the load equation

$$e_t = R_b i_a + E_b \tag{4.78}$$

For simplicity, let us assume that the field current i_f remains constant after the generator is connected to the battery load at $t = 0$. Combining eqs. 4.75 and 4.78, we obtain

$$(L_a + L_s)\frac{di_a}{dt} + \left(R_a + R_s + R_b - K_f \frac{N_s}{N_f} v\right) i_a = K_f i_f v - E_b \tag{4.79}$$

Expressed in operational form, the transform of the load current is given by

$$i_{a(s)} = \frac{K_f i_f v - E_b}{\left(R_a + R_s + R_b - K_f \dfrac{N_s}{N_f} v\right)(1 + s\tau)s} \qquad \text{amperes} \tag{4.80}$$

where the effective time constant τ is

$$\tau = \frac{L_a + L_s}{\left(R_a + R_s + R_b - K_f \dfrac{K_s}{N_f} v\right)} \qquad \text{seconds} \tag{4.81}$$

If this time constant is positive, the load current approaches its steady-state value in a decaying exponential transient. But if

$$\left(K_f \frac{N_s}{N_f} v\right) > (R_a + R_s + R_b) \tag{4.82}$$

the load current transient is characterized by an increasing exponential. Thus to operate stably, it is necessary that the slope R_b of the load characteristic (eq. 4.78) be greater than the slope of the steady-state terminal characteristic, that is

$$R_b > \left(N_f \frac{N_s}{N_f} v - R_a - R_s\right) \tag{4.83}$$

Examination of Fig. 4.27c shows that this condition is met if the load is a simple resistance.

4.5.3 Self-Excited or Shunt Generator

The separately excited generator requires an external source of direct current which may not always be readily available. Since the armature produces a voltage, let us examine the possibility of using this as a source for the required field current.

Suppose the machine of Fig. 4.28a is operated at constant speed v and that its generated voltage e_g is related to the field current i_f by the curve of Fig. 4.28b. Because of the hysteresis in the magnetic material of the machine, there may be a residual flux producing a generated voltage e_{go} at $i_f = 0$. The field circuit, containing an adjustable resistance R_e, may then be connected across the armature terminals in such a way that the field current that flows tends to increase the flux. If there is no load connected to the armature, the buildup of the field current is governed by the equation

$$e_g = (R_f + R_e + R_a)i_f + \frac{d\lambda_f}{dt} \qquad\qquad (4.84)$$

where the field flux linkage λ_f is related to the field current by a curve similar in shape to the $e_g - i_f$ curve. Rearranging eq. 4.84 into the form

$$\frac{d\lambda_f}{dt} = e_g - (R_f + R_e + R_a)i_f \qquad\qquad (4.85)$$

we note that the rate of increase of field flux linkage is proportional to the difference between the generated voltage e_g for the value of field current flowing and the voltage drop in the circuit resistance. As long as the generated voltage curve in Fig. 4.28b is above the straight line representing the drop in the field circuit resistance, the field flux (and consequently the generated voltage) continues to rise. Steady state is reached at the intersection point p of the two curves; at this point, the voltage generated is just sufficient to produce a steady flow of the required field current through the circuit resistance. The rate of voltage buildup with time may be predicted by use of the numerical method introduced in Section 2.1.1. A typical curve is shown in Fig. 4.28c. The time required for voltage buildup is considerably longer than for a separately excited machine.

The steady-state terminal voltage on no-load can be controlled over a limited range by adjusting the value of the series resistance R_e in the field circuit. As R_e is increased, the intersection point p in Fig. 4.28b moves down the open-circuit curve. If the resistance is made too large, the intersection occurs at a point that is only slightly greater than the residual voltage e_{go}. The value of resistance that causes the resistance line in Fig. 4.28b to lie along the approximately linear part of the magnetization curve is known as the critical field circuit resistance.

When a load is connected to the terminals of the generator of Fig. 4.28a, the terminal voltage e_t is reduced because of the drop across the resistance R_a. This causes a reduction in the field current i_f, which in turn causes a further reduction in the generated and terminal voltages. The new

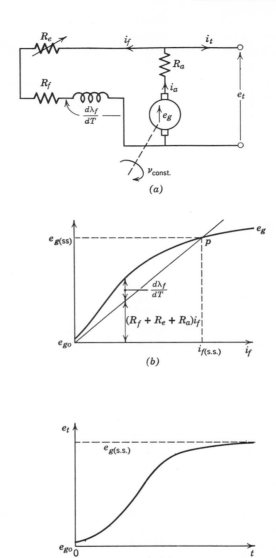

Fig. 4.28 (*a*) Self-excited generator. (*b*) Buildup and final steady state of generated voltage. (*c*) Typical terminal voltage transient during buildup.

steady-state operating point is governed by the equations

$$e_t = e_g - R_a i_a \qquad (4.86)$$

and

$$e_t = (R_f + R_e)i_f \qquad (4.87)$$

plus the nonlinear magnetization curve relating e_g and i_f. As shown in Fig. 4.29a, the steady-state terminal voltage e_t for a given armature current i_a has a value such that the field current i_f that flows (eq. 4.87) produces a generated voltage e_g (from the magnetization curve), which is $R_a i_a$ greater than e_t (eq. 4.86). The armature current i_a, which corresponds

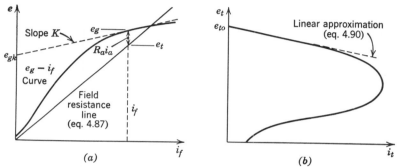

(a)   (b)

Fig. 4.29   (a) Determination of the terminal characteristic (b) of a self-excited or shunt generator.

to any value of terminal voltage e_t, may therefore be found by dividing the vertical distance between the magnetization and field resistance curves in Fig. 4.29a by R_a. The terminal current i_t is

$$i_t = i_a - i_f \qquad (4.88)$$

Figure 4.29b shows a typical terminal characteristic for a self-excited generator. Note that the maximum steady-state terminal current is limited by the maximum vertical separation between the magnetization and field resistance curves. If the field resistance is increased to decrease the no-load terminal voltage, the maximum terminal current is considerably reduced.

The linear portion of the terminal characteristic of Fig. 4.29b may be predicted analytically by approximating the magnetization curve of Fig. 4.29a by the equation

$$e_g = e_{gk} + Ki_f \qquad (4.89)$$

Substitution of eqs. 4.89, 4.88, and 4.87 into eq. 4.86 gives the relation

$$e_t = \frac{e_{gk} - R_a i_t}{1 - (K - R_a)/(R_f + R_e)}$$

$$= e_{to} - \left[\frac{R_a}{1 - (K - R_a)/(R_f + R_e)}\right] i_t \qquad (4.90)$$

Comparison of this relation with that of a separately excited generator (eq. 4.58) shows that the voltage drop with load is greater for the self-excited generator by an amount that depends on the relative values of the slope K and the field circuit resistance $R_f + R_e$. It is therefore advantageous to design a self-excited generator to have an abrupt saturation in its magnetic circuit and to operate the generator well into the saturated region.

4.5.4 Compound Self-Excited Generator

The large voltage drop on load of a self-excited generator can be counteracted by the addition of a series field winding, as shown in Fig. 4.30a. The result is known as a cumulatively compounded generator. Although the action of the series field is essentially the same as in the separately excited generator with series field (Section 4.5.2), the prediction of performance for the compound generator is somewhat more involved.

Figure 4.30b shows the magnetization and field resistance curves for the machine. The generated voltage e_g is a function of the main field current i_f plus N_s/N_f times the armature current i_a (eq. 4.70). Suppose we approximate the magnetization curve in the region about the point of no-load operation by the straight line

$$e_g = e_{gk} + K\left(i_f + \frac{N_s}{N_f}i_a\right) \tag{4.91}$$

The terminal voltage in the steady state is given by

$$e_t = e_g - (R_a + R_s)i_a \tag{4.92}$$

where

$$i_a = i_t + i_f \tag{4.93}$$

and

$$i_f = \frac{e_t}{R_f + R_e} \tag{4.94}$$

Elimination of all variables but e_t and i_t from eqs. 4.91 to 4.94 gives the following relation for the terminal characteristic.

$$e_t = \frac{e_{gk} + [K(N_s/N_f) - (R_a + R_s)]i_t}{1 - \dfrac{K + K(N_s/N_f) - (R_a + R_s)}{R_f + R_e}} \tag{4.95}$$

From this relation it is seen that the terminal voltage e_t may be made independent of the load current i_t by making

$$K\frac{N_s}{N_f} = R_a + R_s \tag{4.96}$$

Then

$$e_t = \frac{e_{gk}}{1 - [K/(R_f + R_e)]} = e_{to} \tag{4.97}$$

If the number of series field turns is increased beyond the value given in eq. 4.96, the terminal voltage rises as the load current is increased. This

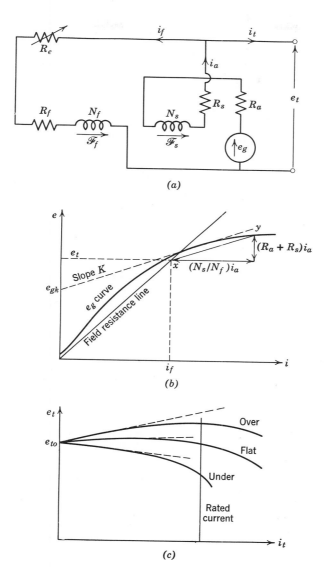

Fig. 4.30   (a) Compound self-excited generator. (b) Construction for determining the terminal characteristic. (c) Typical terminal characteristic for overcompounded, flat compounded, and undercompounded generators. The straight dashed lines represent the approximation of eq. 4.95.

effect is sometimes desired when the load is remote from the generator, since the voltage drop in the connecting transmission line can be compensated by the rise in the terminal voltage of the generator.

In contrast with the self-excited shunt generator of Section 4.5.3, it is preferable to have a gradual rather than an abrupt saturation in the magnetic system of a compound generator. Examination of eq. 4.96 shows that the number of series field turns required is inversely proportional to the slope K. It is, however, necessary that the slope K be sufficiently less than the field circuit resistance $R_f + R_s$ so that a stable no-load operating point is established.

The range of application of the terminal relation of eq. 4.95 is limited since it is dependent on the linearization of eq. 4.91. The terminal characteristic may be derived graphically from Fig. 4.30b if a prediction over a wider load range is required. Suppose the machine is to operate at the terminal voltage e_t and field current i_f of the point x. With an armature current i_a, the effective magnetization of the machine is dependent on $[i_f + (N_s/N_f)i_a]$. This magnetization produces a generated voltage e_g, which must be $(R_a + R_s)i_a$ volts above the terminal voltage e_t (eq. 4.92) and must be at a point y on the magnetization curve. The armature current i_a that fulfills this requirement may be found by drawing a line xy of slope $(R_a + R_s)/(N_s/N_f)$ from a point x, where the terminal voltage is e_t. The length of this line is proportional to the armature current i_a that flows at this value of terminal voltage. Lines of the same slope may be drawn from different points x on the field resistance line to find corresponding values of armature current.

Figure 4.30c shows typical terminal characteristics for compound generators. When the terminal voltage at rated current is equal to the no-load voltage, the generator is said to be flat compounded. With overcompounding, the terminal voltage at rated load is greater than at no-load. Undercompounding results in a terminal characteristic that is somewhere between the flat compounded case and that of a simple shunt generator.

If a generator has sufficient series field turns to provide overcompounding, the degree of compounding may be reduced in the steady state by shunting the series field circuit with a suitable resistor, thus bypassing part of the current.

A differentially compounded generator is one in which the series field connections of Fig. 4.30a are reversed. The terminal characteristic of this generator is of the same general shape as that of a shunt generator (Fig. 4.29b) but with a reduced value of maximum terminal current. It finds a limited field of application with loads that are frequently short circuited, such as welders.

4.5.5 Parallel Operation of Generators

It is occasionally necessary to operate two or more generators in parallel to supply a common load. An example is found in a multiengined aircraft that has a generator coupled to each of its engines. In parallel operation, the major question is whether the generators will share the load stably and equally if they are similar, or in the proper proportion if they are different in rating.

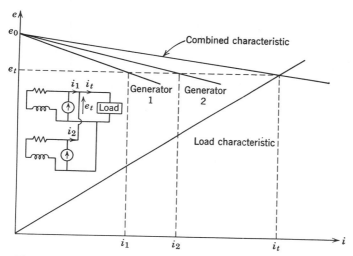

Fig. 4.31 Division of load between two parallel shunt generators.

Figure 4.31 shows the steady-state terminal characteristics of two shunt or undercompounded generators delivering currents i_1 and i_2. The resistances of the shunt field circuit have been adjusted to provide equal voltages at no-load. When they are connected in parallel, the generators have a common terminal voltage e_t, and the load current i_t is

$$i_t = i_1 + i_2 \qquad (4.98)$$

As shown in Fig. 4.31, the operating point of a load occurs at the intersection of the load characteristic with the terminal characteristic of the paralleled generators. The current taken by each generator is the value corresponding to the common terminal voltage e_t. If the machines do not share the load in proportion to their ratings, the terminal characteristics may be changed by changing the compounding or by adding series resistance to one of the machines.

The terminal characteristics of Fig. 4.31 apply only for the steady state. To demonstrate the stability of the parallel arrangement, it is necessary to consider the transient behavior. In the transient state, the terminal voltage-current relationship may be expressed as

$$e_{10} - L_1 \frac{di_1}{dt} - R_1 i_1 = e_t \tag{4.99}$$

and

$$e_{20} - L_2 \frac{di_2}{dt} - R_2 i_2 = e_t \tag{4.100}$$

where e_{10} and e_{20} are the no-load voltages of the two machines, L_1 and L_2 are the effective internal inductances, and R_1 and R_2 are equal to the negative slopes of the steady-state terminal characteristics of Fig. 4.31.

For simplicity let us consider the case when the net load is zero, $i_t = 0$. When the two machines are connected in parallel with slightly different values of no-load voltages e_{10} and e_{20}, rearrangement of eqs. 4.99 and 4.100, with $i_1 = -i_2$, gives

$$(L_1 + L_2) \frac{di_1}{dt} + (R_1 + R_2) i_1 = e_{10} - e_{20} \tag{4.101}$$

The solution of eq. 4.101 shows that the current i_1 approaches a small steady-state value in a transient, which is characterized by a decaying exponential of time constant τ where

$$\tau = \frac{L_1 + L_2}{R_1 + R_2} \tag{4.102}$$

The system is therefore stable.

In contrast, suppose two overcompounded generators are connected in parallel. The transient terminal relations for these are of the form

$$e_{10} - L_1 \frac{di_1}{dt} + R_1 i_1 = e_t \tag{4.103}$$

and

$$e_{20} - L_2 \frac{di_2}{dt} + R_2 i_2 = e_t \tag{4.104}$$

where R_1 and R_2 are the positive slopes of the steady-state terminal characteristics of the two machines. Under the same no-load conditions as before

$$(L_1 + L_2) \frac{di_1}{dt} - (R_1 + R_2) i_1 = e_{10} - e_{20} \tag{4.105}$$

The solution of this equation includes an increasing exponential of time constant τ where τ is given in eq. 4.102. The current of one machine increases exponentially, operating as a generator; the current of the other increases exponentially in the opposite direction, operating as a motor.

Two overcompounded generators may be operated in parallel successfully if their series fields are connected in parallel. The load current then divides between the two series fields in inverse proportion to their resistances in the steady state or in inverse proportion to their operational impedances in the transient state. On no-load, the machines operate as two shunt generators in parallel.

4.5.6 Voltage Control

Shunt and compound generators are generally used in situations where an essentially constant voltage is required for a load or for a d-c distribution system, for example, laboratory, automobile, aircraft. If the speed of the prime mover is relatively constant, the terminal voltage of a shunt generator—or more particularly a compound generator—may be sufficiently constant for some applications. But if the prime mover speed is not accurately controlled, auxiliary means are necessary to regulate the output voltage. The field resistance can, of course, be adjusted manually as the speed or load vary, or, one of a number of types of automatic voltage regulator may be employed. These regulators differ primarily in the means used to adjust the resistance in the main field circuit. In some types, an electromechanical relay is used to short out a section of the external resistance when the voltage is too low and to reinsert it when the voltage is too high. In others, an electromechanical actuator adjusts the contact point on a rheostat or varies the pressure on a pressure-sensitive rheostat.

Separately excited generators are used when a continuously variable or reversible terminal voltage is required. In these situations, the generator is used as a power amplifier, and the important features are the accuracy and speed with which the terminal voltage follows changes in the signal voltage applied to the field circuit.

The transient relationship between the terminal voltage e_t and the field voltage e_f of a separately excited generator was developed in Section 4.5.1. Neglecting the armature-circuit time constant τ_a in eq. 4.67, the operational form of this relation for a magnetically linear generator is

$$e_{t(s)} = \frac{R_L}{R_L + R_a} \frac{K_f v}{R_f} \frac{1}{1 + s\tau_f} e_{f(s)} \qquad (4.106)$$

The steady-state voltage amplification of the generator depends upon the speed v, which may vary as the torque varies. It is also dependent on the load resistance R_L, which may not be constant. Because of magnetic nonlinearity, the effective value of K_f may change appreciably causing a proportional change in the e_t/e_f ratio. In the transient state, the time variation of the output voltage is delayed with respect to the input voltage signal because of the field time constant τ_f. All of these effects reduce the accuracy with which the terminal voltage reproduces, proportionally, the form of the voltage signal applied to the field.

The accuracy and speed of response can be improved considerably if the generator is incorporated in a closed-loop feedback system, as shown in Fig. 4.32. In this system it is desired that the load voltage e_t be pro-

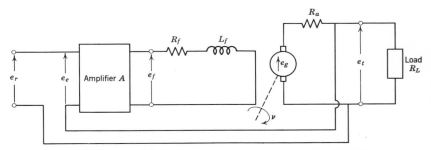

Fig. 4.32　A closed-loop system for voltage control of a generator.

portional to an input voltage signal e_r. The difference or error between the desired voltage e_r and the actual terminal voltage e_t is

$$e_e = e_r - e_t \tag{4.107}$$

This error voltage e_e is applied to the input of a power amplifier, which may be of electronic or magnetic type, or may be another separately excited generator. Let us assume that the amplifier is linear and has no significant time constants. Then

$$e_f = Ae_e \tag{4.108}$$

where A is the voltage amplification of the amplifier. Combining eqs. 4.108 and 4.106, the terminal voltage is related to the error voltage by the transfer function

$$e_{t(s)} = \frac{K}{1 + s\tau_f}\, e_{e(s)} \tag{4.109}$$

where

$$K = \frac{AR_L K_f v}{(R_L + R_a)R_f} \tag{4.110}$$

From eqs. 4.107 and 4.109, the operational relationship between the actual and desired load voltage is

$$e_{t(s)} = \frac{K}{K + 1}\, \frac{1}{(1 + s\tau')}\, e_{r(s)} \tag{4.111}$$

where

$$\tau' = \tau_f/(K + 1) \tag{4.112}$$

The overall voltage amplification K may be made much greater than unity by appropriate choice of the amplification A. Comparison of eqs. 4.111 and 4.106 shows that the effective time constant of the closed-loop system is much lower than that of the generator alone. In addition if $K \gg 1$, the ratio of e_t to e_r in eq. 4.111 for the steady state becomes essentially independent of the value of K. Thus, the accuracy of voltage control is only slightly affected by changes in speed, load, voltage amplification A, or in K_f caused by magnetic nonlinearity.

It might appear from eq. 4.111 that this voltage control system could be made perfect by continued increase of the amplification K. There are, however, several limitations in a practical system. One such is the maximum voltage $\hat{e}_f$ that the amplifier can produce. The maximum rate of change with time of the field current is therefore $\hat{e}_f/L_f$. Another limitation arises from the fact that the other time constants in the armature circuit and the amplifier become significant as the speed of response of the system is increased. An excessive value of K then leads to oscillation in the output voltage.

4.5.7 Cross-Field Generators

The power amplification of a separately excited generator is normally in the range of 20 to 200. Where a higher power amplification is required, two generators may be used in tandem, the first providing the field power of the second. An attractive alternative to this arrangement is a cross-field generator that combines the properties obtainable from two tandem generators into one machine.

To visualize the action of a cross-field generator, let us begin with the simple two-pole generator shown in Fig. 4.33a. A small magnetomotive

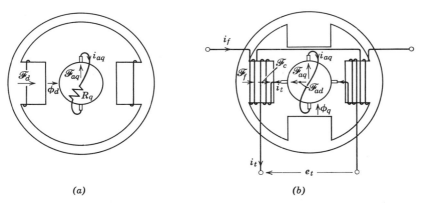

(a)   (b)

Fig. 4.33   The evolution of cross-field machines. (a) Two-pole generator with shorted armature. (b) Compensated cross-field generator.

force on the poles of this generator produces enough flux and generated voltage to cause a large current i_{aq} to flow in the short-circuited armature path. In most commutator machines the magnetomotive force $\mathscr{F}_{aq}$ this current produces would be regarded as a nuisance. In the cross-field machine it is exploited by placing poles in the quadrature axis so that it can establish a flux ϕ_q, as shown in Fig. 4.33b. Rotation of the armature through this flux ϕ_q causes a generated voltage in the armature circuit between two additional brushes placed in the direct axis of the machine. Thus, a large output voltage can be produced with very little excitation from the main field coils. When a load is connected to the output, the resultant magnetomotive force $\mathscr{F}_{ad}$ from the load current in the armature acts to oppose the main field. This effect may be counteracted by use of a series or compensating winding in the main poles.

Now let us examine the generator performance analytically. A magnetomotive force $\mathscr{F}_d$ per pole in the direct axis of the machine produces a flux ϕ_d in the main poles of

$$\phi_d = \frac{\mathscr{F}_d}{\mathscr{R}_g} \qquad \text{webers} \qquad (4.113)$$

where, assuming magnetic linearity, $\mathscr{R}_g$ is the reluctance of an air gap. From eq. 4.23 with $p = 2$ and $a = 2$, the generated voltage e_{gq} in the armature circuit between the shorted brushes is

$$e_{gq} = \frac{N\nu}{\pi} \phi_d \qquad \text{volts} \qquad (4.114)$$

where N is the number of armature turns and ν is the speed. If R_q is the resistance of the shorted armature circuit, and L_q is its inductance, the short-circuit current is given in operational form by

$$i_{aq(s)} = \frac{1}{R_q(1 + s\tau_q)} e_{gq(s)} \qquad \text{amperes} \qquad (4.115)$$

where $\tau_q = L_q/R_q$. The magnetomotive force $\mathscr{F}_{aq}$ per pole that this armature current produces in the quadrature axis is, from eq. 4.32,

$$\mathscr{F}_{aq} = \frac{N}{2} \frac{i_{aq}}{2} \qquad \text{amperes/pole} \qquad (4.116)$$

and, if all poles are similar,

$$\phi_q = \frac{\mathscr{F}_{aq}}{\mathscr{R}_g} \qquad \text{webers} \qquad (4.117)$$

The generated voltage e_{gd} produced by this flux in the output circuit is

$$e_{gd} = \frac{N\nu}{\pi} \phi_q \qquad \text{volts} \qquad (4.118)$$

The no-load output voltage is therefore related to the field current i_f in the main field coils of N_f turns by combining eqs. 4.113 to 4.118 (with $\mathscr{F}_d = N_f i_f$) to give

$$e_{gd(s)} = \frac{K}{1 + s\tau_q}\, i_{f(s)} \qquad \text{volts} \qquad (4.119)$$

where

$$K = \frac{N^3 v^2 N_f}{4\pi^2 \mathscr{R}_g{}^2 R_q} \qquad \text{volts/ampere} \qquad (4.120)$$

The shape of the no-load magnetization characteristics is similar to that of a normal generator.

Suppose a load of resistance R_L is connected to the output terminals. If the output circuit of the generator has an internal resistance of R_d, the load current is

$$i_t = \frac{e_{gd}}{R_d + R_L} \qquad \text{amperes} \qquad (4.121)$$

The time constant arising from the inductance of this armature circuit has been neglected, partly because the load resistance is normally large and partly because the inductance is made very small by the action of the compensating winding.

The load current i_t produces a magnetomotive force $\mathscr{F}_{ad}$ per pole of

$$\mathscr{F}_{ad} = \frac{Ni_t}{4} \qquad \text{amperes/pole} \qquad (4.122)$$

which can be essentially canceled by an opposing magnetomotive force produced by placing compensating windings of $N/4$ turns, carrying the load current i_t, on each of the two direct-axis poles. Moreover, this effectively eliminates any magnetic coupling between the main or control field circuit and the output circuit.

If the field resistance is R_f and its inductance is L_f, the field current is related to the field voltage by

$$i_{f(s)} = \frac{1}{R_f(1 + s\tau_f)}\, e_{f(s)} \qquad \text{amperes} \qquad (4.123)$$

where $\tau_f = L_f/R_f$. From eqs. 4.119 and 4.123, the terminal voltage e_t, with load resistance R_L, is related to the control field voltage by

$$e_{t(s)} = \frac{R_L}{R_d + R_L}\frac{K}{R_f}\frac{1}{(1 + s\tau_q)(1 + s\tau_f)}\, e_{f(s)} \qquad \text{volts} \qquad (4.124)$$

The steady-state power amplification of this fully compensated cross-field generator* is

$$\frac{P_t}{P_f} = \frac{e_t^2/R_L}{e_f^2/R_f} \approx \frac{K^2 R_f}{R_L} \qquad (4.125)$$

assuming $R_L \gg R_d$.

A typical value of power amplification is about 10,000, comparable to the product of the amplifications of two normal generators. The most important time constant is τ_q associated with the quadrature axis. The armature circuit in this axis has a low resistance R_q and its inductance is significant because of the presence of the quadrature-axis poles. Typical values of this time constant are in the range 0.02 to 0.2 second. Because the power amplification is so high, the control field coil requires much less space than in a normal generator. The use of smaller conductors increases its resistance without changing its inductance. Thus the field time constant τ_f is generally much less than τ_q and may often be neglected.

If a cross-field generator is used without a compensating coil, its terminal characteristics are quite different from those of a compensated machine. From eq. 4.119, the generated voltage in the output circuit is

$$e_{gd(s)} = \frac{K}{N_f} \frac{1}{(1 + s\tau_q)} \mathscr{F}_{d(s)} \qquad \text{volts} \qquad (4.126)$$

The magnetomotive force $\mathscr{F}_d$ per pole on the direct axis is the difference between the control-field magnetomotive force and $\mathscr{F}_{ad}$ in eq. 4.122

$$\mathscr{F}_d = N_f i_f - \frac{N}{4} i_t \qquad (4.127)$$

If eqs. 4.121, 4.126, and 4.127 are combined, the load current i_t is related to the field current i_f by

$$i_{t(s)} = \frac{4(N_f/N)}{\left[1 + \dfrac{4N_f(R_d + R_L)}{NK}\right]\left\{1 + \dfrac{s\tau_q}{1 + [NK/4N_f(R_d + R_L)]}\right\}} i_{f(s)} \qquad (4.128)$$

Unless the load resistance R_L is very high,

$$R_d + R_L \ll \frac{NK}{4N_f} \qquad (4.129)$$

and the generator behaves as a current source with an output current proportional to its field current. As the field current is increased, the load

* Known by the trade name Amplidyne, patented by General Electric Co.

current increases proportionally until the terminal voltage is limited by magnetic saturation. A typical characteristic is shown in Fig. 4.34.

From eqs. 4.128 and 4.129 it can be seen that the effective time constant of the uncompensated cross-field generator* is much lower than the time constant τ_q of the compensated machine (eq. 4.124). But since the magnetomotive force of the control field must equal the magnetomotive force of the armature output circuit, the power amplification is much lower than in a compensated machine and is about the same as for a normal generator.

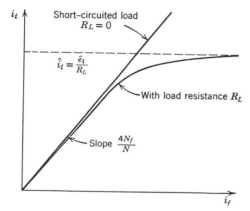

Fig. 4.34 Relation between load current i_t and field current i_f for an uncompensated cross-field generator.

To provide proper commutation in a cross-field machine, it is necessary to introduce interpoles in the centers of the main poles. The magnetic system of a practical cross-field machine is thus somewhat more complex than the one shown in Fig. 4.33b. The compensating winding is sometimes distributed in pole-face slots so that its magnetomotive force distribution will more nearly approximate that of the armature. It is normal to provide several control field windings, possibly with different current ratings, to allow for the summation of a number of input signals.

4.6 PERFORMANCE OF MOTORS

In the study of motors our interest is focused on the relations governing the torque and speed. The extensive use of commutator motors derives from the wide range of accurate speed and torque control that they can provide. In contrast, the synchronous and induction motors (to be discussed in Chapter 5) are essentially constant-speed machines.

* Known as metadyne.

Figure 4.35 shows an equivalent circuit of a commutator or direct-current machine. For convenience in discussing motors, the assigned direction of the armature current i_a has been chosen so that when e_a and i_a are positive, power is entering the armature. The circuit layout has been rearranged (as compared with Fig. 4.20) so that the direction of power flow, when operating as a motor, is from left to right. And, on the shaft, the torque directions have been assigned so that the electromagnetic torque T produced by the motor opposes the mechanical loss and load torque components.

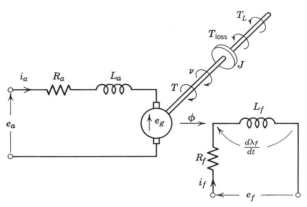

Fig. 4.35   Equivalent circuit of commutator motor.

The terminal variables e_a, i_a, e_f, i_f, T, and v of the machine are related by the three equations

$$e_f = R_f i_f + \frac{d\lambda_f}{dt} \qquad \text{volts} \tag{4.130}$$

$$e_a = K_a \phi v + L_a \frac{di_a}{dt} + R_a i_a \qquad \text{volts} \tag{4.131}$$

and $$T_L = K_a \phi i_a - J \frac{dv}{dt} - T_{\text{loss}} \qquad \text{newton-meters} \tag{4.132}$$

The field flux linkage λ_f and the quantity $K_a \phi$ are generally nonlinear functions of the field current i_f, as shown in Figs. 4.23a and 4.24a. When the machine is operated in the magnetically linear range, these functions may be expressed as

$$\lambda_f = L_{fif} \qquad \text{webers} \tag{4.133}$$

and $$K_a \phi = K_{fif} \qquad \text{volts/radian per second} \tag{4.134}$$

In the steady state, with i_f, i_a, and v constant, the speed is given from eqs. 4.131 and 4.132 by

$$v = \frac{e_a - R_a i_a}{K_a \phi}$$

$$= \frac{e_a}{K_a \phi} - \frac{R_a T}{(K_a \phi)^2} \qquad \text{radians/second} \qquad (4.135)$$

where

$$T = T_{\text{loss}} + T_L \qquad (4.136)$$

Several possible methods of speed control can be visualized from this expression. The steady-state speed can be controlled directly by controlling the voltage e_a applied to the armature (*armature voltage control*). If the armature circuit resistance R_a is small, the speed is seen to be essentially independent of the load torque. The speed may also be controlled by varying the field current i_f and therefore the flux ϕ in eq. 4.135 (*field control*). As a third possibility, the resistance R_a of the armature circuit may be augmented by a series resistor, thus altering the speed-torque relationship (*armature resistance control*). By the use of series field windings, the flux ϕ in eq. 4.135 can be made wholly or partially dependent on the armature current i_a (*series and compound motors.*) The performance of motors operated with these various types of speed-torque control is discussed in the following sections.

4.6.1 Armature-Voltage Control

Many manufacturing, traction, and processing operations require continuous control of the speed from standstill to maximum speed in both directions of rotation. Armature-voltage control of a d-c motor provides one of the best drives for such operations. The field circuit is connected to a direct-voltage source and the field current is generally set at a constant value I_f, which produces the maximum designed value of flux ϕ in the machine. The armature circuit is supplied from a variable direct-voltage source, which may be a controlled rectifier, an electronic amplifier, a magnetic amplifier, a d-c generator, or a compensated cross-field generator.

Let us assume that the armature source is capable of maintaining any value of voltage e_a independent of the current i_a drawn from it. Then, from eq. 4.135, the steady-state speed v of the machine is related approximately to the voltage e_a and the electromagnetic torque T by

$$v = \frac{e_a}{K_a \phi} - \frac{R_a T}{(K_a \phi)^2} \qquad \text{radians/second}$$

Figure 4.36a shows the steady-state speed-voltage relationship. If the torque T is zero, the speed is linearly proportional to the applied voltage and reverses when the applied voltage is reversed. When the machine is operating as a motor supplying a constant positive torque, the speed-voltage relation is slightly shifted to the right. The machine may, at certain times, operate as a generator with negative torque, in which case its speed-voltage relation is shifted to the left.

Figure 4.36b shows the relationship between the steady-state speed and the torque at various values of constant applied armature voltage.

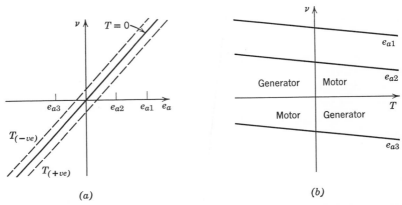

(a)   (b)

Fig. 4.36   Relations between speed ν, torque T, and armature voltage e_a for an armature-voltage controlled motor.

If e_a is set at the rated value for the machine, an increase in torque from zero to rated value normally causes the speed to drop by as little as 1 to 2% for larger machines and by as much as 10 to 30% for small machines.

The linear speed-torque curves of Fig. 4.36b are based on the assumption that the flux ϕ is constant. With large values of armature current, armature reaction (Section 4.4.3) may cause an appreciable reduction in this flux. From eq. 4.135, it can be seen that this reduction in flux tends to counteract the drop in the speed-torque relation and may cause the speed to increase as the torque is increased. With certain types of load, such as a constant-torque load, a rising speed-torque relation is unstable. Thus, normally measures are taken to prevent a significant armature reaction effect. These measures should be effective not only for armature currents up to the steady-state rated value but also for higher currents that may occur intermittently, for example, during starting. Compensating windings are normally fitted for this purpose on large control motors.

Let us now examine the process by which the speed adjusts itself following a change in applied armature voltage or in load torque. As a beginning, consider an unloaded machine $T_L = 0$ with negligible armature inductance L_a and negligible mechanical loss torque. Suppose a steady field current I_f is established and then a voltage $e_a = E_a$ is applied at $t = 0$. From eq. 4.131, with the machine at standstill

$$i_{a(t=0)} = \frac{E_a}{R_a} \quad \text{amperes} \qquad (4.137)$$

(The effect of the armature inductance would be to delay slightly the rise of the current to the value of eq. 4.137.) The armature current i_a reacts with the main pole flux ϕ to produce a torque (eq. 4.30) which, from eq. 4.132, is used entirely to accelerate the machine rotor having a polar moment of inertia J.

$$J \frac{dv}{dt} = K_a \phi i_a \quad \text{newton-meters} \qquad (4.138)$$

As the speed v of the motor increases, an increasing generated voltage

$$e_g = K_a \phi v \quad \text{volts} \qquad (4.139)$$

is produced in the armature circuit. From eq. 4.131, this causes a gradual reduction in the armature current i_a and in the torque produced. Eventually, the speed approaches its final value

$$v_{(t \to \infty)} = \frac{E_a}{K_a \phi} \quad \text{radians/second} \qquad (4.140)$$

and the armature current and torque approach zero. Note that if the loss torque were actually zero, no torque would be required to keep the machine rotating at a constant speed.

The transient speed of this simplified motor may be expressed in operational form by combining eqs. 4.131 and 4.132 with $T_L = 0$, $T_{\text{loss}} = 0$, and $L_a = 0$ to give

$$Jsv_{(s)} = K_a \phi i_{a(s)}$$
$$= \frac{K_a \phi [e_{a(s)} - K_a \phi v_{(s)}]}{R_a}$$

When rearranged, this becomes

$$v_{(s)} = \frac{1}{K_a \phi (1 + s\tau_m)} e_{a(s)} \quad \text{radians/second} \qquad (4.141)$$

in which the "mechanical" time constant is

$$\tau_m = \frac{J R_a}{(K_a \phi)^2} \quad \text{seconds} \qquad (4.142)$$

When e_a is a step voltage E_a applied at $t = 0$, the speed is

$$v = \frac{E_a}{K_a\phi} \left[1 - \epsilon^{-t/t_m}\right] \qquad \text{radians/second} \qquad (4.143)$$

For the same conditions, the armature current is

$$i_a = (E_a/R_a)\epsilon^{-t/\tau_m} \qquad \text{amperes} \qquad (4.144)$$

As would be expected, the mechanical time constant is directly proportional to the polar moment of inertia J of the motor. Control motors are often made with long armatures of small diameter to reduce the value of J (Section 4.8). The time constant is also directly proportional to the armature resistance R_a, since this resistance limits the armature current, which in turn produces the accelerating torque. The value of the mechanical time constant τ_m of an unloaded motor varies from a few milliseconds to a few tenths of a second depending on the motor size. Whereas this might give the impression that the motor speed can be changed very rapidly, it must be noted that often only small changes in speed can safely be made at this time constant. It is only in very small machines with relatively high armature resistance that rated voltage can be applied suddenly to the armature at standstill without exceeding the maximum transient current that the commutator can switch without damage. For larger machines, either the rate of change of the armature voltage e_a must be limited, or additional resistance must be added to the armature circuit. The additional resistance required may increase the effective time constant to several seconds.

Equation 4.144 for the armature current transient is of the same form as would occur with a voltage E_a suddenly applied to a resistance R_a in series with an uncharged capacitance C, where, from eq. 4.142,

$$C = \frac{\tau_m}{R_a}$$

$$= \frac{J}{(K_a\phi)^2} \qquad \text{farads} \qquad (4.145)$$

This suggests that the unloaded motor may be represented by the equivalent circuit of Fig. 4.37a. Using eqs. 4.139 and 4.145, the energy stored in this equivalent capacitance may be shown to be equal to the energy stored in the motor inertia.

$$\frac{1}{2}Ce_g{}^2 = \frac{1}{2}\frac{J}{(K_a\phi)^2}(K_a\phi v)^2$$

$$= \tfrac{1}{2}Jv^2 \qquad \text{joules} \qquad (4.146)$$

The equivalent capacitance C of a motor may be as high as several farads. Unloaded motors are thus occasionally used in the place of capacitators where very high effective capacitance is required for, example, in a filter for a low-voltage, high-current supply.

The transient speed response to changes in either armature voltage or load torque can be obtained, from eqs. 4.131 and 4.132, as

$$v_{(s)} = \left[\frac{1}{K_a\phi(1 + s\tau_m)}\right] e_{a(s)} - \left[\frac{R_a}{(K_a\phi)^2(1 + s\tau_m)}\right](T_{\text{loss}} + T_L)_{(s)}$$

(4.147)

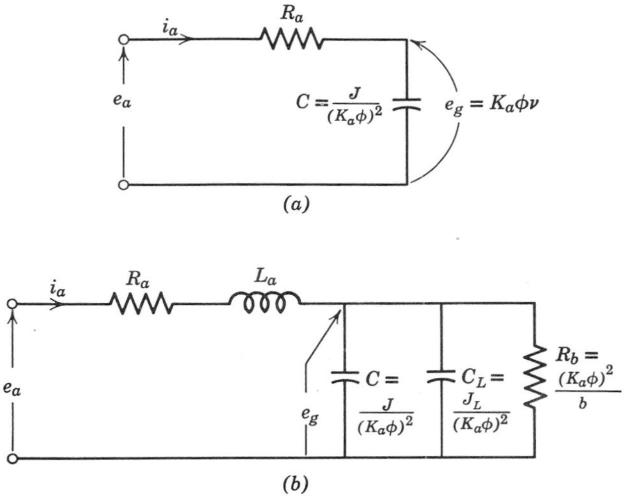

(a)

(b)

Fig. 4.37 Equivalent circuit of d-c motor (a) neglecting rotational losses and armature inductance. (b) Including representation of load inertia, viscous friction load, and armature inductance.

Thus, a step change in either the supply voltage or the load torque is followed by an exponential transient in speed that occurs at the mechanical time constant τ_m.

For a more complete picture of mechanical transient behavior, a description of the transient properties of the mechanical load on the machine is required. The mechanical load on a motor normally has a significant polar moment of inertia J_L. Suppose the steady-state load torque (including the motor loss torque) can be assumed to be linearly proportional to the speed, as would occur with viscous friction. Then

$$T_{\text{loss}} + T_L = J_L\frac{dv}{dt} + bv \qquad \text{newton-meters} \qquad (4.148)$$

Inserting this expression into eq. 4.132 and substituting i_a from eq. 4.131 with $L_a = 0$ gives the speed transfer function relating speed v and armature voltage e_a as

$$v_{(s)} = \frac{1}{K_a\phi\left[1 + \dfrac{bR_a}{(K_a\phi)^2}\right](1 + s\tau_m)}\, e_{a(s)} \qquad \text{radians/second} \quad (4.149)$$

where the mechanical time constant τ_m of the system is

$$\tau_m = \frac{(J + J_L)R_a}{(K_a\phi)^2\left[1 + \dfrac{bR_a}{(K_a\phi)^2}\right]} \qquad \text{seconds} \qquad (4.150)$$

From this it is seen that while the load inertia J_L tends to increase the mechanical time constant, the viscous friction load acts to reduce the time constant. At first it may seem surprising that a motor with a friction load reaches its final speed in a shorter time than one without a load. With a viscous friction load, no torque is required at zero speed. Thus the initial acceleration is the same as for no friction load. But the final speed is somewhat lower and is therefore achieved in a shorter time.

The load characteristic of eq. 4.148 can be incorporated into the equivalent circuit of the motor system, as shown in Fig. 4.37b. Substituting $v = e_g/K_a\phi$ into the speed-torque equation

$$(J + J_L)\frac{dv}{dt} + bv = K_a\phi i_a \qquad (4.151)$$

gives the following relation between the generated voltage e_g and the armature current

$$\left[\frac{J + J_L}{(K_a\phi)^2}\right]\frac{de_g}{dt} + \left[\frac{b}{(K_a\phi)^2}\right]e_g = i_a \qquad (4.152)$$

In the equivalent circuit of Fig. 4.37b, both motor and load inertias are represented by equivalent capacitances, while the viscous friction load is represented by a resistance of

$$R_b = \frac{(K_a\phi)^2}{b} \qquad \text{ohms} \qquad (4.153)$$

Other load characteristics can be reflected into the equivalent circuit by a similar change of variables from speed and torque to generated voltage and current. For example, a constant torque load can be represented as a current source or sink.

4.6.2 Armature and Field Resistance Control

When only a constant-voltage supply is available, the speed and torque characteristics of a d-c motor can be controlled by adjustment of series resistances in the field and armature circuits, as shown in Fig. 4.38. This arrangement is known as the shunt connection of a d-c motor.

To start a shunt-connected motor, it is first necessary to connect the field circuit and establish flux in the machine. The armature circuit may then be connected with sufficient additional resistance R_d to limit the

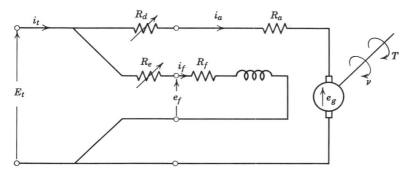

Fig. 4.38   Shunt-connected motor.

initial armature current to the maximum value $\hat{i}_a$ that the commutator can withstand without damage, that is,

$$R_d + R_a = \frac{E_t}{\hat{i}_a} \qquad (4.154)$$

The maximum permissible armature current may be 1.5 to 10 times the continuous rated value.

Assuming no-load and negligible mechanical losses, the speed rises exponentially as given in the expression

$$v = \frac{E_t}{K_a \phi} (1 - \epsilon^{-t/\tau_m}) \qquad \text{radians/second} \qquad (4.155)$$

where the mechanical time constant is

$$\tau_m = \frac{J(R_d + R_a)}{(K_a \phi)^2} \qquad \text{seconds} \qquad (4.156)$$

To minimize the time required for starting, the largest practical value of flux ϕ should be used.

With the relatively large value of armature-circuit resistance, the time constant τ_m (eq. 4.156) may be several seconds. If this resistance is unchanged, the armature current decays exponentially.

$$i_a = \frac{E_t}{R + R_a} \epsilon^{-t/\tau_m} \qquad \text{amperes} \qquad (4.157)$$

A more rapid start can be achieved if the resistance R_d is reduced gradually or in steps as the speed increases. Various types of manual and automatic starters provide this capability. The manual starter of Fig. 4.39 has a spring-loaded contact arm which is rotated clockwise. This provides for the initial connection of the field circuit, the gradual reduction of the series resistance, and the holding of the arm in the zero-resistance position as

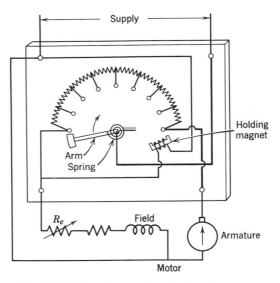

Fig. 4.39   Manual starter for shunt motor.

long as adequate supply voltage is available. Automatic starters perform essentially the same functions by the use of electromagnetic relays that short out sections of the starting resistance, either in a predetermined time sequence, or when the armature current has dropped to a predetermined value.

In steady-state operation, the speed-torque relation for the shunt motor of Fig. 4.38 is obtained by modification of eq. 4.135 as

$$v = \frac{E_t - (R_d + R_a)i_a}{K_a \phi}$$

$$= \frac{E_t}{K_a \phi} - \frac{(R_d + R_a)T}{(K_a \phi)^2} \qquad \text{radians/second} \qquad (4.158)$$

The magnetization curve relating $K_a \phi$ to the field current i_f is of the form shown in Fig. 4.40a. Increase of the external field resistance R_e decreases the field current i_f and the flux ϕ. The consequent drop in the generated voltage causes an increased armature current and torque resulting finally in an increased speed.

Figure 4.40*b* shows steady-state speed as a function of field current for several values of constant load torque. At zero torque, the speed is inversely proportional to the field current over the approximately linear range of Fig. 4.40*a*. As the field current is increased further, the magnetic system becomes saturated, and the speed approaches its minimum value.

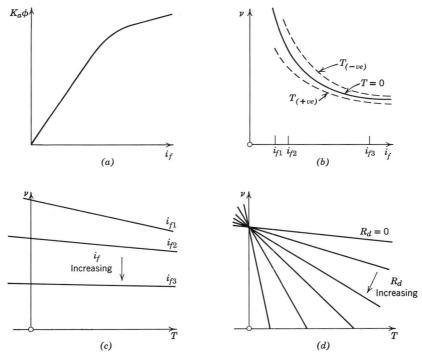

Fig. 4.40 Steady-state terminal characteristics of shunt motor. (*a*) Magnetization curve. (*b*) Speed as a function of field current. (*c*) Speed as a function of torque with field resistance control. (*d*) Speed as a function of torque with armature resistance control.

A positive load torque reduces the steady-state speed by an amount which is inversely dependent upon $(K_a\phi)^2$. The machine may also absorb power from its coupled mechanical system, in which case the speed is greater than the no-load value. Figure 4.40*c* shows the speed-torque relation for several values of field current. It is noted that the speed becomes more dependent on the torque at the high values of speed that correspond to low values of field current.

The maximum speed for a shunt motor is limited by mechanical considerations. Shunt motors are normally built to operate over only a limited speed range up to about 1.5 times the minimum speed value. By special design the speed range with field resistance control can be extended up to about 3 to 6 times the minimum speed value.

Although series resistance in the armature circuit is mainly used for starting only, it may also be used to provide control of the steady-state speed-torque characteristics. Figure 4.40d shows a family of speed-torque curves for various values of the series resistance R_d. This method of speed control is effective only when the motor has a mechanical load. At low values of speed this method of control has very low efficiency. Its use is generally restricted to systems that are operated at low speed for only short periods of time.

Reversal of the direction of rotation requires that the machine be stopped and the connections to either the field or the armature be reversed. Resistance control is therefore not well suited for application requiring continuous reversible control of speed.

4.6.3 Field Voltage Control

One of the disadvantages of armature-voltage control (Section 4.6.1) is that the power amplifier or controlled source must provide all of the power converted in the motor. Since the power required in the field circuit is only a few per cent of the power required by the armature, a control system in which only the field power need be controlled appears advantageous.

Figure 4.41a shows a motor that has its field voltage supplied by an amplifier (electronic or magnetic), Ideally, the armature would be supplied from a constant current source. For small motors, a constant current source may be approximated by using a high resistance in series with a voltage source. Alternatively, a saturable reactor (Section 3.4.3) rectifier system may be used.

A motor with constant armature voltage tends to have an essentially constant steady-state speed. In contrast, a motor with constant armature current produces an essentially constant torque, independent of speed. Assuming magnetic linearity, the electromagnetic torque of the motor in Fig. 4.41a is

$$T = K_f I_a i_f \quad \text{newton-meters} \tag{4.159}$$

where I_a is the constant armature current. Suppose the amplifier output circuit can be represented as a controllable source voltage $e_0 = Ae$ in series with an internal resistance R_0. Then the torque is related to the

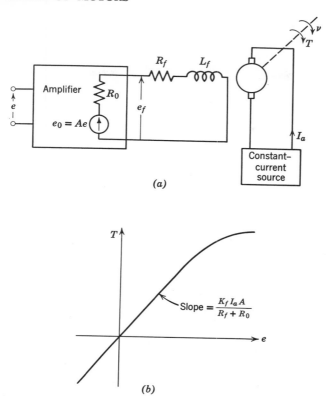

Fig. 4.41 (a) Motor with field voltage control. (b) Relation between steady-state torque T and input voltage e.

amplifier input e by the operational expression

$$T_{(s)} = \frac{K_f I_a A}{(R_f + R_0)(1 + s\tau_f)} e_{(s)} \quad \text{newton-meters} \quad (4.160)$$

where

$$\tau_f = \frac{L_f}{R_f + R_0} \quad \text{seconds} \quad (4.161)$$

The steady-state torque is shown as a function of amplifier input voltage in Fig. 4.41b. The effect of magnetic saturation is noted. Hysteresis may also be significant in this type of control since it may cause a small torque when the amplifier input is zero.

The time constant τ_f in eq. 4.161 depends greatly on the type of amplifier used. If the amplifier acts as a voltage source, the time constant τ_f will be that of the field only L_f/R_f. More rapid response can be achieved if the amplifier has an inherently high internal resistance. Circuits using transistors or pentode vacuum tubes can be designed to have this property.

Suppose that the electromagnetic torque T is absorbed by the motor inertia J and the load which has inertia J_L and a viscous friction constant b.

$$T = (J + J_L)\frac{dv}{dt} + b \qquad \text{newton-meters} \qquad (4.162)$$

The speed of the motor is then given, from eqs. 4.160 and 4.162, as

$$v_{(s)} = \frac{K_f I_a A}{(R_f + R_0)b(1 + s\tau_f)(1 + s\tau_m)} e_{f(s)} \qquad \text{radians/second} \quad (4.163)$$

where

$$\tau_m = \frac{J + J_L}{b} \qquad \text{seconds} \qquad (4.164)$$

It is noted that with constant-armature current, the mechanical time constant is determined by the mechanical properties only.

4.6.4 Series Motors

In a series motor, the armature is connected in series with an appropriately designed series field winding as shown in Fig. 4.42a. The supply is generally a constant-voltage source in series with a starting or controlling resistor R_d. From eq. 4.135, the steady-state speed and torque of the motor are related by

$$v = \frac{E_t}{K_a \phi} - \frac{(R_a + R_s + R_d)}{(K_a \phi)^2} T \qquad \text{radians/second} \qquad (4.165)$$

where $K_a \phi$ is related to the field current i_s by the magnetization curve of Fig. 4.42b. When the motor current is within the linear range of the magnetization curve where

$$K_a \phi = K_f i_s \qquad \text{newton-meters/ampere} \qquad (4.166)$$

the electromagnetic torque is

$$\begin{aligned} T &= K_a \phi i_t \\ &= K_f i_t^2 \qquad \text{newton-meters} \end{aligned} \qquad (4.167)$$

Thus, the motor current increases only as the square root of the torque in contrast with the shunt machine, in which torque and motor current are proportional.

Substitution of eqs. 4.167 and 4.166 into 4.165 gives the steady-state speed-torque relation

$$v = \frac{E_t}{(K_f T)^{\frac{1}{2}}} - \frac{(R_a + R_s + R_d)}{K_f} \qquad \text{radians/second} \qquad (4.168)$$

If we neglect the armature circuit resistance, the speed is inversely proportional to the square root of the torque. An increase in torque is accompanied by an increase in motor current, which in turn causes an increase in the flux of the machine. Figure 4.42c shows typical speed-torque relations for a series motor.

The significant decrease in speed with increase in load torque is desirable for many types of mechanical load. For example, in traction applications

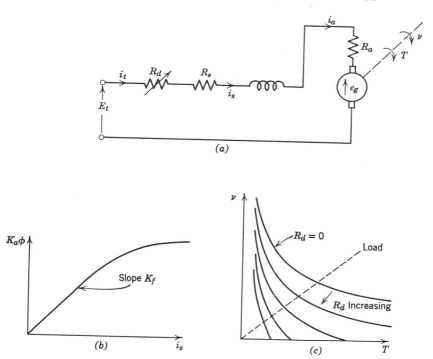

Fig. 4.42 (a) Series motor. (b) Magnetization curve. (c) Typical speed-torque characteristics with resistance control.

a low speed when climbing at high torque and a high speed when running on the level at low torque allows more nearly constant power to be taken from the supply lines. As a further example, consider a punch press that requires a high thrust for a short period. With a series motor drive, most of this intermittent torque is obtained from the inertia J of the system as its speed decreases, and only a small increase in armature current is required. If an essentially constant-speed shunt motor had been used, a large increase in armature current would have occurred during the period of high torque.

Figure 4.42c shows that the speed of a series motor driving a load can be controlled by adjustment of the series resistance R_d. The steady-state speed corresponds with the intersection of the speed-torque characteristics of the motor and the load. From the curves it is evident that the motor must always be connected to a load. If the load is removed, the motor accelerates and the current is reduced. This causes a reduction in flux and a further acceleration to dangerously high speed. In contrast with the shunt motor, a series motor cannot be used as a brake absorbing mechanical power.

It may be noted from eq. 4.167 that reversal of the motor current i_t reverses the flux direction as well as the armature current, and leaves the direction of the torque T unchanged. Suitably designed series motors may therefore be operated on an alternating voltage supply. With an alternating current, the torque T pulsates between zero and twice its average value.

A-c series motors require laminated poles and yokes to prevent excessive eddy-current losses. The series field must have relatively few turns to limit the inductive reactance of the field. The inductive reactance of the armature circuit is reduced by the use of a distributed compensating winding. There are also special problems in the commutation of a-c series motors because of the voltage induced by transformer action in the coils short circuited during commutation.

Figure 4.43a shows a series motor with compensating winding connected to a supply of voltage E_t and frequency ω radians/second. If we assume magnetic linearity (eq. 4.166), the motor current phasor is

$$I_t = \frac{E_t}{(K_f v + R_a + R_s + R_c) + j\omega(L_f + L_q)} \quad \text{amperes} \quad (4.169)$$

where
$$L_q = L_a + L_c - 2L_{ac} \quad \text{henrys} \quad (4.170)$$

The average torque is

$$\bar{T} = K_f I_t I_t{}^*$$
$$= \frac{K_f |E_t|^2}{(K_f v + R_a + R_s + R_c)^2 + (\omega L_f + \omega L_q)^2} \quad \text{newton-meters} \quad (4.171)$$

At zero speed the motor current is limited mainly by the inductive reactance of the windings, which also limits the standstill torque. As the speed increases, the motor current phasor follows a circular locus as shown in Fig. 4.43b. A typical speed torque curve is shown in Fig. 4.43c.

Small series motors that can be used with either direct or alternating current are known as *universal motors*. These are extensively used in hand tools and domestic appliances.

In Fig. 4.43a the compensating windings are connected in series opposition with the armature to reduce the net inductance. If the motor is to be used on alternating current only, essentially the same effect can be achieved by short circuiting the compensating winding as shown in Fig. 4.44a. The armature and compensating windings constitute a two-winding transformer. The short-circuit current in the compensating winding is of

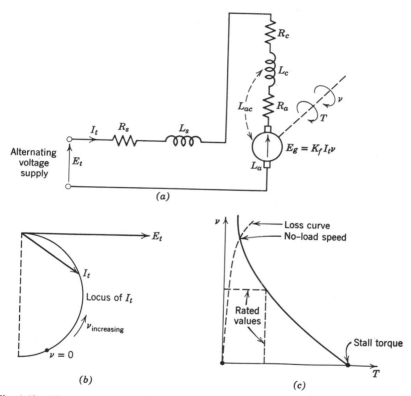

Fig. 4.43 (a) Compensated series motor operating on alternating current. (b) Phasor diagram showing current locus. (c) Speed-torque characteristic.

essentially the same magnitude and phase as it would be if connected in series with the armature. The performance of this inductively compensated motor is essentially identical with that of the normal conductively compensated type.

Figure 4.44b shows another variant of the a-c series motor. The compensating winding is connected in series with the field winding and the armature is short circuited. In this case, the armature forms the short-circuited secondary of a two-winding transformer. Its current is proportional to the compensating-winding current in magnitude, but opposite in phase. Again, its characteristics when operating on alternating current are essentially the same as those of a normally connected series motor. The motor cannot, however, operate with direct current.

Instead of using separate field and compensating windings as in Fig. 4.44*b*, a single distributed winding may be employed as in Fig. 4.44*c*. This winding is located so that it produces the magnetomotive force

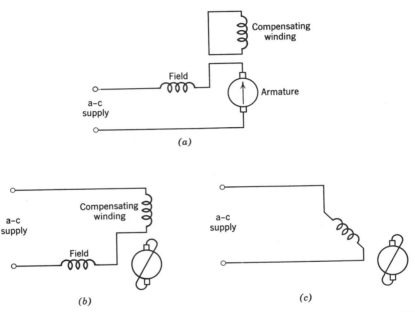

Fig. 4.44 (*a*) Inductively compensated series motor. (*b*) Repulsion motor with separate field and compensating windings. (*c*) Repulsion motor with single stator winding.

required for both the main field and for inducing the appropriate current in the armature. The proportioning between these two functions may be altered by shifting the brush position. In this form, the machine is known as a *repulsion motor*. One of the advantages of a repulsion motor over a normal series motor is that its armature can be designed to operate at any desired current level. By using a low-voltage high-current winding, the difficulties of commutation are greatly reduced. The repulsion-motor principle is incorporated into certain single-phase induction motors (Section 5.8.4) to produce a repulsion-induction motor. The resulting machine has the high starting torque of the series motor and the essentially constant steady-state speed of the induction motor.

4.6.5 Compound Motors

Some applications require a drive having the drooping speed-torque characteristic of the series motor but also require a definite no-load speed as in the shunt motor. These features are combined in the compound motor shown in Fig. 4.45a. The no-load speed is inversely dependent upon

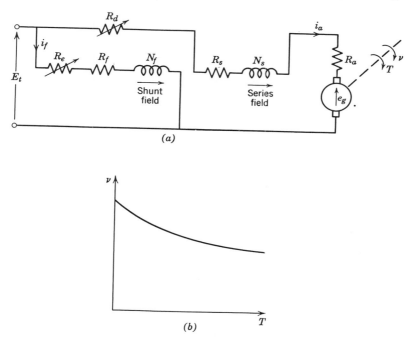

(a)

(b)

Fig. 4.45   (a) Compound motor. (b) Typical speed-torque curve.

the shunt field current as in the shunt machine. As the load torque is increased, the armature current flowing through the series field causes an increase in the pole flux and a consequent decrease in the steady-state speed.

The steady-state speed and torque of the motor are given by the expressions

$$v = \frac{E_t - (R_d + R_s + R_a)i_a}{K_a\phi} \quad \text{radians/second} \quad (4.172)$$

and

$$T = K_a\phi i_a \quad \text{newton-meters} \quad (4.173)$$

where $K_a\phi$ is related to i_f and i_a by a magnetizing curve as shown in Fig. 4.27b. If the machine is operating in the magnetically linear region,

$$K_a\phi = K_f\left(i_f + \frac{N_s}{N_f} i_a\right) \qquad \text{volts/radian per second} \qquad (4.174)$$

The steady-state speed-torque curve may be predicted by choosing values of i_a, determining the value of $K_a\phi$ from either the magnetization curve or from eq. 4.174, and by inserting it into eqs. 4.172 and 4.173. A typical speed-torque relation is shown in Fig. 4.45b.

4.7 CONTROL SYSTEMS USING COMMUTATOR MACHINES

Of all the types of rotating electrical machines, the commutator machine has the greatest flexibility and is therefore the best choice for many control applications. If only a steady relatively uncontrolled electromechanical conversion of energy is required, induction and synchronous machines provide simple economical drives. It is where some property of the output must be controlled, more or less accurately, that commutator machines find their major applications.

In this section a few examples of combinations or systems of commutator machines are introduced to show the potentialities of such systems and to indicate how the system performance is constrained by the limitations of individual machines. The optimization of the performance of these systems requires a number of feedback control concepts that are beyond the scope of the present treatment.

In electric drives, control may be required over any of the available variables. For example, accurate control of the speed of one or a group of motors is required in applications such as machine tools, locomotive and ship propulsion, steel and paper mill drives, and conveyors. Accurate and automatic control of position is required in elevators, machine tools, radar and telescope tracking, to mention only a few examples. Control of torque is required in certain operations such as wire drawing and reeling continuous strips of material. Controlled acceleration may be desired in hoists and elevators to prevent overstress to equipment or personnel.

4.7.1 Example of a Speed Control System

Figure 4.46 shows one of the most widely used speed control systems, known as the *Ward-Leonard* system. A separately excited generator, driven at approximately constant speed, provides power to the armature of a motor that has constant excitation. This system is a particular instance of the armature-voltage control discussed in Section 4.6.1.

To assess the properties and limitations of this system, let us first relate the load speed v_m to the voltage e_f by which the speed is to be controlled. If we assume the generator to be magnetically linear, its generated voltage is given by the operational expression

$$e_{g(s)} = \frac{K_f v_g}{R_f(1 + s\tau_f)} e_{f(s)} \qquad \text{volts} \qquad (4.175)$$

where
$$\tau_f = \frac{L_f}{R_f} \qquad \text{seconds} \qquad (4.176)$$

For simplicity let us assume that the armature inductances produce negligible delay in response, that the mechanical losses in the motor are

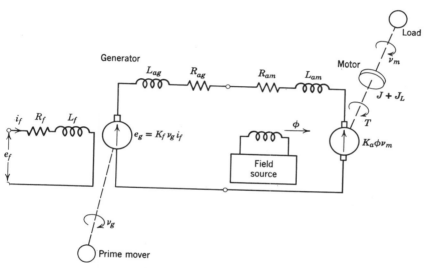

Fig. 4.46 Ward-Leonard system for speed control.

negligible, and that the load consists only of the load inertia J_L and the motor inertia J. Then, from eq. 4.141, the motor speed is

$$v_{m(s)} = \frac{1}{K_a\phi(1 + s\tau_m)} e_{g(s)} \qquad \text{radians/second} \qquad (4.177)$$

where
$$\tau_m = \frac{(J + J_L)(R_{ag} + R_{am})}{(K_a\phi)^2} \qquad \text{seconds} \qquad (4.178)$$

Combining eqs. 4.175 and 4.177 gives

$$v_{m(s)} = \frac{K_f v_g}{R_f(K_a\phi)(1 + s\tau_f)(1 + s\tau_m)} e_{f(s)} \qquad \text{radians/second} \quad (4.179)$$

This shows that if the machines were actually linear, the motor speed would be directly proportional to the field voltage e_f in the steady state and would be delayed in its transient response to variations in e_f by the effects of the generator-field and motor-mechanical time constants. But the magnetization curve of the generator is not linear, since its magnetic system has both saturation and some hysteresis. The speed v_g of the generator prime mover may change with load or because of external causes. The supply of the motor-field current may also change. Thus the

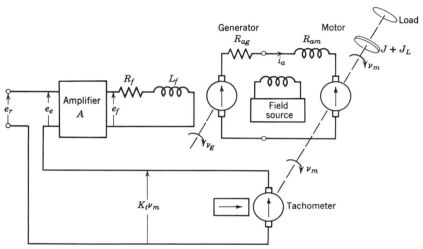

Fig. 4.47   Ward-Leonard system with elementary feedback control.

steady-state speed cannot be accurately related to the field voltage e_f even by a nonlinear calibration curve.

Accurate automatic control of speed in a system such as this first requires that the controlled quantity be measured and second, that the deviation of this controlled quantity from the desired value be used to provide the appropriate corrective action. Figure 4.47 shows one way in which this feedback control of speed can be effected. The motor speed is measured by a tachometer, which is a small d-c generator usually with a permanent magnet field. The output voltage $K_t v_m$ of the tachometer represents the actual value of the quantity to be controlled. This is compared, by subtraction in this case, with a voltage e_r, which represents the desired value of the controlled quantity (speed). The difference or error voltage e_e is applied to the input of a low-power amplifier, which provides the generator field voltage. Thus

$$e_f = A(e_r - K_t v_m) \qquad \text{volts} \qquad (4.180)$$

By combining eqs. 4.180 and 4.179, the operational relationship between the speed v_m and the command voltage e_r becomes

$$v_{m(s)} = \frac{1}{K_t} \frac{K}{(1 + s\tau_f)(1 + s\tau_m) + K} e_{r(s)}$$

$$= \frac{1}{K_t} \left(\frac{K}{1 + K} \right) \frac{1}{s^2 \left(\dfrac{\tau_f \tau_m}{1 + K} \right) + s \left(\dfrac{\tau_f + \tau_m}{1 + K} \right) + 1} e_{r(s)} \quad (4.181)$$

where
$$K = \frac{K_f v_g A K_t}{R_f (K_a \phi)} \quad (4.182)$$

Consider the particular case where a constant voltage $e_r = E_r$ is applied at $t = 0$ to a system that is initially at rest. Let

$$\omega_n = \left(\frac{1 + K}{\tau_f \tau_m} \right)^{\frac{1}{2}} \quad \text{radians/second} \quad (4.183)$$

$$\alpha = \frac{1}{2} \left(\frac{1}{\tau_f} + \frac{1}{\tau_m} \right) \quad \text{second}^{-1} \quad (4.184)$$

and
$$\omega_d = (\omega_n{}^2 - \alpha^2)^{\frac{1}{2}} \quad \text{radians/second} \quad (4.185)$$

Then for the usual operating case of $\alpha < \omega_n$, the speed transient is

$$v_m = \frac{E_r}{K_t} \left(\frac{K}{1 + K} \right) \left[1 - \frac{\omega_n}{\omega_d} \epsilon^{-\alpha t} \cos{(\omega_d t - \theta)} \right] \quad \text{radians/second} \quad (4.186)$$

where $\theta = \cos^{-1} \omega_d / \omega_n$.

Note that the speed response is a damped sinusoidal oscillation. The damping factor α of the this oscillation is dependent upon the system time constants. The frequency ω_d is dependent on the overall amplification factor K, which may be changed by adjusting the voltage amplification A of the amplifier. Figure 4.48 shows the speed as a function of time for three values of K that result in particular values of the relative damping factor α/ω_n. As the amplification is increased, the speed reaches its desired value in a shorter time but also may overshoot it. Too high an amplification produces a severe oscillation; too low an amplification produces a slow response to the command signal. Relative damping ratios in the range 0.5 to 0.75 usually provide satisfactory response.

Since K is normally much greater than unity, small variations in its value produce relatively little effect on the transient response because the natural frequency ω_n is proportional to the square root of $1 + K$. In addition, the steady-state speed becomes relatively independent of K at large values of K (see eq. 4.186) and approaches closely the command signal divided by the tachometer constant.

Various compensating networks can be added to the system of Fig. 4.47 to improve its speed of response without producing undesirable oscillations. But, except for small changes in command signal, the response is limited mainly by the limits of the machines. For example, it is usually necessary to add to the system of Fig. 4.47 a feedback loop that prevents the armature current i_a of the generator and motor from exceeding its

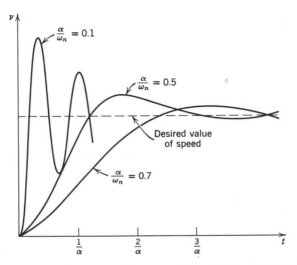

Fig. 4.48   Transient speed response of system of Fig. 4.47 to step command signal.

maximum safe value $\hat{i}_a$. On a purely inertia load, the maximum acceleration of the motor is then limited to

$$\frac{dv_m}{dt} = \frac{(K_a\phi)\hat{i}_a}{J + J_L} \qquad \text{radians/second}^2 \qquad (4.187)$$

If a large change is made in the command signal e_r, the motor-speed changes at the constant rate of eq. 4.187 until it approaches the new desired value. When the armature current becomes less that $\hat{i}_a$, the speed closes on the desired value in a damped sinusoidal manner of the form of Fig. 4.48.

There are many arrangements of machines used in practice to achieve accurate speed control. The amplifier in Fig. 4.47 may be a compensated cross-field generator (Amplidyne). For relatively low power drives (up to about 25 kilowatts) the cross-field machine may replace both the amplifier and the generator.

4.7.2 Example of a Position Control System

Figure 4.49 shows an elementary way in which commutator machines may be used for position control. In this example, the horizontal angle θ of a telescope is to be controlled accurately in response to a command voltage e_r. The controlled quantity θ is measured by use of a rotary potentiometer in this instance, and a voltage e_θ obtained where

$$e_\theta = K_\theta \theta \qquad \text{volts} \qquad (4.188)$$

This voltage is compared with the command voltage e_r by applying each to a field winding of a cross-field generator. If we assume these field windings

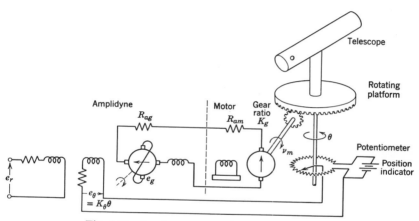

Fig. 4.49 An elementary position control system.

to be identical and the time constants of the generator to be negligibly small, the generated voltage is given by

$$e_g = A(e_r - e_\theta)$$
$$= A(e_r - K_\theta \theta) \qquad \text{volts} \qquad (4.189)$$

The motor speed ν_m is then given by

$$\nu_{m(s)} = \frac{1}{K_a \phi (1 + s \tau_m)} e_{g(s)} \qquad \text{radians/second} \qquad (4.190)$$

The mechanical time constant τ_m depends on the motor inertia J and on the load inertia J_L reflected through the gear ratio K_g (where $K_g < 1.0$). Thus, neglecting mechanical losses,

$$\tau_m = \frac{(J + K_g^2 J_L)(R_{ag} + R_{am})}{(K_a \phi)^2} \qquad \text{seconds} \qquad (4.191)$$

The load speed is related to the motor speed by

$$\frac{d\theta}{dt} = K_g v_m \tag{4.192}$$

From eqs. 4.189, 4.190, and 4.192, the angle θ is related to the command voltage by

$$\theta_{(s)} = \frac{1}{K_\theta} \frac{1}{\left(s^2 \dfrac{\tau_m}{K} + \dfrac{s}{K} + 1\right)} e_{r(s)} \qquad \text{radians} \tag{4.193}$$

where

$$K = A \frac{K_g K_\theta}{K_a \phi} \qquad \text{second}^{-1} \tag{4.194}$$

Equation 4.193 is a second-order equation of the same form as eq. 4.181. The damping factor is

$$\alpha = \frac{1}{2\tau_m} \qquad \text{second}^{-1} \tag{4.195}$$

and the frequency ω_d is

$$\omega_d = (\omega_n^2 - \alpha^2)^{\frac{1}{2}} \qquad \text{radians/second} \tag{4.196}$$

where

$$\omega_n = \left(\frac{K}{\tau_m}\right)^{\frac{1}{2}} \qquad \text{radians/second} \tag{4.197}$$

The transient response of position θ to a step input of voltage e_r has the same form as shown in Fig. 4.48.

Setting $s = 0$ in eq. 4.193 indicates that the steady-state angle θ is equal to the command voltage e_r divided by the potentiometer constant K_θ. Thus in this system there is no steady-state error regardless of the value of K, excepting the error in the measurement of θ. In practice, static friction in the driven system normally produces some steady-state error.

4.8 SOME DESIGN CONCEPTS AND CONSTRAINTS

Design is a complex process in which many factors must be considered. The judgment of the designer is greatly influenced by accumulated experience. The following design concepts are introduced, not to demonstrate the complete process of design, but rather to show approximately how the size and shape of a machine are related to its ratings and parameters.

First let us consider the factors influencing the size and shape of the armature of a commutator machine. From eq. 4.23, the generated voltage is

$$e_g = \frac{Np}{a\pi} \phi v \qquad \text{volts} \tag{4.198}$$

The power P converted in the machine, either as a generator or as a motor, is

$$P = e_g i_a$$

$$= \frac{Np\phi v i_a}{a\pi}$$

$$= \left(\frac{2Ni_a}{a}\right)(p\phi)\left(\frac{v}{2\pi}\right)$$

$$= \left(\begin{array}{c} \text{Total axial current} \\ \text{in armature conductors} \end{array}\right)\left(\begin{array}{c} \text{Total radial} \\ \text{magnetic flux} \end{array}\right)\left(\begin{array}{c} \text{Speed in revolutions} \\ \text{per second} \end{array}\right)$$

(4.199)

The amount of current that can be carried in the slotted armature is limited by the ability to conduct away the heat produced in the conductors, without exceeding the maximum allowable temperature of the insulation. For organic insulating materials—such as cotton, paper and many varnishes—this maximum temperature is about 105°C. For inorganic materials—such as mica, asbestos, and glass fiber bonded with silicone varnishes—the maximum temperature is about 180°C. The heat produced in the conductors must be transferred to the cooling air, which may have a temperature as high as 40°C for normal applications. Most of the temperature drop between the conductors and the cooling air is concentrated at the interface between the air and the armature surface. The amount of heat that can be removed per unit of temperature drop ΔT and per unit of surface area is the convection coefficient h. With air cooling, the value of this coefficient may be about 30 to 50 watts per meter²-°C.

For the machine of Fig. 4.50, the allowable power loss in the armature conductors is given by

$$P_L = h\,\Delta T 2\pi r l \qquad \text{watts} \qquad (4.200)$$

From the dimensions of Fig. 4.50, the cross-sectional area available for armature conductors in the slots is

$$A_c = 2\pi r b\left(\frac{d}{t+d}\right)k_s \qquad \text{meters}^2 \qquad (4.201)$$

where k_s is the space factor or ratio of net conductor area in a slot to the total slot area. Its value depends on the type of insulation and the shape of the conductors (round or rectangular) and is often between 0.3 and 0.6. The allowable current density J in the conductors depends mainly on the limiting temperature of the insulation used. Equating $A_c J$ to the total axial current in eq. 4.199 gives

$$\frac{2Ni_a}{a} = A_c J = 2\pi r q \qquad \text{amperes} \qquad (4.202)$$

where
$$q = Jk_s b\left(\frac{d}{t + d}\right) \qquad \text{amperes/meter} \qquad (4.203)$$

The circumferential current density q is the number of amperes in the armature conductors per meter of its circumference.

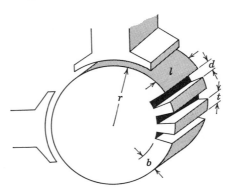

Fig. 4.50 Dimensions of armature.

From eq. 4.202, the power dissipated in the conductors imbedded in the armature surface is

$$P_L = \rho J^2 A_c l$$
$$= \rho J 2\pi r q l \qquad \text{watts} \qquad (4.204)$$

Equating the power loss expressions in eqs 4.200 and 4.204 gives

$$q = \frac{h\,\Delta t}{\rho J} \qquad \text{amperes/meter} \qquad (4.205)$$

As expected, the allowable circumferential current density q is directly dependent on the heat convection capability of the surface. The inverse dependence on conductor current density J is perhaps unexpected, unless it is realized that an increase of current density J decreases the depth b of conductor-filled slot that can be employed with a fixed value of loss per unit of surface area. Typical values of current density J are in the range of 2 to 5 amperes per millimeter^2. The circumferential current density q is normally within the range of 10 to 40 amperes per millimeter of periphery. If we know the insulating material, the ambient temperature, and the conductor resistivity ρ at operating temperature, a compatible set of values for J and q can be chosen using eq. 4.205.

The total radial magnetic flux $p\phi$ of eq. 4.199 is limited by the total cross-sectional area available at the bases of the teeth. The flux density at the tooth base cannot exceed about 2.0 to 2.2 webers/meter². In machines of large radius, the tooth width is almost constant. Thus with $d = t$, the average air-gap flux density B_g could be about 1.0 webers/meter². In small machines, because of the smaller area available at the tooth base, the average gap density B_g may be as low as 0.6 webers/meter². Of the total curved surface area of the armature, a fraction α, generally 0.6 to 0.7, is covered by the poles. Thus

$$p\phi = 2\pi r l B_g \alpha \qquad \text{webers} \qquad (4.206)$$

Combining eqs. 4.201 and 4.203, the volume of the active part of the armature is

$$V_a = \pi r^2 l$$
$$= \frac{P}{2q B_g \alpha v} \qquad \text{meter}^3 \qquad (4.207)$$

where P is the rated power of the machine. Note from the foregoing discussion that the circumferential current density q is limited by the temperature limit of the insulating material, and the flux density B_g is limited by saturation in the magnetic material. Thus the volume and therefore, to some extent, the cost of a machine is inversely dependent on its speed v. Wherever a choice may be made, the highest practical speed rating should therefore be selected for a motor drive. In special circumstances, the maximum speed may be limited by the mechanical stresses in the armature materials.

Having estimated the armature volume, the question of shape arises. For large high-speed machines, the maximum radius may be limited by the difficulty of holding the conductors in the slots against the centrifugal forces. However, if a low polar moment of inertia J is required, the radius should be made as small as feasible, since J is roughly proportional to $r^4 l$. Conversely, a high-inertia machine may be required for impact-load applications.

Normally, it is desirable to have approximately square pole faces. Thus

$$l \approx \frac{2\pi r \alpha}{p} \qquad (4.208)$$

The shape then depends on the choice of the number of poles. Increasing the number of poles reduces the flux per pole and thus reduces the required thickness of the armature core and yoke. This increase also reduces the armature magnetomotive force $\mathscr{F}_a$ per pole and thus the required field magnetomotive force $\mathscr{F}_f$ per pole (Section 4.4.3), since $\mathscr{F}_f$ generally must be 1.0 to $1.5\mathscr{F}_f$ to prevent excessive armature reaction effect. But increasing the number of poles also increases the frequency of flux alternation in the armature and thus increases the eddy-current and hysteresis losses. At the high flux densities that are used, this frequency generally should not exceed 30 to 50 cycles per second. A large number of

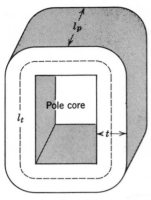

poles increases the number of brush sets, decreases the required commutator length, and increases either the required number of commutator segments or the voltage per segment. This example of the choice of number of poles demonstrates the interplay of the many factors that must be compromised in reaching a design judgment.

Let us now examine briefly some of the design features of the field system. The flux ϕ per pole is given by eq. 4.206 if the number of poles and armature dimensions are known. By use of a reasonable value of flux density, the cross-sectional area of the pole may be determined. As mentioned previously, the magnetomotive force $\mathscr{F}_f$ per pole is deter-

Fig. 4.51   Dimensions of field coil.

mined largely by the armature magnetomotive force $\mathscr{F}_a$, which is, from eqs. 4.20 and 4.32

$$\mathscr{F}_a = \frac{\pi r q}{p} \qquad \text{amperes/pole} \qquad (4.209)$$

Thus the air gap is adjusted to obtain the appropriate reluctance $\mathscr{R}_g$ per pole of the magnetic system.

$$\mathscr{R}_g = \frac{\mathscr{F}_f}{\phi} \approx 1.0 \text{ to } 1.5\frac{\mathscr{F}_a}{\phi} \qquad \text{amperes/weber} \qquad (4.210)$$

Figure 4.51 shows the general dimensions of a field coil. Its thickness t is limited by the available space between poles (allowing for interpoles if required) or by cooling considerations. With t determined, the length of the mean turn of the field coil is fixed. This leaves only the length l_p of the coil, and therefore of the pole core to be determined. Using a current density J (usually 1 to 3 amperes per millimeter²) and a space factor k_s, the cross-sectional area of the field coil is related to the required magneto-motive force by

$$t l_p = \frac{\mathscr{F}_f}{J k_s} \qquad \text{meter}^2 \qquad (4.211)$$

For shunt generators and motors, the resistance R_f of the field must be such that somewhat less than rated armature voltage is required to produce the required field current. If the conductor resistivity is ρ, the number of field turns per pole N_f to give a resistance R_f per field coil may be derived from

$$R_f = \frac{N_f^2 l_t}{t l_p k_s} \quad \text{ohms} \tag{4.212}$$

The inductance L_f of each field coil is given by

$$L_f = \frac{N_f^2}{\mathscr{R}_g} \quad \text{henrys} \tag{4.213}$$

Thus the field time constant is

$$\tau_f = \frac{L_f}{R_f}$$

$$= \frac{t l_p k_s}{\rho \mathscr{R}_g l_t} \quad \text{seconds} \tag{4.214}$$

Note that the field time constant is dependent on the dimensions of the field coil but is independent of its number of turns N_f.

An alternative expression for the field time constant may be obtained by substituting from eqs. 4.211 and 4.210 into 4.214.

$$\tau_f = \frac{\mathscr{F}_f}{J} \frac{1}{\rho \mathscr{R}_g l_t}$$

$$= \frac{\phi}{J \rho l_t} \quad \text{seconds} \tag{4.215}$$

Suppose all dimensions of a machine are multiplied by a factor K. Equation 4.204 indicates that the rated power of the machine increases as the dimension cubed (K^3). With constant flux density in the pole core, the pole flux ϕ in eq. 4.212 is proportional to area, that is, K^2, while the length of mean turn is proportional to length, that is, K. The current density J and the resistivity ρ are essentially constant. Thus with machines of the same shape but of increasing size, the field time constant is expected to increase roughly in proportion to length, that is K, or in proportion to the cube root of the power rating.

Problems

4.1 In Fig. 4.1a, suppose the field coil has 2500 turns and carries a current of $i_f = 1.2$ amp. Let each air gap have a radial length of 2 mm and let $r = z = 5$ cm. The magnetic material may be assumed ideal.

(a) If the loop current i is 40 amp, determine the torque on the loop when it is within the air gap.

(b) If the loop revolves at 20 r/sec, determine the electromotive force in the loop when it is within the air gap.

(c) For the conditions of parts (a) and (b), determine the rate at which energy is being converted. *Ans.:* 23.7 W.

4.2 For the elementary machine of Fig. 4.1a, suppose that the field current i_f is zero and that a current i flows in the rotatable loop.

(a) Draw a rough sketch of the magnetic field that is produced in one of the air gaps by the current i when the loop position θ is about 330°, that is, in the position shown in Fig. 4.1a.

(b) Does the loop experience a torque in the condition described in part (a), and, if so, in what direction does it act?

(c) For what position θ of the loop is the torque caused by the current i alone equal to zero?

(d) For the condition of part (a) is the average value of the radial component of flux density within the conductor equal to zero? Consider the possibility of determining the torque on the loop using eq. 1.51.

(e) If the current i is constant, show that the work done in rotating the loop through one revolution is equal to zero.

4.3 Figure P4.3 shows a cross-section of a simple electrical brake. The rotor winding consists of two shorted loopes, each having a resistance of 0.005 Ω. Each of the stator poles covers a 90° arc of the rotor. The rotor

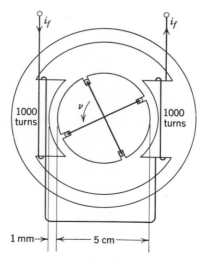

Fig. P4.3

length is 5 cm. The magnetic material in the stator and rotor may be considered ideal, fringing flux may be neglected, and the magnetic field produced by the shorted loops may be ignored.

(a) Derive expressions for the electromotive force and for the current in each of the shorted loops during the interval that the loop sides are under the poles.

(b) Show that the total power dissipated in the two loops is essentially constant throughout each revolution, provided the speed v and the field current i_f are constant.

(c) Derive an expression for the electromagnetic torque acting on the rotor.

(d) What field current is required to provide a braking power of 200 W when the speed is 400 rad/sec.   *Ans.:* 0.8 amp.

4.4 Figure P4.4 shows the dimensions of the teeth, slots and, air gap of a slotted-rotor machine. The stator and the rotor each may be regarded

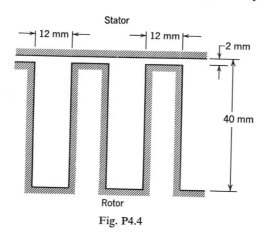

Fig. P4.4

as surfaces of constant magnetic potential. By use of the curvilinear-squares technique, sketch the magnetic field around a tooth and slot. Use this sketch to determine the approximate value of the effective air-gap length.   *Ans.:* $g' \approx 2.8$ mm.

4.5 Figure P4.5 gives the dimensions in centimeters of a d-c machine. The rotor has 116 slots, each containing 2 conductors. The cross-sectional area of each conductor is 0.515 cm². A lap-winding connection is used. Each field coil has 1280 turns, and all field coils are connected in series.

(a) Determine the reluctance of each air gap. The empirical expression given in Section 4.2 may be used to find the effective air-gap length.

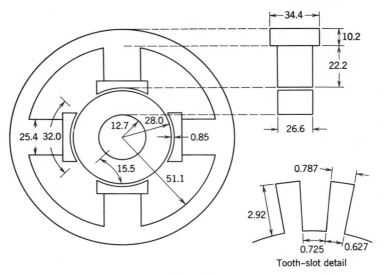

Fig. P4.5

(b) If we neglect all reluctances except those of the air gaps, determine the air-gap flux ϕ per unit of field current i_f.   *Ans.:* 0.0148 Wb/amp.

(c) Determine the winding constant K_f for the machine.

(d) Determine the generated voltage per unit of the product of field current and speed (that is, the constant K_f) when the machine is operating in its linear range.   *Ans.:* 0.546 V-sec/amp-rad.

(e) Suppose the normal magnetization curve for the magnetic material in all parts of the machine can be represented by the relation

$$B = 1.9 + 2\,\mu_0 H \qquad \text{Wb/m}^2 \quad \text{for} \quad B > 1.9$$

The objective in this part of the analysis is to predict the curve relating $K_a\phi$ to the field current i_f. It is evident from the dimensions given in Fig. P4.5 that the teeth will experience saturation well before other parts of the magnetic system. Let us assume that all the flux is confined to the teeth. First determine the value of $K_a\phi$ for which a flux density of 1.9 Wb/m² is just reached at the base of the tooth.   *Ans.:* 2.48 Wb.

(f) The magnetomotive force required for the tooth can be evaluated by integrating the magnetic field intensity H with respect to distance over the length of each tooth. With the simplified *B-H* relation given in part (e), only that part of the tooth having $B > 1.9$ need be considered. Evaluate the tooth magnetomotive force for about three values of tooth-base flux density between 1.9 and 2.5 Wb/m². Determine the flux constant

$K_a\phi$ and the field current i_f for each of these conditions and plot an appropriate graph relating $K_a\phi$ and i_f.

Ans.: As a check, one point on the graph should be about 3.25, 9.8.

(g) Suppose the machine is operated at a flux for which the field current is about 40% greater than that required for the air gap alone. If the rotor conductors can be operated continuously at a current density of 400 amp/cm², estimate the rated torque for the machine.

(h) If the speed of the machine is 1200 r/min, estimate the rated voltage and the rated power for the machine. *Ans.:* 325 kW.

4.6 You are given a commutator machine which has no nameplate to indicate its rating. Examination of the machine reveals the following data: 4 poles each with a pole-face area of 25 cm by 20 cm; 150 bars on the commutator; armature coils wave wound with 2 turns/coil. It is estimated that a reasonable value of flux density at the pole face would be 1 Wb/m². The cross-sectional area of each armature conductor appears to be adequate to carry about 50 amp. If the machine is to be operated at 500 r/min, estimate
  (a) the rated voltage
  (b) the rated torque
  (c) the rated power
Ans.: 50 kW.

4.7 A d-c, 4-pole, wave-wound machine is rated for 230 V and 5 kW at a speed of 1200 r/min. Its normal field current is 0.5 amp.

(a) If the speed could be increased to 1500 r/min, what would be the rated voltage and power of the machine?

(b) If the armature coils were reconnected to form a lap winding, what would be the rated voltage and power at 1200 r/min?

(c) Suppose a machine is built, identical in all respects to the one described, except that the axial length of the poles and the armature is doubled. Determine the rated voltage, the rated power and the required field current for this revised machine. *Ans.:* 460; 10; 0.5.

4.8 A d-c machine is driven at a constant speed of 1170 r/min. The open-circuit armature voltage e_t is measured for a set of values of the field current i_f, giving the following data:

i_f(amp)	0.1	0.2	0.3	0.4	0.5	0.6	0.7	0.8
e_t(V)	55	110	161	218	265	287	303	312

(a) Determine the flux quantity $K_a\phi$ for the machine when its field current is 0.7 amp.

(b) If we neglect the saturating effect of armature magnetomotive force, what electromagnetic torque will this machine produce with a field current of 0.7 amp and an armature current of 25 amp?   *Ans.:* 62 newton-m.

(c) Estimate the electromagnetic torque per unit of the product of field current and armature current when the machine is operating in its magnetically linear range.   *Ans.:* 4.46 newton-m/amp².

4.9 A d-c machine has the following nameplate data and physical properties: 550 V, 275 kW, 900 r/min, 6 poles, wave-wound armature winding in 180 slots with 8 conductors in each slot, 70% of the armature surface covered by poles.

(a) Find the armature magnetomotive force per pole at rated armature current.   *Ans.:* 30,000 amp.

(b) Find the number of conductors that should be placed in each pole face to provide an adequate compensating winding.   *Ans.:* 84.

(c) Estimate the number of turns required on each of 6 commutating poles to provide a flux density of 0.5 Wb/m² across an effective gap length of 0.5 cm at rated armature current if the machine has no compensating winding.

(d) Repeat part (c) supposing the machine to have the compensating winding of part (b).   *Ans.:* 22.

4.10 A commutator machine has the following physical properties: 6 poles, 2000 turns per field coil, 10 Ω resistance per field coil, all field coils connected in series, armature of radius 5 cm and axial length 5 cm. pole face area 20 cm², effective air-gap length 2 mm, armature wave wound with 300 turns, each turn having a resistance of 8 milliohms. The rotor has a mass of 15 kg, and its effective radius of gyration is estimated to be 3 cm. The armature inductance, the mechanical friction, and saturation in the magnetic material may all be ignored. It is estimated that the leakage flux between adjacent poles is about 15% of the air-gap flux.

(a) Determine the inductance of the field circuit.   *Ans.:* 34.6 henrys.

(b) Determine the field circuit resistance, the armature circuit resistance, the constant K_f, and the polar moment of inertia.

(c) Write three differential equations that relate the instantaneous values of the 6 terminal variables of this machine: terminal voltage e_t, field voltage e_f, armature current i_a, field current i_f, shaft torque T, and rotational speed v. Include the numerical values of all parameters in these equations.

4.11 The open-circuit voltage of a d-c generator when driven at a speed of 200 rad/sec with rated field current is 85 V. The resistance of the armature circuit is 4.3 Ω. The air-gap flux in the machine may be assumed to be independent of the armature current. Suppose a resistive load of 50 Ω is connected to the armature terminals when the machine is being driven at 260 rad/sec with rated field current. What will be the power delivered to the load?

Ans.: 208 W.

4.12 The field circuit of a machine has an inductance of 18.4 henrys and a resistance of 9 Ω.

(a) Suppose the field circuit is supplied from a 125 V source in series with a resistor that is adjusted to give a steady-state field current of 10 amp. In what time after this source is connected will the field current reach 9 amp?

Ans.: 3.4 sec.

(b) A resistor is often connected across a field circuit to protect the insulation on the field coils from the excessive voltage that might occur when a switch connecting the field circuit to its supply is opened. Suppose the insulation of the field coils of this machine will safely withstand a maximum voltage of 2000 V. What value of protective resistance is required to limit the induced voltage to this value if the initial current in this field is 10 amp?

Ans.: 191 Ω.

4.13 A source of low and variable frequency up to 5 c/s is required to supply a sinusoidal voltage of 115 V rms to a 50-Ω resistive load. An available commutator machine has a rating of 200 V (d-c), 500 W, and 1200 r/min. This machine requires a field current of 0.2 amp to provide rated terminal voltage on no-load at rated speed. The machine may be regarded as magnetically linear. Other parameters for the machine are: armature resistance 5 Ω, armature inductance 1.1 henrys, field resistance 800 Ω, and field inductance 40 henrys. A low-frequency electronic oscillator having negligible internal impedance is connected to the field. The machine is driven at rated speed.

(a) Determine the rms value of the field voltage that is required at a frequency of 5 c/s.

Ans.: 221 V.

(b) Determine the phase shift between the load voltage and the field voltage for the condition of part (a).

Ans.: 89.5°.

(c) Determine the power amplification of the machine when operating at 5 c/s.

Ans.: 15.

(d) Compare the power amplification in part (c) with that obtained at frequencies below about 0.5 c/s.

4.14 A d-c generator operated at rated speed has a power amplification of 100 and a voltage amplification (armature voltage per unit of field voltage) of 10. Its field time constant is 0.1 sec, and its armature time constant is negligible. The field circuit is connected as shown in Fig. P4.14 so that the field voltage e_f is equal to a control voltage e_c minus the terminal voltage e_t.

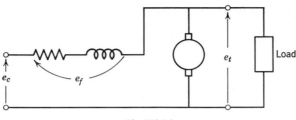

Fig. P4.14

(a) Determine the voltage amplification e_t/e_c of the system.
Ans.: 0.909.
(b) Determine the power amplification of the system.
(c) Determine the effective time constant of the system.
Ans.: 9.09 msec.
(d) Show that the power amplification per unit time constant is unchanged by the reconnection of the field circuit.
(e) Suppose the speed of the rotating amplifier system of Fig. P4.14 is increased by 50%. Determine the new values of voltage amplification, power amplification, and effective time constant for the system.

4.15 The following data describe the open-circuit magnetization characteristic of a d-c generator operating at 1500 r/min.

i_f(amp)	0	0.5	1.0	2.0	3.0	4.0	5.0
e_t(V)	10	40	80	135	172	199	220

The resistance of the field circuit is 44 Ω, and the resistance of the armature circuit is 0.035 Ω.

(a) Suppose the field is supplied from a 200-V source in series with a variable resistor having a range from 0 to 25 Ω. What will be the maximum and minimum values of no-load terminal voltage that can be obtained?
Ans.: 211; 168.
(b) Suppose the machine is separately excited to provide a no-load terminal voltage of 200 V. Determine the terminal voltage when a load current of 200 amp is being supplied.
(c) Suppose the generator is self-excited using the variable resistor of part (a) in series with the field circuit. What will be the maximum and minimum values of no-load terminal voltage that can be obtained?
Ans.: 220; 131.
(d) Suppose the generator is self-excited and adjusted to give a no-load terminal voltage of 200 V. Determine the terminal voltage when the load current is 200 amp. *Ans.:* 186.

(e) With the field circuit adjusted as in part (d), estimate the maximum load current that can be obtained from the machine terminals. What value of load resistance would produce this maximum current condition? *Ans.:* about 0.08 Ω.

(f) Plot a few points on a curve, relating terminal voltage and terminal current for the machine when self-excited and having a no-load voltage of 200 V. Suppose the machine is used to charge a battery that has an internal voltage of 175 V and an internal resistance of 0.1 Ω. Estimate the value of the battery current. *Ans.:* 145 amp.

4.16 Suppose the generator described in Prob. 4.15 is provided with a series field, the ratio of series-field turns to shunt-field turns being 0.005. The series field is connected so as to asist the shunt field.

(a) If the no-load voltage is 200 V, estimate the terminal voltage when the load current is 100 amp. *Ans.:* 212,

(b) Determine the ratio of series-field turns to shunt-field turns for which the load voltage will be essentially independent of load current at a value of 200 V. *Ans.:* About 0.0017.

4.17 Two-100-kW, 600-V shunt generators are operated electrically in parallel. Machine A has a no-load voltage of 680 V and a voltage of 600 V at rated load. Machine B has a no-load voltage of 700 V and provides 600 V at rated load. The reduction in load voltage may be assumed to be linearly proportional to load current for both machines. Determine the load voltage and the power supplied by each of the machines when they supply a combined load current of 250 amp. *Ans.:* 622 V.

4.18 In the voltage control system of Fig. 4.32, the generated voltage in the machine is 120 V/amp of field current. The armature resistance is 1.5 Ω the field resistance is 25 Ω and the field inductance is 4 henrys. The amplifier has a voltage amplification A of 10.

(a) Suppose the control voltage e_r is held constant at 100 V. With no-load in the generator, what is its output voltage? *Ans.:* 97.95 V.

(b) Repeat part (a) when a load of 20 Ω is connected. *Ans.:* 97.8 V.

(c) Compare the change in output voltage between no-load and full load with that which would occur with constant-field current in the generator.

(d) If a step change is made in the control voltage, at what time constant will the output voltage across the 20-Ω load change? *Ans.:* 0.0035 sec.

(e) Suppose the amplifier has a maximum output voltage of 80 V. If the system is initially at rest and a constant-control voltage of 100 V is applied, what will be the initial rate at which the open-circuit terminal voltage will rise? *Ans.:* 2400 V/sec.

4.19 A d-c generator has two sets of field coils. The magnetic system of the machine may be considered linear. At rated speed, the generated voltage is 100 V/amp of current in field A and 20 V/amp of current in field B. The field circuit resistances are 105 Ω for field A and 0.5 Ω for field B. Field A is connected directly across the armature terminals and field B is supplied from a separate source. The armature resistance is 0.05 Ω.

(a) Find the current in field B to produce an output voltage of 100 V on no-load.   *Ans.:* 0.24 amp.

(b) Find the voltage amplification of the generator on no-load.

(c) If the output voltage on no-load is 100 V, what will be the output voltage when the output current is 20 amp?   *Ans.:* 79 V.

4.20 A d-c generator has two identical sets of field coils, each of which has a resistance of 100 Ω and an inductance of 20 henrys. The two field coils on each pole may be considered to have perfect coupling. The generated voltage is 90 V/amp of current in either of the field circuits. The generator supplies a 2-Ω resistive load. Armature resistance is negligible.

(a) Suppose only one set of field coils is used to excite the machine. Derive a transfer function giving the output voltage in terms of the control voltage on the field. Determine the voltage amplification per unit. of time constant.   *Ans.:* 4.5.

(b) Repeat part (a) with both fields connected in parallel.

(c) Repeat part (a) with one field connected across the armature and a control voltage applied to the other field.

(d) Determine the power amplification (ratio of load power to control field power) per unit of time constant for the systems of (a), (b), and (c). *Ans.:* 202.5, 202.5, and 1025.

(e) Suppose the speed of the generator is increased by a factor 1.111 for the connection described in part (c). Derive a transfer function relating the output voltage to the control voltage.

4.21 A cross-field generator of the type shown in Fig. 4.33 has the following physical properties: 250 control-winding turns per pole, each control coil having a resistance of 5 Ω; reluctance of 2.5 $\times$ 10^5 amp/Wb in each air gap; resistance of 0.5 Ω between opposite brushes on the armature; 250 turns in the armature winding. The generator is driven at a speed of 50 r/sec.

(a) Determine the total number of turns required in compensating coils for complete compensation of the machine.

(b) Determine the voltage amplification of the fully compensated machines operating with no-load   *Ans.:* 31.25.

(c) Determine the time constant of the control field.   *Ans.:* 0.05 sec.

(d) Determine the time constant of the shorted quadrature-axis winding. The armature magnetomotive force $\mathscr{F}_{aq}$ may be assumed to act on the complete cross section of the quadrature axis poles.   *Ans.:* 0.0625 sec.

(e) Suppose the cross-field generator is connected to a 10-Ω resistive load. Determine the power amplification of the generator.   *Ans.:* 887.

(f) It is desired to reduce the value of one of the two time constants of this machine. This can be done either by adding a resistance of 0.5 Ω in the short-circuited armature circuit or by adding a 10-Ω resistance in the field circuit. Which of these possibilities will give the larger value of power amplification?

4.22   Figure P4.22 shows a section of a cross-field machine that has no windings on its poles. A voltage e_d is applied between one pair of armature

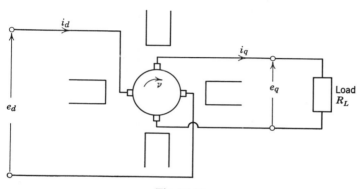

Fig. P4.22

brushes, and a load of resistance R_L is connected to the other pair of brushes. The armature has N turns. The effective reluctance of each air gap is $\mathscr{R}$, and the resistance measured between an opposite pair of brushes is R_a.

(a) Derive an expression relating the load current i_q to the supply voltage e_d, and show that the load current is essentially independent of the load resistance.

(b) Derive an expression relating the supply voltage e_d and the supply current i_d. Show that the input current has its minimum when the load is a short circuit.

(c) If $N = 240$ turns, $\nu = 200$ rad/sec, $\mathscr{R} = 10^5$ amp/Wb and, $R_a = 0.5\ \Omega$, determine the input and output powers for a 200-V source and an 8-Ω load resistance.   *Ans.:* 3850 W: 3450 W.

(d) For the condition of part (c) determine the required shaft torque.

4.23   A small commutator motor with a permanent-magnet field rotates at 20 r/sec when its armature voltage is held at 60 V. Its rotational losses are negligible. The armature resistance is 5 Ω, the armature inductance is 0.1 henry, and the polar moment of inertia is 0.005 kg-m².

(a) Draw an equivalent circuit for this machine of the form shown in Fig. 4.37b.

(b) Develop a transfer function relating the speed in rad/sec to the armature voltage.

(c) Determine the characteristic roots of the transfer function of part (b).   *Ans.:* 10.1 and 39.8 sec⁻¹.

(d) If the motor is initially at rest, determine its speed 0.05 sec after a 20-V source is connected to its terminals.

4.24   A d-c motor is used to rotate a load having a polar moment of inertia of 0.8 kg-m² and requiring negligible rotational torque. The motor has a polar moment of inertia of 0.05 kg-m², an armature resistance of 0.5 Ω, and negligible armature inductance and rotational losses. The field current is supplied from a constant-current source. When the armature voltage is maintained at 60 V, the motor has a steady-state speed of 120 rad/sec.

(a) At a certain time the armature voltage is increased to 80 V. Determine the speed of the motor 1 sec after the change is made.

Ans.: 138 rad/sec.

(b) Suppose that after the armature voltage has been maintained at 60 V for some time, a mechanical load requiring a constant torque of 5 newton-m is connected. Determine the speed of the motor 1 sec after the change is made.   *Ans.:* 115.6 rad/sec.

4.25   The starter for a d-c motor consists of a single resistor, the value of which is adjusted to limit the maximum armature current during the start to twice the rated value. The motor has a permanent-magnet field which provides a generated voltage of 200 V at a speed of 1800 r/min. The rated armature current is 18 amp, and the armature circuit resistance is 1.2 Ω. The polar moment of inertia of the motor and its connected load is 2.5 kg-m². Rotational losses, armature circuit inductance, and the effects of armature magnetomotive force may be neglected. The supply voltage is 200 V. For how long a time should the starting resistor be left in the circuit if the armature current is to rise to just twice its rated value when the starting resistor is shorted out?   *Ans.:* 19 sec.

4.26   A 120-V shunt motor requires a supply current of 12.6 amp when operated with no mechanical load. Its armature circuit resistance is 0.038 Ω. The motor draws a supply current of 212 amp when its mechanical load is connected.

(a) By making any reasonable assumptions, estimate the conversion efficiency of the motor drive.

(b) Suggest measurements that might be made to permit a more accurate estimate of efficiency.

4.27 The starting motor on a jet aircraft engine is geared to the engine rotor shaft through a 1:5 speed increaser. The polar moment of inertia of the engine rotor is 0.4 kg-m². The windage and friction torque of the engine rotor is 0.02 newton-m/rad per sec. The starting motor produces a torque of 0.8 newton-m/amp of armature current. Its armature circuit resistance is 0.8 Ω. The polar moment of inertia of the motor armature is 0.01 kg-m². If a 100-V d-c supply is used, how long a time is required for the engine to reach its starting speed of 250 rad/sec?   *Ans.:* 8.07 sec.

4.28 A small d-c machine is to be used to provide a short pulse of constant electrical power to a load of resistance R. By use of an armature supply of E volts the machine is first brought up to its full speed v_0 with a constant field current i_{f0}. The machine is then disconnected from its supply and connected to the load R. Suppose the machine is magnetically linear, has negligible armature inductance, and is lossless. Let the polar moment of inertia be J.

(a) Show that the field current required to maintain constant power in the load is given by the expression

$$ i_f = i_{f0} \left[1 - \frac{2E^2 t}{RJv_0^2} \right]^{-\frac{1}{2}} \quad \text{amp} $$

(b) If the field current can be raised to twice its initial value, for how long a time can the constant power be maintained, and what will be the machine speed at the end of the pulse?

4.29 It is desired to use a certain series motor to drive a load requiring a torque of 4 newton-m at a speed of 25 r/sec. A 200-V d-c supply is available. A test on the machine at standstill shows that a shaft torque of 4 newton-m can be produced by a terminal current of 5 amp and a terminal voltage of 10 V. The rotational losses of the machine are considered negligible. What value of resistance is required in series with the 200-V supply to meet the required load condition?   *Ans.:* 12.9 Ω.

4.30 A 4-pole series-wound fan motor rotates at 100 rad/sec and takes 20 amp from its 200-V supply when its field coils are connected in series. In order to increase the speed of the system, it is decided to reconnect the field coils into two parallel groups, each group having two coils in series. The fan load requires a mechanical power that varies as the cube of the speed. The motor may be considered magnetically linear and all motor losses may be ignored. Determine the new values of motor speed and motor current. *Ans.:* 118.9 rad/sec; 33.6 amp.

4.31 A load requiring a constant torque of 30 newton-m is driven by a series motor supplied from a 200-V source. The combined resistance of the armature and series field of the motor is 0.3 Ω. When tested at standstill, a motor current of 25 amp produces a shaft torque of 10 newton-m. Further tests show that the motor has negligible magnetic saturation up to a field current of about 50 amp. Determine the speed at which the load is driven. *Ans.:* 270 rad/sec.

4.32 A small universal series motor produces a standstill torque of 2 newton-m when carrying a direct current of 3 amp. The total resistance between its terminal is 2.5 Ω and the total inductance is 0.04 henry. Magnetic linearity may be assumed and rotational losses may be ignored. Suppose this machine is connected to a 115 V rms, 60-c/s alternating-voltage source.

(a) Determine the starting torque for the machine.
Ans.: 12.5 newton-m.

(b) Determine the mechanical power produced when the motor current is 3 amp rms. *Ans.:* 294 W.

(c) Determine the input power factor for the condition of part (b).
Ans.: 0.92.

4.33 A radar antenna is supported on a turntable, which is to be revolved at a variable speed in either direction of rotation; the following drive system is suggested. A diesel motor is to be used to drive a separately excited d-c generator, which in turn is to supply power to the armature of a separately excited d-c motor. The motor is to be connected to the turntable through a 40:1 reduction gear. The effective load on the motor shaft is estimated to be 0.04 newton-m/r/min of the motor shaft. The generator and motor are identical, each having an armature resistance of 0.47 Ω and negligible friction losses. The open-circuit magnetization characteristic at 1200 r/min of each of the machines is

i_f(amp)	0	0.2	0.4	0.6	0.8	1.0	1.2
e_t(V)	0	108	183	230	254	267	276

The diesel motor has a no-load speed of 1000 r/min. Its speed drops by 2 r/min for each newton-m of its shaft torque.

(a) The radar system is to be provided with a control by which the generator field current can be adjusted to any value up to 1.2 amp in either direction. You are to provide a graph showing the relationship between antenna speed and generator field current. The motor field current is to be set at a constant value of 0.8 amp.

Ans.: 23 r/min at $i_f = 1.2$ amp.

(b) If the d-c machines have a nominal rating of 250 V and 5 kW at 1200 r/min, consider their ability to rotate the antenna continuously at maximum speed without overheating.

4.34 In the speed control system of Fig. 4.47, the motor speed is measured by a tachometer that produces 0.2 V/rad per sec. The electronic amplifier has a voltage amplification A. The generator has a field resistance of 20 Ω, a field inductance of 1 henry, and an armature resistance of 4 Ω. The generated voltage is 100 V/amp of field current. The motor has an armature resistance of 4 Ω and produces 1 newton-m of torque per amp of armature current. The polar moment of inertia of the motor and its load is 2 kg-m². Friction losses in both motor and load may be neglected. The armature inductance of the motor and the generator may also be neglected.

(a) Develop a transfer function relating the load speed v_m to the control voltage e_r.

(b) Determine the amplification A required to provide a relative damping ratio α/ω_n of 0.7.   *Ans.*: 163.

(c) Suppose the system is initially at rest and a constant control voltage of 10 V is applied. Sketch the speed as a function of time and determine the time required to reach the final steady-state speed for the first time. The amplification of part (b) may be used.   *Ans.*: 0.234 sec.

(d) Suppose the amplifier has a maximum output voltage of 28 V. Repeat part (c) with this limitation imposed.   *Ans.*: About 7 sec.

4.35 Figure P4.35 shows a system for positioning the magnetic reading head over the desired track on a disk memory of a computer. The head is moved 2.5 mm for each revolution of the motor shaft. The position of the

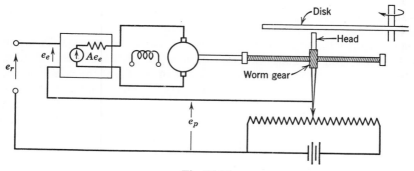

Fig. P4.35

head is measured by a linear potentiometer which gives an output voltage of 1 V/cm of displacement from the extreme left position of the head. The motor has an armature resistance of 12 Ω and negligible armature inductance. The polar moment of inertia of the motor and its load is 10^{-5} kg-m². The friction torque may be neglected. The motor produces a torque of 0.1 newton-m/amp of armature current. The amplifier has a voltage amplification of A and an internal resistance of 10 Ω.

(a) Develop a transfer function relating the position of the head to the control voltage.

(b) Determine the voltage amplification A required to produce a relative damping ratio of 0.5. *Ans.: 113.5.*

(c) A change in head position is initiated by a step change in the control voltage e_r. Estimate the time required for the head to remain within 5% of its desired position. *Ans.: 0.123 sec.*

4.36 A design is required for a d-c motor to drive a steel rolling mill. The steady-state rating of the motor is estimated to be 2 MW at 900 r/min. Electrical power is available from a controlled rectifier at a maximum direct voltage of 550 V. From previous experience with this type of drive, it is decided to use 6 poles having approximately square pole faces.

(a) Choose any reasonable values for the average air-gap flux density and for the linear current density on the armature surface. Estimate the diameter of the armature and the length of the armature core.

(b) Estimate the number of armature turns required using either a wave or a lap winding.

(c) Determine the cross-sectional area of the armature conductors using a current density of about 3 amp/mm².

4.37 A control motor is required to operate from a 28-V supply and to provide a torque of 0.5 newton-m at 200 r/sec. To achieve a low polar moment of inertia, the armature length is to be twice the armature diameter.

(a) By choosing any reasonable values for the operating densities in the machine, estimate the dimensions of the armature.

(b) Assume that the average density of the rotor material is about 8000 kg/m³, and estimate the polar moment of inertia of the armature. It may be assumed that the polar moment of inertia of the commutator, shaft and end connections is about equal to that of the cylinder of magnetic material. *Ans.: About 2×10^{-5} kg-m².*

REFERENCES

Burns, R. A., and R. M. Saunders, *Analysis of Feedback Control Systems.* McGraw-Hill, New York, 1955.

Carter, F. W., "The Magnetic Field of the Dynamo-Electric Machine." *Journal, Institution of Electrical Engineers*, London, **64,** 1926.

Langsdorf, A. S., *Principles of D-C Machines.* McGraw-Hill, New York, 1959.

Legros, R. and A. V. J. Martin, *Transform Calculus for Electrical Engineers.* Prentice-Hall, Englewood Cliffs, N.J., 1963.

Liuschitz-Garik, M. and C. C. Whipple, *Electric Machinery*, Vol. 1, D. Van Nostrand, Princeton, N.J., 1946.

Pestarini, J. M., *Metadyne Statics.* Technology Press and John Wiley and Sons, New York, 1952.

Say, M. G., *Rotating Amplifiers.* George Newnes, London, 1954.

Say, M. G. *Electrical Engineering Design Manual.* Chapman and Hall, London, 1962.

Thaler, G. J. and R. G. Brown, *Analysis and Design of Feedback Control Systems* (second edition). McGraw-Hill, New York, 1961.

Tustin, A., *Direct Current Machines for Control Systems.* Macmillan, New York, 1952.

Chapter 5
POLYPHASE MACHINES

5.1 GENERAL MAGNETIC AND WINDING ARRANGEMENTS

In this chapter various types of induction and synchronous machines are introduced. All of these machines have distributed windings carrying alternating currents on either the stator or rotor, or both. Because of their many common features, it is convenient to treat all synchronous and induction machines as a group or class. Our first step in the study of this class of machines is an examination of some of the factors that determine the shape of the magnetic structure and the distribution of the windings. The magnetic fields are then analyzed and a general circuit model is developed. By applying various constraints to the machine variables, this circuit model is then used to demonstrate and predict the performance of several types of induction and synchronous machines.

In Chapter 1, some simple torque-producing mechanisms using magnetic materials were discussed. Let us first examine the evolution of polyphase machines from these elementary systems. Figure 5.1 shows a simple magnetic system with a concentrated coil on each of its stator and rotor members. The torque of this system may be found using the energy conservation approach (Section 1.5.3). Assuming the magnetic system to be linear, we can express the flux linkages of the stator and rotor coils in terms of self- and mutual inductances as

$$\begin{aligned} \lambda_s &= L_s i_s + L_{sr} i_r \\ \lambda_r &= L_{sr} i_s + L_r i_r \end{aligned} \qquad \text{webers} \qquad (5.1)$$

Suppose the rotor is moved through an incremental angular displacement $d\theta$. Neglecting the resistances of the coils, the electric energy input to the system is, from eq. 1.94

$$\begin{aligned} dW_{\substack{\text{elec.} \\ \text{input}}} &= i_s \, d\lambda_s + i_r \, d\lambda_r \\ &= i_s \, d(L_s i_s + L_{sr} i_r) + i_r \, d(L_{sr} i_s + L_r i_r) \\ &= (L_s i_s \, di_s + i_s^2 \, dL_s + L_{sr} i_s \, di_r + i_s i_r \, dL_{sr} \\ &\quad + L_{sr} i_r \, di_s + i_r i_s \, dL_{sr} + L_r i_r \, di_r + i_r^2 \, dL_r) \end{aligned} \qquad (5.2)$$

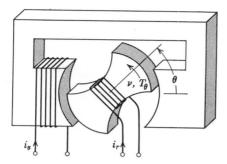

Fig. 5.1   Elementary machine with stator and rotor windings.

From eq. 1.98, the increase in magnetic energy stored in the system is

$$dW_{\text{stored}} = d(\tfrac{1}{2}L_s i_s^{\,2} + \tfrac{1}{2}L_r i_r^{\,2} + L_{sr}i_s i_r)$$

$$= \left(L_s i_s\, di_s + \frac{i_s^{\,2}}{2}\, dL_s + L_r i_r\, di_r + \frac{i_r^{\,2}}{2}\, dL_r \right.$$

$$\left. + L_{sr}i_s\, di_r + L_{sr}i_r\, di_s + i_s i_r\, dL_{sr} \right) \qquad (5.3)$$

Thus, the mechanical output energy is given by

$$dW_{\substack{\text{mech.}\\\text{output}}} = dW_{\substack{\text{elec.}\\\text{input}}} - dW_{\text{stored}}$$

$$= \frac{i_s^{\,2}}{2}\, dL_s + \frac{i_r^{\,2}}{2}\, dL_r + i_s i_r\, dL_{sr} \qquad (5.4)$$

and the torque is given by

$$T = \frac{dW_{\substack{\text{mech.}\\\text{output}}}}{d\theta}$$

$$= \frac{i_s^{\,2}}{2}\frac{dL_s}{d\theta} + \frac{i_r^{\,2}}{2}\frac{dL_r}{d\theta} + i_s i_r \frac{dL_{sr}}{d\theta} \qquad (5.5)$$

Let us now examine the conditions under which each of the three terms in eq. 5.5 can produce a useful torque in a rotating machine. The first two terms represent reluctance torques of the type discussed in Section 1.7.4. Suppose i_s is an alternating current of angular frequency ω_s. The quantity $i_s^{\,2}$, when expanded, contains a constant term plus a term of frequency $2\omega_s$. If the average torque of the rotating machine is not to be zero, $dL_s/d\theta$ must contain a component that varies at the frequency $2\omega_s$.

Figure 5.2a shows that the stator circuit inductance of the machine of Fig. 5.1 oscillates with a period of π radians about an average value. It may be expressed as a Fourier series with a constant term plus terms in $\cos 2\theta$, cos 4θ, ... Thus, $dL_s/d\theta$ contains only terms in sin 2θ, sin 4θ, ... If $\theta = \nu t$, the first and largest of these terms can be exploited if

$$2\theta = 2\nu t = \pm 2\omega_s t$$

or $$\nu = \pm \omega_s \qquad \text{radians/second}$$

(5.6)

Torque may also be produced from the sin 4θ, sin 6θ, ..., terms in $dL_s/d\theta$ at the lower speeds of $\nu = \pm \omega_s/2$, $\nu = \pm \omega_s/3$, ... However, if one of these lower speeds is desired, it is preferable to redesign the mag-

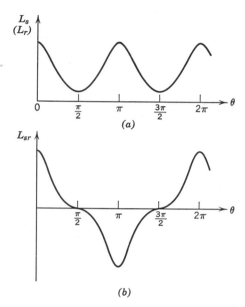

Fig. 5.2 Self-inductances L_s and L_r and mutual inductances L_{sr} of Fig. 5.1 as functions of rotor angle θ.

netic structure to have an appropriate number of poles on its stator or rotor to accentuate the desired term in $dL_s/d\theta$. The basic speed of operation would then be equal to ω_s divided by the number of pairs of poles.

Machines that depend for their torque on the first term of the torque expression of eq. 5.5 can operate only at certain speeds that are directly related to the stator supply frequency. They are therefore purely synchronous machines. Polyphase reluctance machines using this torque mechanism are discussed in Section 5.6.

A similar reasoning applies for torque developed from the second term of eq. 5.5. The variation of rotor inductance L_r with angle is of the same general form as that shown for the stator inductance in Fig. 5.2a. If the rotor current i_r has a frequency ω_r, torque can be developed only at the speeds

$$v = \pm\omega_r, \pm\frac{\omega_r}{2}, \pm\frac{\omega_r}{3}, \ldots \qquad \text{radians/second} \qquad (5.7)$$

The third term of eq. 5.5 offers somewhat greater flexibility in the values of speed at which useful torque can be produced. The product of two alternating currents i_s and i_r contains terms of the frequencies $\omega_s \pm \omega_r$. From Fig. 5.2b, the mutual inductance L_{sr} of the machine of Fig. 5.1 can be expressed as a Fourier series. The first and largest term of this series varies as cos θ. Thus $dL_{sr}/d\theta$ contains a term in sin θ. With $\theta = vt$, torque can be produced at any of the speeds

$$v = \pm(\omega_s \pm \omega_r) \qquad \text{radians/second} \qquad (5.8)$$

A machine that exploits the third term in eq. 5.6 can therefore operate either forward or backward at speeds equal to the sum or difference of the two supply frequencies. At any of these speeds the torque consists of a constant term plus several oscillatory terms. Submultiples of the speeds of eq. 5.8 can also be obtained by the use of several pairs of alternately wound poles in the magnetic structure of the machine.

From the foregoing discussion, some of the structural features of practical a-c machines can be inferred. Equations 5.6, 5.7, and 5.8 indicate that generally only one of the three torque terms of eq. 5.5 can be exploited in a given machine, because the speeds at which each produces torque are different. One notable exception occurs when either ω_s or ω_r equals zero, that is, when one of the windings carries direct current. The salient-pole synchronous machine discussed in Section 5.6.3 develops both a reluctance torque and a mutual inductance torque.

Most a-c machines derive their torque from the rate of change of mutual inductance between their stator and rotor windings. One of the reasons for this choice is that the magnitude of the variation of mutual inductance with angle is generally much larger than the variations of the self-inductances (see Fig. 5.2). A second and major reason for the use of the mutual inductance term is that it is necessary in the operation of induction machines (Section 5.4). In these machines the frequency of the currents produced by induction in the shorted rotor windings is automatically related to the speed, thus permitting operation over a wide speed range with a single-frequency stator supply.

If only the mutual inductance torque is to be exploited, the torques arising from changes in self-inductance are generally undesirable. Over most of the speed range these reluctance torque components are oscillatory and therefore useless. At the few values of speed for which they do produce average torque they may interfere with the desired performance.

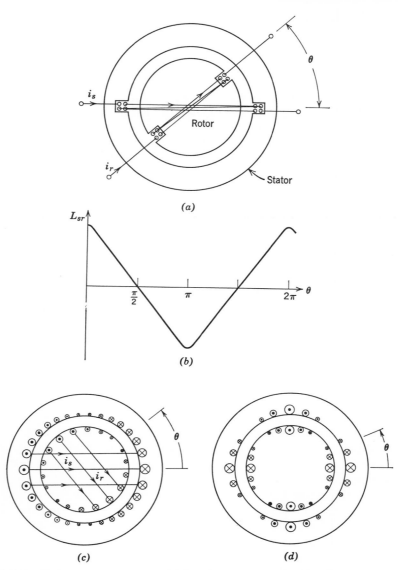

Fig. 5.3   (a) Cylindrical machine with concentrated windings. (b) Variation of mutual inductance L_{sr} with angle θ for concentrated windings of (a). (c) Cylindrical machine with sinusoidally distributed windings. (Turns density is suggested by the size of the circles.) (d) A four-pole sinusoidally wound machine.

The self-inductances of the stator and rotor windings may be made essentially independent of rotor position by the use of cylindrical magnetic structures for both stator and rotor, as shown in Fig. 5.3a. By neglecting the effects of the slots in which the windings are placed, the reluctances of the magnetic paths as seen by the stator and rotor windings in Fig. 5.3a are independent of the rotor position.

With the concentrated windings of Fig. 5.3a, the mutual inductance L_{sr} varies in the approximately linear manner shown in Fig. 5.3b. The Fourier series of L_{sr} therefore contains terms in cos θ, cos 3θ, ... It is desirable to eliminate the higher harmonic terms of this series, as they produce only oscillatory torque terms. Since this cannot now be done by changing the shape of the magnetic structure, it must be accomplished by distributing the windings. As might be expected, a sinusoidally varying mutual inductance can be achieved if the turns of the windings are distributed so that the turns density varies sinusoidally, as suggested by Fig. 5.3c. In a practical machine, various approximations to this ideal sinusoidal distribution are used.

The machine of Fig. 5.3c is described as a two-pole machine because the magnetic flux is directed outward in half of the machine and inward in the other half. Its possible speeds are those of eq. 5.8. Submultiples of these speeds may be obtained by arranging the winding to produce a large even number p of magnetic poles. Figure 5.3d shows a four-pole winding arrangement. For a p-pole machine, the mutual inductance L_{sr} varies as cos $(p\theta/2)$. Thus the basic speeds of operation of such a machine are

$$\nu = \pm \frac{2}{p}(\omega_s \pm \omega_r) \qquad \text{radians/second} \qquad (5.9)$$

The final step in this evolution of the structure of polyphase machines is the introduction of several symmetrically placed distributed windings on either or both of the stator and rotor. These windings normally carry balanced sets of polyphase currents. The basic reason for the use of polyphase windings is that they can produce a revolving magnetic field, as discussed in Section 4.1.3. This revolving field is an essential requirement for induction machines.

There are several other advantages in the use of polyphase windings. With only a single winding on each of the stator and rotor, there are oscillatory torque components in addition to the average torque. With polyphase windings carrying balanced currents, these oscillatory components are canceled out, leaving only a constant unidirectional torque. The direction of this torque is determined by the sequence in which the windings are energized. Another advantage is that more efficient use can be made of the space on the air-gap periphery of the stator and rotor.

With several symmetrically placed distributed windings, the density of conductors around the periphery becomes essentially constant.

5.2 MAGNETIC FIELD ANALYSIS

In this section we analyze, approximately, the magnetic field in a cylindrical machine with polyphase distributed windings. The objective in this analysis is to relate the terminal voltages and terminal currents of the windings to the torque and speed of the machine. Since the machine is a magnetic system like a transformer, we expect that the voltage-current relationships can be expressed in terms of winding inductances and ideal transformations, that is, an equivalent circuit. To find these inductances, we first examine the magnetic field produced by currents in distributed windings and then find the resultant flux linkages of the windings.

5.2.1 Magnetomotive Force Distribution

Let us consider the field produced by a single, two-pole distributed stator winding as shown in Fig. 5.4. It is assumed that the stator has a large number of slots and that the N_s turns of the winding are distributed in these slots so that the number of conductors per unit of angle varies approximately sinusoidally around the stator. For the winding shown in Fig. 5.4 and designated as a, the conductor density is assumed to be

$$n_a = \frac{N_s}{2}\cos\theta \qquad \text{conductors/radian} \qquad (5.10)$$

For convenience, conductors carrying positive winding current i_a away from the observer are considered to be positive.

Consider the path shown in Fig. 5.4. The magnetomotive force in a clockwise excursion around this path is equal to the total enclosed current

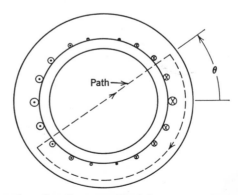

Fig. 5.4 The magnetomotive force produced by a sinusoidally distributed stator winding.

directed away from the observer. Thus

$$\mathscr{F}_{\text{path}} = \int_{\theta-\pi}^{\theta} \frac{N_s}{2} \cos\theta \, i_a \, d\theta$$

$$= N_s i_a \sin\theta \qquad \text{amperes} \qquad (5.11)$$

This shows the expected result that a sinusoidally distributed winding produces a sinusoidally distributed magnetomotive force.

Now consider a stator with m_s windings, each sinusoidally distributed and each having N_s turns, and mutually displaced ahead of each other around the periphery by $2\pi/m_s$ radians in the sequence a, b, c, ... Figure 5.5 shows the particular and important case of $m_s = 3$. For

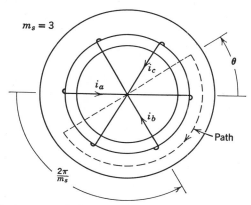

Fig. 5.5 Three-phase stator winding. (Center turn of each sinusoidally distributed winding shown).

simplicity, only the center turn of each winding is shown. If the winding currents are i_a, i_b, i_c, ..., the magnetomotive force around the path at angle θ is, by superposition,

$$\mathscr{F}_\theta = N_s i_a \sin\theta + N_s i_b \sin\left(\theta - \frac{2\pi}{m_s}\right) + N_s i_c \sin\left(\theta - \frac{4\pi}{m_s}\right) + \cdots \quad (5.12)$$

Suppose the winding currents are a balanced m_s-phase set with peak amplitude $\hat{I}_s$, sequence a, b, c, ..., and frequency ω_s.

$$i_a = \hat{I}_s \sin\left(\omega_s t + \alpha_s\right)$$

$$i_b = \hat{I}_s \sin\left(\omega_s t + \alpha_s - \frac{2\pi}{m_s}\right)$$

$$i_c = \hat{I}_s \sin\left(\omega_s t + \alpha_s - \frac{4\pi}{m_s}\right) \qquad \text{amperes} \qquad (5.13)$$

$$\cdots$$

Substituting these into eq. 5.12 yields the total magnetomotive force of a polyphase winding with balanced currents as

$$
\begin{aligned}
\mathscr{F}_\theta &= N_s \hat{I}_s \bigg[\sin(\omega_s t + \alpha_s) \sin\theta + \sin\left(\omega_s t + \alpha_s - \frac{2\pi}{m_s}\right) \sin\left(\theta - \frac{2\pi}{m_s}\right) \\
&\quad + \sin\left(\omega_s t + \alpha_s - \frac{4\pi}{m_s}\right) \sin\left(\theta - \frac{4\pi}{m_s}\right) + \cdots \bigg] \\
&= \frac{N_s \hat{I}_s}{2} \bigg[m_s \cos(\omega_s t + \alpha_s - \theta) + \cos(\omega_s t + \alpha_s + \theta) \\
&\quad + \cos\left(\omega_s t + \alpha_s + \theta - \frac{4\pi}{m_s}\right) + \cos\left(\omega_s t + \alpha_s - \frac{8\pi}{m_s}\right) + \cdots \bigg]
\end{aligned}
$$

$$(5.14)$$

By choosing any value of m_s equal to or greater than 3, it can easily be demonstrated that the sum of all but the first term in the bracketed part of eq. 5.14 is zero. Thus, the magnetomotive force produced by a set of balanced polyphase currents in a symmetrical set of sinusoidally distributed windings is

$$
\mathscr{F}_\theta = \frac{N_s \hat{I}_s m_s}{2} \cos(\omega_s t + \alpha_s - \theta) \qquad \text{amperes} \qquad (5.15)
$$

Equation 5.15 describes a revolving magnetic field. At any instant in time, the magnetomotive force $\mathscr{F}_\theta$ is distributed sinusoidally around the machine. The maximum value of magnetomotive force occurs for a path at

$$
\theta = \omega_s t + \alpha_s \qquad \text{radians} \qquad (5.16)
$$

As time t passes, the magnetomotive force distribution advances as a space wave of unchanging shape and magnitude around the machine. In Fig. 5.5, with the phase currents rising in the sequence $a, b, c, \ldots$, this revolving space wave proceeds counterclockwise around the machine at an angular velocity equal to the angular frequency ω_s of the stator supply current. The effect of the polyphase winding is therefore similar to that of a permanent-magnet stator rotating at angular velocity ω_s. The direction of rotation of this revolving field can be reversed by reversing the sequence of the currents.

Let us now consider the magnetomotive force produced by a polyphase winding on the rotor. Suppose there are m_r phase windings, each with N_r sinusoidally distributed turns. As shown in Fig. 5.6, the phase windings are displaced $2\pi/m_r$ radians apart, the sequence being $A, B, C, \ldots$. Let the rotor currents be a balanced m_r-phase set with

$$i_A = \hat{I}_r \sin(\omega_r t + \alpha_r),$$
$$i_B = \hat{I}_r \sin\left(\omega_r t + \alpha_r - \frac{2\pi}{m_r}\right) \quad (5.17)$$
$$\cdots$$

Then, by analogy with eq. 5.15, the magnetomotive force of the rotor windings for the path shown in Fig. 5.6 is

$$\mathcal{F}_\gamma = \frac{N_r \hat{I}_r m_r}{2} \cos(\omega_r t + \alpha_r - \gamma) \quad \text{amperes} \quad (5.18)$$

where γ is the angular position of the path measured with respect to the phase A reference axis on the rotor.

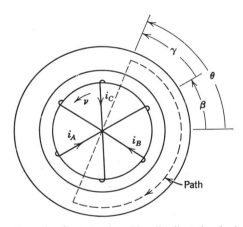

Fig. 5.6 The magnetomotive force produced by distributed polyphase rotor windings.

As the total magnetomotive force along any path in the machine is the sum of the magnetomotive forces produced by the stator and rotor windings, it is convenient to express the rotor magnetomotive force of eq. 5.18 in terms of the stator reference angle θ. As shown in Fig. 5.6, let

$$\theta = \beta + \gamma \quad \text{radians} \quad (5.19)$$

Then eq. 5.18 becomes

$$\mathcal{F}_\theta = \frac{N_r \hat{I}_r m_r}{2} \cos(\omega_r t + \alpha_r + \beta - \theta) \quad \text{amperes} \quad (5.20)$$

At standstill, β is a constant β_0. Equation 5.20 then represents a sinusoidally distributed magnetic field rotating in a forward (counterclockwise) direction at an angular velocity of ω_r radians per second. If, however, the rotor itself is rotating at angular velocity ν in a forward direction,

$$\beta = \nu t + \beta_0 \qquad \text{radians} \qquad (5.21)$$

where β_0 represents the rotor position at $t = 0$. The rotor magnetomotive force then becomes

$$\mathscr{F}_\theta = \frac{N_r \hat{I}_r m_r}{2} \cos\left[(\omega_r + \nu)t + \alpha_r + \beta_0 - \theta\right] \qquad \text{amperes} \quad (5.22)$$

This represents a magnetic field which is rotating forward at an angular velocity $\omega_r + \nu$ as seen by a stationary observer.

A comparison of eqs. 5.15 and 5.22 shows that identical magnetomotive force distribution can be produced by either the stator or the rotor currents provided three conditions are met, namely,

$$\nu = \omega_s - \omega_r \qquad \text{radians/second} \qquad (5.23)$$

$$\frac{\hat{I}_r}{\hat{I}_s} = \frac{N_s m_s}{N_r m_r} \qquad (5.24)$$

and
$$\alpha_r = \alpha_s - \beta_0 \qquad (5.25)$$

The first condition (eq. 5.23) is one of the speeds at which eq. 5.8 indicates that torque can be produced in a two-pole machine. (For a p-pole machine, eq. 5.23 is replaced by eq. 5.9.) In further analysis we will be concerned only with situations where this condition is met.

The second condition represents the current ratio of a polyphase transformer connected with different numbers of primary and secondary phases (Section 3.3.3). The magnetizing current for the machine may be provided equally from either the stator or the rotor windings if the magnitudes of the balanced polyphase magnetizing currents are related by eq. 5.24.

The third condition of eq. 5.25 merely states that, when the axis of phase A on the rotor is shifted forward by an angle β_0 at $t = 0$, the magnetomotive force produced by the rotor currents is similarly shifted forward in angle θ.

Another way of expressing these conditions is that, when a given rotor magnetomotive force is viewed from the stator, it is impossible to tell whether it is produced (1) by a stationary rotor carrying polyphase currents of frequency $\omega_r = \omega_s$, (2) a rotor rotating at speed $\nu = \omega_s$ carrying direct current in its windings, or (3) a rotor with winding currents of frequency ω_r rotating at speed $\nu = \omega_s - \omega_r$. These three situations represent the operation of the machine (1) as a transformer, (2) as a synchronous machine, and (3) as an induction machine.

The total magnetomotive force acting on the magnetic system at any instant and at any angle θ may be found by adding the stator and rotor contributions of eqs. 5.15 and 5.22. These contributions are both sinusoids in θ rotating at a common angular velocity ω_s if the condition of eq. 5.23 applies. They may thus be added conveniently in vector form. Figure 5.7 shows vectors representing the magnitudes and positions in angle θ of the peak values of the stator and rotor magnetomotive forces. The reference axis for this vector diagram has been chosen so that each vector is oriented

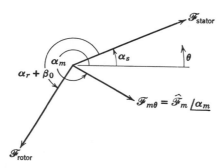

Fig. 5.7 Space vector diagram showing stator, rotor, and magnetizing magnetomotive forces.

in the same direction as the magnetomotive force in the machine diagram (Fig. 5.5 or 5.6) at $t = 0$.*

The vector addition of the stator magnetomotive force $\mathscr{F}_{s\theta}$ and the rotor magnetomotive force $\mathscr{F}_{r\theta}$ in Fig. 5.7 gives the net or magnetizing magnetomotive force

$$\mathscr{F}_{m\theta} = \hat{\mathscr{F}}_m \cos(\omega_s t + \alpha_m - \theta \qquad \text{amperes} \qquad (5.26)$$

From eq. 5.15, this magnetizing force can be considered as the result of a magnetizing component of the stator current. In phase a, this current component would be

$$i_{ma} = \hat{I}_{ms} \sin(\omega_s t + \alpha_m) \qquad \text{amperes} \qquad (5.27)$$

where

$$\hat{I}_{ms} = \frac{2\hat{\mathscr{F}}_m}{N_s m_s} \qquad \text{amperes} \qquad (5.28)$$

* It should be noted that magnetomotive force is a scalar quantity. The space vectors of Fig. 5.7 represent the sinusoids in space of this quantity just as a phasor represents a sinusoid in time of a scalar, such as current.

5.2.2   Flux Linkages and Inductances

Now that we have determined the magnetomotive force acting in the machine, the next step is to determine the magnetic flux density it produces. Consider a path like that shown in Fig. 5.6. If the magnetic material is regarded as perfect, all the magnetomotive force (eq. 5.26) is absorbed at the two air gaps. Making allowance for the slotting of both stator and rotor (see Section 4.2), we let the effective length of each air gap be g'.

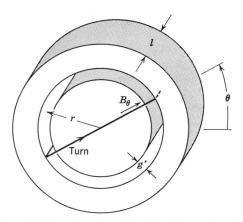

Fig. 5.8   The determination of the flux linkage of a winding.

Then, because of the symmetry of the machine, the magnetic field intensity directed outward across the air gap at angle θ is

$$H_\theta = \frac{\mathscr{F}_{m\theta}}{2g'} \qquad \text{amperes/meter} \qquad (5.29)$$

The corresponding magnetic flux density in the air gap is, from eq. 5.26,

$$\begin{aligned} B_\theta &= \mu_0 H_\theta \\ &= \hat{B}\cos(\omega_s t + \alpha_m - \theta) \qquad \text{webers/meter}^2 \end{aligned} \qquad (5.30)$$

where $\hat{B} = \mu_0 \mathscr{F}_m / 2g'$.

We may now find the flux linkages this air-gap flux density produces in a stator or rotor winding. Consider a single turn, as shown in Fig. 5.8, with its "positive" side at θ and its "negative" side at $\theta + \pi$. If r is the radius at the air gap and l is the axial length of the magnetic system, the flux linkage of this turn is

$$\begin{aligned} \lambda_{\text{turn}} &= \int_\theta^{\theta+\pi} B_\theta l r \, d\theta \\ &= -2\hat{B}lr \sin(\omega_s t + \alpha_m - \theta) \qquad \text{webers} \end{aligned} \qquad (5.31)$$

The conductor distribution for the winding of phase a of the stator is given in eq. 5.10. Integration over the band of conductors in phase a gives its flux linkage due to the air-gap flux density as

$$\lambda_{ma} = \int_{-\pi/2}^{\pi/2} \frac{N_s}{2} \cos \theta \lambda_{\text{turn}} \, d\theta$$

$$= \frac{\pi}{2} N_s \hat{B} l r \sin (\omega_s t + \alpha_m) \qquad \text{webers} \qquad (5.32)$$

The flux linkages of the windings $b, c, \ldots,$ of the stator have the same magnitude but are delayed by phase angles of $2\pi/m_s, 4\pi/m_s, \ldots$. In addition to these flux linkages due to air-gap flux, there are additional flux linkages of the windings due to leakage flux around the conductors in the slots. These are considered in Section 5.2.5.

The flux linkages of the rotor windings may similarly be found by considering first a single turn at an angle γ in Fig. 5.6. From eqs. 5.19 and 5.30, the radial flux density at an angle γ is

$$B_\gamma = \hat{B} \cos (\omega_s t + \alpha_m - \beta - \gamma) \qquad \text{webers/meter}^2 \qquad (5.33)$$

The flux linkage of a turn at angle γ is then

$$\lambda_{\text{turn}} = \int_\gamma^{\gamma+\pi} B_\gamma l r \, d\theta$$

$$= -2\hat{B} l r \sin (\omega_s t + \alpha_m - \beta - \gamma) \qquad \text{webers} \qquad (5.34)$$

For phase A on the rotor, the conductor distribution is

$$n_A = \frac{N_r}{2} \cos \gamma \qquad \text{conductors/radian} \qquad (5.35)$$

Thus the flux linkage of phase winding A due to the air-gap flux density is

$$\lambda_{mA} = \int_{-\pi/2}^{\pi/2} \frac{N_r}{2} \cos \gamma (-2\hat{B} l r) \sin (\omega_s t + \alpha_m - \beta - \gamma) \, d\gamma$$

$$= \frac{\pi}{2} N_r \hat{B} l r \sin (\omega_s t + \alpha_m - \beta) \qquad \text{webers} \qquad (5.36)$$

For the windings $B, C, \ldots$ of the rotor, the flux linkages are delayed by phase angles of $2\pi/m_r, 4\pi/m_r, \ldots$.

It is convenient for analysis to relate the flux linkages directly to the winding currents. Suppose the machine is magnetized by a balanced set of stator currents, the current in phase a being i_{ma} as given by eq. 5.27. From eqs. 5.26, 5.27, 5.28, 5.30, and 5.32, the flux linkage of winding a

is found to be

$$\lambda_{ma} = \frac{\pi}{2} N_s \left(\frac{\mu_0}{2g'} N_s \frac{\hat{\imath}_{ms}}{2} m_s \right) lr \sin(\omega_s t + \alpha_m) \qquad \text{webers} \qquad (5.37)$$

The magnetizing inductance of the machine with balanced polyphase magnetizing current, as seen from the stator, is therefore

$$L_{ms} = \frac{\lambda_{ma}}{i_{ma}}$$

$$= N_s^2 \mu_0 \frac{\pi m_s}{8} \frac{lr}{g'} \qquad \text{henrys} \qquad (5.38)$$

It can be shown that this expression also applies for a p-pole machine if N_s is the number of turns per pole pair per phase.

By analogy, if the machine is magnetized by a balanced set of polyphase currents in the rotor windings, the magnetizing inductance per phase, as seen from the rotor, is

$$L_{mr} = N_r^2 \mu_0 \frac{\pi m_r}{8} \frac{lr}{g'} \qquad \text{henrys} \qquad (5.39)$$

The per-phase values of magnetizing inductance given in eqs. 5.38 and 5.39 are useful when dealing with balanced winding currents. When the currents are not balanced, the self- and mutual inductances of the individual windings may be required. If only the stator winding a carries a current i_a, its magnetomotive force (eq. 5.11) may be used in eqs. 5.30, 5.31, and 5.32 to obtain the flux linkage λ_{aa}. The self-magnetizing inductance of winding a, due to air-gap flux, is

$$L_{aa} = N_s^2 \mu_0 \frac{\pi}{4} \frac{lr}{g'} \qquad \text{henrys} \qquad (5.40)$$

The mutual magnetizing inductances between windings a, b, c, ... of the stator are

$$L_{ab} = L_{aa} \cos \frac{2\pi}{m_s} ; \quad L_{ac} = L_{aa} \cos \frac{4\pi}{m_s} ; \quad \cdots \qquad (5.41)$$

By analogy, the self- and mutual magnetizing inductances of the rotor windings are

$$L_{AA} = N_r^2 \mu_0 \frac{\pi}{4} \frac{lr}{g'} \qquad \text{henrys} \qquad (5.42)$$

and

$$L_{AB} = L_{AA} \cos \frac{2\pi}{m_r} , \ldots . \qquad \text{henrys} \qquad (5.43)$$

5.2.3 Effect of Magnetic Saturation

To make efficient use of the magnetic material in the machine, it is generally necessary to operate it at reasonably high values of maximum flux density. The assumption of ideal magnetic material that we have made thus far is therefore not valid over the whole range of operation. From Fig. 5.9a, it can be seen that the highest values of flux density occur in the stator and rotor teeth. The magnetic field intensity of at least the teeth should therefore be included in a calculation of the flux density B_θ produced in the air gap by the magnetomotive force $\mathscr{F}_{m\theta}$ acting along a path at angle θ.

Calculation of the effect of magnetic saturation is somewhat tedious but the process is relatively simple. For a given value of the air-gap flux density B_θ, averaged over teeth and slots, the actual flux density along the stator and rotor teeth may be found. Corresponding values of magnetic field intensity H may be found from a $B-H$ curve for the magnetic material. The magnetic field intensity may then be integrated with respect to distance around the path shown in Fig. 5.9a, making allowance also for the field intensity in the yoke and core if these are significant. The result is the magnetomotive force $\mathscr{F}_{m\theta}$ required in the path to support the given averaged value of air-gap density B_θ. If this process is repeated for a number of values of B_θ, the curve of Fig. 5.9b is obtained.

Figure 5.9c shows the magnetomotive force $\mathscr{F}_{m\theta}$ of the path as a function of the angle θ. With sinusoidally distributed windings, this magnetomotive force is a sinusoidal function of θ for any values of the stator or rotor currents. Figure 5.9d shows the corresponding spatial distribution of the average air-gap density B_θ, derived by the use of the curve of Fig. 5.9b.

With magnetic saturation, the flux density B_θ is flat topped. For purposes of analysis, it may be represented as a Fourier series, replacing eq. 5.30 by

$$B_\theta = \hat{B}_1 \cos (\omega_s t + \alpha_m - \theta)$$
$$- \hat{B}_3 \cos 3(\omega_s t + \alpha_m - \theta) + \cdots \quad \text{webers/meter}^2 \quad (5.44)$$

By analogy with eqs. 5.31 and 5.32, the flux linkage of a turn at angle θ is

$$\lambda_{\text{turn}} = \int_\theta^{\theta+\pi} B_\theta lr \, d\theta$$

$$= -2lr \left[\hat{B}_1 \sin (\omega_s t + \alpha_m - \theta) - \frac{\hat{B}_3}{3} \sin 3(\omega_s t + \alpha_m - \theta) + \cdots \right]$$

and the flux linkage of winding a of the stator is $\qquad\qquad (5.45)$

$$\lambda_{ma} = \int_{-\pi/2}^{\pi/2} \frac{N_s}{2} \cos \theta \lambda_{\text{turn}} \, d\theta$$

$$= \hat{\lambda}_{ms} \sin (\omega_s t + \alpha_m) \quad \text{webers} \quad (5.46)$$

where $\qquad\qquad \hat{\lambda}_{ms} = \frac{\pi}{2} N_s \hat{B}_1 lr \qquad\qquad\qquad (5.47)$

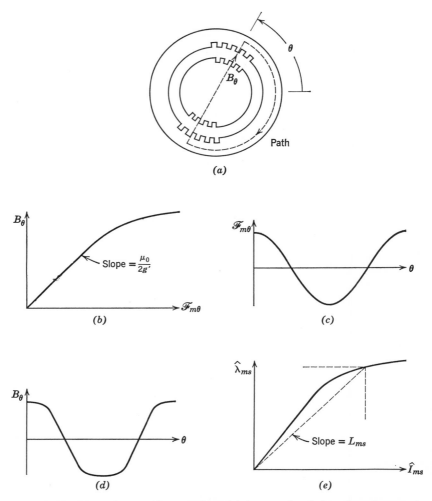

Fig. 5.9 The effect of magnetic saturation. (a) A general path in a slotted magnetic structure. (b) Average air-gap flux density B_θ as a function of the path magnetomotive force $\mathscr{F}_{m\theta}$. (c) Sinusoidal distribution of $\mathscr{F}_{m\theta}$ with angle θ. (d) Nonsinusoidal distribution of flux density B_θ with angle θ. (e) Relation between magnetizing flux linkage λ_{ms} and magnetizing current $\hat{I}_{ms}$.

Note that the higher harmonic terms of the flux density B_θ make no contribution to the flux linkage of the sinusoidally distributed winding. The winding can be linked only by a flux density that has the same spatial period of sinusoidal distribution as the winding. It is therefore a property of a sinusoidally wound machine that a balanced set of sinusoidal currents in its windings produces sinusoidally varying flux linkages even though the magnetic structure is nonlinear.

By Fourier analysis, the fundamental component $\hat{B}_1$ of the flux density B_θ may be found for a number of values of peak magnetizing force $\hat{\mathscr{F}}_m$. A curve such as Fig. 5.9e relating the magnetizing flux linkage λ_{ms} (eq. 5.47) and the stator magnetizing current $\hat{I}_{ms}$ (eq. 5.28) may be produced. The linear part of this curve has the slope L_{ms} determined in eq. 5.38 for the magnetically linear machine. In the magnetically nonlinear range, the magnetizing inductance L_{ms} is henceforth denoted as

$$L_{ms} = \frac{\hat{\lambda}_{ms}}{\hat{I}_{ms}} \qquad \text{henrys} \qquad (5.48)$$

With increased saturation, the value of the magnetizing inductance decreases.

5.2.4 Practical Winding Arrangements

The previous analysis was based on the assumption of sinusoidally distributed windings. Even at best, a compromise must be made with this idealization because the practical number of slots is limited. Figure 5.10a shows one way in which an approximately sinusoidal winding for one phase can be arranged. Ideally, the desired conductor density for an N_s-turn, two-pole winding is

$$n = \frac{N_s}{2} \cos \theta \qquad \text{conductors/radian} \qquad (5.49)$$

In a practical winding with S slots, the number of conductors N_q in the qth slot can be made equal to

$$N_q = \int_{q(2\pi/S)}^{(q+1)(2\pi/S)} \frac{N_s}{2} \cos \theta \, d\theta \qquad (5.50)$$

Where $S = 12$, as in Fig. 5.10a, the result is two sets of three coils having $0.25N_s$, $0.183N_s$, and $0.067N_s$ turns, respectively. The coils are connected in series.

The magnetomotive force distribution produced by this winding is shown in Fig. 5.10b. Even with the small number of slots, the result is reasonably close to sinusoidal form. In practice, coil 3 might be omitted or its turns amalgamated with those of coil 2. This concentric type of winding is widely used in small machines in which each of the coils has a relatively large number of turns of small flexible wire. It is also used in the rotor winding of high-speed synchronous machines (see Fig. 5.29).

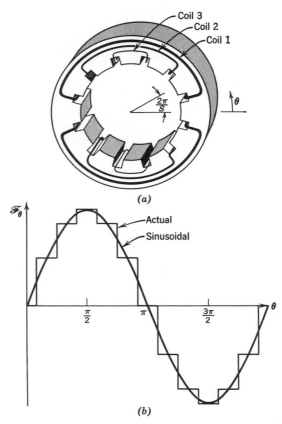

(a)

(b)

Fig. 5.10 (a) Concentric winding for twelve-slot stator. (b) Magnetomotive force distribution.

The production and installation of coils in larger machines is greatly simplified if all the coils are identical in shape and number of turns. Although this might appear to impose a severe restriction, we shall find that approximately sinusoidal magnetomotive force distribution can be produced by identical-coil windings whose turns distribution is far from sinusoidal. As an extreme case consider the m-phase winding of Fig. 5.11a in which each phase has only one coil of N turns. The magnetomotive force distribution of phase 0 is shown in Fig. 5.11b. This can be expressed as a Fourier series of space harmonics.

$$\mathcal{F}_{00} = \frac{4}{\pi} N i_0 \left(\sin \theta + \frac{\sin 3\theta}{3} + \frac{\sin 5\theta}{5} + \cdots \right) \tag{5.51}$$

If

$$i_0 = \hat{I} \sin \omega t \tag{5.52}$$

the magnetomotive force of phase 0 can be expressed as

$$\mathcal{F}_{00} = \frac{4}{\pi} N\hat{I} \sum_{h=1}^{h=\infty} \sin(\omega t) \frac{\sin(h\theta)}{h} \tag{5.53}$$

where h denotes the order of the space harmonics and is a series of odd numbers. The kth phase is displaced by $k2\pi/m$ radians from phase 0 and

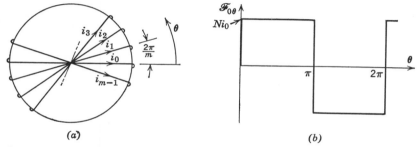

(a)   (b)

Fig. 5.11 (a) m-phase winding with single coil of N turns per phase. (b) Magnetomotive force of zero phase winding.

its current is delayed by a similar phase angle of $k2\pi/m$ radians. Thus the magnetomotive force produced by the kth phase is

$$\begin{aligned}
\mathcal{F}_{k\theta} &= \frac{4}{\pi} N\hat{I} \sum_{h=1}^{h=\infty} \frac{1}{h} \sin\left(\omega t - \frac{k2\pi}{m}\right) \sin h\left(\theta - \frac{k2\pi}{m}\right) \\
&= \frac{2N\hat{I}}{\pi} \sum_{h=1}^{h=\infty} \frac{1}{h}\left[\cos\left\{\omega t - h\theta + (h-1)\frac{k2\pi}{m}\right\} \right. \\
&\qquad \left. - \cos\left\{\omega t + h\theta - (h+1)\frac{k2\pi}{m}\right\}\right]
\end{aligned} \tag{5.54}$$

The total magnetomotive force of the winding is then given by the summation

$$\mathcal{F}_\theta = \sum_{k=0}^{k=m-1} \mathcal{F}_k = \mathcal{F}_{1\theta} + \mathcal{F}_{3\theta} + \mathcal{F}_{5\theta} + \mathcal{F}_{h\theta} + \cdots \tag{5.55}$$

This rather formidable double summation produces a simple result. With $h = 1$, the fundamental space distribution is

$$\mathscr{F}_{1\theta} = \frac{2mN\hat{I}}{\pi} \cos(\omega t - \theta) \qquad \text{amperes} \qquad (5.56)$$

A comparison of this equation with eq. 5.15 shows that the concentrated windings of N turns produce the same fundamental revolving field as would $(4/\pi)N$ sinusoidally distributed turns. This represents a significant saving in the number of required turns.

Of the various space harmonic terms, the only ones that do not sum to zero are those for which $(h \pm 1)/m$ is an integer. Thus

$$\mathscr{F}_{h\theta} = \frac{2mN\hat{I}}{\pi h} \cos(\omega t - h\theta) \quad \text{for} \quad \frac{h-1}{m} = \text{integer}$$

$$= \frac{2mN\hat{I}}{h} \cos(\omega t + h\theta) \quad \text{for} \quad \frac{h+1}{m} = \text{integer} \qquad (5.57)$$

Note that the lowest order of space harmonic is $h = m - 1$ for an even number of phases or $h = 2m - 1$ for an odd number of phases. In addition, the amplitude of the hth harmonic is only $1/h$ of that of the fundamental. Thus, if the number of phases is large, the space harmonics in the total magnetomotive force wave are generally negligible. This feature is significant in squirrel-cage induction machines where the rotor winding consists of b solid bars connected to shorting end rings. For purposes of analysis, this winding may be considered as a $m_r = b/2$ phase winding of one concentrated turn (or the equivalent of $4/\pi$ sinusoidally distributed turns) per phase. If b is large, the effects of the space harmonics may be neglected.

For windings that are connected to external supplies or loads, the normal number of phases is either three or four. (The system generally called two-phase is actually an asymmetrical half of a four-phase system.) Concentrated coils for windings with such low numbers of phases produce significant space harmonics. In these windings, the space harmonics are controlled by the distribution and pitch of the coils.

Suppose the coils of an m-phase winding are distributed in the S-slots so that each phase winding occupies a pair of bands as shown in Fig. 5.12a. The number of mutually displaced coils (n) per phase is $S/2m$ for an odd number of phases or S/m for an even number of phases. Each of the coils has N/n turns and all coils of a phase are connected in series. The magnetomotive force distribution produced by this winding is compared with the ideal sinusoid in Fig. 5.12b. Analytically, the magnetomotive force of each coil has a rectangular form that can be expressed as a

Fourier series of odd harmonics as in eq. 5.51. The total magnetomotive force of the winding may be found conveniently by the addition of space vectors.

Figure 5.12c shows the summation of n vectors representing the fundamental components produced by the n coils. The phase displacement between these vectors is $\alpha = 2\pi/S$. From the geometrical construction,

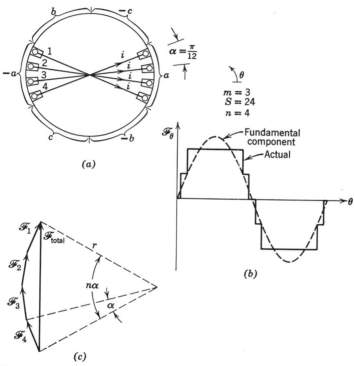

Fig. 5.12 (a) Distributed three-phase winding. (b) Magnetomotive force of winding. (c) Summation of fundamental space vectors of magnetomotive force.

note that each vector forms the chord of a circle of radius r over an angle α, while the total vector is a chord of the same circle over an angle $n\alpha$. Thus, from eq. 5.51,

$$\hat{\mathscr{F}}_{1(\text{coil})} = 2r \sin \frac{\alpha}{2} = \frac{2Ni}{\pi n} \tag{5.58}$$

and

$$\hat{\mathscr{F}}_{1(\text{total})} = 2r \sin \frac{n\alpha}{2}$$

$$= K_{1d} \frac{2}{\pi} Ni \tag{5.59}$$

where the fundamental distribution factor K_{1d} is

$$K_{1d} = \frac{\sin (n\alpha/2)}{n \sin (\alpha/2)} \tag{5.60}$$

A distributed winding of N turns therefore produces the same fundamental space wave as a concentrated winding of $K_{1d}N$ turns, or as a sinusoidally distributed winding of N_1' turns, where

$$N_1' = \frac{4}{\pi} K_{1d}N \tag{5.61}$$

For a three-phase winding in which the phase band is $\pi/3$ radians, K_{1d} is between 0.955 and 1.0. For a four-phase winding, the phase band is $\pi/2$ radians and the fundamental distribution factor may be as low as 0.9.

The vectors of the unwanted space harmonics are displaced from each other by an angle $h\alpha$ for the hth harmonic. Thus, the distribution factor for the hth harmonic is

$$K_{hd} = \frac{\sin (hn\alpha/2)}{n \sin (h\alpha/2)} \tag{5.62}$$

This harmonic distribution factor is always less than unity and may be small for certain space harmonics.

An effective means of minimizing one or more space harmonics is the use of coils that span less than π radians for a two-pole machine (or $2\pi/p$ radians for a p-pole machine) as shown in Fig. 5.13a. For an S-slot machine, the span of a coil may be $\pi - \beta$ where β is any multiple of $2\pi/S$ radians. The magnetomotive force for a path at θ of a short-pitched coil of N turns is shown in Fig. 5.13b. The maximum value of space harmonic h is

$$\mathscr{F}_h = \frac{2}{\pi} \int_{\beta/2}^{\pi-\beta/2} Ni \sin (h\theta) \, d\theta$$

$$= K_{hp} \frac{2}{\pi} \frac{Ni}{h} \tag{5.63}$$

where the pitch factor K_{hp} for harmonic h is

$$K_{hp} = \cos \frac{h\beta}{2} \tag{5.64}$$

By the proper choice of β, the pitch factor of a particular harmonic may be made equal to zero. For example, to eliminate all fifth space harmonic, β is made equal to $\pi/5$ or $36°$. In a 30-slot machine, this would involve short pitching the coil by three slots. The effect of short pitching on the fundamental component is small, as β is relatively small and $\cos(\beta/2) \approx 1.0$.

The effects of short pitching and distribution can be combined into a single winding factor K_{hw} where

$$K_{hw} = K_{hd}K_{hp} \tag{5.65}$$

for the harmonic of order h. A winding of N distributed and short-pitched turns then has the same fundamental space wave as a winding of $K_{1w}N$ concentrated turns or $(4/\pi)K_{1w}N$ sinusoidally distributed turns.

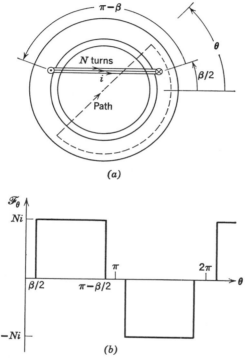

(a)

(b)

Fig. 5.13 (a) Short-pitched coil of N turns. (b) Magnetomotive force of coil.

In a p-pole machine all the coils of a particular phase are normally connected in series. In the stator winding, both ends of each winding may be brought out to terminals, or the winding may be internally connected in star or mesh. A polyphase rotor winding is usually internally connected so that the number of required slip rings is equal to the number of phases. But a neutral connection from a star-connected rotor winding can be brought out on an extra slip ring if required.

5.2.5   Leakage Inductances

The useful part of the magnetic field in a machine is normally only that which produces mutual flux linkage between stator and rotor windings. But, in addition, there are significant amounts of leakage flux that link one of the windings but not the others.

Figure 5.14 shows several of the regions in which leakage flux linkage may occur. These include (*a*) leakage flux within the slot, (*b*) leakage flux

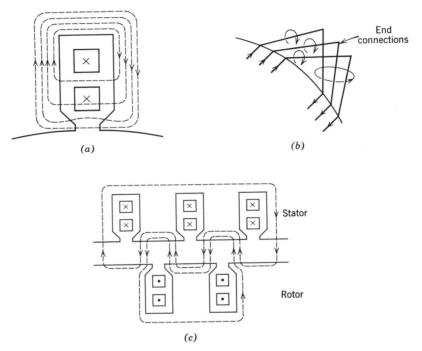

(*a*)   (*b*)

(*c*)

Fig. 5.14   Leakage flux patterns (*a*) in slot. (*b*) Around end connections. (*c*) Around group of phase coils following zigzag air-gap path.

around the end connections of the coils, and (*c*) leakage that follows a zigzag path between stator and rotor tooth faces along the air gap. Except for the presence of the magnetic material, this zigzag leakage is similar to that between two adjacent windings of a transformer (Section 3.1.4).

In Section 5.4.1 we see that the starting current, the starting torque, and the maximum torque of induction machines are all determined by the leakage inductances of the windings. For synchronous machines, the leakage inductances determine the maximum short-circuit currents and also influence the control of terminal voltage. Thus accurate methods of predicting leakage inductances are necessary to the machine designer. For the limited purposes of this treatment, we need only obtain a general picture of the relation between the leakage inductances and the dimensions.

Consider one side of an N-turn coil situated in a slot, as is shown in Fig. 5.15. Let us assume that the magnetic material is perfect and that the

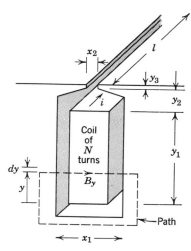

Fig. 5.15 The calculation of slot leakage inductance.

flux crosses the slot horizontally. The magnetomotive force of a path at height y is

$$\mathscr{F}_y = Ni\frac{y}{y_1} \quad \text{for} \quad y < y_1$$
$$= Ni \quad \text{for} \quad y > y_1 \quad \text{amperes} \quad (5.66)$$

The flux density at height y is

$$B_y = \frac{\mu_0 \mathscr{F}_y}{x_1} \quad 0 < y < (y_1 + y_2)$$
$$= \frac{\mu_0 \mathscr{F}_y}{x_2} \quad (y_1 + y_2) < y < (y_1 + y_2 + y_3) \quad \text{webers/meter}^2 \quad (5.67)$$

Noting that for $y < y_1$ the flux due to B_y links only y/y_1 of the N conductors, we find that the approximate flux linkage resulting from slot leakage around the two sides of a coil can be expressed as

$$\lambda_{\text{slot}} = 2\int_0^{y_1} B_y \frac{y}{y_1} Nl\, dy + 2\int_{y_1}^{y_1+y_2+y_3} B_y Nl\, dy$$

$$= 2\int_0^{y_1} \frac{\mu_0 N^2 il}{x_1}\left(\frac{y}{y_1}\right)^2 dy + 2\int_{y_1}^{y_1+y_2} \frac{\mu_0 N^2 il}{x_1}\, dy + 2\int_{y_1+y_2}^{y_1+y_2+y_3} \frac{\mu_0 N^2 il}{x_2}\, dy$$

$$= 2N^2\mu_0 li\left(\frac{y_1}{3x_1} + \frac{y_2}{x_1} + \frac{y_\gamma}{x_2}\right) \qquad \text{webers} \qquad (5.68)$$

The slot leakage inductance λ_{slot}/i is therefore dependent on the ratio of slot depth to slot width. Partial closure of the slot as shown in Fig. 5.15 causes a considerable increase in slot leakage inductance. But it has the desirable effect of increasing the magnetizing inductance by reducing the effective length g' of the air gap (eq. 5.38).

In a two-layer winding, a slot contains the sides of two coils. If the coils are fully pitched, these coil sides carry the same phase current, and the total contribution of the two sides to the leakage inductance may be determined as in eq. 5.68. If the coils, however, are short pitched, some slots contain coil sides of two different phases. In this case, we can calculate the self-flux linkages of each phase and the mutual flux linkages between phases.

The zigzag leakage inductance is proportional to the air-gap area, the square of the number of turns, and the inverse of the effective air-gap length. These are the same factors that determine the magnetizing inductance (eq. 5.38). The number of times that the zigzag flux crosses the air gap is dependent on the number of slots per phase. Thus, to a first approximation, the zigzag leakage inductance of a winding is equal to the self-magnetizing inductance of eq. 5.40, divided by the square of the number of slots per phase. In machines that have only a few slots per phase, this zigzag inductance may make a large contribution to the total leakage inductance.

There is one other flux in the machine that crosses the air gap but generally produces no mutual flux linkage. This is the flux produced by any space harmonics of the magnetomotive force of the winding (Section 5.2.4). The harmonic leakage inductance of a winding is found by summing the self-flux linkages per unit of current of all these space harmonics. With good winding design, this contribution to the leakage inductance can be made negligible. But in an extreme case, such as a full-pitched, three-phase concentrated winding, the harmonic leakage inductance may be about 10% of the self-magnetizing inductance.

The paths of all the components of leakage flux are at least partially in air. Thus the leakage flux linkage of a winding is usually linearly proportional to the winding current, and the leakage inductance generally may be considered as a constant. If, however, the teeth of the machine are highly saturated by mutual flux, the reluctances of the leakage paths are increased and the effective leakage inductance is decreased.

5.3 EQUIVALENT CIRCUITS

Our general picture of a polyphase machine at this stage consists of a cylindrical magnetic structure with slotted stator and rotor. Both the rotor and the stator carry three or more identical symmetrically placed phase windings placed in an approximately sinusoidal distribution in the slots. In Section 5.2 the flux linkages of these windings were related to the stator and rotor currents, and inductance parameters were derived. These parameters and relationships can now be collected in an equivalent circuit model of the machine.

At standstill, a polyphase machine behaves as a polyphase transformer. It is therefore to be expected that the equivalent circuit of a polyphase machine at standstill will be similar to those developed for the transformers discussed in Chapter 3. Therefore, let us first examine this already familiar mode of operation. We may then incorporate the effects of rotation into our equivalent circuit model to provide a basis for the analysis of induction and synchronous machines.

5.3.1 Equivalent Circuit at Standstill

Figure 5.16 shows a single-phase equivalent circuit for a polyphase machine with stationary rotor. This circuit applies only for the condition that all voltages and currents in the m_s-phase stator and m_r-phase rotor are balanced. The circuit represents the terminal relationships between phase a on the stator and phase A on the rotor.

Let us suppose, for the present, that the rotor windings are open circuited and that a balanced supply voltage E_s of angular frequency ω_s is applied to the stator terminals. The phasor E_s represents the terminal voltage on stator phase a. The current I_s in this phase flows through the resistance R_s of the winding. The voltage produced in phase a by the rate of change of its leakage flux linkages is $j\omega_s L_{Ls} I_s$, where L_{Ls} is the stator leakage inductance per phase (Section 5.2.5).

With the rotor open circuited, all of the stator current I_s can be considered as magnetizing current I_{ms}. From eq. 5.27, let the magnetizing current in phase a be

$$i_{ma} = \hat{I}_{ms} \sin(\omega_s t + \alpha_m) \qquad \text{amperes} \qquad (5.69)$$

From eqs. 5.37 and 5.38, the useful flux linkage produced in phase a by

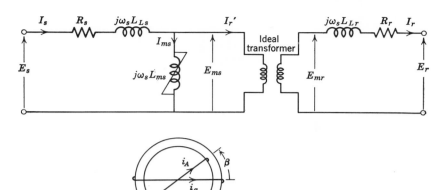

Fig. 5.16   Equivalent circuit of polyphase machine at standstill.

$$\text{Voltage } 1: \frac{N_r}{N_s} \underline{/-\beta}$$

$$\text{Current } 1: \frac{N_s m_s}{N_r m_r} \underline{/-\beta}$$

$$\text{Impedance } 1: \left(\frac{N_r}{N_s}\right)^2 \frac{m_r}{m_s}$$

$$\text{Power } 1: \frac{m_s}{m_r}$$

the stator magnetizing currents is

$$\lambda_{ma} = L_{ms}\hat{I}_{ms} \sin{(\omega_s t + \alpha_m)} \qquad \text{webers} \qquad (5.70)$$

where L_{ms}, the magnetizing inductance per phase for the stator, is described in the magnetically nonlinear range by a curve of the form shown in Fig. 5.9. The induced voltage in phase a is

$$e_{ma} = \frac{d\lambda_{ma}}{dt}$$

$$= \omega_s L_{ms} I_{ms} \cos{(\omega_s t + \alpha_m)} \qquad \text{volts}$$

or in phasor form

$$E_{ms} = j\omega_s L_{ms} I_{ms} \qquad \text{volts} \qquad (5.71)$$

The eddy-current and hysteresis losses in the magnetic material of the machine can be included in the equivalent circuit by inserting an appropriate resistance R_{ms} parallel with the magnetizing inductance L_{ms}.

From eq. 5.30, the air-gap flux density B_θ produced by the magnetizing current of eq. 5.69 is

$$B_\theta = \hat{B} \cos (\omega_s t + \alpha_m - \theta) \qquad \text{webers/meter}^2 \qquad (5.72)$$

From eq. 5.32, the stator flux linkage is

$$\lambda_{ma} = \frac{\pi}{2} N_s \hat{B} l r \sin (\omega_s t + \alpha_m) \qquad \text{webers} \qquad (5.73)$$

and the induced voltage is

$$e_{ma} = \omega_s \frac{\pi}{2} N_s \hat{B} l r \cos (\omega_s t + \alpha_m) \qquad (5.74)$$

The corresponding induced voltage in winding A of the rotor is, from eq. 5.36,

$$e_{mA} = \frac{d\lambda_{mA}}{dt}$$

$$= \frac{d}{dt}\left[\frac{\pi}{2} N_r \hat{B} l r \sin (\omega_s t + \alpha_m - \beta) \right] \qquad \text{volts} \qquad (5.75)$$

where β is the angle by which the axis of rotor phase A leads the axis of stator phase a, as shown in Fig. 5.6. At standstill, the angle β is constant and

$$e_{mA} = \omega_s \frac{\pi}{2} N_r \hat{B} l r \cos (\omega_s t + \alpha_m - \beta) \qquad \text{volts} \qquad (5.76)$$

Comparison of eqs. 5.74 and 5.76 shows that the induced voltages in the rotor and stator are related by the phasor expression

$$E_{mr} = \frac{N_r}{N_s} \underline{/-\beta} \, E_{ms} \qquad \text{volts} \qquad (5.77)$$

This expression specifies the voltage ratio of the ideal transformer in Fig. 5.16. Except for the phase shift, the voltage ratio is equal to the turns ratio, as expected in any transformer. We can visualize the origin of the phase shift β by noting that the air-gap flux density of eq. 5.72 can be regarded as a distributed magnetic field of constant magnitude, rotating in a forward direction at angular velocity ω_s. After producing maximum flux linkage in the stator winding a, it must rotate forward by β radians before it produces maximum flux linkage in the rotor winding A.

The m_r-phase rotor winding has a leakage inductance L_{Lr} and a resistance R_r per phase. If a balanced load is connected to the rotor terminals, a current I_r at angular frequency $\omega_r = \omega_s$ flows. As in a transformer, the magnetomotive force from this rotor current I_r can be considered to be equivalent to that produced by a component of current I_r' in the m_s-phase stator. The relation between I_r and I_r' is the current ratio of the ideal transformer. Expressing eqs. 5.24 and 5.25 in phasor form yields

$$I_r = \frac{N_s\, m_s}{N_r\, m_r} \underline{/-\beta}\; I_r' \qquad \text{amperes} \qquad (5.78)$$

The magnitude of this current ratio is the inverse of the turns ratio if the number of phases on the rotor and stator are equal. Since the rotor is shifted forward by an angle β, a rotating field produced by currents in its windings is ahead of one produced by currents of the same phase angles in the corresponding stator windings.

We note from eqs. 5.77 and 5.78 that the current ratio is dependent on the number of phases, but the voltage ratio is not. Unless the numbers of stator and rotor phases are equal, the current ratio is not the inverse of the voltage ratio, and the ideal transformer is not power invariant. The complex power U_{ms} per phase leaving the stator is related to the complex power U_{mr} per phase entering the rotor by

$$U_{mr} = P_{mr} + jQ_{mr} = I_r E_{mr}{}^*$$

$$= \left(\frac{N_s\, m_s}{N_r\, m_r} \underline{/-\beta}\; I_r'\right)\left(\frac{N_r}{N_s} \underline{/\beta}\; E_{ms}{}^*\right)$$

$$= \frac{m_s}{m_r} I_r' E_{ms}{}^*$$

$$= \frac{m_s}{m_r}(P_{ms} + jQ_{ms}) = \frac{m_s}{m_r} U_{ms} \qquad (5.79)$$

For analysis, it is often convenient to transfer impedances across ideal transformers. Suppose that $E_{mr} = Z_r I_r$, where the impedance Z_r is a complex number. Then from eqs. 5.77 and 5.78,

$$E_{ms} = \frac{N_s}{N_r} \underline{/\beta}\; E_{mr}$$

$$= \frac{N_s}{N_r} \underline{/\beta}\; Z_r \frac{N_s\, m_s}{N_r\, m_r} \underline{/-\beta}\; I_r'$$

$$= \left(\frac{N_s}{N_r}\right)^2 \frac{m_s}{m_r} Z_r I_r' \qquad (5.80)$$

Thus the rotor impedance per phase Z_r may be represented by an equivalent impedance per phase Z_r' on the other side of the ideal transformer, the impedance ratio being given by

$$Z_r' = \left(\frac{N_s}{N_r}\right)^2 \frac{m_s}{m_r} Z_r \qquad \text{ohms} \qquad (5.81)$$

In the equivalent circuit of Fig. 5.16, the magnetizing inductance has been placed on the stator side of the ideal transformer. The equivalent magnetizing inductance L_{mr} of eq. 5.39 could just as easily have been placed on the rotor side of the transformation.

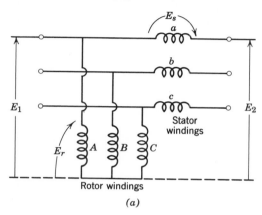

(a)

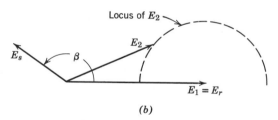

(b)

Fig. 5.17 (a) Three-phase induction regulator. (b) Phasor diagram showing locus of variable output voltage.

From the equivalent circuit, it is evident that a stationary polyphase machine can be used as a phase shifter. It may also be used as a source of variable polyphase voltage when connected as an induction regulator (Fig. 5.17). In this application, the primary windings, usually on the rotor, are connected to the supply; the stator windings are connected in series with the supply. As the rotor is shifted through $180°$, the output voltage E_2 folllows a circular locus of variable magnitude, as shown in Fig. 5.17b. With identical stator and rotor windings, the output voltage may be adjusted from about zero to $2E_1$. The advantage of induction regulators over variable autotransformers (Section 3.4.1) is that continuous stepless variation of the voltage can be obtained and that no sliding electric connections are required. (For 180° rotation, connections to the rotor are made through flexible leads.) The disadvantages of induction regulators arise from their higher leakage inductance and higher magnetizing current.

5.3.2 Equivalent Circuit for Rotating Machine

Rotation of the polyphase machine does not change its inductance and resistance parameters, but it does change the relationship between the stator and rotor voltages and frequencies. Suppose the rotor has an angular velocity v. Then, for a two-pole machine, the angle β between the reference phase A on the rotor and the reference phase a on the stator is

$$\beta = vt + \beta_0 \qquad \text{radians} \tag{5.82}$$

Proceeding in the same manner as in the analysis at standstill (Section 5.3.1), let us consider a machine with open-circuited rotor windings. The stator magnetizing current of eq. 5.69 produces the air-gap flux density of eq. 5.72, the stator flux linkage of eq. 5.73, and the induced voltage in stator phase a of

$$e_{ma} = \omega_s \frac{\pi}{2} N_s \hat{B} lr \cos(\omega_s t + \alpha_m) \qquad \text{volts} \tag{5.83}$$

From eqs. 5.75 and 5.82, the corresponding induced voltage in rotor winding A is

$$e_{mA} = \frac{d}{dt}\left[\frac{\pi}{2} N_r \hat{B} lr \sin(\omega_s t + \alpha_m - \beta)\right]$$

$$= \frac{d}{dt}\left\{\frac{\pi}{2} N_r \hat{B} lr \sin[(\omega_s - v)t + \alpha_m - \beta_0]\right\}$$

$$= (\omega_s - v)\frac{\pi}{2} N_r \hat{B} lr \cos[(\omega_s - v)t + \alpha_m - \beta_0] \qquad \text{volts} \tag{5.84}$$

The magnetic field of eq. 5.72 revolves forward at an angular velocity ω_s. But, since the rotor has a forward angular velocity v, the flux linkages of the rotor windings change at a rate of $\omega_s - v$ only. The rotor frequency becomes

$$\omega_r = \omega_s - v \qquad \text{radians/second} \tag{5.85}$$

and the induced voltage in the rotor is proportional to this frequency.

If the stator and rotor voltages of eqs. 5.83 and 5.84 are represented by the phasors E_{ms} and E_{mr}, the induced voltage ratio becomes

$$E_{mr} = \frac{N_r}{N_s}\left(\frac{\omega_s - v}{\omega_s}\right)\angle{-\beta_0}\, E_{ms} \qquad \text{volts} \tag{5.86}$$

Since E_{mr} and E_{ms} are phasors of different frequency, the angle β_0 serves merely as a convenient means of relating their phase angles at $t = 0$.

Suppose that a balanced load is now connected to the rotor terminals. A current I_r at frequency ω_r flows in the rotor windings. The magneto-motive force produced by these currents rotates forward at an angular

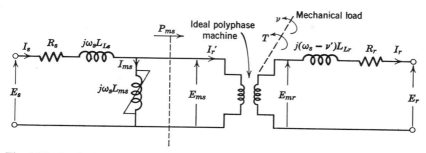

Fig. 5.18 Equivalent circuit of polyphase machine rotating at angular velocity ν. $\left(\nu' = \dfrac{p\nu}{2}\right)$.

$$\text{Voltage 1}: \frac{N_r}{N_s}\left(\frac{\omega_s - \nu'}{\omega_s}\right)\angle -\beta_0'$$

$$\text{Current 1}: \frac{N_s}{N_r}\frac{m_s}{m_r}\angle -\beta_0$$

$$\text{Impedance 1}: \left(\frac{N_r}{N_s}\right)^2 \frac{m_r}{m_s}\left(\frac{\omega_s - \nu'}{\omega_s}\right)$$

$$\text{Power 1}: \frac{m_s}{m_r}\left(\frac{\omega_s - \nu'}{\omega_s}\right)$$

$$\text{Frequency } \omega_s:(\omega_s - \nu') \quad \text{or} \quad \omega_s:\omega_r$$

velocity ω_r with respect to the rotor or $\omega_r + \nu = \omega_s$ with respect to the stator. From eqs. 5.24 and 5.25, the same magnetomotive force can be produced by a phasor current I_r' in the stator windings if

$$I_r = \frac{N_s}{N_r}\frac{m_s}{m_r}\angle -\beta_0\, I_r' \tag{5.87}$$

Comparison of eqs. 5.87 and 5.78 shows that the current ratio of the machine is independent of the rotor speed ν.

Figure 5.18 shows the single-phase equivalent circuit of the balanced polyphase machine rotating at speed ν. The equivalent circuit consists of resistances and inductive impedances that may be considered as the imperfections of the machine plus an ideal polyphase machine defined by its voltage and current ratios. Except for its voltage ratio, the ideal polyphase machine is similar to the ideal transformer of Fig. 5.16.

Again, for analytical purposes, it is convenient to be able to transfer impedances across the ideal polyphase machine. If the rotor circuit has a balanced impedance Z_r per phase at frequency ω_r, it may be replaced by an equivalent impedance Z_r' on the other side of the ideal machine. The impedance ratio is the voltage ratio (eq. 5.86) divided by the current ratio (eq. 5.87), that is,

$$Z_r' = \left(\frac{N_s}{N_r}\right)^2 \frac{m_s}{m_r}\left(\frac{\omega_s}{\omega_s - \nu}\right)Z_r \qquad \text{ohms} \qquad (5.88)$$

For a p-pole machine, the quantity ν in eqs. 5.86 and 5.88 should be replaced by the equivalent angular velocity ν' of a two-pole machine, where

$$\nu' = \frac{p}{2}\nu \qquad \text{radians/second} \qquad (5.89)$$

5.3.3   Torque

There are several ways by which the torque produced by a polyphase machine may be determined. One method is by the application of the principle of conservation of energy to the equivalent circuit of Fig. 5.18. Of the total power entering the m_s-phase stator windings, a certain amount is lost in the stator resistances, and in hysteresis and eddy-current effects if included. The remainder is

$$m_s P_{ms} = \mathcal{R}_e(m_s I_r' E_{ms}^*) \qquad \text{watts} \qquad (5.90)$$

Because this power crosses the air gap it is thus generally called the air-gap power.

The power that is absorbed in the electrical circuits of the m_r-phase rotor is

$$
\begin{aligned}
m_r P_{mr} &= \mathcal{R}_e(m_r I_r E_{mr}^*) \\
&= \mathcal{R}_e\left[m_r\left(\frac{N_s}{N_r}\frac{m_s}{m_r}\,\underline{/-\beta_0}\,I_r'\right)\left(\frac{N_r}{N_s}\frac{\omega_s - \nu'}{\omega_s}\,\underline{/\beta_0}\,E_{ms}^*\right)\right] \\
&= \frac{\omega_s - \nu'}{\omega_s}\,m_s P_{ms} \qquad \text{watts} \qquad (5.91)
\end{aligned}
$$

where ν' is the equivalent speed of a two-pole machine as given in eq. 5.82. Thus, of the total power crossing the air gap, only a fraction $(\omega_s - \nu')/\omega_s$ is transformed into electric power in the rotor windings. If energy, and therefore power, is to be conserved, the remaining fraction must be the mechanical power. Thus

$$P_{\text{mech.}} = \frac{\nu'}{\omega_s}(m_s P_{ms}) \qquad \text{watts} \qquad (5.92)$$

The torque is then derived from eqs. 5.92 and 5.89 as

$$T = \frac{P_{\text{mech.}}}{v}$$

$$= \frac{p}{2} \frac{m_s P_{ms}}{\omega_s}$$

$$= \mathscr{R}_e \left[\frac{p}{2} \frac{m_s I_r' E_{ms}^*}{\omega_s} \right] \qquad \text{newton-meters} \qquad (5.93)$$

For balanced operation, the torque on the rotor of a polyphase machine is therefore equal to the total air-gap power multiplied by the number of pairs of poles and divided by the angular velocity ω_s of the stator current. Alternatively, the torque is equal to the air-gap power divided by the angular velocity $(2/p)\omega_s$ of the rotating field of the machine.

The fact that the torque of a balanced polyphase machine does not contain oscillatory terms can be established by inference. We know that the total instantaneous power in a balanced polyphase system contains no oscillatory terms. The distributed rotating magnetic field in the machine has a constant magnitude and therefore has a constant stored energy. The electric power output to the balanced system connected to the rotor windings is also constant. Thus it follows that the mechanical power and torque must also be constant.

Whereas the energy conservation approach allows a simple derivation of a torque expression, it gives little insight into the mechanism of torque production. Let us therefore examine qualitatively the means by which the winding currents interact with the magnetic field to produce torque. For simplicity, let us neglect the winding resistances and leakage inductances in the equivalent circuit of Fig. 5.18. Suppose a balanced supply of voltage E_s is connected to the stator and a balanced resistive load of R ohms per phase is connected to the rotor. From eq. 5.88, this rotor load is equivalent to a resistive load R' on the stator side of the ideal machine where

$$R' = \left(\frac{N_s}{N_r} \right)^2 \frac{m_s}{m_r} \left(\frac{\omega_s}{\omega_s - v'} \right) R \qquad \text{ohms} \qquad (5.94)$$

The phasor diagram of Fig. 5.19a shows the phase relations between the stator voltage E_s, the stator current I_s, and the equivalent stator component I_r' of the rotor current. It also shows the phasor of stator flux linkage λ_{ms}.

Sinusoidal magnetomotive force distributions are produced in the machine by the currents I_s and I_r'. The sum of these two magnetomotive forces is the magnetizing magnetomotive force that may be considered the result of the magnetizing current I_{ms}. Figure 5.19b shows a space vector diagram of these magnetomotive forces. The relative positions in space of these sinusoidal magnetomotive force distributions are identical to the relative phases of the corresponding current phasors of Fig. 5.19a with one exception. The vector representing the rotor magnetomotive force is directed opposite to the rotor current phasor I_r' because we have

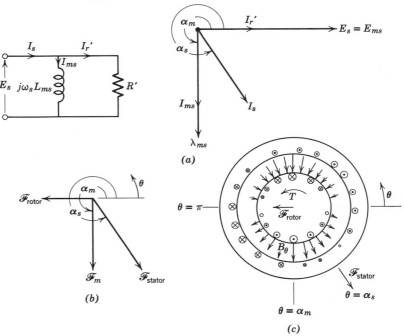

Fig. 5.19 (*a*) Phasor diagram of simplified machine. (*b*) Space vector diagram showing magnetomotive forces. (*c*) Distribution of stator and rotor currents and air-gap flux density.

chosen to direct the current I_r' in the equivalent circuit of Fig. 5.19a out of the rotor winding.

Figure 5.19c shows the instantaneous winding current distributions in the stator and rotor that produce the magnetomotive forces of Fig. 5.19b. It also shows the resultant magnetic field produced in the air gap.

If the rotor conductors were on the surface of a smooth cylindrical rotor, they would react directly with the air-gap flux density to produce a positive or counterclockwise torque T as shown in Fig. 5.19c. As the conductors are normally imbedded in slots, the torque acts on the magnetic material of the rotor teeth rather than on the conductors.

The direction of the torque on the rotor is such as to increase the flux linked by the rotor currents that are flowing at any instant. In Fig. 5.19c, the torque tends to align the magnetomotive force axis of the rotor currents $\theta = \pi$ with the axis of the maximum air-gap flux density $\theta = \alpha_m$.

If the load in Fig. 5.19a had been inductive rather than resistive, the phasors I_s, I_r', and I_{ms} would all have had a phase angle of $-\pi/2$. The magnetomotive force axis of the rotor currents would then be at $\theta = \pi/2$; the axis of maximum air-gap flux density would also be at $\theta = -\pi/2$. It can be seen that this condition produces no torque on the rotor. This conclusion is consistent with eq. 5.93 as no power crosses the air gap.

Throughout the analysis of this polyphase machine, it has been assumed that the flux density is radially directed across the air gap as shown in Fig. 5.19c. This is a reasonable analytical approximation, but if it were true, there would be no torque produced on the magnetic material of the rotor and stator. By the use of the flux source-sink concepts of Section 1.7.3, a radial flux density would produce only radially directed forces. The torque-producing forces actually act on the tooth edges, as shown in Fig. 4.2c of Section 4.1.2, as a result of the tangential components of the asymmetric fringing fields around the teeth.

5.4 POLYPHASE INDUCTION MACHINES

In a polyphase induction machine, the stator windings are connected to a balanced polyphase supply. The rotor windings are either internally short circuited or connected through slip rings to a balanced passive impedance. The distinctive feature of the induction machine is that the rotor currents are produced by induction from the stator.

The principles of operation of an induction motor may be summarized as follows. The balanced stator supply of frequency ω_s radians per second sets up a magnetic field in the machine that revolves at an angular velocity of $(2/p)\omega_s$ radians per second. This field induces voltages in the rotor windings, the frequency ω_r of these voltages depending on the relative velocities of the magnetic field and the rotor. The current that flows in each rotor winding is equal to the induced voltage divided by the combined impedance at the rotor frequency ω_r of the winding and of any external network. This rotor current reacts with the magnetic field to produce torque. The torque causes the machine to accelerate in the direction of the field rotation. As the speed ν of the rotor approaches the speed $\nu_s = (2/p)\omega_s$ of the field, the rotor frequency ω_r approaches zero. Thus the induced voltages, the rotor currents, and the torque also approach zero.

For a motor to develop positive torque, the rotor must rotate more slowly than the revolving magnetic field, that is, it must slip backward with respect to the revolving field. The term slip s is used to denote the slip speed in per unit of the synchronous or revolving field speed v_s. Thus

$$s = \frac{(2/p)\omega_s - v}{(2/p)\omega_s} = \frac{v_s - v}{v_s} \qquad \text{per unit} \qquad (5.95)$$

Alternatively, slip can be expressed in terms of the equivalent rotational speed v' of a two-pole machine, using eq. 5.89.

$$s = \frac{\omega_s - v'}{\omega_s} \qquad \text{per unit} \qquad (5.96)$$

Since the rotor frequency ω_r is $\omega_s - v'$,

$$\omega_r = s\omega_s \qquad \text{radians/second} \qquad (5.97)$$

With no load torque, an induction machine normally operates with negligible slip at essentially its synchronous speed v_s. When a mechanical load is connected, the rotor slows down, thus increasing the slip, the rotor frequency, the induced voltage, the rotor current, and finally the torque to the value required by the load. If the rotor is driven at a speed greater than that of the revolving field, the slip is negative. The induced rotor voltage is reversed in polarity as compared with an equal positive slip. The rotor current polarity is also reversed leading to a torque in the direction opposite to the direction of rotation. Thus above synchronous speed v_s the machine operates as a generator.

In an induction motor with shorted rotor windings, only a small induced voltage is required to produce rated rotor current and torque. Thus the operating value of slip is usually small (0.02 to 0.05). The speed is essentially constant, reducing only slightly with increased load torque. This essentially constant-speed feature, combined with its self-starting capability, makes the induction motor suitable for the majority of applications in which continuous control of speed is not required. It may be provided with means of limited speed control, as discussed later in Section 5.4.5.

The polyphase induction motor is the simplest, most rugged and economical type of electromechanical converter. The magnetic structures of both the stator and the rotor are made of laminated material since alternating flux is present in both. To minimize the magnetizing current, the air gap is made as small as possible (0.5 to 1 millimeter) and the tops of the slots are often partially closed, as shown in Fig. 5.15. Different numbers of slots are generally used in the stator and rotor structures to avoid reluctance torque components.

The stator is generally wound for three-phase operation. There are two major types of rotor windings. The *wound-rotor type* has a conventional three-phase winding brought out through three slip rings. The *squirrel-cage rotor* consists of a number of uninsulated bars in slots connected to shorting end rings. In most of the smaller induction motors, the bars and end rings are made of cast aluminum. For larger machines, copper or copper alloy bars are brazed to end rings of a similar material.

5.4.1 Current, Torque, and Speed Relations

For purposes of analysis, a polyphase induction machine may be regarded as having four terminal variables—the stator voltage E_s per phase, the stator current I_s per phase, the torque T, and the speed v. The relationships of these variables may be determined from equivalent circuit models of the machine.

Figure 5.20*a* shows an equivalent circuit of a polyphase machine with shorted rotor windings. The ratios for the ideal polyphase machine have been expressed in terms of slip s using eqs. 5.96 and 5.97. As compared with the general equivalent circuit of Fig. 5.18, the phase shift angles β_0 have been omitted from the voltage and current ratios, as there is no need to know the relative phase angles of rotor and stator quantities in an induction machine.

Suppose a balanced voltage E_s is applied to the stator terminals. We wish to determine the stator current I_s and the torque T as functions of the speed v. As we are not directly interested in the rotor voltages and currents, it is convenient to transfer the rotor impedance across the ideal machine using eq. 5.88. Thus

$$Z_r' = \left(\frac{N_s}{N_r}\right)^2 \frac{m_s}{m_r} \frac{1}{s} (R_r + j\omega_r L_{Lr})$$

$$= \frac{R_r'}{s} + j\omega_s L_{Lr}' \qquad \text{ohms} \qquad (5.98)$$

where

$$L_{Lr}' = \left(\frac{N_s}{N_r}\right)^2 \frac{m_s}{m_r} L_{Lr} \qquad \text{henrys} \qquad (5.99)$$

and

$$R_r' = \left(\frac{N_s}{N_r}\right)^2 \frac{m_s}{m_r} R_r \qquad \text{ohms} \qquad (5.100)$$

In the resultant equivalent circuit of Fig. 5.20*b*, the voltage on the rotor side of the ideal machine is zero, but its current is the actual rotor current per phase. The voltage on the stator side of the ideal machine is thus also equal to zero, excepting only the indeterminate condition of $s = 0$, for which the voltage ratio of the ideal machine is $1 = 0$. If the rotor current is not specifically required, the ideal machine may therefore be replaced by a short circuit as shown in Fig. 5.20*c*.

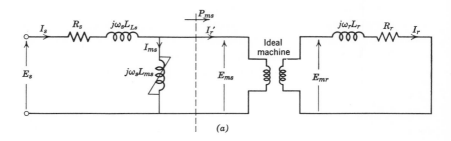

(a)

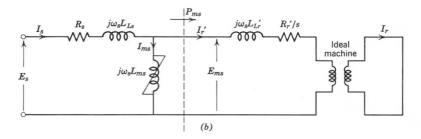

(b)

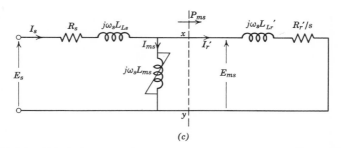

(c)

Fig. 5.20   Simplified equivalent circuits for a polyphase induction machine. In (a)

$$\text{Voltage } 1 : \left(\frac{N_r}{N_s}\right)s$$

$$\text{Current } 1 : \left(\frac{N_s}{N_r}\right)\frac{m_s}{m_r}$$

$$\text{Impedance } 1 : \left(\frac{N_r}{N_s}\right)^{2}\left(\frac{m_r}{m_s}\right)s$$

$$\text{Power } 1 : \frac{m_s}{m_r}s$$

$$\text{Frequency } \omega_s : \omega_r \quad \text{or} \quad \omega_s : s\omega_s$$

Let us now derive an expression for the torque. From eq. 5.93, the torque can be determined from the air-gap power P_{ms}, which in turn may be expressed in terms of E_{ms} and I_r'. On first examination, it might appear that the calculation of these quantities would be complicated by the magnetizing inductance L_{ms}, which is a nonlinear function of the magnetizing current. A sufficiently accurate calculation may generally be obtained by choosing an average value of the magnetizing impedance $j\omega_s L_{ms}$ for the expected range of E_{ms} or I_{ms}, and assuming it to remain constant. Thévenin's theorem may then be applied at the nodes x and y of Fig. 5.20c, to produce the circuit of Fig. 5.21a in which

$$E_e = \frac{j\omega_s L_{ms}}{R_s + j\omega_s(L_{Ls} + L_{ms})} E_s \qquad \text{volts} \qquad (5.101)$$

and

$$R_e + jX_e = \frac{j\omega_s L_{ms}(R_s + j\omega_s L_{Ls})}{R_s + j\omega_s(L_{Ls} + L_{ms})} \qquad \text{ohms} \qquad (5.102)$$

Since $L_{ms} \ll L_{Ls}$, a moderate inaccuracy in the value of L_{ms} has little effect on this Thévenin equivalent.

From Fig. 5.21a, the current I_r' is

$$I_r' = \frac{E_e}{(R_e + R_r'/s) + j(X_e + X_{Lr}')} \qquad \text{amperes} \qquad (5.103)$$

As the air-gap power P_{ms} is equal to the power in the resistance R_r'/s, the torque is, from eqs. 5.93, 5.95, and 5.103,

$$T = \frac{p}{2} \frac{m_s P_{ms}}{\omega_s}$$

$$= \frac{p}{2} \frac{m_s}{\omega_s} \frac{R_r'}{s} |I_r'|^2$$

$$= \frac{m_s}{v_s} \frac{R_r'}{s} \frac{E_e^2}{(R_e + R_r'/s)^2 + (X_e + X_{Lr}')^2} \qquad \text{newton-meters} \quad (5.104)$$

Figure 5.21b shows a typical relation between torque and speed. When the motor operates at its synchronous speed $v_s = (2/p)\omega_s$, the slip s is zero and the torque of eq. 5.104 is zero. For small values of s, the resistance R_r'/s is very large, and the torque can be approximated by

$$T \approx \frac{m_s}{v_s} \frac{|E_e|^2}{R_r'} s \qquad \text{newton-meters} \qquad (5.105)$$

In this region of linear torque-slip relationship, the rotor current (eq. 5.103) is essentially proportional to slip s, and the phase of the rotor

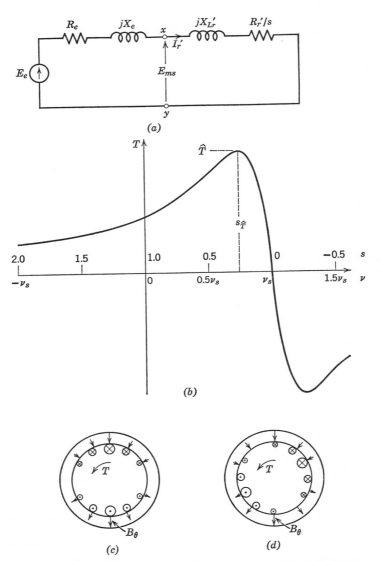

Fig. 5.21 (a) An equivalent circuit for determining torque. (b) Typical torque-speed relation. (c) Relationship of air-gap field B_θ and rotor current for low values of slip, and (d) for high values of slip.

current is such as to be most effective in producing torque, as shown in Fig. 5.21c.

As the slip s is increased, the rotor current I_r increases in magnitude; however, it also lags in phase behind the induced rotor voltage because of the increased rotor reactance at the higher rotor frequency. As shown in Fig. 5.21d, the rotor current is then in a less effective position relative to the air-gap field to produce torque. At the extreme phase lag of 90° no torque would be produced.

The condition for maximum torque corresponds to the condition for maximum air-gap power. This occurs when, in Fig. 5.21a,

$$\frac{R_r'}{s} = [R_e^2 + (X_e + X_{Lr}')^2]^{\frac{1}{2}} \qquad \text{ohms} \qquad (5.106)$$

or at a slip of

$$s_{\hat{T}} = \frac{R_r'}{[R_e^2 + (X_e + X_{Lr}')^2]^{\frac{1}{2}}} \qquad \text{per unit} \qquad (5.107)$$

The maximum torque is, from eq. 5.104,

$$\hat{T} = \frac{m_s}{2\nu_s} \frac{|E_e|^2}{R_e + [R_e^2 + (X_e + X_{Lr}')^2]^{\frac{1}{2}}} \qquad \text{newton-meters} \quad (5.108)$$

Except in very small machines, $R_e \ll (X_e + X_{Lr}')$ and the maximum torque can be approximated by

$$\hat{T} = \frac{m_s}{2\nu_s} \frac{|E_e|^2}{X_e + X_{Lr}'} \qquad \text{newton-meters} \qquad (5.109)$$

This shows that the maximum torque an induction motor can develop is limited principally by the stator and rotor leakage reactances and is independent of the rotor circuit resistance.

For large values of slip where $(R_e + R_r'/s) \ll (X_e + X_{Lr}')$, the torque of eq. 5.104 may be approximated by

$$T = \frac{m_s}{\nu_s} \frac{R_r'}{s} \frac{|E_e|^2}{(X_e + X_{Lr}')^2} \qquad \text{newton-meters} \qquad (5.110)$$

For this range, the torque varies approximately inversely as the slip.

When operating as an induction generator with negative values of slip s, the torque characteristics are given approximately by eqs. 5.105, 5.109, and 5.110.

The stator current I_s may be readily found with the aid of the circuit of Fig. 5.22a. As the equivalent rotor current I_r' is known (eq. 5.103), the rotor circuit of Fig. 5.20c has been replaced by an equivalent current source. Except in the smallest machines, the stator resistance R_s has a

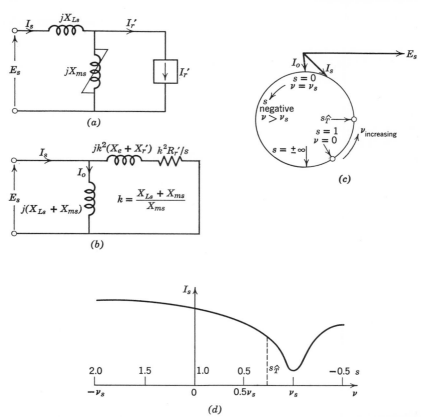

Fig. 5.22 (a) An equivalent circuit for determining stator current. (b) An equivalent circuit of the machine as seen from the stator terminals. (c) The locus of the stator current. (d) The stator current as a function of speed ν.

negligible effect on current magnitudes and has therefore been omitted for simplicity. To apply superposition to Fig. 5.22a, it is necessary to linearize the circuit by choosing an appropriate average value of magnetizing reactance X_{ms}. Then

$$I_s = \frac{E_s}{j(X_{Ls} + X_{ms})} + \frac{X_{ms}}{X_{ms} + X_{Ls}} I_r' \qquad \text{amperes} \qquad (5.111)$$

If eq. 5.101 for E_e is substituted into eq. 5.103 with R_s neglected, and the result is substituted into eq. 5.111, the stator current is

$$I_s = \frac{E_s}{j(X_{Ls} + X_{ms})} + \left(\frac{X_{ms}}{X_{Ls} + X_{ms}}\right)^2 \frac{E_s}{(R_r'/s) + j(X_e + X_{Lr}')} \qquad \text{amperes}$$

$$(5.112)$$

At a slip of $s = 0$, the stator current of eq. 5.112 is the magnetizing current only. This may contain a small in-phase component due to the eddy-current and hysteresis losses that were neglected in the equivalent circuits. The second component of the stator current in eq. 5.112 can be considered to flow in a circuit branch that consists of a constant inductive reactance in series with a variable resistance, as shown in the equivalent circuit of Fig. 5.22b. The stator current therefore follows a circular locus as the slip s of the machine changes as shown in Fig. 5.22c. The stator current-speed relation for a machine having the torque-speed relation of Fig. 5.21b is shown in Fig. 5.22d. Except in the region $2s_{\hat{T}} > s > -2s_{\hat{T}}$, the stator current is limited mainly by the stator and rotor leakage reactances and is approximately constant.

If $X_{Ls} \ll X_{ms}$, the equivalent circuit of Fig. 5.22b is essentially the same as that of Fig. 5.20c, with the magnetizing reactance moved out to the stator terminals. For large induction machines, X_{Ls} is generally less than about 0.05 X_{ms} and the above approximation generally leads to a valid and simple analysis. For small machines, the stator leakage reactance X_{Ls} may be as high as $0.1X_{ms}$ and the more accurate circuit of Fig. 5.22b may be required.

5.4.2 Losses and Efficiency

Let us follow the power flow through an induction motor with the aid of the equivalent circuit of Fig. 5.23a. The power input to the stator is

$$P_{\text{input}} = \mathcal{R}_e[m_s I_s E_s{}^*] \qquad \text{watts} \tag{5.113}$$

There is a loss of power in the stator windings of

$$P_{\substack{\text{stator} \\ \text{winding}}} = m_s R_s |I_s|^2 \qquad \text{watts} \tag{5.114}$$

where R_s is the resistance of each phase winding at the operating temperature and frequency. With large conductors and/or high operating frequency, the alternating magnetic field within the conductor drives the current toward the conductor surface (skin effect) and increases the effective resistance of the conductor.

The remaining power, that is, the input minus the stator winding loss, is transferred to the magnetic field of the machine. Part of this is dissipated as hysteresis and eddy-current loss in the magnetic material of the stator. The eddy-current loss is approximately proportional to the square of each of the flux density, the frequency ω_s, and the lamination thickness, as shown in eq. 2.37. The hysteresis loss is proportional to the frequency and is nonlinearly dependent on the flux density. It is convenient to consider the losses in the stator magnetic material as arising from two separate fluxes, the first being the mutual flux, which produces the voltage E_{ms} in Fig. 5.23a, and the second being the stator leakage flux produced by the stator current I_s. The first component can then be represented by the resistance R_{ms} connected across the voltage E_{ms} as in Fig. 5.23a, and

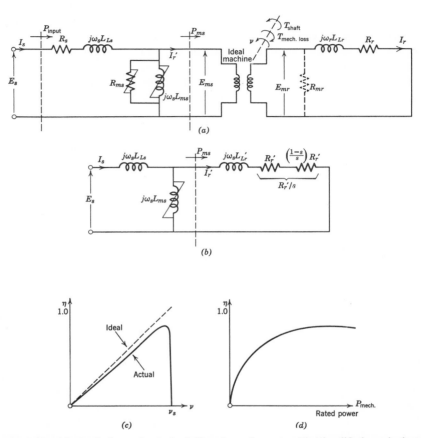

Fig. 5.23 (a) Equivalent circuit including loss elements. (b) Simplified equivalent circuit. (c) Efficiency η as a function of rotor speed v. (d) Efficiency η as a function of mechanical power output.

the second can be included by an appropriate increase in the effective resistance R_s of the stator winding. If the losses were from eddy currents only, the resistances representing the losses would be constant for any voltage or frequency, as shown in Section 2.2. For the usual operation at constant frequency, the hysteresis losses are frequently assumed to vary as flux density squared also so that constant resistances can represent the total loss in the magnetic material at any voltage within the normal range of operation.

Of the power P_{ms}, which crosses the air gap, a part is dissipated in the magnetic material of the rotor. Again, this loss may be represented by a resistance R_{mr} connected across the voltage E_{mr} of the rotor. As these losses are dependent on the frequency ω_r of the rotor, they may be negligible at normal operating speeds where the rotor frequency is very low.

The power loss in the rotor windings is

$$P_{\substack{\text{rotor} \\ \text{winding}}} = m_r R_r I_r^2 \quad \text{watts} \tag{5.115}$$

At normal operating speeds, the rotor frequency ω_r is low, and the rotor resistance per phase R_r is essentially the d-c value. But at the higher rotor frequencies associated with starting and acceleration to operating speed, the effective rotor resistance may be considerably increased by skin effect.

When the losses in the rotor windings and magnetic material have been deducted from the air-gap power, the remaining power is that which is converted into mechanical form. Part of this is lost in windage and friction losses, which are dependent on the speed. The rest is the mechanical output power.

The efficiency of an induction motor is highly dependent on the operating speed relative to the synchronous speed, that is, on the slip. Suppose all losses are neglected except those in the rotor windings. In Fig. 5.23b, the air-gap power (and also the input power) is

$$P_{ms} = m_s \frac{R_r'}{s} |I_r'|^2 \quad \text{watts} \tag{5.116}$$

The rotor winding loss is

$$P_{\substack{\text{rotor} \\ \text{winding}}} = m_s R_r' |I_r'|^2 \quad \text{watts} \tag{5.117}$$

Thus the mechanical power is

$$P_{\text{mech.}} = P_{ms} - P_{\substack{\text{rotor} \\ \text{winding}}}$$

$$= \frac{1-s}{s} R_r' |I_r'|^2 \quad \text{watts} \tag{5.118}$$

and the mechanical load can be represented by the resistance $R_r'(1-s)/s$ as shown in Fig. 5.23b. From eqs. 5.118 and 5.116, the ideal efficiency, neglecting all but rotor winding losses, is

$$\eta_{\text{ideal}} = \frac{P_{\text{mech.}}}{P_{ms}}$$

$$= (1-s) \quad \text{per unit} \tag{5.119}$$

This relation, shown in Fig. 5.23c, leads us to the conclusion that an induction motor must operate near its synchronous speed if a high efficiency is to be obtained. For this reason, the slip for normal full-load operation is made less than 0.05 for most polyphase induction motors. When an induction motor is used in a variable-speed drive (Section 5.4.5), the efficiency is relatively low over much of the speed range.

If the stator winding, hysteresis, eddy-current, and mechanical losses are included, the actual efficiency is lower than the ideal efficiency of eq. 5.119 as shown in Fig. 5.23c. Under normal operating conditions, only the portion of this curve between no-load ($s \simeq 0$) and full-load is of interest. The efficiency may then be more appropriately expressed as a function of mechanical output power, as shown in Fig. 5.23d. The maximum efficiency of a polyphase induction motor may be as high as 95% in large machines.

5.4.3   Measurement of Parameters

The equivalent circuit parameters of a wound-rotor induction machine may be found in much the same manner as those of a transformer (Section 3.1.3). For a large machine the magnetizing reactance X_{ms} is much larger than the stator leakage reactance X_{Ls}. In the equivalent circuits of Fig. 5.20, the magnetizing branch may be moved out to the stator terminals without appreciable change in the overall voltage-current relationships. A test with the rotor open circuited and stationary gives the magnetizing reactance and its associated resistance representing losses in the magnetic materials. It also gives the voltage ratio and therefore the approximate value of the turns ratio (N_r/N_s) of the machine. This open-circuit test normally would be made over a range of values of supply voltage because of the nonlinearity of the magnetizing branch.

It may be seen, from Fig. 5.20b, that a test with the rotor short circuited and at standstill ($s = 1.0$) gives the total impedance $(R_s + R_r') + j(X_{Ls} + X_{Lr}')$ as seen from the stator, provided this impedance is small in comparison with the magnetizing impedance. The stator and rotor resistances may be found separately by d-c measurement. Normally, it is not necessary to separate the leakage reactances. The turns ratio N_r/N_s may also be determined approximately from the current ratio I_s/I_r.

In smaller machines, where the leakage reactance may not be negligible in comparison with the magnetizing reactance, a reasonably accurate equivalent circuit may generally be obtained by assuming that the stator leakage reactance X_{Ls} is equal to the equivalent rotor leakage reactance X_{Lr}'.

It is not possible to perform an open-circuit test on an induction machine that has an internally shorted rotor. Instead, the machine is operated at no-load where the slip is just sufficient to produce the mechanical loss torque. The quadrature component of the input current is then essentially equal to the magnetizing current and the in-phase component mainly represents the loss in the stator magnetic material, the mechanical loss, and the loss in the stator windings. If this last loss term is calculated and deducted, the remaining loss may generally be regarded as a constant for normal constant-voltage, essentially constant-speed operation.

The standstill test on a squirrel-cage motor gives the short-circuit impedance, as seen from the stator shown previously. By measuring the d-c stator resistance, we may deduce the effective rotor resistance R_r'.

We note that the turns ratio is not obtainable from these tests on a squirrel-cage motor. It is not, however, required for a prediction of the machine performance.

For machines in which the stator leakage reactance X_{Ls} cannot be neglected in relation to the magnetizing reactance X_{ms}, the previous no-load and standstill tests give the parameters of the equivalent circuit of Fig. 5.22b. (If required, the stator resistance R_s and a loss resistance R_{ms} may be added to this circuit.) Although the quantity k cannot be determined from the measurements, the performance of the machine can be predicted from this equivalent circuit.

For comparative purposes, it is usually best to express the equivalent circuit impedances in per unit of a base impedance Z_{1b} for the machine, which is given by

$$Z_{1b} = \frac{|E_s|_{\text{rated}}}{|I_s|_{\text{rated}}} \quad \text{ohms} \tag{5.120}$$

where E_s is the phase or line-to-neutral voltage. Then, for example,

$$X_{ms} = \frac{X_{ms}(\text{ohms})}{Z_{1b}} \quad \text{per unit} \tag{5.121}$$

For a large induction machine, a typical value of the magnetizing reactance X_{ms} might be in the range of 2 to 3 per unit, indicating that the no-load current is about 0.3 to 0.5 of rated stator current. The combined leakage reactance $X_{Ls} + X_{Lr}'$ as seen from the stator may be as low as about 0.12 to 0.2 per unit for large machines. With full voltage applied to the stator, the starting current at standstill can then be in the range from five to eight times rated value. For smaller machines, the leakage reactance is normally higher. The stator resistance is normally about 0.005 to 0.02 per unit for large machines and becomes progressively higher as the machine rating is reduced. The equivalent rotor resistance R_r' for a squirrel-cage machine is generally in the range 0.02 to 0.05 per unit. From eq. 5.116 we see that if 1 per-unit power is to cross the air gap with 1 per-unit equivalent rotor current I_r', the per-unit rotor resistance must be equal to the desired value of slip s.

5.4.4 Squirrel-Cage Rotors

Squirrel-cage rotors consist of bare copper, aluminum, or alloy bars inserted or cast into slots in the magnetic material of the rotor. At both ends, these bars are connected to shorting end rings.

The rotor resistance R_r per phase (and its equivalent resistance R_r' as seen from the stator) can be varied over a wide range by appropriate choice of the size and material of the rotor bars. The selection of an appropriate value for the rotor resistance involves an interesting design compromise. If the machine is to have a high efficiency, it must have a low operating value of slip s (eq. 5.119). From eq. 5.105 we note that as the effective rotor resistance R_r' is reduced, the slip s required to produce a given torque is reduced. On the other hand, we note from eq. 5.110 that for large values of slip, the torque is directly proportional to the effective rotor resistance R_r'. Thus a high rotor resistance is required to produce high starting torque, but a low rotor resistance is desired for high running efficiency.

We need not accept this compromise between efficiency and starting torque. The rotor bars can be so designed that their effective resistance is much higher at standstill than at full-speed operation. One frequently used arrangement of rotor bars is the double squirrel cage, shown in Fig. 5.24a. Both sets of bars are connected to shorting end rings. The upper bars are small in cross section and may be made of a high-resistivity material. Thus they have a high resistance. These bars are placed close to the rotor surface producing a high-reluctance path for leakage flux and therefore a low leakage inductance. The lower bars are larger and have a low resistance. The narrow slot between the upper and lower bars provides a low-reluctance leakage path and thus a high leakage inductance. At high values of rotor frequency, for example, at standstill, very little of the rotor current flows in the lower bars because of their high reactance. Under this condition, the effective resistance as seen by the stator is that of the high-resistance upper bars. With the low rotor frequencies that accompany normal high-speed operation, the rotor reactances are negligible, and most of the rotor current flows in the low-resistance lower bars.

An equivalent circuit for a double-cage rotor may be readily developed using the methods discussed in Section 2.4. Two bars spaced $2\pi/p$ radians apart on the rotor periphery may be considered as one of the m_r-phase windings of the rotor. In the magnetic equivalent circuit of Fig. 5.24b, $\mathscr{F}_1$ and $\mathscr{F}_2$ represent the magnetomotive forces of the upper and lower

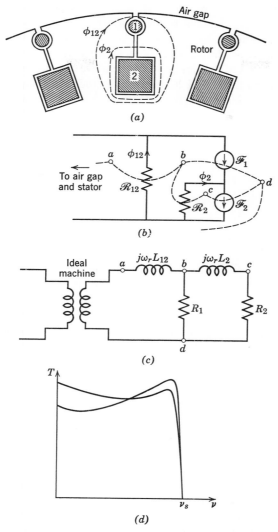

Fig. 5.24 (a) Double squirrel-cage-rotor bar arrangement. (b) Magnetic equivalent circuit. (c) Electric equivalent circuit of rotor. (d) Typical torque-speed curves.

bars. $\mathscr{R}_2$ is the reluctance of the path of the leakage flux that links only the lower bar, and $\mathscr{R}_{12}$ is the reluctance of the leakage path that encircles both upper and lower bars. Using the topological principle of duality (Section 2.4.2), the equivalent electric circuit of Fig. 5.24c is developed for the rotor. Since $L_2 \gg L_{12}$, the rotor impedance at high values of rotor frequency ω_r is approximately $R_1 + j\omega_r L_{12}$. At low values of rotor frequency, the rotor reactances are negligible, and the rotor impedance per phase is essentially R_1 in parallel with R_2.

By adjusting the relative areas and materials of the two sets of bars and the dimensions of the slot between them, we can achieve a combination of high starting torque and high running efficiency. Figure 5.24d shows some typical torque-speed characteristics that can be obtained. Refinements can be added to the equivalent circuit of Fig. 5.24 to include the effects of resistance and leakage inductance of the end rings.

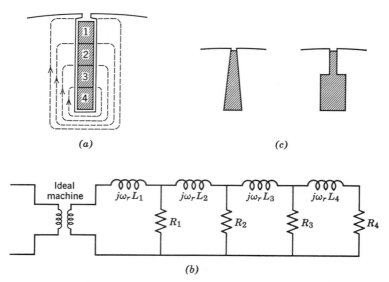

Fig. 5.25 (a) Deep-bar rotor construction. (b) An equivalent circuit for a deep-bar rotor. (c) Other deep-bar shapes.

A torque-speed relation similar to that of a double-cage rotor may be achieved by the use of deep, narrow rotor bars as shown in Fig. 5.25a. This conductor arrangement may be analyzed approximately by considering each conductor as a number of parallel sections. Leakage flux produced by current in the top section encounters a relatively high-reluctance path whereas leakage fluxes produced by the lower sections encounter progressively lower reluctances. At high rotor frequencies for which the leakage impedance predominates, the current is concentrated toward the top of the conductor and the effective rotor resistance is high. At low rotor frequencies, the current is approximately uniformly distributed and the effective rotor resistance is low. Figure 5.25b shows that the equivalent electric circuit of a bar divided into a number of sections is in the form of a ladder network. For a rectangular bar divided into a number of equal sections, the inductance and resistance associated with each section is the same. Other shapes of bars, such as those shown in Fig. 5.25c, may also be used to advantage. This deep-bar construction is particularly suitable for use with rotors whose conductors and end rings are cast.

An effective change in rotor resistance with frequency can be obtained only if the bars are sufficiently deep. At normal power frequencies (50 to 60 cycles/second), the minimum effective depth is about 1 centimeter. The reason for this can be seen by considering all rotor dimensions to be multiplied by a factor k. Then the leakage inductance would be multiplied by k, but the resistances of conductor sections would be multiplied by $1/k$. If the bar is too small, the current distribution in sections of the bar is determined by the resistances of the sections rather than by their inductive reactances at the standstill rotor frequency.

5.4.5 Speed and Torque Control

A polyphase induction motor with a shorted rotor winding and a constant-supply voltage can drive a given mechanical load at a constant steady-state speed, which is usually near synchronous speed. If control of speed is required, arrangements must be made to vary some parameter of the motor or some property of the supply.

Speed control may be achieved by the use of a wound-rotor induction motor with a variable polyphase resistance connected to its rotor terminals. The effect of added rotor-circuit resistance can be appreciated by examining eqs. 5.104 and 5.112 and the equivalent circuits of Figs. 5.21a and 5.22b. We note that both the torque and the stator current are functions of the rotor-circuit resistance divided by the slip s. Thus, if the rotor-circuit resistance is multiplied by a factor k, the same values of torque and stator current will occur at k times the original value of slip.

Figure 5.26 shows a set of torque-speed curves for a wound-rotor induction motor with constant-supply voltage and various values of rotor-circuit resistance. The intersections of these curves with the torque-speed characteristic of a load represent the steady-state conditions that are obtained for each value of external rotor resistance. It is evident that this method of speed control is effective only when the motor is mechanically loaded; on no-load, the steady-state speed approaches its synchronous value ν_s. This method of speed control wastes a considerable proportion of the input power except when operating near synchronous speed (eq. 5.119). This inefficiency is, however, of minor importance if the drive is used only intermittently at low speed.

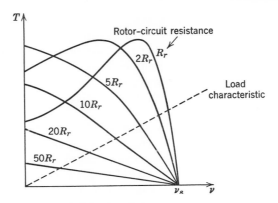

Fig. 5.26. Torque-speed curves for wound-rotor induction motor with variable rotor-circuit resistance; R_r is the winding resistance alone.

Speed control of some mechanical loads can be achieved using a squirrel-cage induction motor with variable supply voltage. We note from eq. 5.104 that the torque at any value of speed is proportional to the square of the supply voltage. Figure 5.27 shows a family of torque-speed curves for a double-cage or deep-bar induction motor with several values of supply voltage. If the torque required by the mechanical load rises as the speed increases, speed control can be achieved. The intersections of curves in Fig. 5.27 represent stable operating speeds; a slight reduction in speed causes the motor to produce more torque than is required by the load, the difference torque acting to accelerate the motor back to the operating speed. It can readily be seen that this method of control would

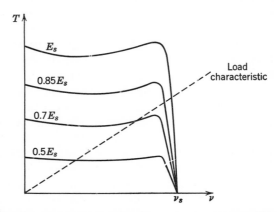

Fig. 5.27 Torque-speed curves for double-cage induction motor with variable supply voltage. E_s represents the rated supply voltage.

not be effective with a mechanical load that required a substantially constant torque at all values of speed.

The supply voltage may be controlled manually by the use of an induction regulator (Fig. 5.17) or a polyphase autotransformer (Section 3.4.1) with adjustable tappings. Alternatively, the supply voltage may be controlled electrically by the use of polyphase saturable reactors (Section 3.4.3), controlled rectifiers, or magnetic frequency doublers (Section 3.4.5). Closed-loop feedback control of speed may be employed with any of these voltage controllers.

Essentially ideal control of speed can be obtained by control of the supply frequency. The synchronous speed then varies directly with the supply frequency, and the load is driven efficiently at a speed near synchronism. Variable frequency supply can be obtained from variable-speed synchronous generators, commutator frequency changers, electronic inverters, or cycloconverters. At present, the major limitation of these systems is the complexity and therefore the cost of the frequency conversion equipment.

If the line frequency is varied, the supply voltage should be varied more or less proportionately to maintain essentially constant flux in the machine. If the supply voltage is made directly proportional to frequency, the maximum torque (eq. 5.108) remains essentially constant except for very low frequencies, at which the leakage reactance is no longer large in comparison with the stator resistance.

Another method of rough speed control, applicable to squirrel-cage motors, involves changing the number of poles (p) of the stator winding. This can be accomplished by the provision of two independent stator windings with different numbers of poles. Alternatively, the connections of appropriately designed stator coils may be changed to change the effective number of poles. The most common type of reconnection doubles the number of poles and halves the synchronous speed. With more complex switching of connections, other ratios of synchronous speeds can be obtained. Although this method does not provide continuous control of speed, it is simple, efficient, and adequate for many drives.

5.4.6 Starting and Transient-Speed Characteristics

When an induction motor at standstill is connected to a rated-voltage supply, the stator current may be 3 to 8 times its rated value. Most induction motors are designed to withstand the mechanical forces and heating that accompany this high current during the limited time required for starting. Thus in contrast with d-c machines, induction motors may safely be started by connecting the stator terminals directly to the supply. But unless the internal impedance of the power supply is sufficiently low, the high starting current may cause a substantial transient drop in the local-supply voltage, with consequent disturbance to the operation of other apparatus. When this voltage drop is too large to permit across-the-line starting, various means can be employed to reduce the line current during the starting period.

One common type of starter consists of a polyphase step-down auto-transformer. Suppose, for example, that the stator voltage is reduced to 0.8 of its rated value during the starting period. The stator current is also reduced to 0.8 of the value that would occur with rated-voltage

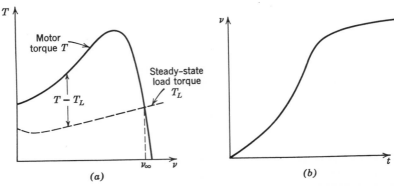

Fig. 5.28   Starting transient of induction motor. (a) Torque-speed curves of motor and load. (b) Speed-time curve during starting.

starting. The supply current on the other side of the $1:0.8$ ratio transformer is then only 0.64 of the value that would occur with across-the-line starting. The starting torque, being proportional to the square of the stator voltage, would also be 0.64 of the rated-voltage value.

There are several other means that can be used to reduce the line current during starting. Resistance or inductive-reactance elements may be inserted in series with the supply. This method may be more economical than the use of an autotransformer but it provides less starting torque per unit of line current. Another method consists of connecting the three stator phase windings in star during starting and in delta for full-speed operation. This method provides $1/\sqrt{3}$ times rated voltage and therefore only one-third of the rated-voltage torque during starting.

Another problem associated with starting is determining the time required to accelerate the motor and its mechanical load from standstill to the steady-state operating speed. Figure 5.28a shows the steady-state torque produced by the motor and the steady-state torque required by the load over this speed range. Because of the relatively high inertia of the motor and its load, the change in speed during one cycle of the supply frequency is usually very small. In addition, the initial electrical transients decay in a time that is usually negligible in comparison with the starting time. Thus the electrical system normally can be considered to be in a slowly varying steady state during the starting period, and the steady-state expression of eq. 5.104 may be used to determine the motor torque T produced at any value of speed v.

The speed-time relation during starting may be found by solution of the equation

$$J\frac{dv}{dt} = T - T_L \qquad \text{newton-meters} \qquad (5.122)$$

where J is the rated polar moment of inertia of the motor and its load, T is the torque produced by the motor at speed v, and T_L is the steady-state torque required by the load at speed v. The time t required to accelerate from standstill to a speed v is given by

$$t = J\int_0^v \frac{1}{T - T_L}\,dv \qquad \text{seconds} \qquad (5.123)$$

This integration may be performed graphically or by the use of numerical methods (see example in Section 2.1.1). A typical speed-time curve during starting is shown in Fig. 5.28b.

Speed transients also occur following sudden changes in the mechanical load torque. Suppose, for example, that the load torque is increased suddenly from zero to a constant value T_L on a motor of inertia J which is initially operating at synchronous speed v_s. From eq. 5.105, the motor torque near synchronous speed can be approximated by

$$T = \frac{m_s}{v_s}\frac{|E_e|^2}{R_r'}s$$
$$= K_s s$$
$$= K\frac{(v_s - v)}{v_s} \qquad \text{newton-meters} \qquad (5.124)$$

Substituting from eq. 5.124 into eq. 5.122 gives

$$\frac{Jv_s}{K}\frac{dv}{dt} + v = v_s - \frac{T_L v_s}{K} \qquad (5.125)$$

The speed-time solution of this linear equation is

$$v = v_s - T_L\frac{v_s}{K}(1 - \epsilon^{-t/\tau_m}) \qquad \text{radians/second} \qquad (5.126)$$

where the mechanical time constant τ_m is

$$\tau_m = \frac{Jv_s}{K} \quad \text{seconds} \quad (5.127)$$

It can be seen that a motor which has a low-resistance rotor not only has a smaller speed change with change in load but also adjusts more rapidly to the new value of speed.

5.5 POLYPHASE SYNCHRONOUS MACHINES

The general polyphase machine discussed earlier in this chapter consists of a cylindrical magnetic structure with distributed polyphase windings placed in slots on both the stator and the rotor. It was shown that such a machine produces torque only when its speed v is

$$v = \frac{2}{p}(\omega_s - \omega_r) \quad \text{radians/second} \quad (5.128)$$

where p is the number of poles, and ω_s and ω_r are the frequencies of the balanced polyphase currents in the stator and rotor, respectively. In Section 5.3.1, we examined the operation of this machine at standstill as a polyphase phase-shifting transformer with $\omega_r = \omega_s$. In Section 5.4 we considered its operation as an induction machine in which the rotor currents at the appropriate frequency ω_r are obtained at any speed v by induction.

In this section we consider the important group of machines in which one set of windings, usually that on the rotor, is supplied with direct current, thus making the rotor frequency ω_r equal to zero. These are then called the field windings by analogy with d-c machines. Under this constraint, energy conversion can take place in the machine only when the speed v and the stator frequency ω_s are related by

$$v = \frac{2}{p}\omega_s \quad \text{radians/second} \quad (5.129)$$

that is, when the rotor of the machine is revolving synchronously with the revolving magnetic field produced by the stator currents.

There are several reasons for choosing to supply the rotor rather than the stator windings with direct current. Winding space is less constrained on the stator side of the air gap. The windings connected to the a-c power system usually operate at a voltage that is considerably higher than that of the d-c field system and thus require more space for insulation. These windings are also subject to high transient currents and must have adequate mechanical strength. This can be provided more easily on the stationary member. Furthermore, only two slip rings are required to supply direct current to the rotor whereas three or more connections must be brought out from a three-phase winding. It is only in some small synchronous machines that the direct current is supplied to the stator.

The stator winding of a synchronous machine is similar to that of a polyphase induction machine and normally has three phases. The field winding on the rotor is required to produce a distributed magnetomotive force that is fixed in position relative to the rotor. Thus only a single rotor winding is required.

Synchronous machine rotors are of two basic types. Figure 5.29 shows a cylindrical rotor with a single distributed winding. This type is used in high-speed machines such as steam-turbine-driven alternators. Salient-pole rotors have concentrated windings on their poles. This latter type of rotor is used in lower-speed applications.

Since the salient-pole machine combines the properties of the cylindrical-rotor synchronous machine and the reluctance-type synchronous machine, discussion of this type is postponed until Section 5.6. The analysis to follow assumes a cylindrical rotor, but its results apply approximately to most salient-pole machines as well.

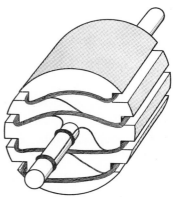

Fig. 5.29 Cylindrical rotor for synchronous machine.

5.5.1 Equivalent Circuits

Figure 5.30 shows schematically the magnetic structure and windings of a cylindrical-rotor, two-pole, synchronous machine. Each of the three stator windings has N_s sinusoidally distributed turns. The single rotor winding has N_r distributed turns. Let us examine the magnetic fields produced by these windings.

Suppose a balanced set of currents of frequency ω_s flows in the stator windings, the current in phase a being

$$i_a = \hat{I} \sin (\omega_s t + \alpha) \tag{5.130}$$

From eq. 5.15, the magnetomotive force produced in the machine by these currents is

$$\mathcal{F}_\theta = \frac{m_s N_s \hat{I}}{2} \cos (\omega_s t + \alpha - \theta) \tag{5.131}$$

This magnetomotive force is sinusoidally distributed around the machine and revolves forward, in the direction of positive angle θ, at an angular velocity of ω_s radians per second. The flux linkages produced in the stator windings by this magnetomotive force change sinusoidally with time, causing an induced voltage in those windings.

Now suppose the rotor is rotated at an angular velocity of ν radians per second so that the angle β of the rotor winding A is related to that of the stator winding a by

$$\beta = \nu t + \beta_0 \tag{5.132}$$

If $\nu = \omega_s$, the rotor is rotating synchronously with the revolving field. The flux linkage of the rotor winding is constant and no voltage is induced in it. The rotor frequency has become equal to zero.

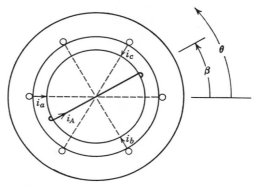

Fig. 5.30. Magnetic structure and windings of a two-pole cylindrical-rotor, synchronous machine.

Now suppose a direct current i_A is made to flow in the rotor winding. From eqs. 5.11, 5.19, and 5.132, the magnetomotive force produced by this winding is

$$\mathscr{F}_\theta = N_r i_A \sin(\theta - \beta)$$
$$= N_r i_A \sin(\theta - \nu t - \beta_0)$$
$$= N_r i_A \cos\left(\nu t + \beta_0 + \frac{\pi}{2} - \theta\right) \tag{5.133}$$

A comparison of eqs. 5.131 and 5.133 shows that if $\nu = \omega_s$, the magnetic effect of the d-c winding on the synchronous rotating rotor is equivalent to that of a balanced set of currents of frequency ω_s in the stator windings. If this equivalent current in stator phase a is designated as

$$i_a = \hat{I}_r' \sin(\omega_s t + \alpha_r') \tag{5.134}$$

then

$$\hat{I}_r' = \frac{2}{m_s} \frac{N_r}{N_s} i_A \tag{5.135}$$

and

$$\alpha_r' = \beta_0 + \frac{\pi}{2} \tag{5.136}$$

For later analysis, it is convenient to designate the field current i_f as

$$i_f = -i_A \tag{5.137}$$

Expressed in phasor notation, the stator equivalent of the field current i_f is given by

$$
\begin{aligned}
I_r' &= \frac{\hat{I}_r'}{\sqrt{2}} \big/\!\underline{\alpha_r'} \\
&= \frac{\sqrt{2}}{m_s} \frac{N_r}{N_s} i_f \big/\!\underline{\beta_0 - \pi/2} \\
&= n' i_f \big/\!\underline{\beta_0 - \pi/2} \qquad \text{amperes} \tag{5.138}
\end{aligned}
$$

where n' is the current ratio linking the rms value of the equivalent stator current component I_r' to the value of the direct field current i_f.

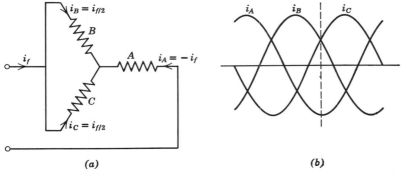

(a)   (b)

Fig. 5.31   (a) Connection of three-phase winding as the field of a synchronous machine. (b) Instant in a three-phase set of currents corresponding to connection of (a).

A three-phase rotor winding may be used as the field system by connecting it as shown in Fig. 5.31a. This connection reproduces the phase currents that occur at the instant shown in Fig. 5.31b where

$$i_A = -i_f \tag{5.139}$$
$$i_B = i_C = i_f/2 \tag{5.140}$$

For this connection, it can be shown that n' in eq. 5.138 is replaced by

$$n' = \frac{3}{\sqrt{2}m_s} \frac{N_r}{N_s} \tag{5.141}$$

The electrical behavior of the synchronous machine can now be described by the equivalent circuit of Fig. 5.32. This circuit is a simplification of that of the general polyphase machine shown in Fig. 5.18. In the rotor section of the circuit, the voltage e_{mf} is that produced by the rate of change of mutual linkage in the rotor winding. In the steady state this induced voltage is zero, and the field current i_f is related to the field voltage by

$$i_f = \frac{e_f}{R_f} \qquad \text{amperes} \qquad (5.142)$$

The current i_f in the rotor is equivalent in effect to a component of stator current I_r' of frequency ω_s, the current ratio being that of eq. 5.138 (or 5.141). The magnetizing current I_{ms} is equal to the sum of the stator

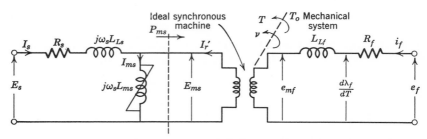

Fig. 5.32 Equivalent circuit of cylindrical-rotor, synchronous machine. (Current ratio n' given in eqs. 5.138 and 5.141.)

Voltage $1:0$

Current $n'\big/\beta_0 - \pi/2 : 1$

Inductance $1 : \sqrt{2}\, n'\, \dfrac{N_r}{N_s}$

Power $1:0$

Frequency $\omega_s : 0$

current I_s and the equivalent I_r' of the rotor current. The voltage induced in the stator winding by the air-gap flux of the machine is

$$E_{ms} = j\omega_s L_{ms} I_{ms} \qquad \text{volts} \qquad (5.143)$$

Because of magnetic saturation, particularly in the region of the stator teeth, the magnetizing inductance L_{ms} is nonlinearly related to the magnetizing current as shown earlier in Fig. 5.9e.

The stator and rotor variables of Fig. 5.32 are linked by an ideal synchronous machine transformation, which represents the behavior of a machine with no winding resistances, no leakage inductances, and no magnetizing current. The current ratio is that derived in eq. 5.138 (or 5.141). The voltage ratio states only that the induced voltage e_{mf} in the field windings is zero for any steady-state value of the stator voltage E_{ms}. In the steady state, no power is transferred across the air gap to the rotor windings. Because the rotor frequency is zero, impedances transferred from stator to rotor are equal to zero. It is, however, possible and useful to transfer inductances across the transformation. The maximum value of mutual flux linkage per phase in the field winding is related to the mutual flux linkage of a stator winding by the turns ratio $N_r : N_s$. The inductance ratio is the flux linkage ratio divided by the maximum current ratio. For example, the magnetizing inductance L_{mr} as seen by the field circuit is given by

$$L_{mr} = \sqrt{2} n' \frac{N_r}{N_s} L_{ms} \qquad \text{henrys} \qquad (5.144)$$

The equivalent circuit of Fig. 5.32 may be replaced by the simple form of Fig. 5.33a, in which the effect of the field is represented simply by a sinusoidal current source at frequency ω_s. The magnitude of this current source is directly proportional to the field current (eq. 5.138). The phase

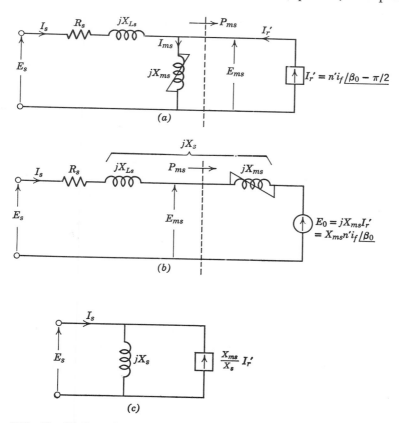

Fig. 5.33 Simplified steady-state equivalent circuits for cylindrical-rotor, synchronous machines. (a) Form derived from general circuit of Fig. 5.32. (b) Thévenin equivalent of (a). (c) Norton equivalent of (b), assuming X_{ms} constant and $R_s = 0$.

angle of the current source is $\beta_0 - \pi/2$, where β_0 is the angle by which the field reference axis leads the stator reference axis at the chosen reference time designated as $t = 0$.

In general, the magnetizing reactance $\omega_s L_{ms}$ must be regarded as a nonlinear function of the magnetizing current I_{ms} or of the induced voltage E_{ms}. If, however, the machine is operated over a reasonably narrow range of values of the voltage E_{ms}, a suitable average value of the magnetizing reactance may be chosen for this range. If the equivalent circuit of Fig. 5.33a is linearized in this way, an alternative form of equivalent circuit may be derived by the use of Thévenin's theorem. This circuit, shown in Fig. 5.33b, consists of an impedance in series with an alternating voltage source E_0. The voltage E_0 is given by

$$E_0 = jX_{ms}n'i_f\underline{/\beta_0 - \pi/2}$$
$$= X_{ms}n'i_f\underline{/\beta_0} \qquad \text{volts} \qquad (5.145)$$

Note that the voltage E_0 is directly proportional to the field current i_f, and that its angle is equal to the rotor-axis position at $t = 0$.

The sum of the stator leakage reactance and the magnetizing reactance is commonly known as the synchronous reactance X_s of the machine.

$$X_s = X_{Ls} + X_{ms} \qquad \text{ohms} \qquad (5.146)$$

In many analyses, it is simpler not to separate the two components of the synchronous reactance. But it must be recalled that the magnetizing reactance X_{ms} in both eq. 5.145 and eq. 5.146 must be assigned a value that is appropriate for the operating value of the voltage E_{ms}.

Figure 5.33c shows another form of equivalent circuit that is useful in analyses, for which the magnetizing reactance is considered as a constant and the stator resistance is neglected. It is developed by application of Norton's theorem to the stator terminals of either of the other circuits.

5.5.2 Torque

The torque T of a synchronous machine may be derived by applying the principle of energy conservation to the equivalent circuits of Fig. 5.32 or 5.33. As none of the air-gap power P_{ms} is transferred to the rotor windings, all of it must be converted into mechanical power. Using eqs. 5.93 and 5.129, the torque produced by a p-pole, m_s-phase synchronous machine is given by

$$T = \frac{p}{2}\frac{m_s}{\omega_s}P_{ms}$$
$$= \mathscr{R}_e\left[-\frac{p}{2}\frac{m_s}{\omega_s}I_r'E_{ms}{}^*\right] \qquad \text{newton-meters} \qquad (5.147)$$

As no power is dissipated in the inductive reactances of Fig. 5.33, the power P_{ms} may be derived from several other sets of current and voltage variables. For example, in Fig. 5.33b the torque may be expressed as

$$T = \mathscr{R}_e \left[\frac{p}{2} \frac{m_s}{\omega_s} I_s E_0^* \right] \qquad \text{newton-meters} \qquad (5.148)$$

The torque may also be derived by considering the reaction between the field winding and the magnetic field in the air gap. As there is no reluctance torque, the torque on the rotor may be derived from the rate of change of the mutual flux linkage of the field winding with respect to the rotor angle β.

$$T = i_f \frac{d\lambda_{mf}}{d\beta} \qquad \text{newton-meters} \qquad (5.149)$$

From eq. 5.30, let the air-gap flux density distribution for a two-pole machine be

$$B_\theta = \hat{B} \cos (\omega_s t + \alpha_m - \theta) \qquad \text{webers/meter}^2 \qquad (5.150)$$

The corresponding flux linkage of the N_r-turn, phase A rotor winding is given in eq. 5.36. Note that the polarity of the field winding was reversed in eq. 5.137, making $i_f = -i_A$, thus the mutual flux linkage of the field winding is

$$\lambda_{mf} = - \frac{\pi}{2} N_r \hat{B} l r \sin (\omega_s t + \alpha_m - \beta) \qquad (5.151)$$

Thus

$$T = i_f \frac{d\lambda_{mf}}{d\beta}$$

$$= i_f \frac{\pi}{2} N_r \hat{B} l r \cos (\omega_s t + \alpha_m - \beta) \qquad (5.152)$$

By inserting the expression for β of eq. 5.132, the torque is given by

$$T = i_f \frac{\pi}{2} N_r \hat{B} l r \cos (\beta_0 - \alpha_n) \qquad \text{newton-meters} \qquad (5.153)$$

The torque expressions of eqs. 5.147 and 5.153 may be shown to be identical, for $p = 2$ by substituting, first from eq. 5.74, expressed in phasor form,

$$E_{ms} = \frac{1}{\sqrt{2}} \omega_s \frac{\pi}{2} N_s \hat{B} l r \underline{/\alpha_m + \pi/2} \qquad (5.154)$$

and also, from eq. 5.138,

$$I_r' = \frac{\sqrt{2}}{m_s} \frac{N_r}{N_s} i_f \underline{/\beta_0 - \pi/2} \qquad (5.155)$$

To examine the torque properties of a synchronous machine, let us suppose that the machine is rotating at synchronous speed and that its stator terminals are connected to a constant-voltage polyphase supply of frequency ω_s. For simplicity, let us neglect the effects of the stator resistance R_s and stator leakage reactance X_{Ls}. Then, referring to the equivalent circuit of Fig. 5.33a, the voltage E_{ms} is assumed to be equal to E_s and is constant in magnitude and phase. The necessary magnetizing current

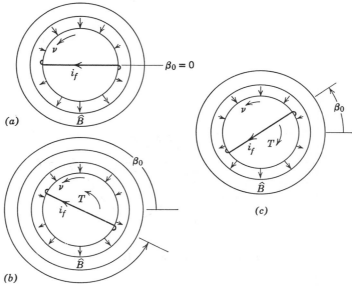

Fig. 5.34 Torque on a synchronous machine rotor. (a) Condition for zero torque ($\beta_0 = 0$). (b) Torque in direction of rotation (motor action). (c) Torque opposite to direction of rotation (generator action).

I_{ms} is provided by a combination of the stator and field currents. Let us assign a phase angle of zero to E_{ms} in eq. 5.154, thus making $\alpha_m = -\pi/2$. The machine then has a constant air-gap flux density (eq. 5.150), the maximum value of which occurs at $\theta = \alpha_m = -\pi/2$ for $t = 0$, as shown in Fig. 5.34a. From eq. 5.153, zero torque occurs when the rotor is in the position where $\beta_0 = 0$. This is to be expected, since in Fig. 5.34a, the rotor flux linkages are at the maximum value in this position.

If a mechanical load is applied to the machine shaft, the rotor decelerates momentarily, thus causing the rotor angle β_0 to become negative in value. From eq. 5.153 in which $\alpha_m = -\pi/2$, this results in a positive torque T, which acts to arrest the deceleration and supply the required load torque. The rotor angle β_0 then automatically adjusts itself until the torque produced by the machine equals the torque required at steady state by the mechanical load. Under this condition, shown in Fig. 5.34b the machine is operating as a synchronous motor.

The machine may also be operated as a generator if its shaft is driven by a prime mover. Torque applied by the prime mover accelerates the rotor, causing its position to move forward relative to the magnetic field. With a positive value of β_0, the machine torque in eq. 5.153 becomes negative, that is, against the direction of rotation as shown in Fig. 5.34c. Again, the angle β_0 adjusts itself so that the torque produced by the machine just balances the prime mover torque.

The relation between the torque T and the rotor angle β_0 is shown in Fig. 5.35, assuming a constant voltage E_{ms} and a constant field current

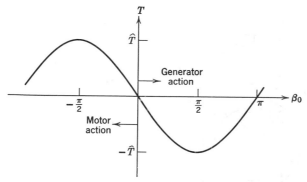

Fig. 5.35   Relation between torque T and rotor angle β_0. (Maximum torque T given in eqs. 5.153 and 5.147.)

i_f. As a generator, maximum torque occurs at $\beta_0 = \pi/2$ while, as a motor, maximum torque occurs at $\beta_0 = -\pi/2$. The value of the maximum torque is directly proportional to the maximum flux density $\hat{B}$ in the machine (eq. 5.153). It is also directly proportional to the field current i_f. The maximum torque that a synchronous machine can produce is therefore limited by saturation in its magnetic material and by heating in its windings.

5.5.3   Measurement of Parameters

Prediction of the steady-state performance of a synchronous machine is dependent on a knowledge of the values of its parameters. From the equivalent circuit of Fig. 5.33a, the parameters are the stator resistance R_s, the stator leakage reactance X_{Ls}, the magnetizing reactance X_{ms}, and the current ratio n'. Since most synchronous machines have a single field winding, the techniques for obtaining the parameters are somewhat different from those employed with polyphase induction machines.

The stator resistance R_s per phase may be measured at the operating temperature using direct current. If the stator conductors are large in cross-section or the frequency ω_s is high, the a-c resistance is somewhat greater than the d-c value because of local eddy currents. The resistance R_s has little effect on the terminal performance of the machine. Knowledge of its value is important mainly in the determination of losses and efficiency.

This leaves three parameters to be determined. The current ratio n' is a constant. The stator leakage reactance may also be regarded as constant for the normal range of stator current. It may, however, be subject to

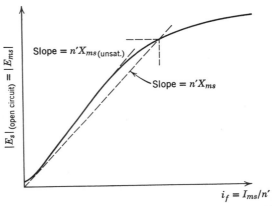

Fig. 5.36   Open-circuit magnetization curve of synchronous machine.

magnetic saturation at high values of stator current. The magnetizing reactance X_{ms} includes the effect of magnetic saturation arising from the mutual flux and is therefore nonlinearly dependent on the air-gap voltage E_{ms}. Since the performance of a synchronous machine is sensitive to the value of X_{ms}, an accurate determination of X_{ms} as a function of E_{ms} is important.

Let us first see what information can be obtained from an open-circuit test. Suppose the machine is driven at synchronous speed with its stator terminals open circuited. Figure 5.36 shows a typical relationship of the open-circuit terminal voltage E_s to the field current i_f. From Fig. 5.33a it can be seen that, with $I_s = 0$, the open-circuit terminal voltage is equal to the air-gap voltage E_{ms}. Also, all the field current i_f is used to magnetize the machine. Thus the abscissa of Fig. 5.36 is a measure of I_{ms}/n'. For a particular value of E_{ms}, the appropriate value of the magnetizing reactance X_{ms} is

$$X_{ms} = \frac{E_{ms}}{n'i_f} \qquad \text{ohms} \qquad (5.156)$$

where i_f is the field current corresponding to E_{ms}. When the current ratio n' is determined (from a test to be described later) it can be inserted into eq. 5.156, to give X_{ms}.

The curve of Fig. 5.36 shows a small effect of residual magnetism near $i_f = 0$. A significant part of the curve is approximately linear, and the constant value of X_{ms}, which applies over this linear region, is known as the unsaturated magnetizing reactance. To make efficient use of the magnetic material, most synchronous machines are operated at values of E_{ms}, which are in the nonlinear or saturated region of Fig. 5.36.

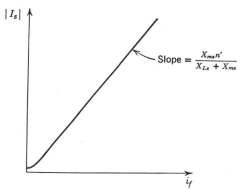

Fig. 5.37 Short-circuit curve of synchronous machine (the unsaturated value of magnetizing reactance X_{ms} applies).

Let us now examine the results of a test in which the stator terminals are short circuited and the magnitude of the stator current I_s is measured as a function of the field current. A typical curve is shown in Fig. 5.37. Analysis of the circuit of Fig. 5.33a shows that

$$I_s = \frac{-jX_{ms}}{R_s + jX_{Ls} + jX_{ms}} I_r' \qquad (5.157)$$

In this short-circuit test, the voltage E_{ms} is usually well below the saturated region in Fig. 5.36, and thus the unsaturated value of X_{ms} is appropriate for use in eq. 5.157. Since $R_s \ll (X_{Ls} + X_{ms})$, eq. 5.157 may be replaced by the simpler magnitude relation

$$|I_s| = \frac{X_{ms}}{X_{Ls} + X_{ms}} n' i_f \qquad \text{amperes} \qquad (5.158)$$

To determine the parameters X_{Ls}, X_{ms}, and n', a third relation is needed in addition to eqs. 5.156 and 5.158. If the equivalent circuit of the machine were linear, no additional information would be obtained by performing other terminal tests and measurements. But the fact that the magnetizing reactance X_{ms} has an identifiable nonlinear relationship to the voltage E_{ms} allows us to devise a further test that gives the required information. Suppose an inductive polyphase load with negligible resistance is connected to the stator terminals, and is adjusted, at each value of field current i_f, to obtain a constant magnitude of the stator current I_s. Normally, the rated value of stator current would be chosen. The lower curve in Fig. 5.38 shows the measured relation between the magnitude E_s of the stator voltage and the field current i_f for this zero power factor, inductive-load test.

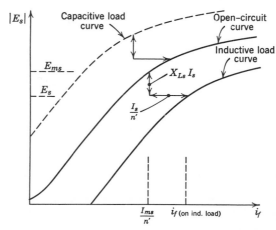

Fig. 5.38 The terminal voltage $|E_s|$ as a function of field current i_f, with no-load and with zero-power factor loads at constant stator current I_s.

The results of the open-circuit test (Fig. 5.36) are also shown in Fig. 5.38. It is noted that the two curves are similar in shape but that the zero power factor curve is shifted downward and to the right of the open-circuit curve. Inspection of the equivalent circuit of Fig. 5.33a shows that, with a purely inductive load and R_s negligible, the voltage across the leakage reactance X_L is in phase with the terminal voltage E_s. Thus

$$|E_s|_{\substack{\text{(zero} \\ \text{p.f. load)}}} = |E_{ms}| - |X_{Ls}I_s| \qquad (5.159)$$

and

$$|I_r'| = |I_{ms}| + |I_s| \qquad (5.160)$$

Dividing all terms in eq. 5.160 by the current ratio n' gives

$$i_{f\substack{\text{(zero} \\ \text{p.f. load)}}} = i_{f(Ems)} + \frac{|I_s|}{n'} \qquad (5.161)$$

Thus the zero power factor, inductive-load curve in Fig. 5.38 is shifted downward by $X_{Ls}I_s$ volts and to the right by I_s/n' amperes with respect to the open-circuit curve. If one of these curves is copied on transparent graph paper, its best fit on the other curve may be found. Knowing the magnitudes of the shifts between the two curves and the magnitude of the stator current I_s used in the test, we may find the values of the leakage reactance X_{Ls} and the current ratio n'.

A zero power factor capacitive load may also be used to obtain these parameters. In Fig. 5.38, the capacitive-load curve is shifted upward by $X_{Ls}I_s$ volts and to the left by I_s/n' amperes with respect to the open-circuit curve.

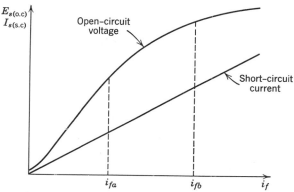

Fig. 5.39 Open-circuit stator voltage and short-circuit stator current as function of field current.

With some synchronous machines, we find that the zero power factor, inductive-load curve is not identical in shape to the open-circuit curve for high values of field current. This is an indication of the inadequacy of the simple equivalent circuit of Fig. 5.32, which is based on the assumption that all the magnetic saturation is due to mutual flux. At high values of field current, the rotor leakage flux adds to the mutual flux to produce magnetic saturation in the rotor. This effect may be included in the equivalent circuit of Fig. 5.32 by connecting a nonlinear inductance, representing the rotor magnetic system, across the terminals of the voltage denoted as $d\lambda_f/dt$. This inductance and the leakage inductance L_{Lf} may then be transferred across the ideal machine, to produce a modified form of the equivalent circuit of Fig. 5.33a.

In many analyses it is convenient to use the simple voltage-source equivalent circuit of Fig. 5.33b, the value of the synchronous reactance X_s being chosen at an appropriate average value for the expected range of the induced voltage E_{ms}. Let us consider how this synchronous reactance may be measured. Figure 5.39 shows the results of open-circuit and short-circuit tests on a machine. In the magnetically linear region of operation of the machine, the unsaturated synchronous reactance may be measured simply as the ratio of the open-circuit voltage to the short-circuit current at a constant value of field current. By assuming $R_s \ll X_s$ we find that

$$X_{s(\text{unsat.})} = \left. \left| \frac{E_{s(\text{o.c})}}{I_{s(\text{s.c})}} \right| \right|_{\substack{i_f = \text{constant} \\ i_f \leq i_{fa}}} \tag{5.162}$$

Let us now consider what reactance is obtained if the ratio of eq. 5.162 is taken in the nonlinear or saturated region of operation, at $i_f = i_{fb}$ for example. From the equivalent circuit of Fig. 5.33a, the relations for the open and short-circuit tests are

$$E_{s(\text{o.c.})} = E_{ms} = jX_{ms(E_{ms})}I_r' \tag{5.163}$$

and

$$I_{s(\text{s.c.})} = -\frac{X_{ms(\text{unsat.})}}{X_{Ls} + X_{ms(\text{unsat.})}} I_r' \tag{5.164}$$

The ratio of the open-circuit voltage to the short-circuit current is

$$\left| \frac{E_{s(\text{o.c.})}}{I_{s(\text{s.c.})}} \right| = X_{Ls}\left(\frac{X_{ms(E_{ms})}}{X_{ms(\text{unsat.})}} \right) + X_{ms(E_{ms})} \tag{5.165}$$

Thus if the open-circuit test is made at a particular value of the voltage E_{ms}, the reactance obtained from eq. 5.165 is not the correct value $[X_{Ls} + X_{ms(E_{ms})}]$ of synchronous reactance for that voltage but has a somewhat lower value. In other words, the value of X_s obtained is appropriate for a value of induced voltage somewhat greater than the value of E_{ms} at which the open-circuit measurement was made. In many machines, the leakage reactance X_{Ls} is much smaller than the magnetizing reactance X_{ms}. Equation 5.165 gives a reasonably accurate measure of the synchronous reactance applicable for the induced voltage E_{ms} used in the measurement. Since the leakage and magnetizing parts of this synchronous reactance are not separated in the open-circuit and short-circuit measurements, it is necessary in analysis to estimate the operating value of E_{ms} using an estimate of the value of leakage reactance, and then to choose the appropriate value of synchronous reactance X_s.

In large synchronous machines, the stator leakage reactance X_{Ls} is generally between 0.1 and 0.25 per unit based on the machine rating. The magnetizing reactance X_{ms} may be as low as 0.4 per unit and may be as high as 2.5, per unit, depending on the intended application of the machine. An average value is about 1.0 per unit. The stator resistance depends on the size of the machine and may be as low as 0.0025 per unit in large synchronous generators.

5.5.4 Steady-State Terminal Characteristics

A synchronous machine operating in a steady state with balanced polyphase currents and voltages has six terminal variables: the stator phase voltage E_s and the stator phase current I_s (both of which are phasors), the field voltage e_f and field current i_f, the torque T, and the speed v. The steady-state field voltage and current are simply related by

$$e_f = R_f i_f \qquad (5.166)$$

The speed v is known and is usually a constant. The remaining variables still provide a wide variety of terminal relationships. In this section we examine a few of the more important characteristics.

Most synchronous generators and motors operate with approximately constant terminal voltage. Let us therefore first examine their properties under this constraint. Suppose a synchronous machine is accelerated by a prime mover to a speed v of

$$v = \frac{2}{p}\,\omega_s \qquad \text{radians/second} \qquad (5.167)$$

where ω_s is the frequency in radians per second of the available supply. By increasing the field current i_f the magnitude of the open-circuit terminal voltage E_s in the stator phase windings may be made equal to that of the available supply. The phase angle of the terminal voltage E_s may be altered by momentary changes in the speed v. Using some synchronizing device such as a synchroscope, we can connect the machine terminals to the supply when the voltages are equal both in magnitude and in phase. In making this connection, the phase sequence of the machine must, of course, be the same as that of the supply.

At the condition of synchronization just described, the variables of the equivalent circuit of Fig. 5.40a are as shown in the phasor diagram of Fig. 5.40b. The stator current I_s is zero, and all the magnetizing current is provided by the field. The prime mover torque is just sufficient to provide the mechanical losses of the machine and the eddy-current losses in the stator. Since these losses are small, particularly in large machines, they are neglected in the analysis to follow. The effects of the stator resistance are also-neglected. If the prime mover is removed, the operating condition is still represented approximately by Fig. 5.40b.

Suppose the field current i_f is now reduced. The equivalent field current I_r' is then insufficient to magnetize the machine and some magnetizing current is drawn from the supply, as shown in Fig. 5.40c. As the field current is reduced the inductive current taken by the machine increases. In this condition, the machine acts as a variable inductive load on the supply and is said to be underexcited.

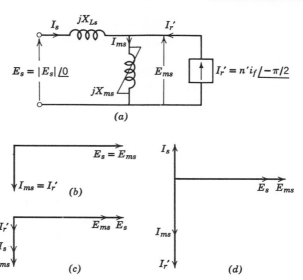

Fig. 5.40 Operation of machine as synchronous reactor or condenser. (*a*) Equivalent circuit. (*b*) Condition at synchronization. (*c*) With reduced field current (underexcited) —action as inductive load. (*d*) With increased field current (overexcited)—action as capacitive load.

If the field current is increased beyond the value required for synchronization, not all of the field current is required to magnetize the machine. The voltage E_{ms} becomes greater than E_s, causing the stator current to lead the stator voltage by $\pi/2$ radians, as shown in Fig. 5.40*d*. In this condition the machine acts as a capacitive load on the supply and is said to be overexcited.

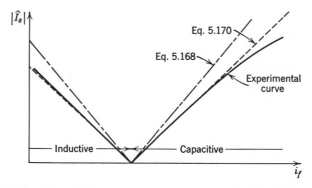

Fig. 5.41 Relationship of stator current I_s to field current i_f for unloaded synchronous machine.

Figure 5.41 shows a typical experimental relationship between the magnitude of the stator current and the field current for a synchronous machine with zero torque. Let us consider how this relationship may be predicted using the equivalent circuit of Fig. 5.40a. The nonlinear magnetizing branch of this circuit may be represented by a curve relating E_{ms} and I_{ms}, as shown in Fig. 5.42. The most accurate method of analysis consists of (1) choosing a value of I_s, (2) calculating the induced voltage $E_{ms} = E_s - jX_{Ls}I_s$, (3) finding the value of I_{ms} corresponding to E_{ms} from the curve of Fig. 5.42, (4) evaluating $I_r' = (I_{ms} - I_s)$ and (5) finding the field current $i_f = I_r/n'$.

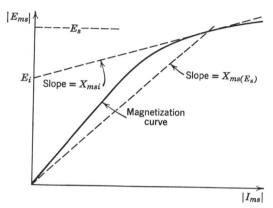

Fig. 5.42 Magnetization curve of synchronous machine shown with two linear approximations.

The phasor diagrams of Fig. 5.40 suggest that the variation of E_{ms} from E_s is reasonably small. Let us therefore consider linearizing the equivalent circuit by fixing the magnetizing reactance X_{ms} at the value that applies for $E_{ms} = E_s$. In this approximation, the magnetization curve is represented by the straight line of slope $X_{ms(E_s)}$ shown in Fig. 5.42. The principle of superposition may then be applied to the linearized circuit of Fig. 5.40a. Assigning a reference angle of zero to the phasor E_s, the stator current is

$$I_s = \frac{E_s}{j(X_{Ls} + X_{ms})} - \frac{X_{ms}}{X_{Ls} + X_{ms}} I_r'$$

$$= -j\frac{|E_s|}{X_{Ls} + X_{ms}} + j\frac{X_{ms}}{X_{Ls} + X_{ms}} n' i_f \qquad (5.168)$$

This solution, shown in Fig. 5.41, predicts a higher value of stator current than actually obtains over the whole range of field current.

A better linear approximation to the magnetization curve can be obtained by letting

$$E_{ms} = E_i + jX_{msi}I_{ms} \qquad (5.169)$$

where X_{msi} is an incremental magnetizing reactance equal to the slope of the magnetization curve at $E_{ms} = E_s$. The intercept voltage E_i is considered to be a phasor with the same phase angle as E_{ms}. Inserting eq. 5.169 into $I_s = (I_{ms} - I_r')$ gives, after some manipulation,

$$I_s = -j\frac{|E_s| - |E_i|}{X_{Ls} + X_{msi}} + j\frac{X_{msi}}{X_{Ls} + X_{msi}}n'i_f \qquad (5.170)$$

This result, shown in Fig. 5.41, is reasonably accurate except for high values of stator current I_s, for which the voltage E_{ms} differs considerably from E_s.

Unloaded synchronous machines are often used in power transmission systems for power factor correction. Such machines are called synchronous condensers or synchronous phase modifiers. As most loads on a power system are inductive, these synchronous condensers are used primarily as adjustable capacitive loads. But since high-voltage transmission lines are capacitive when operated at low-load, synchronous condensers may also be required to operate as inductive loads. The same feature of power factor control is obtained with all synchronous motors and generators. It is this feature that provides the major advantage of synchronous machines over other types. In contrast, the induction machine acts as an inductive load on the system when operating as a motor or as a generator.

Let us now consider the characteristics of the machine when acting as an electromechanical energy converter. Figure 5.43*a* shows an equivalent circuit for the machine. For simplicity in analysis, all losses are neglected and the magnetizing reactance X_{ms} is assumed to be constant. Suppose the machine is initially unloaded and that its field current is fixed at a value that produces the overexcited condition shown in the phasor diagram of Fig. 5.43*b*. If a mechanical load is applied to the machine, its rotor is momentarily retarded, thus reducing the rotor angle β_0 to a value less than zero.

By superposition, the stator current I_s in Fig. 5.43*a* is given by

$$I_s = \frac{E_s}{j(X_{Ls} + X_{ms})} - \frac{X_{ms}}{X_{Ls} + X_{ms}}I_r' \qquad (5.171)$$

As the angle β_0 becomes negative, the locus of the phasor I_r' moves through a circular arc as shown in Fig. 5.43*c*. Since the stator current I_s in eq. 5.171 is equal to a constant term minus a term proportional to I_r', it also moves through a circular locus as shown. In the condition designated

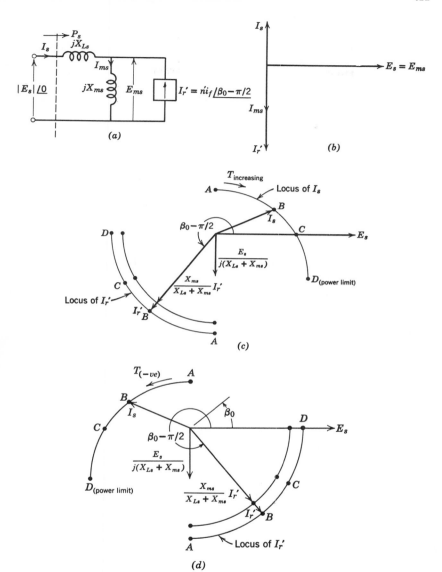

Fig. 5.43 Phasor diagrams and loci for synchronous machine with constant field current. (a) Equivalent circuit. (b) No-load condition. (c) Loci as a motor. (d) Loci as a generator.

as B, the stator current I_s has a component that is in phase with the terminal voltage E_s, indicating that power is entering the machine. This results in a positive value of torque T to supply the mechanical load. The stator current at B also has a capacitive component but it is somewhat less than that at the condition A of no-load.

At condition C in Fig. 5.43c, the machine is operating at unity power factor. Further gradual increase in the load torque causes a further decrease in angle β_0 to condition D. At this point we note that the inphase component of the stator current has reached its maximum value. Thus the power input and the torque are also at their maximum values. Any further addition of load causing a further decrease in the rotor angle β_0 results in a decrease in input power and torque. The machine then decelerates continuously and loses synchronism with the supply. Condition D represents the maximum value of power and torque that the machine can provide with the given values of field current and stator voltage and with a gradually increased load. It is therefore called the *steady-state stability limit* of the machine acting as a motor. It is noted that, at condition D in Fig. 5.43c, β_0 is $-\pi/2$ radians and the phasor I_r' is in phase opposition to the stator voltage E_s. From eq. 5.171, the maximum power at this condition is

$$\hat{P}_s = \frac{X_{ms}}{X_{Ls} + X_{ms}} |I_r'| |E_s| \qquad \text{watts per phase} \qquad (5.172)$$

Now suppose a prime mover is connected to the synchronous machine, and torque is applied to increase the rotor angle β_0 from its no load position. As shown in Fig. 5.43d, the phasors I_r' and I_s again follow circular loci. At condition A the machine is on no-load and acts as a capacitive load on the system. At B, the stator current has a component in phase opposition to the stator voltage. Power is therefore being delivered from the machine to the supply, and the torque developed by the machine is negative. At C, the machine is acting as a unity power factor generator. At D, the maximum power output of the generator for the given values of stator voltage and field current is reached. Any further increase in prime mover torque accelerates the machine to a larger value of β_0. But, since the machine torque decreases the acceleration of the generator continues until the prime mover torque is removed. Condition D therefore represents the steady-state stability limit of the machine acting as a generator. Since the machine has been assumed to be lossless, the stability limits as a motor and as a generator are predicted to be equal. The effect of the losses is negligible in most large machines.

The terminal properties of synchronous generators and motors, operating with constant stator voltages, may be represented graphically in a number of useful ways. From eq. 5.171, the complex power U_s per phase entering the machine is

$$U_s = P_s + jQ_s$$
$$= I_s E_s{}^*$$
$$= \frac{|E_s|^2}{j(X_{Ls} + X_{ms})} - \frac{X_{ms}}{X_{Ls} + X_{ms}} I_r' E_s{}^* \qquad (5.173)$$

If the stator voltage and field current are constant, the only variable in eq. 5.173 is the angle $\beta_0 - \pi/2$ of the phasor I_r'. Thus the complex power

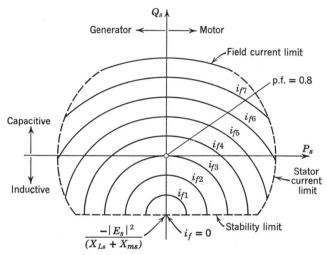

Fig. 5.44 Circle diagram showing power P_s and reactive power Q_s into synchronous machine at various constant values of field current. Terminal voltage E_s constant.

follows a circular locus, the radius of which is directly proportional to the field current. Figure 5.44 shows a family of these circular loci. The field current that is necessary to operate the machine at any given power and power factor, as a motor or as a generator, may be interpolated from this chart. It is also convenient to indicate on the chart the limits of its steady-state operation. These are (1) the maximum power or stability limit, (2) the limit on the field current to prevent overheating, and (3) the limit on the stator current to prevent overheating.

The torque on a synchronous generator is generally determined by the setting of its prime mover whereas the torque on a motor is determined by its mechanical load. The power of the synchronous machine is thus fixed externally. The only available control over the machine performance is

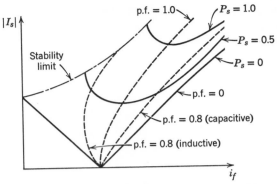

Fig. 5.45 Loci of stator current magnitude as a function of field current for various values of input or output power and various values of power factor.

the adjustment of the field current to convert the required power at the desired power factor. Figure 5.45 shows the magnitude of the stator current as a function of field current for a number of values of power and power factor. The curve for zero power is the same as shown in Fig. 5.41. These curves may be predicted from the equivalent circuit by the methods described earlier in this section.

From eq. 5.173, the power P_s entering the stator of a lossless synchronous machine is

$$P_s = \mathscr{R}_e\left[\frac{|E_s|^2}{j(X_{Ls} + X_{ms})} - \frac{X_{ms}}{X_{Ls} + X_{ms}} I_r' E_s^*\right]$$

$$= -\frac{X_{ms}}{X_{Ls} + X_{ms}} n' i_f |E_s| \sin \beta_0 \qquad \text{watts/phase} \qquad (5.174)$$

This relationship between stator power and rotor angle, shown in Fig. 5.46, is similar to the torque-angle relationship shown in Fig. 5.35. As the

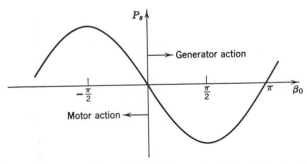

Fig. 5.46 Relation between stator power and rotor angle (machine assumed lossless).

rotor angle β_0 approaches $\pi/2$ or $-\pi/2$, a large change in angle produces only a small change in stator power. The machine is very sensitive to small disturbances and may easily lose synchronism. Most synchronous machines are therefore operated in such a way that the magntiude of the rotor angle is less than $\pi/3$ radians and many operate with β_0 in the region of $\pi/6$ radians. To achieve this, the field current i_f in eq. 5.174 must be maintained

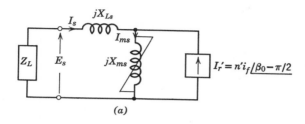

(a)

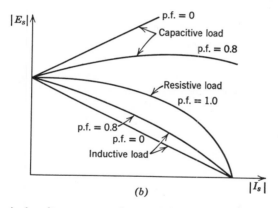

(b)

Fig. 5.47 Terminal voltage-current characteristics of synchronous generator with constant field current and variable load.

at a sufficiently high value to make the power limit considerably greater than the operating power.

Small synchronous generators are frequently used to supply independent electric loads. The important feature of these generators is their ability to maintain essentially constant terminal voltage as the electric load changes. Suppose a load of impedance Z_L is connected to a synchronous generator, as shown in Fig. 5.47a. If the magnetizing reactance X_{ms} is assumed to remain constant at some appropriate average value, the magnitude of the stator voltage is given by

$$|E_s| = |Z_L I_s|$$

$$= \left| \frac{Z_L X_{ms}}{Z_L + j(X_{Ls} + X_{ms})} n' i_f \right| \qquad \text{volts} \qquad (5.175)$$

Suppose the field current is maintained at a constant value. If the stator voltage magnitude is not to vary excessively with variation in the load impedance Z_L, it is necessary that the synchronous reactance $(X_{Ls} + X_{ms})$ be substantially lower in value than the load impedance $|Z_L|$. Since, at rated load, $|Z_L|$ has a value of 1.0 per unit, a synchronous impedance much less than 1.0 per unit is desired for these machines. This is accomplished by the use of a large air gap to decrease the value of the magnetizing reactance.

Figure 5.47*b* shows the terminal voltage $|E_s|$ as a function of the terminal current $|I_s|$ for loads of various power factors. We note that inductive loads cause a rapid drop in terminal voltage as the load is increased. Capacitive loads, on the other hand, may cause a rise in voltage with increasing load. If the generator is to operate with constant field current, it is therefore desirable to maintain a load power factor that is near unity or possibly leading (capacitive). If the variations in terminal voltage with constant field current are in excess of tolerable limits, it is necessary to employ some form of automatic voltage regulator to adjust the field current as the terminal voltage tends to change.

5.5.5 Electrical Transient Performance

Because either the terminal voltage or the power factor of a synchronous machine can be controlled by adjusting its field current, it is important to know how rapidly the machine responds to changes in its field-supply voltage. It is also important to know what stator currents flow after there has been a sudden change, such as a short circuit, at the stator terminals. In this section we examine some of these electrical transient problems.

Let us first consider a synchronous machine that is being driven at synchronous speed with its stator terminals open circuited. At what rate do its field current i_f and its stator voltage E_s build up after a direct-voltage source of constant voltage E_f is connected to its field terminals?

If the magnetizing inductance L_{ms} is transferred across the ideal synchronous machine in the equivalent circuit of Fig. 5.32, the result is the circuit shown in Fig. 5.48*a*, where L_{mr} is given in eq. 5.144. This inductance is constant in magnitude if the machine is operating in its magnetically linear region. Since the stator current is zero, the current i_s' reflected on the

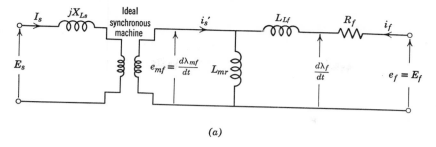

(a)

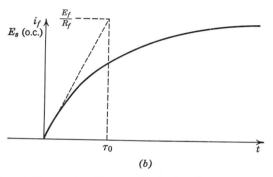

(b)

Fig. 5.48 Transient currents with open-circuited synchronous machine. (a) Equivalent circuit. (b) Field current and open-circuit stator voltage as function of time after field voltage applied. In (a),

Current ratio $n':1$

$$\text{Inductance ratio } 1 : \sqrt{2}\, n'\, \frac{N_r}{N_s}$$

other side of the transformation is also zero. If the field source is connected at $t = 0$.

$$E_f = \frac{d\lambda_f}{dt} + R_f i_f$$

$$= (L_{Lf} + L_{mr})\frac{di_f}{dt} + R_f i_f$$

from which
$$i_f = \frac{E_f}{R_f}(1 - \epsilon^{-t/\tau_0}) \qquad \text{amperes} \qquad (5.176)$$

The exponential current-time relation is shown in Fig. 5.48b. The time constant, given by

$$\tau_0 = \frac{L_{Lf} + L_{mr}}{R_f} \qquad \text{seconds} \qquad (5.177)$$

is normally called the open-circuit (transient) time constant of the machine. The open-circuit stator voltage is directly proportional to the field current (eq. 5.145).

The effect of magnetic nonlinearity may be included by use of numerical methods as described in Section 2.1. For small changes in the open-circuit stator voltage about an average value, the incremental magnetizing inductance as defined in Fig. 5.42 and eq. 5.169 may be used. This results in a somewhat smaller value of the time constant τ_0.

The value of the open-circuit time constant τ_0 is generally in the range of 3 to 9 seconds for large synchronous machines. It decreases as the size of the machine decreases and may be less than 0.1 second in small laboratory machines.

Now let us consider connecting a field source to a machine with its stator short circuited. To determine the transient currents in this situation, it is convenient to shift the stator inductance L_{Ls} across the ideal transformation (using a relation similar to eq. 5.144) to give the equivalent circuit of Fig. 5.49a. For simplicity, the stator resistance is neglected. Before $t = 0$, the stator flux linkage λ_s is zero. After $t = 0$, this flux linkage continues to be zero because

$$e_s = \frac{d\lambda_s}{dt} = 0 \tag{5.178}$$

Thus the flux linkage λ_s' reflected on the other side of the transformation is also zero.

$$\lambda_s' = \frac{N_r}{N_s} \lambda_s = 0 \tag{5.179}$$

The ideal transformation may therefore be considered as a short circuit as seen from the rotor side. The inductances L_{Ls}' and L_{mr} are effectively in parallel.

Continuing our assumption of magnetic linearity, we find the field current to be

$$i_f = \frac{E_f}{R_f}(1 - \epsilon^{-t/\tau'}) \qquad \text{amperes} \tag{5.180}$$

where
$$\tau' = \frac{1}{R_f}\left(L_{Lf} + \frac{L_{Ls}'L_{ms}}{L_{Ls}' + L_{ms}}\right) \qquad \text{seconds} \tag{5.181}$$

This is known as the short-circuit (transient) time constant of the machine. Its value is generally in the range of 0.6 to 3.0 seconds for large synchronous machines.

The field current i_f divides between the elements L_{Ls}' and L_{mr}, to give

$$i_s' = -\frac{L_{mr}}{L_{Ls}' + L_{mr}} i_f \tag{5.182}$$

If the rotor angle is β_0 at $t = 0$, the stator current in phase a is given by

$$i_a = \sqrt{2}n'i_s' \sin\left(\omega_s t + \beta_0 - \frac{\pi}{2}\right) \qquad (5.183)$$

Figure 5.49b shows the stator current as a function of time. The envelope of this current increases exponentially at time constant τ'. Since this time

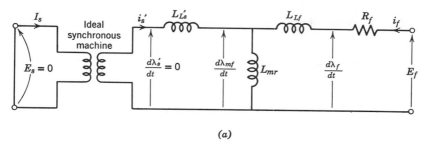

(a)

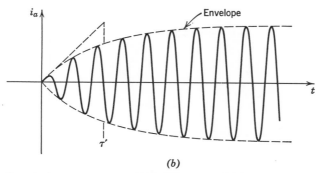

(b)

Fig. 5.49 Transient currents with a short-circuited synchronous machine. (a) Equivalent circuit. (b) Stator current in phase a after field voltage applied.

$$\text{Current ratio } n' \underline{/\beta_0 - \pi/2} : 1$$

$$\text{Inductance ratio } 1 : \sqrt{2}n' \frac{N_r}{N_s}$$

constant is normally large in comparison with the period $2\pi/\omega_s$ of the stator current, it is reasonable to continue to represent the stator current as a phasor. Thus from eqs. 5.180, 5.182, and 5.183 the magnitude of the stator current phasor is

$$|I_s| = \frac{n'L_{mr}}{L_{Ls}' + L_{mr}}\,i_f$$

$$= \frac{X_{ms}}{X_{Ls} + X_{ms}}\,n'\frac{E_f}{R_f}(1 - e^{-t/\tau'}) \qquad \text{amperes} \qquad (5.184)$$

Let us now consider a synchronous machine that is initially unloaded and excited with a field current $i_f = E_f/R_f$. Suppose a polyphase short circuit is applied to the stator terminals at time $t = 0$. A knowledge of the maximum current that flows in the stator is important in the mechanical design of the stator windings and also in the specification of circuit breakers in the power system to which the machine may be connected.

The total flux linkage λ_f of the field winding in Fig. 5.49a cannot change instantaneously. It has been shown that, with the stator terminals

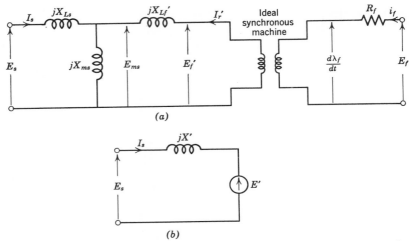

(a)

(b)

Fig. 5.50 (a) Equivalent circuit for prediction of stator current following a short circuit. (b) Simplified equivalent circuit assuming constant field flux linkage.

short circuited, the field flux linkage changes at a time constant τ', which may have a value of several seconds. In a number of situations, we are interested in the events that occur in a relatively short time after the short circuit is applied. For example, circuit breakers normally operate after only a few cycles of the supply frequency following a short circuit. For such short periods of time, it is often reasonable to assume that the field flux linkage λ_f remains constant at the value that obtained before $t = 0$.

In the equivalent circuit of Fig. 5.50a the field leakage inductance has been transferred across the ideal transformation using eq. 5.144.

$$X_{Lf}' = \omega_s L_{Lf}'$$

$$= \frac{\omega_s}{\sqrt{2}n'} \frac{N_s}{N_r} L_{Lf} \tag{5.185}$$

The constant field flux linkage λ_f can be considered to produce a constant voltage E_f' of frequency ω_s on the stator side of the transformation. The magnitude of this voltage is

$$|E_f'| = \frac{\omega_s}{\sqrt{2}} \frac{N_s}{N_f} \lambda_f \qquad \text{volts} \tag{5.186}$$

To determine the stator current, we can apply Thévenin's theorem to Fig. 5.50a to give the simplified equivalent circuit of Fig. 5.50b, in which

$$E' = \frac{X_{ms}}{X_{Lf}' + X_{ms}} E_f' \qquad \text{volts} \tag{5.187}$$

and

$$X' = X_{Ls} + \frac{X_{ms} X_{Lf}'}{X_{ms} + X_{Lf}'} \qquad \text{ohms} \tag{5.188}$$

We note that E' is equal to the open-circuit voltage at the stator terminals before the short circuit is applied. The quantity X' is known as the transient reactance of the machine. Its value is normally in the range 0.15 to 0.5 per unit for large machines. Division of jX' into E gives the stator current phasor immediately after the short circuit.

$$I_s = \frac{E'}{jX'} \qquad \text{amperes} \tag{5.189}$$

The stator current does not remain at the value given in eq. 5.189, but decays at the short-circuit time constant τ' toward its steady-state value. From eqs. 5.184 and 5.145.

$$\begin{aligned} I_{s(\text{steady state})} &= \frac{X_{ms} n'}{X_{Ls} + X_{ms}} \frac{E_f}{R_f} \quad \beta_0 - \pi/2 \\ &= \frac{E_0}{X_s} \end{aligned} \tag{5.190}$$

Thus the stator current phasor is given by

$$I_s = \frac{E_0}{X_s} + \left(\frac{E'}{X'} - \frac{E_0}{X_s} \right) \epsilon^{-t/\tau'} \qquad \text{amperes} \tag{5.191}$$

From eqs. 5.177, 5.181, and 5.188 it can be shown that

$$\tau' = \frac{X'}{X_s} \tau_0 \qquad \text{seconds} \tag{5.192}$$

Figure 5.51 shows the short-circuit current in the windings of a three-phase stator. The alternating component is as described by eq. 5.191. But there is an additional transient component that arises because the total flux linkage of each of the stator windings cannot change instantaneously. If the stator resistance were zero, these flux linkages would remain constant in the short-circuited windings at the values that existed in each

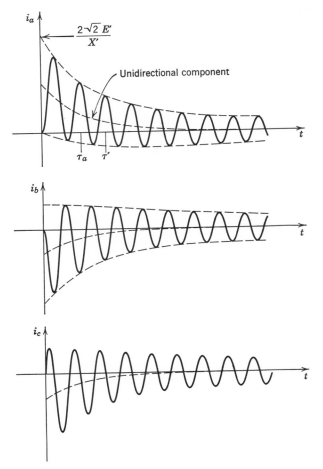

Fig. 5.51   Stator currents after three-phase short circuit at $t = 0$.

at the instant of short circuit. Because of the finite stator resistance, these flux linkages decay exponentially toward zero at the stator or armature time constant τ_a. This time constant is equal to the inductance per phase as seen from the stator terminals divided by the stator resistance per phase. This can be shown to be

$$\tau_a = \frac{X'}{R_s \omega_s} \qquad \text{seconds} \qquad (5.193)$$

where X' is the transient reactance given in eq. 5.188. The value of this time constant is in the range 0.1 to 0.4 second for large machines.

From Fig. 5.51 we note that the maximum value of short-circuit stator current can approach the value

$$\hat{i}_s = 2\sqrt{2}\,\frac{E'}{X'} \qquad \text{amperes} \qquad (5.194)$$

if the period of the current is very short in comparison with the time constants τ' and τ_a. This value may occur if the short circuit occurs at the instant the flux linkage in a phase winding is approximately at its maximum value, as shown for phase a in Fig. 5.51. The maximum current occurs at about $\omega_s t = \pi/2$.

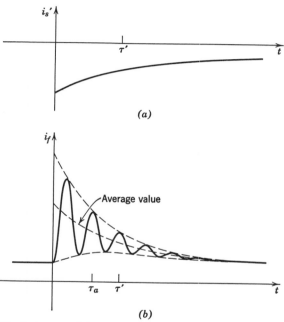

Fig. 5.52 (a) Equivalent i_s' of fundamental-frequency component of stator current I_s during short circuit. (b) Field current during short circuit.

The sinusoidal component of the stator current I_s rises abruptly at $t = 0$ and then decays at time constant τ' toward its steady-state value. The equivalent i_s' of this stator current reflected to the rotor side of the ideal transformation of Fig. 5.49a is shown in Fig. 5.52a. If the total flux linkage λ_f of the field winding is to remain constant through the instant $t = 0$ of short circuiting, the field current must also increase suddenly. Figure 5.52b shows the field current as a function of time. In addition to a transient component similar to that of Fig. 5.52a, it contains a funda- mental component that compensates for the unidirectional transient component in the stator currents. The envelope of this fundamental-frequency component decays at the armature time constant τ_a. The average field current rises abruptly at $t = 0$ and then decays at the short-circuit constant τ' to its original value.

During the first few cycles, the short-circuited current in the stator may be somewhat greater than that shown in Fig. 5.51 because of the effect of other conducting paths in the rotor that also preserve their flux linkages through the instant of short circuit. In a machine such as a high-speed synchronous generator, which has an unlaminated rotor, these paths are in the conducting magnetic material. In other synchronous machines, these paths consist of the damper or amortisseur windings, which are built into the rotor to assist in starting and to damp out mechanical oscillations (Section 5.5.6).

Figure 5.53a shows the short-circuit current in a stator phase, the instant of short circuiting being chosen to produce no unidirectional component in that phase. The current consists of a "subtransient" component which decays at the subtransient time constant τ'' of the damper windings, a "transient" component which decays at time constant τ', and a steady-state component. To predict the short-circuit current including the subtransient component, we must extend the equivalent circuit of the machine, as shown in Fig. 5.53b. The leakage inductance of the damper winding is L_{LD} and its resistance is R_D, both quantities being referred to the number of turns N_r of the field winding. At the instant of short circuit the flux linkage λ_D of the damper winding remains constant as does that of the field winding. If we accept the same concepts as were used to develop the equivalent circuit of Fig. 5.50a, the machine can be represented by the equivalent circuit of Fig. 5.53c in which

$$X'' = \omega_s \left(L_{Ls} + \frac{1}{\dfrac{1}{L_{ms}} + \dfrac{1}{L_{Lf}'} + \dfrac{1}{L_{LD}'}} \right) \qquad \text{ohms} \qquad (5.195)$$

known as the subtransient reactance of the machine. The voltage E'' is the open-circuit stator voltage before the short circuit. The subtransient component of the stator current $(E''/X'' - E'/X')$ decays at the subtransient time constant

$$\tau'' = \frac{1}{R_D} \left(L_{LD} + \frac{1}{\dfrac{1}{L_{Lf}} + \dfrac{1}{L_{mr}} + \dfrac{1}{L_{Ls}'}} \right) \qquad \text{seconds} \qquad (5.196)$$

The value of X'' is slightly less than that of X' for machines with damper windings or solid rotors. The usual range is 0.1 to 0.4 per unit for large

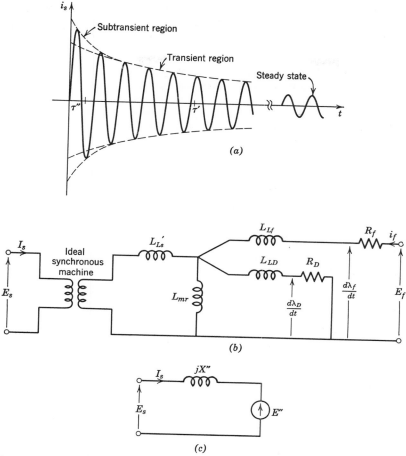

Fig. 5.53 (a) Short-circuit current including subtransient component. (b) Equivalent circuit including representation of damper windings. (c) Simplified subtransient equivalent circuit.

machines. Because of the relatively small amount of conducting material in the damper windings as compared with the field windings, the resistance R_D in Fig. 5.53b is generally much greater than R_f. The time constant τ'' is therefore relatively short (0.01 to 0.05 seconds). The subtransient component is significant in determining maximum short-circuit currents and in determining the current to be interrupted by fact-acting circuit breakers.

The transient and subtransient parameters of a synchronous machine are normally measured by applying a short circuit and recording the phase currents as a function of time. This record may be analyzed most readily by subtracting the peak steady-state current from the current envelope and plotting the remainder on semilogarithmic graph paper as a function of time. The values of X' and τ' can be determined from the straight portion of this graph. Similarly, the values of X'' and τ'' may be found by plotting the difference between the actual current envelope and an extrapolation of the envelope in the transient region.

Another situation of practical importance is the determination of the transient drop in the terminal voltage of a generator when a large inductive load (such as a starting induction motor) is connected to its terminals. Suppose the load can be approximated by an inductive reactance X_e. Neglecting subtransient effects and stator resistance, we find the terminal voltage phasor immediately after the load is connected from Fig. 5.50b to be

$$E_{s(\text{near} \atop t=0)} = \frac{X_e}{X_e + X'} E' \quad \text{volts} \tag{5.197}$$

where X' is the transient reactance and E' is the open-circuit stator voltage before connection of the load.

If the field voltage E_f remains constant, the terminal voltage eventually falls to

$$E_{s(t \to \infty)} = \frac{X_e}{X_e + X_s} E_0 \quad \text{volts} \tag{5.198}$$

where E_0 is given in eq. 5.145. The transition occurs at a time constant τ, which is intermediate in value between τ' and τ_0. By a simple extension of eq. 5.192,

$$\tau = \frac{X_e + X'}{X_e + X_s} \tau_0 \quad \text{seconds} \tag{5.199}$$

Figure 5.54 shows how the magnitude of the stator voltage might change after the connection of a load. If the terminal voltage is to be restored to its original value, some form of voltage regulator must be employed. The equivalent circuit of Fig. 5.50a is in a convenient form for transient studies of voltage regulator action. With a constant inductive load of reactance X_e, the equivalent source current I_r' is related to the applied field voltage e_f by the operational expression

$$|I_r'|_{(s)} = n' i_{f(s)}$$
$$= n' \frac{1}{R_f(1 + s\tau)} e_{f(s)} \tag{5.200}$$

where τ is given in eq. 5.199. If the load reactance X_e changes, it is the voltage E_f' in Fig. 5.50a that remains constant during the change. The current I_r' jumps to a new value at the instant of load change.

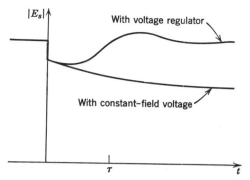

Fig. 5.54 Stator voltage following the sudden application of an inductive load.

The equivalent circuit of Fig. 5.50a applies for all types of loads. Although the single-time-constant relation of eq. 5.200 is strictly applicable only to purely inductive loads, it gives a reasonable approximation for most normal resistive-inductive loads if the value of its time constant τ is appropriately chosen. Figure 5.54 shows the response that might be expected after the sudden application of a load in the terminal voltage of a generator fitted with a high-speed voltage regulator.

5.5.6 Electromechanical Transient Performance

An important class of synchronous machine problems is concerned with predicting the ability of the machine to remain in synchronism with the power system after a sudden change in its operating condition. For a motor, the disturbance may arise either from a sudden change in its mechanical load torque or from the loss of its electrical supply for a few cycles. For a generator, the most severe disturbances arise from short circuits on the power system resulting in loss of electrical power output from the machine.

The dynamic behavior of a synchronous machine is reflected in the differential equation

$$J \frac{dv}{dt} = T + T_{\text{shaft}} \qquad \text{newton-meters} \qquad (5.201)$$

where T is the torque produced by the machine windings and T_{shaft} is the torque applied to its shaft, both being measured in the direction of positive speed v. The mechanical losses may be incorporated into the term T_{shaft}.

If synchronism is to be maintained following a disturbance to the system, the instantaneous speed v of the rotor cannot vary appreciably from its synchronous value v_s. The frequency ω_s may therefore be considered as approximately constant during most electromechanical transient studies. Because of the high inertia J of the machine and of the mechanical system connected to it, the changes in speed during one cycle of the electrical supply are relatively small. During a mechanical oscillation, the electrical part of the system may therefore be analyzed by the use of phasor methods.

For a two-pole machine, the rotor position at any instant is denoted as β where

$$\beta = \omega_s t + \beta_0 \qquad \text{radians} \tag{5.202}$$

Suppose we consider ω_s to be a constant and allow β_0, which is a measure of the rotor position relative to the rotating field, to vary with time. If the machine has p poles, the angle β is $p/2$ times the rotor angle, and the speed v of the rotor is given by

$$v = \frac{2}{p}\frac{d\beta}{dt}$$

$$= \frac{2}{p}\omega_s + \frac{2}{p}\frac{d\beta_0}{dt} \qquad \text{radians/second} \tag{5.203}$$

The acceleration is then given by

$$\frac{dv}{dt} = \frac{2}{p}\frac{d^2\beta_0}{dt^2} \qquad \text{radians/second}^2 \tag{5.204}$$

Equation 5.201 may now be expressed in terms of the variable β_0. The torque T produced by the machine may be expressed, from eq. 5.147, as

$$T = \frac{p}{2}\frac{m_s}{\omega_s} P_{ms} \qquad \text{newton-meters} \tag{5.205}$$

The question now arises as to the correct electrical representation of the machine. From Section 5.5.5, we note that a synchronous machine connected to a constant-voltage power system responds to changes in its electrical operating condition at the time constant τ' of eq. 5.181. In large machines this short-circuit time constant may be several seconds in duration. In the same machines, the period of mechanical oscillation is generally found to be of the order of 0.5 to 2 seconds. We can often obtain a solution of sufficient accuracy by assuming the field flux linkage λ_f to remain constant during the first mechanical oscillation. This allows the use of the transient equivalent circuit of Fig. 5.50. With small synchronous machines, the transient time constant τ' may be substantially less than the mechanical oscillation period. In this case, it is appropriate to consider the field current i_f to be constant and use a steady-state equivalent circuit such as that in Fig. 5.33.

In the following analysis it is assumed that the transient equivalent circuit of Fig. 5.50 provides an adequate representation of the electrical system. Assigning the angle β_0 to the source voltage E' and an angle of zero to E_s, the air-gap power P_{ms} per phase directed from stator to rotor is given by

$$P_{ms} = \mathscr{R}e[I_s E'^*]$$

$$= \mathscr{R}e\left[\frac{E_s - E'}{jX'} E'^*\right]$$

$$= -\frac{|E_s|\,|E'|}{X'}\sin\beta_0 \qquad \text{watts} \qquad (5.206)$$

This power varies sinusoidally with angle β_0, but its maximum value is considerably larger than that given for steady-state operation. Substitution

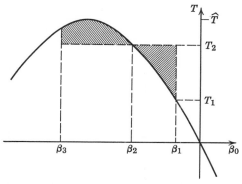

Fig. 5.55 Equal-area method of determining the stability of a synchronous machine.

from eq. 5.206 into eq. 5.205 gives the torque-angle relation shown in Fig. 5.55 for which

$$\hat{T} = \frac{p}{2}\frac{m_s}{\omega_s}\frac{|E_s|\,|E'|}{X'} \qquad \text{newton-meters} \qquad (5.207)$$

As our first example of an electromechanical transient, let us consider a synchronous motor connected to a constant voltage supply E_s. Suppose that, at $t = 0$, the mechanical load torque is suddenly increased from T_1 to T_2. The condition before $t = 0$, neglecting mechanical losses in the machine, is

$$T = -T_{\text{shaft}} = T_1 \qquad (5.208)$$

and

$$\beta_0 = \beta_1$$

When the load torque is increased to T_2, the rotor decelerates toward $\beta_0 = \beta_2$, where the torque T produced in the machine equals T_2. But kinetic energy is being removed from the mechanical system during this deceleration. The change ΔW_k in the kinetic energy is equal to the net torque on the machine, integrated with respect to the mechanical angle $2/p\ \beta_0$. In the interval $\beta_1 > \beta_0 > \beta_2$, this change is

$$\Delta W_k = \frac{2}{p} \int_{\beta_1}^{\beta_2} (T - T_2)\, d\beta_0 \qquad \text{joules} \qquad (5.209)$$

At $\beta_0 = \beta_2$, the speed of the machine is somewhat less than synchronous speed. Thus angle β_0 continues to decrease. But now the torque T produced by the machine is greater than T_2, and the net torque acts to accelerate the machine and restore its lost kinetic energy. The speed reaches its synchronous value again at $\beta_0 = \beta_3$, for which the total change in kinetic energy is zero.

$$\Delta W_k = \frac{2}{p} \int_{\beta_1}^{\beta_3} (T - T_2)\, d\beta_0 = 0 \qquad (5.210)$$

that is, where

$$\int_{\beta_1}^{\beta_2} (T - T_2)\, d\beta_0 + \int_{\beta_2}^{\beta_3} (T - T_2)\, d\beta_0 = 0 \qquad (5.211)$$

In Fig. 5.55, this condition exists when the two shaded areas, which represent the magnitudes of the two integrals in eq. 5.211, are equal. When this condition can be met, the machine remains in synchronism.

At $\beta_0 = \beta_3$ the machine is being accelerated; when β_0 again reaches β_2 the speed is above synchronous value. The angle therefore swings beyond β_2 and, in the absence of any damping torque, again reaches its initial value β_1 and repeats the oscillation. In practice, the oscillation in β_0 is eventually damped out, and the steady-state condition is $\beta_0 = \beta_2$.

Suppose we consider a slightly different situation in which the initial-load torque T_1 is reduced but the final-load torque T_2 is unchanged. As shown in Fig. 5.56, the energy represented by the area between the load torque line T_2 and the T-β_0 curve in the interval $\beta_1 > \beta_0 > \beta_2$ cannot be restored by the time acceleration ceases at $\beta_0 = \pi - \beta_2$. The angle β_0 therefore continues to decrease, and the machine can be expected to come to a standstill.

The graphical or equal-area solution, shown in Figs. 5.55 and 5.56, is adequate for determining whether synchronism can be maintained following many simple disturbances to both generators and motors. But it does not give a complete solution for the mechanical transient in that β_0 is not determined as a function of time. It is therefore not adequate for situations involving a sequence of system changes that occur at specific times.

As an example of a system in which the angle β_0 must be found as a function of time, let us consider a generator connected to a power system containing a number of other generators. Suppose a short circuit occurs in the power system. By reducing the terminal voltage $|E_s|$ (possibly to zero), the short circuit reduces the electrical power output of the machine (eq. 5.206). The prime-mover torque, however, continues to act, and the machine is accelerated. Within a short time, generally from 0.05 to 0.5 second, the relays of the power system detect and locate the short circuit,

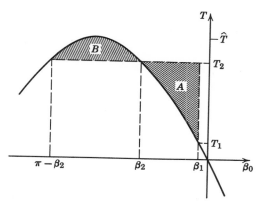

Fig. 5.56 A situation where synchronism is lost. Area B < Area A.

and the circuit breakers disconnect the faulty section of the system. The power output capability of the generator is then restored.

To determine whether the generator remains in synchronism with the power system, the equation

$$J \frac{2}{p} \frac{d^2\beta_0}{dt^2} = T_{\text{shaft}} + T \qquad (5.212)$$

must be solved for β_0 as a function of time. As the torque T is a nonlinear function of the angle β_0, a numerical solution is generally obtained. The shaft torque applied by the prime mover, in the direction of rotation, continues at a constant value until some change is made in the prime-mover control valves. The machine torque T in the faulted condition at $t = 0$ may be found by analysis of the electrical system for the angle β_0, which obtains at that time. The accelerating torque at that time is then $(T_{\text{shaft}} + T)$ where T is a negative quantity (or possibly zero). If it is assumed that this accelerating torque remains essentially constant for a short time interval Δt, the angle β_0 at $t = \Delta t$ may be found by solution of the now linearized eq. 5.212. The calculation may then be repeated for succeeding intervals of time taking into account changes in the electrical system as they occur.

Figure 5.57 shows typical curves of the angle β_0 as a function of time for a generator after a short circuit on its connected power system. It is noted that the ability of the generator to remain in synchronism is dependent on the time required for the circuit breakers to operate.

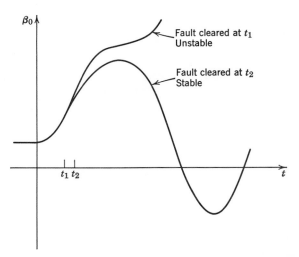

Fig. 5.57 Variation of rotor angle β_0 of synchronous generator after short circuit on power system.

If the disturbance to the machine is small, the change in its angle β_0 is also small. As shown in Fig. 5.58a, the torque-angle relation may be linearized for small excursions in β_0 away from a value β_1 by use of the approximation

$$\sin \beta_0 = \sin \beta_1 + \cos \beta_1 (\beta_0 - \beta_1) \tag{5.213}$$

Insertion of this approximation into eqs. 5.206 and 5.207 converts eq. 5.212 to the form

$$J \frac{2}{p} \frac{d^2\beta_0}{dt^2} = T_{\text{shaft}} - \hat{T} \sin \beta_1 - \hat{T} \cos \beta_1 (\beta_0 - \beta_1) \tag{5.214}$$

Suppose we consider a motor in which the shaft torque is suddenly changed by a small increment from T_1 to T_2 as shown in Fig. 5.58b. After $t = 0$, the system is then described by the linear differential equation

$$J \frac{2}{p} \frac{d^2\beta_0}{dt^2} + (\hat{T} \cos \beta_1)\beta_0 = (T_1 - T_2) - (\hat{T} \cos \beta_1)\beta_1 \tag{5.215}$$

for which the solution is

$$\beta_0 = \beta_1 + \frac{(T_1 - T_2)}{\hat{T}\cos\beta_1}(1 - \cos\omega_n t) \qquad \text{radians} \qquad (5.216)$$

As shown in Fig. 5.58c, the angle β_0 oscillates about an average value $\beta_0 = \beta_2$ at an angular velocity of

$$\omega_n = \left[\frac{\hat{T}\cos\beta_1}{(2/p)J}\right]^{\frac{1}{2}} \qquad \text{radians/second} \qquad (5.217)$$

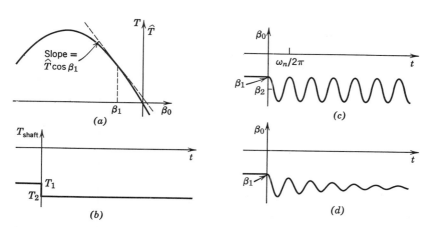

Fig. 5.58 (a) Linearization of torque-angle relation about $\beta_0 = \beta_1$. (b) Step change of load torque on synchronous motor. (c) Undamped oscillation of rotor angle β_0. (d) Damped oscillation of rotor angle β_0.

For a p-pole machine, the rotor speed would be

$$\nu = \nu_s + \frac{2}{p}\omega_n \qquad \text{radians/second} \qquad (5.218)$$

This mechanical oscillation would continue indefinitely if it were not for the damping action that arises from losses in the machine and from speed-dependent torque in the load. The most important damping action arises from currents that are induced in the short-circuited rotor windings as the speed departs from its synchronous value. In Fig. 5.21b, it can be seen that the torque produced by an induction machine near synchronous speed can be approximated by

$$T_i = T'(\nu_s - \nu) \qquad \text{newton-meters} \qquad (5.219)$$

where T is the slope of the torque-speed curve at $v = v_s$. Substitution from eq. 5.203 into eq. 5.219 gives

$$T_i = T'\left(v_s - \frac{2}{p}\omega_s - \frac{2}{p}\frac{d\beta_0}{dt}\right)$$

$$= -T'\frac{d\beta_0}{dt} \qquad \text{newton-meters} \qquad (5.220)$$

If this torque is included, the dynamic behavior of the synchronous machine is represented by the differential equation

$$J\frac{2}{p}\frac{d^2\beta_0}{dt^2} + T'\frac{d\beta_0}{dt} = T_{\text{shaft}} + T \qquad (5.221)$$

Figure 5.58d shows the effect the damping term might have on the small oscillation we considered earlier.

A part of the induction torque of eq. 5.220 is produced by currents induced in the field windings that generally may be considered to be effectively short circuited for slip-frequency currents. In machines with solid iron rotors, torque is produced by induced currents in the magnetic material. In many synchronous machines, a damper or amortisseur winding consisting of bars connected to shorting end rings is fitted into slots on the rotor surface. Such a winding is usually required in a synchronous motor to damp out mechanical oscillations. It is also used for starting synchronous motors (Section 5.6.3).

Sustained mechanical oscillations of considerable amplitude can occur in a synchronous machine that has a periodically varying shaft torque. Examples of such situations include generators connected to a power system and driven by reciprocating engines, and also motors driving reciprocating compressors. The torque oscillations are normally not sinusoidal but may be resolved into a Fourier series of torque harmonics. Serious mechanical oscillations may occur if the frequency of one of these torque harmonics is approximately equal to the natural oscillation frequency ω_n of the machine (eq. 5.217).

5.5.7 Permanent-Magnet and Hysteresis Machines

The excitation for a synchronous machine may be provided by the use of permanent-magnetic material in the rotor. This eliminates the requirement for a source of direct field current and also eliminates the necessity for rotor slip rings.

The main features of the performance of permanent-magnet synchronous machines may be illustrated by an analysis of the simple machine shown in

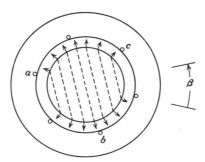

Fig. 5.59   Cross section of permanent-magnet machine with cylindrical rotor.

Fig. 5.59. The stator is of normal cylindrical slotted construction and carries polyphase distributed windings. The rotor of this elementary machine consists of a solid cylinder of a permanent-magnetic material such as Alnico or ferrite (Section 1.6.6). The rotor has been uniformly magnetized so as to produce an approximately sinusoidal distribution of air-gap flux density.

An equivalent circuit for this type of machine may be developed most simply by analogy with that of a cylindrical rotor machine with a field winding, such as that shown in Fig. 5.33a. Since the machines are similar from the air gap outward, the equivalent circuit for a permanent-magnet machine, shown in Fig. 5.60a, includes the stator resistance R_s per phase

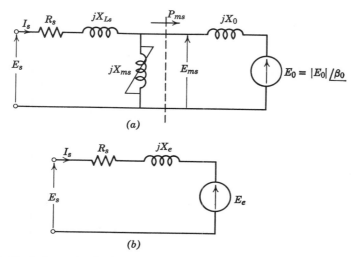

Fig. 5.60 (a) Equivalent circuit for permanent-magnet machine. (b) Simplified Thévenin equivalent.

the stator leakage reactance X_{Ls} per phase, and a magnetizing reactance X_{ms}, which represents the reluctances of the air gap, the stator teeth and slots, and the stator yoke.

All that is now required is an adequate representation of a permanent-magnet rotor. In a synchronous machine with constant field current, the rotor acts as a source of constant distributed magnetomotive force in series with the nonlinear reluctance of the rotor magnetic material. When converted into an electric equivalent circuit, as in Fig. 5.33a, the constant magnetomotive force becomes a constant current source I_r', and the reluctance becomes a contribution to the magnetizing reactance X_{ms} connected in parallel with the current source. In Section 2.5.2, it was shown that a permanent magnet with the flux-magnetomotive force relation of Fig. 2.26b could be represented approximately and within limits by either a magnetomotive force $\mathscr{F}_0$ in series with a linear reluctance $\mathscr{R}_0$ (Fig. 2.26c), or by a flux source ϕ_0 in parallel with a reluctance $\mathscr{R}_0$ (Fig. 2.26d). The first of these two models is identical in form with that of a rotor with field windings. The equivalent circuit of Fig. 5.33a could therefore be used to represent a premanent-magnet machine. But since the flux of a permanent magnet remains more nearly constant than its magnetomotive force, it is generally preferable to use the flux-source model for the magnet. The form of the electric circuit that is equivalent to this magnetic circuit may be found by the duality concept described in Section 2.4.2. The flux source ϕ_0 with its parallel reluctance $\mathscr{R}_0$ becomes a voltage source E_0 in series with a linear reactance X_0, as shown in Fig. 5.60a. If the rotor angle β in Fig. 5.59 is

$$\beta = \omega_s t + \beta_0 \tag{5.222}$$

the phase angle of the constant source voltage E_0 in Fig. 5.60 is β_0.

For simplicity in determining terminal behavior, the Thévenin equivalent of Fig. 5.60b may be used with

$$E_e = \frac{X_{ms}}{X_{ms} + X_0} E_0 \quad \text{volts} \tag{5.223}$$

and

$$X_e = X_{Ls} + \frac{X_{ms}X_0}{X_{ms} + X_0} \quad \text{ohms} \tag{5.224}$$

provided the magnetizing reactance X_{ms} can be regarded as constant.

In contrast with the normal synchronous machine, the permanent-magnet machine has no provision for adjustment of its excitation. When it is used as a generator, it is therefore desirable to have the lowest possible value of equivalent reactance X_e. To provide this, the stator should have relatively open slots to maximize the reluctance to stator leakage flux and the rotor material should have a low value of recoil permeability. To maximize the voltage E_e, the magnetizing reactance X_{ms} would be made large in value by the use of a short air gap.

The linear model of a permanent magnet in Fig. 2.26b is valid only if its output flux is greater than the limit value ϕ_a. Similarly, the equivalent circuit of Fig. 5.60a has a constant source voltage E_0 only if the voltage E_{ms} produced by the magnet flux remains greater than a limit value corresponding to ϕ_a. If the machine terminals are short circuited at any time, the voltage E_{ms} may fall below this limit and part of the permanent-magnet flux may be destroyed, necessitating a remagnetization of the

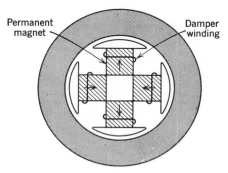

Fig. 5.61   Permanent-magnet machine with four-pole salient-pole rotor and damper windings.

rotor. From this point of view a high value of stator leakage reactance is desirable. It can thus be seen that a compromise is required in the design of these machines.

The rotors of most permanent-magnet machines are of the salient-pole type shown in Fig. 5.61. Because of the low recoil permeability of the permanent-magnet material, the reluctance torque produced by the machine is not large, and the previous analysis applies with reasonable accuracy. If a short circuit on the stator windings can be cleared within a few cycles of stator frequency, the demagnetizing effect on the magnet of the short-circuit current can be counteracted by placing a large conducting loop or damper around each magnet. A change in the magnet flux is inhibited by a large induced current in this damper winding. The short-circuit time constant of this damper winding must be large enough to prevent the flux reaching the limit value before the fault is cleared.

5.5.8 Hysteresis Machines

The hysteresis motor is essentially a permanent-magnet machine designed so that the stator magnetomotive force can produce and change the state of magnetization of the rotor material. The rotor may consist of a solid cylinder of permanent-magnetic material (as in Fig. 5.59) or of a ring of permanent-magnet material with or without a soft-iron core.

Suppose the stator windings of the motor are connected to a polyphase supply. The polyphase stator currents produce a magnetomotive force around the path shown in Fig. 5.62a of

$$\mathscr{F}_\theta = \frac{N_s \hat{I}_s m_s}{2} \cos (\omega_s t + \alpha_s - \theta) \qquad \text{amperes} \qquad (5.225)$$

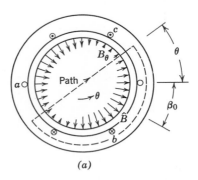

(a)

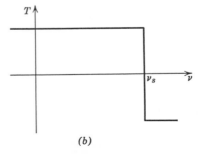

(b)

Fig. 5.62 (a) Cross section of hysteresis machine showing flux density distribution. (b) Torque-speed characteristic of a hysteresis machine.

This is a sinusoidally distributed magnetomotive force rotating in the direction of positive angle θ at angular velocity ω_s. At the instant shown in Fig. 5.62a the maximum magnetomotive force exists for a path at $\theta = 0$.

Suppose the rotor is at standstill. Previous to the instant shown in Fig. 5.62a, the maximum magnetomotive force was applied to the rotor material in the region $\theta < 0$, leaving it with a positive residual flux density $B_\theta = \hat{B}$, the value of which depends on the value of the stator current.

In the region around $\theta = \pi/2$, the material flux density B_θ is at its negative residual value, and the magnetomotive force $\mathscr{F}_\theta$ is small but increasing with time. When $\mathscr{F}_\theta$ becomes large enough to provide the coercive force in the rotor material, the flux density B_θ begins to increase from the negative residual toward the positive residual value.

Only the fundamental component of the nonsinusoidal distributed flux density B_θ produces flux linkage in the sinusoidally distributed stator winding. This fundamental component of B_θ has its maximum value at an angle β_0 behind the angle of maximum magnetomotive force $\mathscr{F}_0$ in Fig. 5.62a. The torque on the rotor acts in the direction of positive θ, tending to align the magnetic axis of the distributed rotor flux density with the magnetomotive force axis of the stator.

The equivalent circuit of Fig. 5.60a may now be used for analysis of the terminal properties of this machine. The source voltage E_0 has a magnitude proportional to the fundamental component of the flux density B_θ in the material and has the phase angle β_0. As in the permanent-magnet machine, the reactance X_0 is proportional to the recoil permeability of the material.

As the machine accelerates toward synchronous speed, the magnitudes and relative positions of the magnetomotive force and flux density distributions remain constant. In the equivalent circuit of Fig. 5.60a, the voltage E_0 remains constant in magnitude and angle. Thus the air-gap power per phase P_{ms} and the torque T also remain constant as shown in Fig. 5.62b. When synchronous speed v_s is reached, the rotor angle β_0 adjusts itself so that the torque produced is equal to the steady-state load torque.

If the machine is driven at a speed greater than its synchronous value, it acts as a generator with a constant positive value of the angle β_0. It thus produces a constant value of electric power P_{ms} per phase and requires a constant shaft torque. The difference between the total electric power $m_s P_{ms}$ and the mechanical power Tv is dissipated as hysteresis loss in the rotor.

The principal advantage of the hysteresis motor is its ability to accelerate high-inertia loads up to synchronous speed. Since its starting current is essentially equal to the operating current at maximum torque and synchronous speed, the time required for starting need not be limited. Examples of its use include timing motors, phonograph motors, and adjustable-torque drives.

5.6 POLYPHASE SYNCHRONOUS-RELUCTANCE MACHINES

The induction and synchronous machines so far discussed in this chapter have had cylindrical rotors and have developed torque by the use of rotor windings or permanent magnets. In Section 1.7.4, we noted that torque could be developed, at synchronous speed, by the use of a non-cylindrical or salient-pole rotor such as that shown in Fig. 5.63. In machines of this type the torque tends to rotate the rotor so as to minimize the reluctance offered by the air gap to the stator magnetomotive force. Such machines are therefore known as reluctance machines.

In this section we first investigate the properties of polyphase reluctance machines with no rotor windings. We then examine the salient-pole

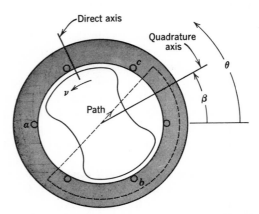

Fig. 5.63   Cross section of two-pole, three-phase reluctance machine.

synchronous machine that has field windings on a salient-pole rotor. This latter type combines the features of the reluctance machine and the cylindrical-rotor synchronous machine.

5.6.1   Analysis and Equivalent Circuit

Figure 5.63 shows a cross section of a two-pole polyphase reluctance machine. Its stator windings are assumed to be sinusoidally distributed and to carry a balanced set of polyphase currents—that in phase a being

$$i_a = \hat{I}_{ms} \sin (\omega_s t + \alpha_{ms}) \qquad \text{amperes} \qquad (5.226)$$

From eq. 5.15, the magnetomotive force around the path shown at angle θ is

$$\mathscr{F}_\theta = \frac{N_s \hat{I}_{ms} m_s}{2} \cos (\omega_s t + \alpha_{ms} - \theta) \qquad \text{amperes} \qquad (5.227)$$

From eq. 5.30, if the magnetic material is assumed to be perfect, the flux density B_θ in the air gap near the stator can be expressed as

$$B_\theta = \frac{\mu_0 \mathscr{F}_\theta}{2g_\theta} \qquad \text{webers/meter}^2 \qquad (5.228)$$

where g_θ is the effective length of the air gap at angle θ. Note that the rotor is symmetrical about $\theta = \beta$ and $\theta = \beta + \pi/2$; thus the inverse of the effective air-gap length may be expressed by a Fourier series of the form

$$\frac{1}{g_\theta} = h_0 - h_2 \cos 2(\theta - \beta) + h_4 \cos 4(\theta - \beta) - \cdots \quad (5.229)$$

If the rotor rotates at synchronous speed, the rotor angle β is

$$\beta = \omega_s t + \beta_0 \quad (5.230)$$

If substitutions from eqs. 5.227, 5.229, and 5.230 are made into eq. 5.228 and the product terms expanded, the air-gap flux density can be expressed in the form

$$
\begin{aligned}
B_\theta = \frac{\mu_0 N_s \hat{I}_{ms} m_s}{4} \Big[& h_0 \cos(\omega_s t + \alpha_{ms} - \theta) \\
& - \frac{h_2}{2} \cos(3\omega_s t + \alpha_{ms} + 2\beta_0 - 3\theta) - \frac{h_2}{2} \cos(\omega_s t - \alpha_{ms} + 2\beta_0 - \theta) \\
& + \frac{h_4}{2} \cos(5\omega_s t + \alpha_{ms} + 4\beta_0 - 5\theta) \\
& + \frac{h_4}{2} \cos(3\omega_s t - \alpha_{ms} + 4\beta_0 - 3\theta) \cdots \Big]
\end{aligned}
\quad (5.231)
$$

In Section 5.2.3 it was shown that flux linkages can be produced in sinusoidally distributed stator windings only by the components of flux density that are similarly distributed in space. Thus, only two components of eq. 5.231 contribute to the stator flux linkage. From eq. 5.32,

$$\lambda_{ma} = \frac{\pi}{8} \mu_0 N_s{}^2 m_s l r \hat{I}_{ms} \left[h_0 \sin(\omega_s t + \alpha_{ms}) - \frac{h_2}{2} \sin(\omega_s t - \alpha_{ms} + 2\beta_0) \right]$$

$$(5.232)$$

The induced voltage in stator winding a is the time rate of change of the flux linkage λ_{ma}. It can be expressed in the phasor form

$$E_{ms} = [j\omega_s L_{m0} - j\omega_s L_{m2} \underline{/2(\beta_0 - \alpha_{ms})}] I_{ms} \qquad \text{volts} \quad (5.233)$$

where $\qquad L_{m0} = \frac{\pi}{8} \mu_0 N_s{}^2 m_s l r h_0 \qquad \text{henrys} \quad (5.234)$

and $\qquad L_{m2} = \frac{\pi}{16} \mu_0 N_s{}^2 m_s l r h_2 \qquad \text{henrys} \quad (5.235)$

The bracketed quantity in eq. 5.233 represents the magnetizing impedance of the reluctance machine. When $\alpha_{ms} = \beta_0 \pm \pi/2$, the direct axis

of the rotor is aligned with the maximum magnetomotive force of the
stator windings and

$$E_{ms} = j\omega_s(L_{m0} + L_{m2})I_{ms}$$
$$= jX_{md}I_{ms} \tag{5.236}$$

where X_{md} is known as the direct-axis magnetizing reactance. When
$\alpha_{ms} = \beta_0$ or $\beta_0 + \pi$, the maximum magnetomotive force acts along the
high-reluctance quadrature axis of the rotor and

$$E_{ms} = j\omega_s(L_{m0} - L_{m2})I_{ms}$$
$$= jX_{mq}I_{ms} \tag{5.237}$$

where X_{mq} is known as the quadrature-axis magnetizing reactance.

With zero torque, the rotor angle adjusts itself to the position $\beta_0 = \alpha_{ms} \pm \pi/2$, where the reluctance offered to the magnetomotive force is

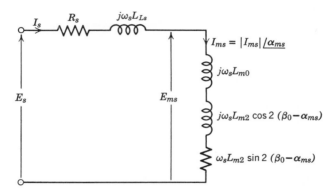

Fig. 5.64   Elementary equivalent circuit for reluctance machine.

a minimum. In this condition the magnetizing impedance is inductive, as
shown in eq. 5.236. If a load torque is applied, the angle β_0 is reduced,
making $\beta_0 < \alpha_{ms} \pm \pi/2$. The magnetizing impedance of eq. 5.233 is then
found to include a positive real part indicating that power is entering the
machine terminals. Alternatively, if the machine is driven so that $\beta_0 > \alpha_{ms} \pm \pi/2$, the magnetizing impedance contains a negative real part
indicating power flow out of the machine terminals. The real part of the
magnetizing impedance has its maximum value when $\beta_0 = \alpha_{ms} \pm \pi/4$.

Figure 5.64 shows a possible equivalent circuit for the polyphase
reluctance machine. A part of the magnetizing reactance and the magnetizing resistance varies as functions of twice the angular difference between
the quadrature-axis position and the position of maximum magnetomotive force. While this equivalent circuit is helpful in understanding the

behavior of the machine, its form is inconvenient for many analyses because some of its parameters depend on the angle α_{ms} of the magnetizing current. It is generally more convenient to choose a voltage such as E_s as a reference for phase angle measurement, as most machines are operated with essentially constant-terminal voltage.

As an alternative approach, let us consider an idealized reluctance machine with negligible stator resistance and stator-leakage reactance. If this machine is connected to a constant-voltage supply, its induced voltage E_{ms} can be considered to be constant and to have a phase angle of zero. From eqs. 5.72 and 5.74, the fundamental component of the air gap flux density that is required to produce the induced voltage E_{ms} with zero phase angle is

$$B_\theta = \hat{B} \cos \left(\omega_s t - \frac{\pi}{2} - \theta \right) \qquad \text{webers/meter}^2 \qquad (5.238)$$

Space harmonics of flux density may exist, but since they produce no flux linkage, they may be ignored. At time $t = 0$, the flux density B_θ is distributed so that the flux linkage of winding a is at its negative maximum value, as shown in the space vector diagram of Fig. 5.65b.

The flux density distribution B_θ in Fig. 5.65b can be considered to consist of two sinusoidally distributed flux densities, $B_{d\theta}$ with its maximum along the direct axis of the rotor and $B_{q\theta}$ with its maximum along the quadrature axis of the rotor. Thus

$$B_{d\theta} = \hat{B} \cos \beta_0 \cos \left[\omega_s t + \beta_0 - \frac{\pi}{2} - \theta \right] \qquad (5.239)$$

and
$$B_{q\theta} = \hat{B} \sin \beta_0 \cos (\omega_s t + \beta_0 - \pi - \theta) \qquad (5.240)$$

The direct-axis component of flux density $B_{d\theta}$ can be considered to result from a similarly distributed magnetomotive force component $\mathscr{F}_{d\theta}$ as shown in Fig. 5.65c. If we let $\alpha_{ms} = \beta_0 - \pi/2$ in eq. 5.227 and in eq. 5.231, the relation between the sinusoidally distributed quantities $\mathscr{F}_{d\theta}$ and $B_{d\theta}$ is found to be

$$\mathscr{F}_{d\theta} = \frac{2}{\mu_0(h_0 + h_2/2)} B_{d\theta} \qquad (5.241)$$

To support the quadrature-axis component of flux density, the stator winding must produce a component of magnetomotive force

$$\mathscr{F}_{q\theta} = \frac{2}{\mu_0(h_0 - h_2/2)} B_{q\theta} \qquad (5.242)$$

The sum of the vectors representing $\mathscr{F}_{d\theta}$ and $\mathscr{F}_{q\theta}$ in Fig. 5.65c gives the total magnetomotive force that must be produced by the stator currents.

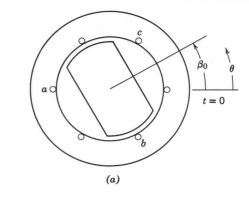

(a)

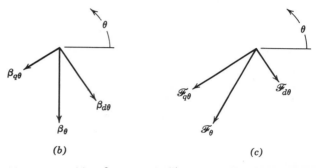

(b)   (c)

Fig. 5.65 (a) Rotor position β_0 at $t = 0$. (b) Space vector diagram of flux density components. (c) Space vector diagram of magnetomotive force components.

Figure 5.66 shows a phasor diagram of the idealized reluctance machine. The flux density components $B_{d\theta}$ and $B_{q\theta}$ of eqs. 5.239 and 5.240 may be considered to produce the two components E_{md} and E_{mq} of the induced voltage E_{ms}, where

$$E_{md} = E_{ms} \cos \beta_0 \ \underline{/\beta_0} \tag{5.243}$$

and
$$E_{mq} = E_{ms} \sin \beta_0 \ \underline{/\beta_0 - \pi/2} \tag{5.244}$$

The direct-axis magnetomotive force of eq. 5.241 required to produce $B_{d\theta}$ may be considered to be produced by a component I_{md} of the stator current. Since the flux density component $B_{d\theta}$ acts along the direct axis, the value of the corresponding magnetizing current component is given, from eq. 5.236, as

$$I_{md} = \frac{E_{md}}{jX_{md}} \tag{5.245}$$

Similarly, from eq. 5.237, the component I_{mq} of the stator current required to produce $\mathscr{F}_{q\theta}$ is

$$I_{mq} = \frac{E_{mq}}{jX_{mq}} \qquad (5.246)$$

The total magnetizing current is given by the phasor sum

$$I_{ms} = I_{md} + I_{mq} \qquad (5.247)$$

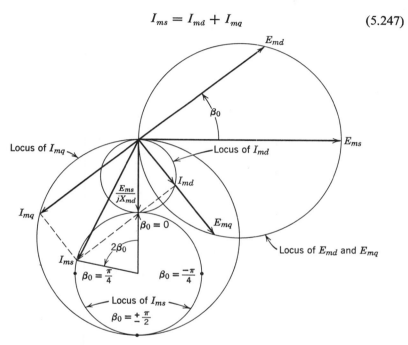

Fig. 5.66 Phasor diagram of reluctance machine showing circular loci of current and voltage components.

As the angle β_0 of the rotor varies over the range $\pi/2 > \beta_0 > -\pi/2$, all of the phasors E_{md}, E_{mq}, I_{md}, and I_{mq} follow circular loci as shown in Fig. 5.66. The magnetizing current I_{ms} also follows a circular locus. Comparison of the locus of I_{ms} with the current locus of an induction machine (Fig. 5.22c) suggests that the reluctance machine can be represented by the equivalent circuit of Fig. 5.67a, which is similar in form to that of an induction machine. Since it is known that the appropriate equivalent circuit consists of a branch jX_{md} in parallel with a variable impedance, eqs. 5.243 to 5.247 may be manipulated to give the magnetizing current expression

$$
I_{ms} = \frac{E_{ms} \cos \beta_0 / \beta_0}{jX_{md}} + \frac{E_{ms} \sin \beta_0 / \beta_0 - \pi/2}{jX_{mq}}
$$

$$
= E_{ms} \left[\frac{\cos^2 \beta_0 + j \cos \beta_0 \sin \beta_0}{jX_{md}} + \frac{\sin^2 \beta_0 - j \sin \beta_0 \cos \beta_0}{jX_{mq}} \right]
$$

$$
= E_{ms} \left[\frac{1}{jX_{md}} + \frac{X_{md} - X_{mq}}{X_{md}X_{mq}} (-\sin \beta_0 \cos \beta_0 - j \sin^2 \beta_0) \right]
$$

$$
= E_{ms} \left[\frac{1}{jX_{md}} + \frac{X_{md} - X_{mq}}{X_{md}X_{mq}(-\cot \beta_0 + j)} \right] \tag{5.248}
$$

(a)

(b)

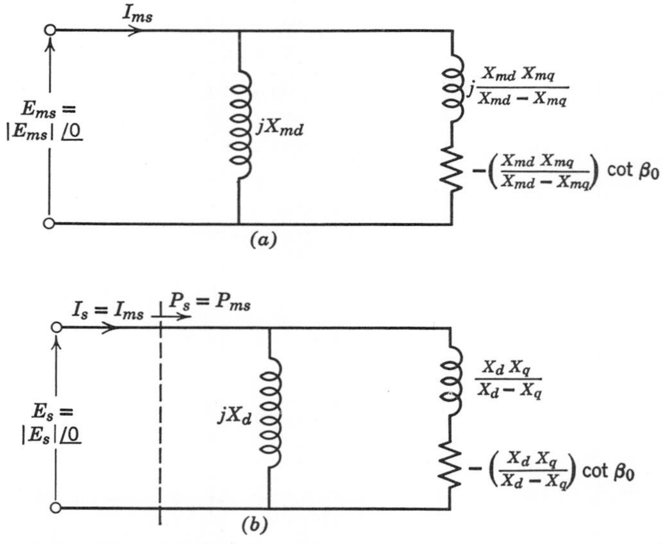

Fig. 5.67 Equivalent circuits for reluctance machine. (a) As seen from air-gap voltage E_{ms}. (b) As seen from stator terminals.

Thus the equivalent circuit of Fig. 5.67a consists of an inductive impedance jX_{md} in parallel with a branch that contains a constant inductive reactance in series with a variable resistance.

When the rotor angle β_0 is zero or π, the resistance in Fig. 5.67a is infinite, and the total magnetizing impedance is equal to jX_{md}. For $\beta_0 = \pm\pi/2$, the resistance is zero and the magnetizing impedance is jX_{mq}. Maximum air-gap power P_{ms} occurs when the resistance is equal to the circuit impedance as seen from the resistance. This condition occurs at $\cot \beta_0 = \pm 1$ or $\beta_0 = \pm \pi/4$, the sign depending on the direction of power flow.

The effect of the stator leakage reactance X_{Ls} is to increase the impedance as seen from the machine terminals. Suppose the terminal voltage E_s is taken as a reference and assigned a phase angle of zero. When the rotor angle β_0 is zero or π, the impedance—looking into the machine—is jX_d where X_d is the direct-axis synchronous reactance given by

$$X_d = X_{Ls} + X_{md} \quad \text{ohms/phase} \tag{5.249}$$

With $\beta_0 = \pm \pi/2$, the impedance as seen from the terminals is jX_q where X_q is the quadrature-axis synchronous reactance is

$$X_q = X_{Ls} + X_{md} \quad \text{ohms/phase} \tag{5.250}$$

At other values of rotor angle β_0, reluctance power is produced, the value depending on the difference between X_d and X_q and on the angle β_0. By analogy with eq. 5.248, the relation between stator current I_s and stator voltage E_s may be written as

$$I_s = I_{ms} = E_s \left[\frac{1}{jX_d} + \frac{X_d - X_q}{X_d X_q (-\cot \beta_0 + j)} \right] \tag{5.251}$$

The equivalent circuit of Fig. 5.67b is identical in form to that of Fig. 5.67a. The reactances X_{md} and X_{mq} as seen from the air-gap voltage E_{ms} have merely been replaced by the reactances X_d and X_q seen from the stator terminal voltage E_s.

5.6.2 Terminal Characteristics

The reluctance machine acts as an energy converter only when operating at synchronous speed. It derives its torque from the tendency of the rotor to align itself with the rotating magnetic field. As the supply voltage is normally constant, the terminal characteristics of interest are those relating the stator current I_s, the torque T, and the rotor angle β_0.

The power input to the machine, derived by use of eq. 5.251, is

$$\begin{aligned} P_s &= \mathscr{R}_e[I_s E_s{}^*] \\ &= \mathscr{R}_e \left[\frac{X_d - X_q}{X_d X_q} \frac{|E_s|^2}{(-\cot \beta_e + j)} \right] \\ &= -\frac{X_d - X_q}{2X_d X_q} |E_s|^2 \sin 2\beta_0 \quad \text{watts/phase} \end{aligned} \tag{5.252}$$

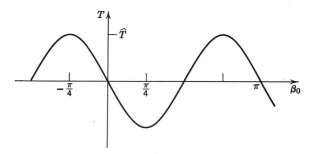

Fig. 5.68   Relation between torque T and rotor angle β_0 for a reluctance machine.

Since the stator resistance has been neglected, eq. 5.252 also represents the air-gap power P_{ms} per phase. Thus, from eq. 5.147, the torque produced by a p-pole machine is

$$T = \frac{p}{2} \frac{m_s}{\omega_s} P_{ms}$$

$$= -\frac{p}{2} \frac{m_s}{\omega_s} \left(\frac{X_d - X_q}{2X_d X_q} \right) |E_s|^2 \sin 2\beta_0 \qquad \text{newton-meters} \quad (5.253)$$

Figure 5.68 shows the relation between the torque and the rotor angle. At zero torque, the stable synchronous conditions are $\beta_0 = 0$ and $\beta_0 = \pi$. Any change in β_0 from either of these positions produces a torque that tends to prevent the change in β_0. Maximum torque as a motor occurs at $\beta_0 = -\pi/4$. As a generator, the maximum torque occurs at $\beta_0 = \pi/4$.

Figure 5.69 shows the locus of the stator current I_s as the rotor angle

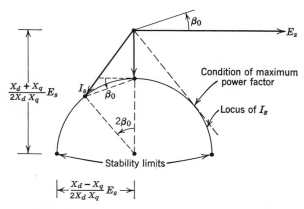

Fig. 5.69   Locus of stator current for reluctance machine.

β_0 varies. From eq. 5.251, this locus is a circle with

$$\text{radius} = \frac{X_d - X_q}{2X_dX_q}|E_s| \qquad \text{amperes} \qquad (5.254)$$

and

$$\text{center} = E_s\left[\frac{1}{jX_d} + \frac{X_d - X_q}{j2X_dX_q}\right]$$

$$= -j\frac{X_d + X_q}{2X_dX_q}E_s \qquad (5.255)$$

At the condition of maximum power input, $\beta_0 = -\pi/4$, the in-phase component of the stator current is seen to be proportional to $X_d - X_q$, whereas the quadrature component is proportional to $X_d + X_q$. Even if

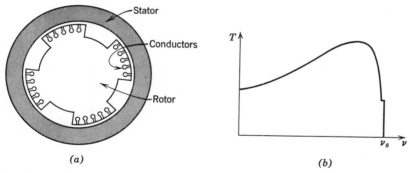

(a)   (b)

Fig. 5.70 (a) Cross section of four-pole reluctance-induction machine. Conductors are shorted by end rings. (b) Torque-speed relation of reluctance-induction machine.

X_q is negligible in comparison with X_d, the power factor at maximum power transfer cannot exceed $1/\sqrt{2}$. It is practically difficult to construct a machine with X_d greater than three to four times X_q. With this limitation, the power factor at all values of loading does not exceed a value of about 0.6.

It is this low power factor feature that limits the use of the purely reluctance machine. Salient-pole rotor construction is, however, incorporated into various types of induction and synchronous machines. One example, shown in Fig. 5.70a, is a squirrel-cage induction machine with sections of the rotor removed. This machine starts and accelerates as an induction machine. As the speed approaches its synchronous value, the reluctance torque oscillates at a low frequency. When this reluctance torque is positive, it acts to accelerate the machine. If the mechanical load and the inertia are small, the machine may reach synchronous speed as a result of

POLYPHASE MACHINES

the half cycle of positive reluctance torque. The machine then runs as a reluctance machine at synchronous speed. Figure 5.70b shows a typical torque-speed curve for the reluctance-induction machine.

The unsaturated values of the reactances X_d and X_q may be measured by applying a reasonably low voltage E_s to the stator terminals and by driving the machine at slightly less than synchronous speed (using, for example, an induction motor having the same synchronous speed). The stator current then varies slowly between a minimum value E_s/X_d and a maximum value E_s/X_q.

As the voltage E_s of the machine is increased, the direct-axis reactance X_d may be substantially reduced by magnetic saturation. The quadrature-axis reactance X_q is much less subject to saturation. It is therefore convenient to consider X_q as a constant and to use the methods described in Section 5.5.3 to determine the appropriate saturated value of X_d for the operating condition of the machine.

5.6.3 Salient-Pole Synchronous Machines

High-speed synchronous machines having two or four poles are usually constructed with cylindrical rotors and distributed field windings of the type shown in Fig. 5.29. At low speeds, a relatively large number of poles is required. It is then simpler to construct the rotor with concentrated field windings placed on salient poles. Figure 5.71 shows a sector of such a machine.

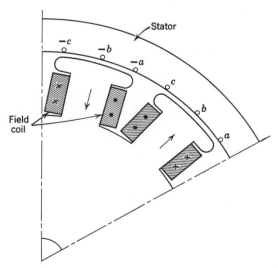

Fig. 5.71 Section of twelve-pole, salient-pole synchronous machine.

The magnetic structure of the salient-pole synchronous machine is that of a reluctance machine. Thus if its field current is zero, it can be represented by the reluctance-machine equivalent circuit of Fig. 5.67b. On the other hand, if the saliency of the magnetic structure is neglected, the machine can be represented by the cylindrical-rotor equivalent circuit of Fig. 5.33c. The salient-pole synchronous machine therefore combines the features of the reluctance machine and the excited-field synchronous machine. Its equivalent circuit, shown in Fig. 5.72, contains a current source that represents the magnetomotive force applied by the field

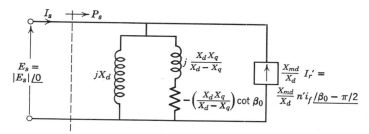

Fig. 5.72 Equivalent circuit for salient-pole synchronous machine.

winding along the direct or pole axis of the rotor. The synchronous reactance X_s of Fig. 5.33c has been replaced by the reluctance-machine representation of Fig. 5.67b. Since both the current source and the magnetizing impedance branch are connected directly to the terminal voltage E_s, they act independently.

The stator current I_s is given, from Fig. 5.72, by

$$I_s = E_s \left[\frac{1}{jX_d} + \frac{X_d - X_q}{X_d X_q(-\cot \beta_0 + j)} \right] - \frac{X_{md}}{X_d} n' i_f \underline{/\beta_0 - \pi/2}$$

$$= E_s \left[\frac{1}{jX_d} - \frac{X_d - X_q}{X_d X_q} \sin \beta_0 \underline{/\beta_0} \right] - \frac{X_{md}}{X_d} n' i_f \underline{/\beta_0 - \pi/2} \quad (5.256)$$

The power P_s entering the machine in the steady state is

$$P_s = \mathscr{R}_e[I_s E_s{}^*]$$

$$= -\frac{X_d - X_q}{2X_d X_q} |E_s|^2 \sin 2\beta_0 - |E_s| \frac{X_{md} n'}{X_d} i_f \sin \beta_0 \qquad \text{watts phase}$$

$$\qquad (5.257)$$

Note that this is equal to the sum of eq. 5.253 and 5.174. If we consider that the air-gap power P_{ms} is equal to P_s, the torque for steady-state operation is given by

$$T = \frac{pm_s}{2\omega_s} P_{ms}$$

$$= \frac{pm_s}{2\omega_s} \left[-\frac{X_d - X_q}{2X_d X_q} |E_s|^2 \sin 2\beta_0 - |E_s| \frac{X_{md} n'}{X_d} i_f \sin \beta_0 \right]$$

$$\text{newton-meters} \quad (5.258)$$

The reluctance torque component depends on the difference between the direct and quadrature-axis synchronous reactances, the stator voltage, and

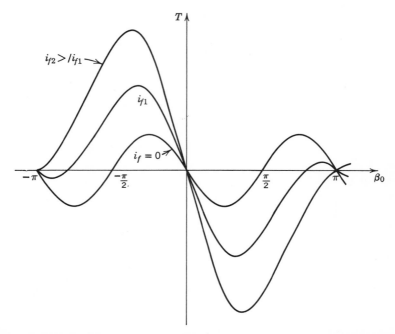

Fig. 5.73 Torque-angle relations for salient-pole synchronous machine in the steady state with several values of field current i_f.

the angle β_0 between the direct axis of the rotor and the net flux linking the reference stator winding. Since the field winding acts on the direct axis only, the field current has no direct influence on the reluctance torque. It may, however, contribute to saturation and thus influence the values of the reactances. The second component of torque in eq. 5.258 depends on the field current, the rotor angle, and on the values of the direct-axis reactances.

Figure 5.73 shows the torque of a salient-pole synchronous machine as a function of rotor angle for several values of field current. In practice, the ratio X_d/X_q is generally less than about 2. Thus when a salient-pole synchronous machine is operating with a reasonably large value of field current, the major part of the torque is produced by the action of the field winding. The maximum torque that the machine can produce is not greatly increased by the presence of reluctance torque. The major influence of the reluctance torque is to cause the maximum torque to occur at a smaller value of rotor angle β_0. The increase in the slope of the torque-angle characteristic in the operating region causes the machine to respond more rapidly to changes in its mechanical load. When the field

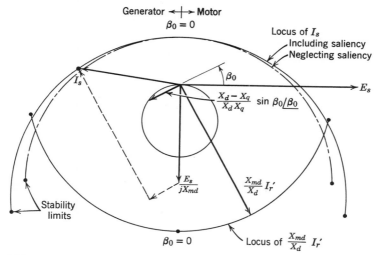

Fig. 5.74   Locus of stator current I_s with constant field current and variable rotor angle β_0.

current is low, the reluctance torque has a considerable effect on the performance of the machine. For example, if the field current in a cylindrical-rotor synchronous condenser (Section 5.5.4) is reduced to zero, the torque is reduced to zero and the machine loses synchronism. But if the machine has some saliency, it can remain in synchronism with zero, or even negative, values of field current. Thus, saliency increases the inductive-load capability of a synchronous condenser.

The electrical behavior of the machine in the steady state may be determined from the equivalent circuit of Fig. 5.72 or from the stator current expression of eq. 5.256. Since the rotor angle β_0 appears twice in the circuit, the simplest analysis is one in which the stator current I_s is predicted for given values of the field current i_f, and the rotor angle β_0. Figure 5.74 shows a phasor diagram of the components of the stator current I_s. As the rotor angle β_0 changes, the stator current I_s follows the locus shown. For comparative purposes, the circular locus from Fig. 5.43 for a machine with zero saliency ($X_q = X_d$) is also shown. It is noted that the input characteristics of the machine are not greatly affected by the saliency. The maximum value of the in-phase component of current is somewhat increased, and the inductive quadrature component of the current at the stability limit is also increased. Since the machine is not normally operated in the region near the stability limit, the effect of saliency can often be neglected in analyses.

Let us now consider the appropriate representation of a salient-pole synchronous machine for transient studies. At the instant of any change in terminal conditions, the flux linkage λ_f of the field winding remains constant. This flux linkage λ_f consists of two components, the field leakage flux and the direct-axis component of the air-gap flux. The total direct-axis flux is restrained from changing by the current that is induced in the field coil. The quadrature-axis flux may, however, change in direct response to the stator magnetomotive force since there is no field coil about the quadrature axis.

Let us first consider a machine in which the field winding is short circuited and which has an initial flux linkage of zero. Suppose that the time constant of the field winding is sufficiently long to keep the flux linkages approximately zero for the transient period of interest, and that we look in at the stator terminals when the rotor angle β_0 is zero. From Fig. 5.50 the machine can then be represented by its transient reactance X' where, from eq. 5.188,

$$X' = X_{Ls} + \frac{X_{md}X_{Lf}'}{X_{md} + X_{Lf}'} \qquad \text{ohms/phase} \qquad (5.259)$$

and X_{Lf}' is the stator equivalent of the field leakage inductance. With zero rotor flux linkage, the voltage E' in Fig. 5.50b is zero. When the rotor angle β_0 is $\pm\pi/2$, the impedance measured at the stator terminals is the quadrature-axis synchronous reactance X_q.

Since the machine has a changing reactance as the rotor angle changes, it produces reluctance torque. This is true even in the cylindrical-rotor machine where $X_q \approx X_d$. In fact, the reluctance torque is generally larger in a cylindrical-rotor machine than in a salient-pole machine for transient operation, since the difference between X' and X_q is larger. For the particular condition of zero rotor flux linkage, the machine may be represented in the transient state by the equivalent circuit of Fig. 5.75a. This circuit is identical with that of the unexcited reluctance machine of Fig. 5.67b, except that X_d has been replaced by X'. Since $X' < X_q$, the reactance in series with the resistance is negative, that is, capacitive. The torque on the rotor is in such a direction as to minimize the reluctance for the air-gap flux or to maximize the magnetizing impedance. Thus the rotor tends to take up either of the positions $\beta_0 = \pm\pi/2$ with the air-gap flux crossing by way of the quadrature axis.

Now let us consider the more general case where the field flux linkage λ_f is maintained at a constant value during the transient period. By analogy with the equivalent circuit of Fig. 5.50, this flux linkage can be considered to produce a constant and proportional induced voltage E'

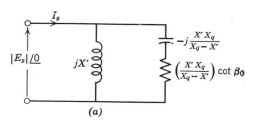

(a)

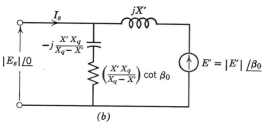

(b)

Fig. 5.75 Equivalent circuits for transient operation including the effect of saliency. (a) With zero field flux linkage. (b) With a constant-field flux linkage.

in series with the direct-axis transient reactance X'. Since the flux corresponding to λ_f is aligned along the direct axis, the phase angle of the voltage E' is equal to the rotor angle β_0. The resultant equivalent circuit is shown in Fig. 5.75b.

The stator current is given from Fig. 5.75b as

$$
\begin{aligned}
I_s &= \frac{X_q - X'}{X_q X'}\frac{E_s}{(\cot\beta_0 - j)} + \frac{E_s - E'}{jX'} \\
&= \frac{X_q - X'}{X_q X'} E_s \sin\beta_0 \underline{/\beta_0} + \frac{E_s - E'}{jX'}
\end{aligned}
\tag{5.260}
$$

The torque produced by the machine in the transient state is

$$
\begin{aligned}
T &= \mathscr{R}_e\left[\frac{pm_s}{2\omega_s} I_s E_s^*\right] \\
&= \frac{pm_s}{2\omega_s}\left[\frac{X_q - X'}{2X_q X'}|E_s|^2 \sin 2\beta_0 - \frac{|E'|\,|E_s|}{X'}\sin\beta_0\right]
\end{aligned}
\tag{5.261}
$$

Note that the reluctance torque opposes the torque due to the field winding in the region $\pi/2 > \beta_0 > -\pi/2$. Figure 5.76 shows the transient torque as a function of the angle β_0. It may be seen that the maximum torque occurs for $|\beta_0| > \pi/2$. This feature is of importance in the maintenance of synchronism immediately following a disturbance to the system. Reference to Fig. 5.56 shows that a large value of torque in the region $-\pi < \beta_0 < \pi/2$

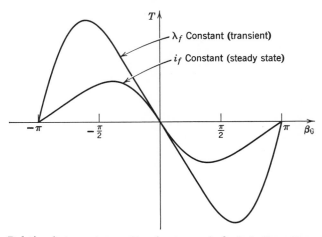

Fig. 5.76   Relation between torque T and rotor angle β_0, including effect of transient and steady-state saliency.

is most useful in restoring the speed of a synchronous motor that has been decelerated by a suddenly applied load. For comparative purposes, the steady-state relation between torque and rotor angle is also shown in Fig. 5.76. This relation applies when the field current is maintained constant, while the transient relation applies when the field flux linkage is maintained constant. The two torque-angle curves are coincident at the condition where the flux linkage of the field is considered to be fixed in value.

Most synchronous motors are of the salient-pole type. To give them a self-starting capability, they are provided with additional windings so that torque may be produced by induction. These windings are normally called damper or amortisseur windings because of their added ability to damp out mechanical oscillations (Section 5.5.6). Figure 5.77 shows a typical winding consisting of bars placed in slots in the pole faces and connected to shorting end rings. Because these windings do not cover the whole surface of the rotor, the induction torque developed during starting is often less than the rated torque of the machine. Thus, synchronous motors must generally be started in an unloaded or only partially loaded condition. During the period of starting, the field winding is short circuited or connected to a small resistance. This contributes to the starting torque and also prevents the induction of high voltages in the field winding which might damage its insulation.

Salient-pole synchronous generators are often fitted with damper windings similar to those shown in Fig. 5.77. These are intended to damp out oscillations in speed, particularly in situations where the prime mover torque is oscillatory. As has already been discussed in Section 5.5.5, these

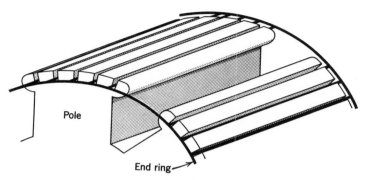

Fig. 5.77 Damper or amortisseur winding on a salient-pole rotor.

damper windings also increase the short-circuit current of the machine, making the subtransient reactance X'' of eq. 5.195 less than the transient reactance X' of eq. 5.188. To some extent, the value of the short-circuit current depends on the angle β_0 at the time of the short circuit. The subtransient reactance as seen along the quadrature axis is somewhat higher than that along the direct axis because the damper winding does not extend over the whole rotor surface.

5.7 POLYPHASE COMMUTATOR MACHINES

Many industrial operations require adjustable-speed drives. This speed-adjustment feature can be provided by the use of d-c commutator machines, as discussed in Section 4.6. But these machines require d-c supplies, whereas the normally available supply is alternating current. A rectifier can sometimes be used to convert the alternating current to direct current, but it is difficult to provide for bilateral flow of power through a rectifier system. Some degree of speed adjustment can be achieved by the use of wound-rotor induction motors with variable rotor-circuit impedance (Section 5.4.5). The speed of such a drive, however, is highly dependent on the load torque. In addition, the drive is inefficient except when operating near synchronous speed.

In this section, we examine several representative types of polyphase commutator machines that operate from a constant-frequency polyphase supply and provide a reasonably wide range of speed adjustment.

5.7.1 Basic Properties of a Polyphase Commutator

Figure 5.78 shows the stator and rotor of a simple type of polyphase commutator machine. The stator has a polyphase distributed winding as in an induction or synchronous machine. The rotor is similar to that of a

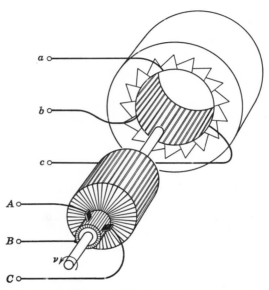

Fig. 5.78 Sketch of stator and rotor of polyphase commutator machine (three-phase, two-pole).

d-c commutator machine (Section 4.3). It normally has a double layer lap or wave winding with all coils connected in series and all coil terminals connected to commutator bars. In contrast with a d-c machine, there are m_r symmetrically placed brushes on the commutator of an m_r-phase, two-pole machine. For a p-pole machine there would be $m_r p/2$ brushes connected in m_r groups. The usual number of phases is three for both stator and rotor.

Let us first examine this machine at standstill. When a polyphase supply is connected to the stator terminals, a magnetic field rotating at ω_s radians per second is produced in a two-pole machine. Suppose each phase of the mesh-connected stator winding has N_s sinusoidally distributed turns. The rotor winding has a total of N uniformly distributed turns. These can be considered as m_r uniformly distributed, mesh-connected phase windings with N/m_r turns per phase. By Fourier analysis, the effective number of sinusoidally distributed turns per phase with $m_r = 3$ can be shown to be

$$N_r' = \frac{12}{\pi^2} N \qquad \text{turns} \tag{5.262}$$

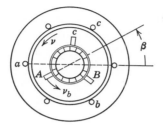

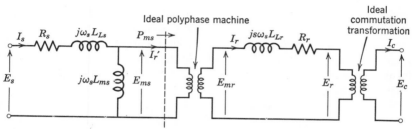

Fig. 5.79   Equivalent circuit for three-phase commutator machine.

Voltage $1:s\dfrac{N_r'}{N_s}$	$1:1\underline{/-\beta}$
Current $1:\dfrac{N_s}{N_r'}$	$1:1\underline{/-\beta}$
Frequency $\omega_s:s\omega_s$	$s\omega_s:\omega_s$
Impedance $1:s\left(\dfrac{N_r'}{N_s}\right)^2$	$1:1$
Power $1:s$	$1:1$

The space harmonics produced by the nonsinusoidal distribution of the rotor winding normally can be neglected because they do not link with the approximately sinusoidal stator winding.

At standstill, the machine has the properties of a phase shifter (Section 5.3.1). The frequency of the voltage induced is ω_s in both stator and rotor. The magnitude of the rotor-induced voltage E_{mr} per phase is N_r'/N_s times that of the stator induced voltage E_{ms}. If the axis of brush A in Fig. 5.79 is advanced β radians with respect to the axis of stator phase

a, the voltage in rotor phase A will be retarded by β radians with respect to the voltage in stator phase a. Thus, at standstill, from eq. 5.77,

$$E_{mr} = \frac{N_r'}{N_s} \underline{/-\beta}\, E_{ms} \qquad \text{volts} \qquad (5.263)$$

It may be noted that this relation is dependent on the angular position of the brushes but is independent of the position of the rotor.

Let us now consider rotating the brush gear at an angular velocity of ν_b radians per second in the same direction as the rotating field while the rotor remains stationary. This does not change the magnitude and frequency of the induced voltage in any rotor coil. But the group of coils having maximum induced voltage is now connected less frequently between a pair of brushes. The frequency of the voltage obtained at the brushes is $\omega_s - \nu_b$ radians per second. At $\nu_b = \omega_s$, a direct voltage is obtained between a pair of brushes. If ν_b is greater than ω_s, the negative frequency $\omega_s - \nu_b$ can be interpreted as a change in the phase sequence of the polyphase brush voltages from $A\,B\,C\,A$ to $A\,C\,B\,A$. In this situation, we note that the frequency at the commutator terminals depends on the relative velocity of the rotating field and the brushes. Although it is used infrequently, the machine can be utilized in this form as a polyphase frequency changer.

Now let us consider another situation in which the rotor is rotating forward at ν radians per second. The induced voltage in any coil of the rotor winding depends on the rate at which its flux linkages change with time. As in the induction machine, the induced voltages in the rotor windings have a frequency of $\omega_s - \nu$ radians per second and are reduced in magnitude by a factor $(\omega_s - \nu)/\omega_s$, (that is, the slip s) as compared with the standstill condition. If the brush gear were also rotated at $\nu_b = \nu$, the terminal conditions would be identical with those of a wound-rotor induction machine, and the brush voltages would have slip frequency $s\omega_s$. If the brush speed ν_b were less than the rotor speed ν, the group of coils having maximum induced voltage would be connected more frequently between a pair of brushes, and the commutator frequency would increase. With stationary brushes, the frequency of the brush voltages would be equal to ω_s.

Thus we note that the magnitude of the commutator voltage depends on the relative velocity $\omega_s - \nu$ between the rotating field and the rotor, whereas the frequency of the commutator voltage depends on the relative velocity $\omega_s - \nu_b$ of the rotating field and the brush gear. In the particular case of stationary brushes $\nu_b = 0$, the commutator voltage always has the same frequency ω_s as does the stator voltage. The commutator therefore provides a means of converting power at rotor frequency $\omega_s - \nu$ to power at the supply frequency ω_s. The same supply may thus be used for both stator and rotor. The phase angle of the voltage on the commutator phase A depends on the brush position β and is β radians behind the corresponding voltage induced by the same flux in phase a of the stator.

From the foregoing discussion, the polyphase commutator machine can be represented by the single-phase equivalent circuit of Fig. 5.79. This circuit is identical with that of a wound-rotor induction machine (Fig. 5.18) except for the addition of an ideal commutator transformation. The frequency ratio of this transformation is from rotor frequency $\omega_s - \nu$ to stator frequency ω_s, that is, $s\omega_s : \omega_s$, where s is the slip (eq. 5.96). The voltage ratio has a magnitude of unity but includes a phase shift β that depends on the brush position relative to stator phase a. The commutator current has the same magnitude as the rotor current but is also shifted in phase by the same angle β. The complex power ratio, being the current ratio multiplied by the conjugate of the voltage ratio, is unity. This is to be expected since the commutator merely rearranges the terminal connections of the rotor winding leaving the power invariant. The impedance ratio is the voltage ratio divided by the current ratio and is also unity. Thus impedances can be shifted unchanged across the ideal commutator transformation.

5.7.2 Terminal Characteristics of Shunt Commutator Machines

Suppose we apply a polyphase voltage E_s of frequency ω_s to the stator terminals and a voltage E_c of the same frequency to the commutator terminals of the machine shown in Fig. 5.78. Since these voltages are obtained from the same supply, they are normally in phase with each other. The torque of the machine can be derived from the air-gap power P_{ms} in Fig. 5.79. To facilitate calculation of the voltage E_{ms} and current I_r' from which this power can be determined, let us transfer the rotor impedance and the commutator voltage to the stator side of the ideal transformations, and also apply Thévenin's theorem to the stator circuit as seen from the terminals of the voltage E_{ms}. By neglecting the stator resistance R_s, the result is the simplified circuit of Fig. 5.80 in which

$$R_r' = R_r\left(\frac{N_s}{N_r'}\right)^2; \quad X_r' = \omega_s L_{Lr}\left(\frac{N_s}{N_r'}\right)^2; \quad E_c' = E_c\frac{N_s}{N_r'}\underline{/\beta} \quad (5.264)$$

and
$$E_e = E_s\frac{X_{ms}}{X_{Ls} + X_{ms}}; \quad X_e = \frac{X_{Ls}X_{ms}}{X_{Ls} + X_{ms}} \quad (5.265)$$

From Fig. 5.80, it can be seen that the current I_r' is zero when $E_e = E_c's$. This condition is fulfilled when the brush angle β is equal to zero and the speed is such as to make the induced voltage in the rotor equal

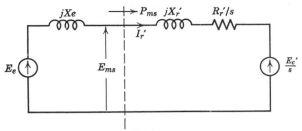

Fig. 5.80   Simplified equivalent of circuit of Fig. 5.79.

to the applied voltage. Since the torque is also zero for this condition, the no-load speed of the commutator machine is, for a two-pole machine,

$$v = (1 - s)\omega_s$$

$$= \left[1 - \frac{X_{Ls} + X_{ms}}{X_{ms}} \frac{N_s}{N_r'} \left| \frac{E_c}{E_s} \right| \right] \omega_s \qquad \text{radians/second} \qquad (5.266)$$

Figure 5.81 shows that the no-load speed is equal to ω_s when E_c equals zero; in this condition, the machine is operating as an unloaded induction motor with shorted rotor. As the commutator voltage E_c is increased, the speed reduces linearly and reverses in direction if E_c is sufficiently large. If the voltage E_c is increased with reversed polarity, the no-load speed increases linearly above the value ω_s.

From Fig. 5.80, the current I_r' is given by

$$I_r' = \frac{E_e - E_c'/s}{(R_r'/s) + j(X_e + X_r')}$$

$$= \frac{E_e}{(R_r'/s) + j(X_e + X_r')} - \frac{E_c'}{R_r' + js(X_e + X_r')} \qquad (5.267)$$

Each of the two terms in eq. 5.267 follows a circular locus as the slip s varies. The total current I_r' also follows a circular locus, the diameter of

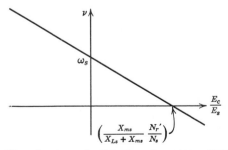

Fig. 5.81   Relation of speed v, on no-load, to the voltage E_c applied to the commutator. (Brush angle $\beta = 0$.)

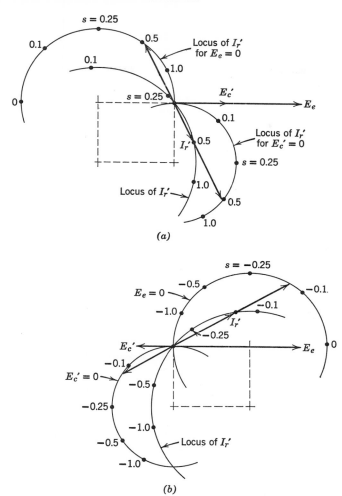

Fig. 5.82 Loci of current I_r' for brush angle $\beta = 0$. (Numerals refer to values of slip.) $R_r' = 0.25(X_e + X_{Lr}')$. (a) No-load speed of $0.7\omega_s$. (b) No-load speed of $1.3\omega_s$.

which is equal to the phasor sum of the phasors representing the diameters of its two components.

Figure 5.82 shows loci of I_r' for two settings of no-load speed, one below and one above the speed ω_s. The magnitude of the component of I_r' that is in phase with the voltage E_e is a measure of the air-gap power and therefore of the torque. In Fig. 5.82a, the voltage E_c' is $0.3E_e$, and zero torque is produced at a slip of 0.3 or a speed of $0.7\omega_s$. As load torque is applied to the machine, the speed reduces, making $s > 0.3$. Note that the current I_r' has an increasingly large lagging phase angle as the torque is increased. The maximum torque for this setting is relatively small.

In Fig. 5.82b, the voltage E_c' has been set at $-0.3E_e$ to give a no-load speed of $1.3\omega_s$, that is, a slip of $s = -0.3$. For this case, the current I_r' is leading for speeds less than $1.3\omega_s$. In addition, the drop in speed to produce a given torque is relatively small. This indicates that this machine operates best in the region above synchronous speed.

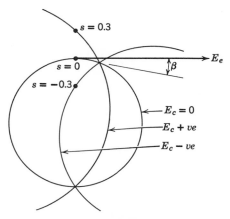

Fig. 5.83   Loci of current I_r' for speed settings above synchronous, at synchronous, and below synchronous for commutator machine.

The power factor and speed regulation for speeds less than ω_s can be improved by shifting the brushes slightly backward so that the voltage E_c' lags E_e by an angle β as shown in Fig. 5.83. This has little effect on the no-load speed values but permits a reasonably good power factor to be maintained at all speeds.

The total stator current can be found by use of superposition in Fig. 5.79. If we neglect R_s,

$$I_s = \frac{E_s}{j(X_{Ls} + X_{ms})} + \frac{X_{ms}}{X_{Ls} + X_{ms}} I_r' \qquad (5.268)$$

where I_r' is given in eq. 5.267. Thus the stator current loci are also circular. Because of the magnetizing current, the loci of I_s are shifted downward with respect to those of I_r' in Fig. 5.83.

Figure 5.84 shows typical torque-speed relations for a polyphase commutator machine at maximum, average, and minimum speed settings. Because of the difficulty of achieving reasonable power factor with large values of commutator voltage, the speed range of this type of machine is

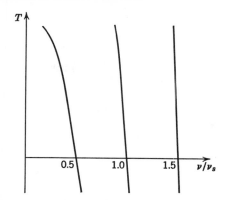

Fig. 5.84 Typical torque-speed relations for commutator motor at maximum, normal, and minimum speed settings.

usually restricted to approximately a $3:1$ range, that is, $0.5\omega_s$ to $1.5\omega_s$ for a two-pole machine.

This motor is usually called a shunt commutator motor because the stator and rotor circuits are in parallel and because of the similarity of its torque-speed characteristics to those of a shunt-connected d-c motor (Section 4.6). The variable voltage applied to the commutator may be obtained as shown in Fig. 5.85 from a polyphase adjustable-ratio transformer (Section 3.4.1) or from an induction regulator. An additional

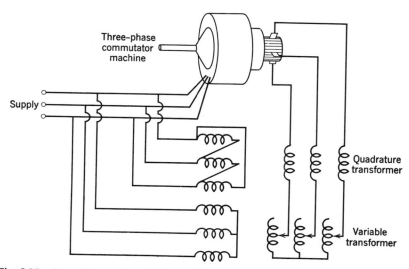

Fig. 5.85 Connections of auxiliary equipment for a shunt commutator machine.

fixed-ratio transformer may be used to provide a small constant component of the voltage E_c leading the stator voltage by $\pi/2$ radians (Section 3.3.1). The effect of this constant-quadrature voltage is to make the power factor less dependent on the speed setting. The leakage reactances of these transformers have a detrimental effect on the machine performances. It can be seen from the equivalent circuit of Fig. 5.79 that a transformer reactance X_t transferred across the ideal commutation transformation and the ideal polyphase machine becomes a reactance $(N_s/N_r')^2 \, X_t/s$ as seen from the stator. At small values of slip s, this reactance becomes relatively large.

5.7.3 Frequency Changers

When power is required at a frequency other than that of the available supply, it may be obtained by use of a commutator frequency changer, as shown in Fig. 5.86a. The rotor of this machine has both a set of slip rings and a commutator. There may be two separate rotor windings, or slip rings and commutator both may be connected to the same winding. In its simplest form, the stator requires no winding and merely provides a low reluctance path for the flux.

If a polyphase set of currents of frequency ω flows into the slip rings,

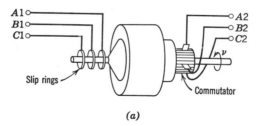

(a)

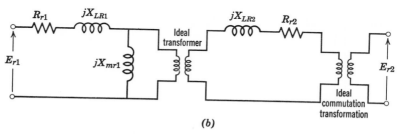

(b)

Fig. 5.86   Connections and equivalent circuit of a rotor-fed frequency changer. In (b),

Voltage $N_{r1}:N_{r2}$	$1:1$
Current $N_{r2}:N_{r1}$	$1:1$
Frequency $\omega_s:\omega_s$	$\omega_s:(\omega_s + \nu)$

the resultant magnetic field rotates at a velocity of ω radians per second (for a two-pole machine) with respect to the rotor. At standstill, the machine operates simply as a transformer or phase shifter. If, however, the rotor is rotated at an angular velocity ν, the frequency of the voltage obtained from the commutator becomes equal to that of the rotating field as seen by the stationary commutator, that is, $\omega + \nu$. The magnitude of the output voltage remains unchanged.

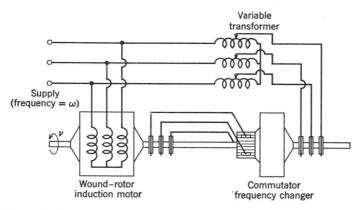

Fig. 5.87 Adjustable speed drive using wound-rotor induction motor and frequency changer (Leblanc system).

The performance of this type of frequency changer can be determined by use of the equivalent circuit of Fig. 5.86b. The two rotor windings act as a transformer with N_{r1} effective turns per phase connected to the slip rings and N_{r2} effective turns per phase connected to the commutator. The frequently changer action is represented by an ideal commutation transformation.

Output frequencies above or below the value ω can be obtained by driving the rotor at positive or negative values of the speed ν. Since the stator is used only as a path for the mutual flux, essentially no power crosses the air gap. The driving motor therefore supplies only the torque required for mechanical losses and for the small eddy-current losses in the stator.

Suppose the frequency changer of Fig. 5.86a is coupled mechanically to a wound-rotor induction motor as shown in Fig. 5.87. The rotor frequency of the induction motor is $\omega - \nu$. By a reversal of the phase sequence of the supply connected to the slip rings of the frequency changer, the commutator output also has a frequency $\omega - \nu$. Thus, the frequency changer may be connected electrically to the induction-motor rotor to supply an injected rotor voltage that is always at the correct slip frequency. This system of machines has characteristics similar to those of the shunt commutator motor discussed in Section 5.7.2. To a first approximation, the power flow through the frequency changer is equal to the power entering the induction machine multiplied by the slip s. Thus, for a small range of speed control about ω, the rating of the frequency changer is relatively small. The magnitude of the commutator voltage may be adjusted by means of a variable-ratio transformer. Its phase may be varied by changing the angle of the brushes.

5.7.4 The Schräge Motor

Suppose the slip rings of the frequency changer of Fig. 5.86a are connected to a supply of frequency ω. If the rotor rotates at a speed ν in a direction opposite to that of the rotating field, the voltages at the commutator have a frequency $\omega - \nu$. Suppose further that the stator of this machine is fitted with a set of distributed polyphase windings. The induced voltages in these windings also have a frequency $\omega - \nu$. If these stator windings were short circuited, the machine would operate as an inside-out induction motor. But if the stator terminals are connected to the commutator, the speed of the machine on no-load adjusts itself to make the slip-frequency voltage induced in the stator equal to the commutator voltage.

To provide for speed adjustment, some means must be included for varying the commutator voltage. A variable-ratio transformer could, of course, be used between the stator and the commutator. In the Schräge motor, the variable voltage is provided by the use of two sets of brushes, as shown in Fig. 5.88a. These two brush sets are mechanically coupled so that as one set rotates forward the other set rotates backward equally. The magnitude of the output voltage between corresponding brushes on the two sets depends on the angle γ between their positions. Its phase is essentially constant but can be altered by rotating all the brushes forward or backward by an angle β.

The appropriate form of the equivalent circuit for a Schräge machine may be derived by examination of its flux paths, as shown in Fig. 5.88b. The slip-ring winding is normally in the bottom of the rotor slots and is assumed to have an independent leakage flux ϕ_1. A mutual leakage flux ϕ_{12} links the slip-ring winding and the commutator winding, which is in the top of the rotor slots. The stator winding has its own leakage flux ϕ_{Ls}. A mutual flux ϕ_m links all the windings. Figure 5.88c shows the corresponding magnetic equivalent circuit. The electric equivalent circuit of Fig. 5.88d is dual in form to that of Fig. 5.88c. The induction action between rotor and stator is represented by an ideal induction machine.

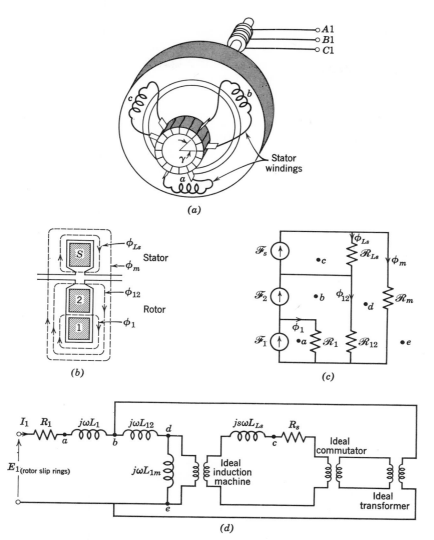

Fig. 5.88 (a) Connections for a Schräge motor. (b) Magnetic flux paths. (c) Magnetic equivalent circuit. (d) Electric equivalent circuit. In (d),

Voltage $N_1:sN_s$		$1:1\underline{/-\beta}$ $N_2:N_1$
Current $N_s:N_1$		$1:1\underline{/-\beta}$ $N_1:N_2$
Frequency $\omega:s\omega$	$s\omega:\omega$	$\omega:\omega$

The frequency-changer action of the commutator is represented by an ideal commutation transformation with a phase shift β, which depends on the mean position of the two brush sets. An ideal transformer is also included to represent the turns ratio between the slip-ring winding of N_1 turns per phase and the N_2 turns per phase of the sections of the commutator winding between the two brush sets spaced γ radians apart.

A comparison of the equivalent circuit of the Schräge motor (Fig. 5.88c) with that of the shunt commutator motor (Fig. 5.79) shows that the two are essentially identical in form, except for the coupling of the slip-ring and commutator currents in the small impedance $R_1 + j\omega L_1$. As would therefore be expected, the performance of the Schräge machine is similar to that of the shunt commutator machine. The relation between the speed ν and the angle γ between the brush sets is of the same form as that shown in Fig. 5.81. Its current loci are circles of the same characteristics as those of the shunt machine, and its torque-speed relations are similar to those of Fig. 5.84. The speed regulation of the Schräge motor is somewhat better than that of the shunt commutator motor because the detrimental effects of the reactance in the external variable-ratio transformer are absent. The speed range at no-load is seldom made greater than 3:1 for the same reasons of power-factor control discussed in Section 5.7.2.

5.8   UNBALANCED OPERATION OF POLYPHASE MACHINES

Throughout this chapter it has been assumed that all the induction, synchronous, reluctance, and commutator machines have operated with balanced polyphase supplies or loads. Although this form of operation represents the normal operating condition of a majority of industrial machines, there are a large number of situations in which machines operate, either temporarily or permanently, in an unbalanced condition. For example, three-phase synchronous generators are in unbalanced operation when one or two phases of the supply connections are opened, when a fault occurs on one or two phases of the connected system, or when the loads are not equally shared among the three phases. Some synchronous generators are designed for single-phase operation only. A polyphase motor can operate in an unbalanced condition when the supply is temporarily lost on one or two of its phases. An ability to predict its torque capability and its currents during this unbalanced condition is important. Then there is the large and important class of induction motors that must operate from the single-phase supply normally provided for domestic and commercial consumers. For purposes of understanding and analysis, these are best considered as polyphase machines operating under unbalanced conditions.

The analysis of unbalanced polyphase systems is facilitated by the use of symmetrical components, an analytical technique derived from the principle of superposition. Suppose, for example, that the unbalanced set of phase voltages E_a, E_b, and E_c shown in Fig. 5.89a are applied to a three-phase star-connected machine. If the behavior of the machine with unbalanced voltages could be represented by a simple network of impedances, analysis

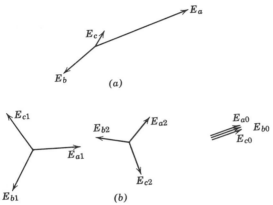

Fig. 5.89 (a) A set of unbalanced three-phase voltages. (b) Positive-, negative-, and zero-sequence components of E_a, E_b, and E_c.

would be relatively simple. But all of the equivalent-circuit models we have developed for polyphase machines are applicable only with balanced voltages and currents. To permit the use of these models, we therefore represent the unbalanced set of voltages as the superposition of three sets, each of three voltages, as shown in Fig. 5.89b. The first of these is a balanced set E_{a1}, E_{b1}, and E_{c1} with a phase sequence $a\,b\,c\,a$, which is denoted as a positive sequence. The second is a balanced set E_{a2}, E_{b2}, and E_{c2} with a negative phase sequence $a\,c\,b\,a$. The third set E_{a0}, E_{b0}, and E_{c0} consists of equal voltages in the three phases and is denoted as the zero-sequence set. The voltage E_a is given by

$$E_a = E_{a1} + E_{a2} + E_{a0} \tag{5.269}$$

It is convenient to state the other voltages in terms of the same quantities E_{a1}, E_{a2}, and E_{a0} so that the number of variables in the analysis will be a minimum. Thus

$$\begin{aligned} E_b &= E_{b1} + E_{b2} + E_{b0} \\ &= \alpha^2 E_{a1} + \alpha E_{a2} + E_{a0} \end{aligned} \tag{5.270}$$

and

$$E_c = \alpha E_{a1} + \alpha^2 E_{a2} + E_{a0} \tag{5.271}$$

where α is a convenient phasor operator defined as

$$\alpha = 1 \; \underline{/2\pi/3} = 1 \; \underline{/120°} \qquad (5.272)$$

If it is understood that all quantities are to be expressed in terms of the components of phase a, the subscript a may be dropped and eqs. 5.269 to 5.271 may be expressed in the matrix form

$$\begin{bmatrix} E_a \\ E_b \\ E_c \end{bmatrix} = \begin{bmatrix} 1 & 1 & 1 \\ \alpha^2 & \alpha & 1 \\ \alpha & \alpha^2 & 1 \end{bmatrix} \cdot \begin{bmatrix} E_1 \\ E_2 \\ E_0 \end{bmatrix} \qquad (5.273)$$

Solution of the three simultaneous equations in eq. 5.273 gives the symmetrical component voltages E_1, E_2, and E_0 as functions of the unbalanced voltages E_a, E_b, and E_c.

$$\begin{bmatrix} E_1 \\ E_2 \\ E_0 \end{bmatrix} = \frac{1}{3} \begin{bmatrix} 1 & \alpha & \alpha^2 \\ 1 & \alpha^2 & \alpha \\ 1 & 1 & 1 \end{bmatrix} \cdot \begin{bmatrix} E_a \\ E_b \\ E_c \end{bmatrix} \qquad (5.274)$$

Our problem now is to determine the response of the machine to each of the three sets of symmetrical component voltages in turn. We have already developed a group of single-phase equivalent circuits that are directly applicable for the positive-sequence balanced set of voltages. If the voltage E_1 is applied to the appropriate equivalent circuit, the positive-sequence current I_1 can be found. These circuits may also be used— sometimes in a modified form—to determine the negative-sequence current I_2 that flows when the negative-sequence voltage E_2 is applied. In Section 5.8.1 single-phase equivalent circuits are developed to represent the machine with negative-sequence voltages and with zero-sequence voltages. By use of these circuits, the negative-sequence current I_2 and the zero-sequence current I_0 may be determined.

The final step in the analysis is to sum the symmetrical components to determine the phase currents I_a, I_b, and I_c. By analogy with eq. 5.273

$$\begin{bmatrix} I_a \\ I_b \\ I_c \end{bmatrix} = \begin{bmatrix} 1 & 1 & 1 \\ \alpha^2 & \alpha & 1 \\ \alpha & \alpha^2 & 1 \end{bmatrix} \cdot \begin{bmatrix} I_1 \\ I_2 \\ I_0 \end{bmatrix} \qquad (5.275)$$

In this section, we also have occasion to deal with so-called two-phase machines. These are, in effect, four-phase machines with an angular spacing of $2\pi/4 = \pi/2$ radians between their distributed windings. But two-phase windings displaced π radians from each other are coincident

in space and may thus be considered as
a single winding. Figure 5.90a shows a
pair of unbalanced voltages E_d and E_q
which might be applied to the direct- and
quadrature-axis windings of a two-phase
machine. These may be resolved into two
sets of balanced voltages, a positive-
sequence set E_1 and $-jE_1$ and a negative-
sequence set E_2 and jE_2, as shown in Fig.
5.90b, where

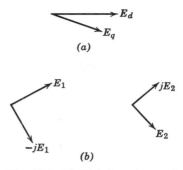

(a)

(b)

Fig. 5.90 (a) Unbalanced set of
two-phase voltages. (b) Positive-
and negative-sequence components
of E_d and E_q.

$$\begin{bmatrix} E_1 \\ E_2 \end{bmatrix} = \frac{1}{2}\begin{bmatrix} 1 & j \\ 1 & -j \end{bmatrix} \cdot \begin{bmatrix} E_d \\ E_q \end{bmatrix} \quad (5.276)$$

The response of the machine to each of
these balanced sets of voltages may be
found by using the appropriate equivalent circuit. The resultant positive-
and negative-sequence currents I_1 and I_2 may then be combined to give
the phase currents I_d and I_q.

$$\begin{bmatrix} I_d \\ I_q \end{bmatrix} = \begin{bmatrix} 1 & 1 \\ -j & j \end{bmatrix} \cdot \begin{bmatrix} I_1 \\ I_2 \end{bmatrix} \quad (5.277)$$

As the method of symmetrical components is based on the principle
of superposition, it is applicable only to linear systems. In machines, the
major source of nonlinearity is in the magnetizing branch. It is therefore
necessary to linearize this parameter by choosing an appropriate average
value.

5.8.1 Sequence Equivalent Circuits

In this section we consider the response of various types of polyphase
machines when positive-, negative-, and zero-sequence voltages or currents
are applied to their terminals. With positive-sequence voltages and
currents, we may use the single-phase equivalent circuits of Fig. 5.20 for
induction machines; Figs. 5.33, 5.50, and 5.53 for synchronous machines—
in the steady, transient, and subtransient states respectively; Fig. 5.67
for reluctance machines, Figs. 5.72 and 5.75 for salient-pole synchronous
machines—in the steady and transient states; and Fig. 5.79 for commutator
machines. These equivalent circuits are applicable for either two or
three-phase machines.

The behavior of most polyphase machines with negative-sequence
voltages and currents may be derived from the equivalent circuit of a
general polyphase machine, shown in Fig. 5.18. A negative-sequence set
of balanced currents of frequency ω_s in the stator winding produces a

sinusoidally distributed air-gap field which rotates in a direction opposite to that produced by positive-sequence currents. Suppose the rotor is rotating in the positive or forward direction at an angular velocity of v radians per second. For a p-pole machine, the frequency of the voltages induced in the rotor windings is $\omega_s + v'$, where $v' = (p/2)v$. Thus the equivalent circuit of Fig. 5.18 is applicable for negative-sequence quantities

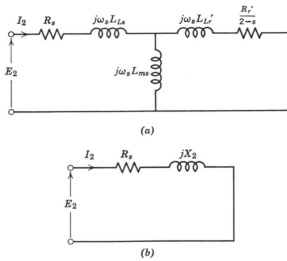

(a)

(b)

Fig. 5.91   Negative-sequence equivalent circuits for (a) a general polyphase machine. (b) Synchronous machine (neglecting rotor resistances).

if $\omega_s - v'$ is replaced by $\omega + v'$. In induction machine terminology, it is convenient to define the slip s for positive-sequence operation as

$$s = \frac{\omega_s - v'}{\omega_s} \tag{5.278}$$

For negative-sequence operation, the corresponding quantity is

$$\frac{\omega_s + v'}{\omega_s} = 2 - s \tag{5.279}$$

When the machine is rotating at synchronous speed in the forward direction, its rotor has a slip of zero, with respect to the field produced by positive-sequence currents, and a slip of 2 per unit with respect to the field produced by negative-sequence currents.

Figure 5.91a shows an equivalent circuit for negative-sequence operation of an induction machine with shorted rotor. This equivalent circuit is also-applicable for the negative-sequence behavior of a machine that has a positive-sequence voltage applied to its rotor terminals as occurs, for example, in commutator machines. By superposition, the positive-sequence rotor voltage produces only positive-sequence currents and is thus equivalent to a short circuit as seen by a negative-sequence set of currents. The circuit of Fig. 5.91a also applies for a synchronous machine with a polyphase rotor winding connected as shown in Fig. 5.31a. A constant direct-voltage source attached to the field terminals acts as a zero impedance to the currents of frequency $2\omega_s$ produced in its rotor by a negative-sequence set of stator voltages. The effective rotor resistance $R_r'/2$ may sometimes be neglected in the representation of a synchronous machine. The negative-sequence performance is then represented approximately by the simplified circuit of Fig. 5.91b, where

$$X_2 = X_{Ls} + \frac{X_{ms} X_{mr}'}{X_{ms} + X_{mr}'} \qquad \text{ohms} \qquad (5.280)$$

When the rotor has only a single field winding as in Figs. 5.29 or 5.71, the negative-sequence rotating field encounters the reluctances of the direct or field axis and the quadrature axis of the rotor, in turn. The alternation between these two reluctances occurs rapidly at ω_s/π times per second. Because of its relatively long time constant, the flux linkage of the field winding may be considered as essentially constant during this rapid alternation. Figure 5.50 shows the positive-sequence equivalent circuit with constant field linkage. With negative-sequence operation, the voltage E_f' would be zero. Thus, when the negative-sequence field acts along the direct axis, the impedance as seen from the stator terminals is approximately $R_s + jX'$, where X' is the transient reactance. When the negative-sequence field acts along the quadrature axis of the rotor that has no winding, the impedance as seen from the stator is $R_s + jX_q$, where X_q is the quadrature-axis synchronous reactance of the machine. The negative-sequence reactance X_2 of the machine is therefore an average of the values X' and X_q. In large salient-pole synchronous generators, its value is about 0.4 to 0.6 per unit. If, however, the rotor is fitted with damper windings or is of unlaminated construction, the negative-sequence reactance is an average of the subtransient reactances X_d'' and X_q'' in the direct and quadrature axis. Its value may then be from 0.1 to 0.3 per unit.

Let us now consider the impedance encountered by zero-sequence currents entering the stator of a polyphase machine. These are equal currents in all the three phases. As shown in Fig. 5.92a, these current components can flow only if the winding is connected in star, with its neutral point connected through some path to the supply neutral. If this neutral path does not exist (as with a delta-connected machine or supply), the zero-sequence currents are zero.

From eq. 5.12, the magnetomotive force produced around a path at angle θ in a three-phase machine with sinusoidally distributed windings is

$$\mathscr{F}_\theta = N_s i_a \sin \theta + N_s i_b \sin \left(\theta - \frac{2\pi}{3}\right) + N_s i_c \sin \left(\theta - \frac{4\pi}{3}\right) \quad (5.281)$$

With zero-sequence currents $i_a = i_b = i_c$, and the magnetomotive force is zero. No mutual flux is produced linking the stator and rotor windings.

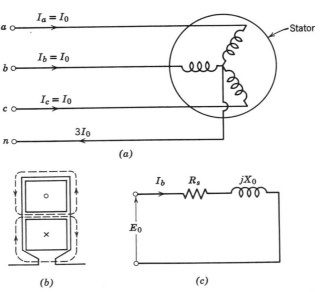

(a)

(b)   (c)

Fig. 5.92 (a) Connection that permits zero-sequence currents to flow. (b) Leakage pattern around slot of short-pitched winding. (c) Zero-sequence equivalent circuit.

The flux linkages of the stator windings result only from leakage around the stator slots and end connections.

The stator leakage reactance X_{Ls}, which has been used in the positive- and negative-sequence equivalent circuits, is a function of the self-leakage inductance L_L of a phase and the mutual leakage inductance L_m between two phases. For positive-sequence currents in the stator

$$jX_{Ls}I_s = j\omega_s L_L I_a + j\omega_s L_m I_b + j\omega_s L_m I_c$$
$$= j\omega_s[L_L + \alpha^2 L_m + \alpha L_m]I_a$$
$$= j\omega_s(L_L - L_m)I_s \quad (5.282)$$

For zero-sequence currents in the stator with $I_a = I_b = I_c = I_0$, the zero-sequence leakage reactance X_0 is given by

$$X_0 = \omega_s(L_L + 2L_m) \quad \text{ohms} \quad (5.283)$$

Consider a three-phase stator winding in which the stator coils span only two-thirds of a full pitch. Half of the coil sides of phase a share their slots with coil sides of phase b; the other half share their slots with phase c. When equal currents flow in the phase windings, each slot has equal and opposite currents in its upper and lower coil sides, as shown in Fig. 5.92b. The net leakage flux is therefore very small. The mutual leakage inductance L_m approaches the value

$$L_m \approx -0.5L_L \qquad \text{henrys} \tag{5.284}$$

and the zero-sequence reactance is very small.

For a full-pitched winding, the conductors of one phase do not share the same slots as those of another phase. Mutual leakage inductance in such a winding arises only from linkages in the end connections and zigzag paths (Fig. 5.14). The zero-sequence reactance X_0 is then only slightly less than the positive-sequence stator leakage reactance X_{Ls}. In large synchronous generators, the value of X_0 may vary between 0.01 and 0.25 per unit.

5.8.2   Synchronous Generator with Unbalanced Load

As a simple example of the use of symmetrical components, let us consider the case of a single-phase load on a synchronous generator. Figure 5.93a shows a load of impedance Z_L connected between phase a and the neutral of a star-connected generator. Figure 5.93b shows positive-, negative-, and zero-sequence equivalent circuits for the generator. The terminal variables of these equivalent circuits are the components E_1, E_2, and E_0 of the phase voltage E_a, and the components I_1, I_2, and I_p of the phase current I_a.

The unbalanced load on the generator is described by the three relations

$$E_a = Z_L I_a \tag{5.285}$$

$$I_b = 0 \tag{5.286}$$

$$I_c = 0 \tag{5.287}$$

These relations may be expressed in terms of the component voltages and currents by use of eqs. 5.273 and 5.275.

$$E_1 + E_2 + E_0 = Z_L(I_1 + I_2 + I_0) \tag{5.288}$$

$$\alpha^2 I_1 + \alpha I_2 + I_0 = 0 \tag{5.289}$$

$$\alpha I_1 + \alpha^2 I_2 + I_0 = 0 \tag{5.290}$$

Subtracting eq. 5.290 from 5.289 gives

$$(\alpha^2 - \alpha)I_1 + (\alpha - \alpha^2)I_2 = 0 \tag{5.291}$$

from which

$$I_1 = I_2 \tag{5.292}$$

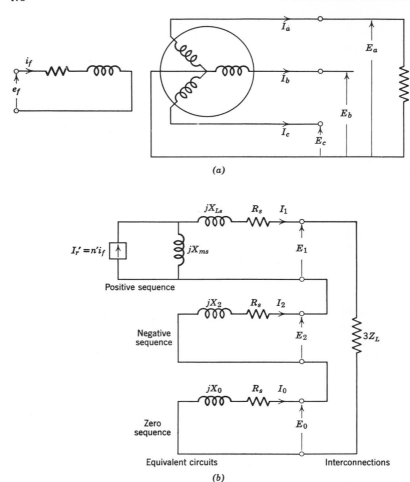

Fig. 5.93 (a) Single-phase load on synchronous generator. (b) Equivalent circuit representation.

Substituting from eq. 5.292 into 5.289 gives

$$(\alpha^2 + \alpha)I_1 + I_0 = 0 \qquad (5.293)$$

from which

$$I_1 = I_0 \qquad (5.294)$$

Since the three components of the current are equal for this type of load, the constraint of eq. 5.288 may be fulfilled by connecting the three sequence networks of Fig. 5.93b in series through an impedance $3Z_L$.

The current components are then given by

$$I_1 = I_2 = I_0 = \frac{jX_{ms}I_r'}{3R_s + j(X_{ms} + X_{Ls} + X_2 + X_0) + 3Z_L} \quad (5.295)$$

The current in phase a is

$$I_a = I_1 + I_2 + I_0$$

$$= \frac{jX_{ms}I_r'}{R_s + j\frac{1}{3}(X_{ms} + X_{Ls} + X_2 + X_0) + Z_L} \quad (5.296)$$

It is noted that the internal reactance of the machine for single-phase loading is somewhat greater than one-third of the synchronous reactance $X_{Ls} + X_{ms}$ per phase that applies for balanced three-phase loading.

Substitution of $I_1 = I_2 = I_0$ into eq. 5.275 shows that the currents in phases b and c are zero. The three phase voltages may be found by determining E_1, E_2, and E_0 from Fig. 5.93b and by substituting these into eq. 5.273.

The performance with other types of unbalanced loads may be analyzed by the same process. It is found that the symmetrical component equations for the load can be represented by a simple interconnection of the sequence networks only when the load is symmetrical with respect to the reference phase a. Thus in analyzing a load Z_L connected between two phases, the unloaded phase would be designated as phase a. The load could then be represented by three constraints

$$I_a = 0 \quad (5.297)$$

$$I_b = -I_c \quad (5.298)$$

and

$$E_b - E_c = Z_L I_b \quad (5.299)$$

Conversion of these three constraints into symmetrical component form shows that this type of load may be represented by the conditions

$$I_1 = -I_2 \quad (5.300)$$

$$I_0 = 0 \quad (5.301)$$

$$E_1 - E_2 = Z_L I_1 \quad (5.302)$$

These constraints may be represented by connecting the positive- and negative-sequence equivalent circuits in parallel through an impedance Z_L.

In the design of a synchronous generator and the specification of its associated circuit breakers, it is important to know the maximum value of short-circuit current that can occur. For such analyses, the subtransient equivalent circuit Fig. 5.53 replaces the steady-state positive-sequence circuit in Fig. 5.93b. By analogy with eq. 5.296, a phase-to-neutral short circuit $Z_L = 0$ results in a phase current of

$$I_a = \frac{E''}{R_s + j\frac{1}{3}(X'' + X_2 + X_0)} \quad \text{amperes} \quad (5.303)$$

For comparison, a three-phase short circuit would result in

$$I_a = \frac{E''}{R_s + jX''} \quad \text{amperes} \quad (5.304)$$

Since the zero-sequence reactance X_0 is usually considerably less than either of the roughly equal reactances X'' and X_2, the phase current with a single-phase short circuit generally exceeds that with a three-phase short circuit.

5.8.3 Polyphase Induction Machine with Unbalanced Supply

Figure 5.94a shows a three-phase star-connected induction machine connected to a balanced star-connected supply. Let us consider the performance of this machine when one of its phase connections is opened. In this system the only unbalance occurs in the linking connections between the source and the machine. Let us therefore examine first the relations governing the voltages and currents of this linking branch only. These are

$$I_a = 0 \quad (5.305)$$
$$E_{bb'} = 0 \quad (5.306)$$
and
$$E_{cc'} = 0 \quad (5.307)$$

If E_1, E_2, and E_0 are the components of the voltages $E_{aa'}$, $E_{bb'}$, and $E_{cc'}$ and I_1, I_2, and I_0 are the components of the currents I_a, I_b, and I_c, these three relations can be restated as

$$I_1 + I_2 + I_0 = 0 \quad (5.308)$$
$$\alpha^2 E_1 + \alpha E_2 + E_0 = 0 \quad (5.309)$$
$$\alpha E_1 + \alpha^2 E_2 + E_0 = 0 \quad (5.310)$$

Addition and subtraction of eqs. 5.309 and 5.310 gives

$$E_1 = E_2 = E_0 \quad (5.311)$$

Figure 5.94b shows the positive-, negative-, and zero-sequence equivalent circuits of the machine and the source. For simplicity, it has been assumed that the source produces a constant positive-sequence voltage, and presents zero impedance to the flow of negative- or zero-sequence currents. A more elaborate representation of the source system, including its internal impedances to positive-, negative-, and zero-sequence currents, could have been used if required. The variables E_1, I_1, E_2, I_2, E_0, and I_0 of the branches between the source and the machine representations in these three circuits are related by eqs. 5.308 and 5.311. These relations can be represented by interconnections of the three equivalent circuits, as shown in Fig. 5.94b.

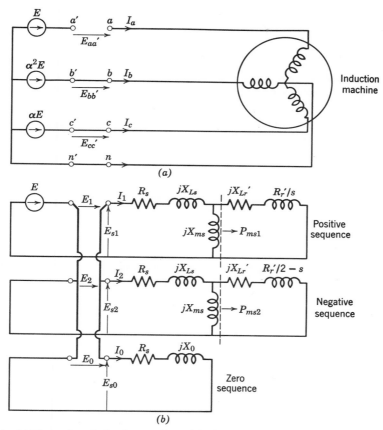

Fig. 5.94   (a) Three-phase induction machine with one phase open. (b) Interconnection of sequence equivalent circuits to represent condition of (a).

In Section 5.8.1 it was shown that the zero-sequence reactance X_0 of a machine is generally small. Examination of Fig. 5.94b shows that the zero sequence impedance $Z_0 = E_{s0}/I_0$ is connected in parallel with the negative-sequence impedance $Z_2 = E_{s2}/I_2$. If the zero-sequence impedance can be regarded as negligible, the sequence voltages E_1, E_2, and E_0 are also negligible. The positive-sequence component I_1 of the phase currents into the machine is then the same as for normal operation on a balanced supply. The power P_{ms1} per phase crossing the air gap in the positive-sequence circuit varies with the slip s and produces a proportional torque in the positive direction of rotation. Since it has been assumed that $E_2 = E_{s2} = 0$, the power P_{ms2} crossing the air gap in the negative-sequence circuit is zero. Thus no torque is produced in the opposite direction. The torque-speed relation of the machine connected as in Fig. 5.94a is then essentially the same as for normal balanced operation. The effect of a small value of zero-sequence reactance X_0 is essentially equivalent to a small increase in the stator leakage reactance, and the maximum torque (eq. 5.108) is only slightly reduced.

The main effect of opening a phase on a machine with a four-wire connection is to make the current in that phase equal to zero and to increase the currents in the other two phases. Again assuming the zero sequence impedance to be negligible, the current components in Fig. 5.94b, are related by

$$I_0 = -I_1 \tag{5.312}$$

and

$$I_2 = 0 \tag{5.313}$$

Then

$$I_a = I_1 + I_2 + I_0 = 0 \tag{5.314}$$

$$I_b = \alpha^2 I_1 + \alpha I_2 + I_0 = \sqrt{3}I_1 \,\underline{/-150°} \tag{5.315}$$

$$I_c = \alpha^2 I_1 + \alpha I_2 + I_0 = \sqrt{3}I_1 \,\underline{/150°} \tag{5.316}$$

Let us now consider the effect of opening the neutral connection $n'n$ in Fig. 5.94a. This would represent a more usual condition of operation because three-phase induction motors do not as a rule have neutral connections brought out. From Fig. 5.94a, the constraint imposed by opening the neutral connection is

$$I_a + I_b + I_c = 0 \tag{5.317}$$

Expressed in symmetrical component form, this becomes $I_0 = 0$. Equal current components cannot flow in the phases since no return path is provided. This constraint may be introduced into the circuit of Fig. 5.94b by open circuiting the zero-sequence network of the machine. The resultant circuit is redrawn in Fig. 5.95a.

When a three-phase machine is provided with only a two-wire single-phase supply, as shown in the connection of Fig. 5.95a, the currents in its stator windings do not produce a rotating magnetic field. When the windings in phases b and c carry the same current, they may be regarded as a single winding. The magnetomotive force produced by the stator current may still be sinusoidally distributed in space about the winding axis, but its magnitude merely pulsates as the current varies sinusoidally. The method of symmetrical components shows that this stationary

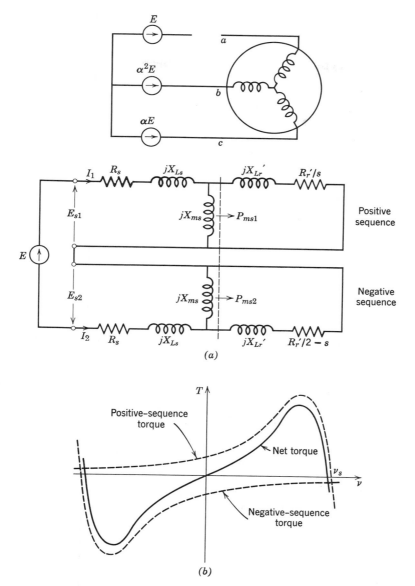

Fig. 5.95 (a) Three-phase machine operating on a single-phase supply. (b) Typical torque-speed relation.

pulsating magnetomotive force may be considered as the sum of two equal sinusoidally distributed rotating magnetomotive forces. The first is due to the positive-sequence component I_1 of the stator phase currents and rotates in a positive direction at angular velocity ω_s. The second is due to the negative-sequence component I_2 of the stator phase currents, and rotates in a negative direction at the same velocity.

At standstill, the slip s is equal to unity, and the positive- and negative-sequence equivalent circuits of Fig. 5.95a are identical. Thus $E_{s1} = -E_{s2} = E/2$ and $P_{ms1} = P_{ms2}$. The average torque T produced by the machine is equal to the difference of the torques produced in the positive direction by the positive-sequence air-gap power P_{ms1} and in the negative direction by the negative-sequence air-gap power P_{ms2}. For a three-phase machine with synchronous speed ν_s,

$$T = \frac{3}{\nu_s}(P_{ms1} - P_{ms2}) \qquad \text{newton-meters} \qquad (5.318)$$

At standstill, the torque is zero. The machine operates simply as a short-circuited single-phase transformer.

Suppose now that the machine is rotated in the positive direction, making $s < 1.0$. Because of the increase in the value of R_r'/s, the impedance $Z_1 = E_{s1}/I_1$ of the positive-sequence circuit in Fig. 5.95a increases. The impedance $Z_2 = E_{s2}/I_2$ of the negative-sequence circuit is somewhat reduced. A positive torque T results, since P_{ms1} exceeds P_{ms2}. As the slip s approaches zero, Z_1 becomes much larger than Z_2, and most of the voltage E appears across the positive-sequence portion of the circuit. As a first approximation, the performance of the machine near synchronous speed may therefore be considered similar to that of the machine on a balanced polyphase supply.

The torque at any value of slip s may be calculated by solving the circuit of Fig. 5.95a to determine the two values of air-gap power P_{ms1} and P_{ms2} and inserting these in eq. 5.318. Figure 5.95b shows a typical torque-speed relation for a squirrel-cage induction motor on a single-phase supply. Note that although the machine has no torque at standstill, it tends to accelerate to synchronous speed in either direction of rotation if it is given a small initial velocity. Note, in addition, that the zero-torque running condition is at slightly below synchronous speed because of the small opposite-sequence torque.

The maximum torque of an induction motor operating on single phase is less than for three-phase operation and occurs at a lower value of speed. It is to some extent dependent on the rotor resistance since the higher the rotor resistance, the larger the negative-sequence torque in the region of maximum torque. This is in contrast with the balanced condition where the maximum torque is independent of the rotor resistance (Section 5.4.1).

The actual torque of the machine consists of the average torque of Fig. 5.95b plus a torque that oscillates at double the stator frequency. This oscillating torque makes unbalanced operation somewhat more noisy than balanced operation.

5.8.4 Single-Phase Induction Motors

Suppose a source voltage E is applied to the direct-axis stator winding of a two-phase induction motor, the quadrature-axis winding being left

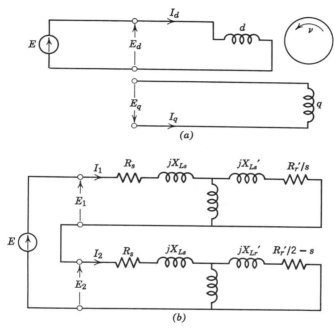

(a)

(b)

Fig. 5.96 (a) Two-phase induction motor with single-phase supply on direct-axis phase. (b) Connection of positive- and negative-sequence equivalent circuits to represent (a).

open circuited as shown in Fig. 5.96a. The constraints applied to the phase voltages and currents are

$$E_d = E \qquad (5.319)$$

and

$$I_q = 0 \qquad (5.320)$$

From eqs. 5.276 and 5.277, these constraints can be expressed in terms of the symmetrical components E_1 and E_2 of the phase voltages, I_1 and I_2, of the phase currents.

$$E_1 + E_2 = E \qquad (5.321)$$

$$-jI_1 + jI_2 = 0 \quad \text{or} \quad I_1 = I_2 \qquad (5.322)$$

In Fig. 5.96*b* the machine is represented by its positive- and negative-sequence equivalent circuits. The constraints of eq. 5.321 and 5.322 on the component variables can be fulfilled by connecting the two circuits in series to a source voltage *E*. The properties of this machine are similar to those of a three-phase machine on a two-wire single-phase supply. The torque-speed relation is of the same form as that shown in Fig. 5.95*b*.

If this motor is to operate satisfactorily from a single-phase supply, some means must be found to produce a starting torque. With only one winding excited, the magnetic field in the machine at standstill merely

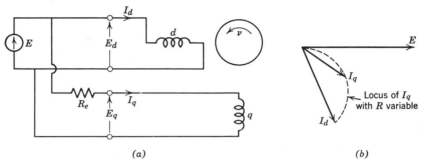

(a) (b)

Fig. 5.97   (*a*) Starting connection for two-phase motor using series resistance. (*b*) Winding currents at standstill.

pulsates. To produce starting torque, a rotating field is required. This can be achieved if the current I_q entering the quadrature-axis winding has a component that is in phase quadrature with the current I_d of the direct-axis winding. One method of accomplishing this is to connect the quadrature-axis winding to the supply through a series resistance R_e, as shown in Fig. 5.97*a*. Suppose that at standstill, the impedance looking into either of the phase windings is $R + jX$. Since X is normally greater than R, the current I_d lags the supply voltage E, as shown in Fig. 5.97*b*. Depending on the value of the series resistance R_e, the quadrature-axis winding current phasor I_q terminates at some point on the circular locus of diameter E/X. The maximum component of I_q in quadrature with I_d occurs at a point when a line parallel to the phasor I_d is tangent to this locus.

This method of starting is employed in the *split-phase induction motor*. Instead of adding a series resistance, the quadrature winding is made of smaller conductors to produce a higher winding resistance. The number of turns N_q on the quadrature winding is generally reduced to about 0.4 to 0.6 of the number N_d on the direct winding. This increases the current I_q and the magnetomotive force produced by the quadrature-winding current. Generally, concentric windings of the type shown in Fig. 5.10a are used. Because of its relatively small conductors, the quadrature winding heats up rapidly and is energized only during starting. A centrifugal switch disconnects the winding when the speed reaches about 75 to 80% of its synchronous value. Alternatively, a relay may disconnect the winding either after a fixed time or when the current drawn by the machine drops to the value associated with about 80% of synchronous speed.

An alternative method of starting makes use of a capacitor connected in series with the quadrature winding, as shown in Fig. 5.98a. If the

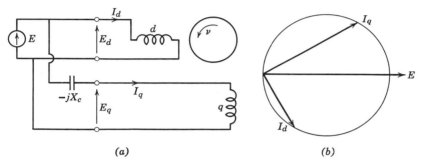

(a)   (b)

Fig. 5.98 (a) Starting connection for two-phase motor using series capacitor. (b) Winding currents at standstill.

impedance looking into either of the identical windings at standstill is $R + jX$, the quadrature-winding current phasor I_q terminates at some point on the circular locus of diameter E/R, shown in Fig. 5.98b. The condition shown applies for the value of capacitive reactance, which causes a phase angle of 90° between the phase currents at standstill. When used with two-phase machines with identical windings, the starting current in the quadrature phase is larger than necessary. In the capacitor-start induction motor, the resistance of the quadrature winding is increased by the use of smaller conductors. In addition, a larger number of turns is used in the quadrature winding to reduce its starting current. By appropriate adjustment of the resistance and the turns ratio an essentially ideal revolving field may be produced at standstill.

Since a fairly large value of capacitance is required, dry electrolytic capacitors are used for starting. These have considerable internal losses on a-c operation and heat up rapidly. A centrifugal switch may be used to disconnect the capacitor at about 75 to 80% of synchronous speed. The efficiency, power factor, and maximum torque of the machine are all improved if a smaller capacitance is used to connect the quadrature winding to the supply during the running condition. An impregnated-paper capacitor is normally used for this continuous duty.

To determine the terminal properties of split-phase and capacitor-start induction motors during the starting period, let us consider the connection of Fig. 5.99a, in which an impedance Z_e is connected between the quadrature winding and the supply. Since the number of turns N_q in the quadrature winding is normally different from the number N_d in the direct winding, the motor itself is unbalanced. Other sources of unbalance in the motor are the differences between the stator winding resistances R_d and R_q and between the stator leakage reactance X_{Ld} and X_{Lq}. Let us therefore conceptually replace the unbalanced motor by one having identical direct and quadrature windings as shown in Fig. 5.99b. The difference in actual winding turns may be represented by an ideal trans-former of ratio $n = N_q/N_d$. The difference in the winding impedances can be represented by a series impedance. For convenience in manipulation, the external impedance Z_e is also transferred across the ideal transformer of ratio n and combined with this series impedance to give

$$Z = \frac{Z_e}{n^2} + \frac{1}{n^2}(R_q + jX_q) - (R_d + jX_{Ld}) \qquad \text{ohms} \qquad (5.323)$$

The variables at the quadrature terminals of the equivalent balanced machine have been designated as E_q' and I_q'.

The symmetrical components of the phase voltages E_d and E_q' are

$$\begin{bmatrix} E_1 \\ E_2 \end{bmatrix} = \frac{1}{2}\begin{bmatrix} 1 & j \\ 1 & -j \end{bmatrix} \cdot \begin{bmatrix} E_d \\ E_q' \end{bmatrix}$$

$$= \frac{1}{2}\begin{bmatrix} 1 & j \\ 1 & -j \end{bmatrix}\begin{bmatrix} E \\ (-E/n - ZI_q') \end{bmatrix} \qquad (5.324)$$

If we insert

$$I_q' = -jI_1 + jI_2 \qquad (5.325)$$

This gives

$$E_1 = \frac{E}{2}\left(1 - \frac{j}{n}\right) - \frac{Z}{2}(I_1 - I_2)$$

and

$$E_2 = \frac{E}{2}\left(1 + \frac{j}{n}\right) + \frac{Z}{2}(I_1 - I_2) \qquad (5.326)$$

Equation 5.326 may be represented by the interconnection of the positive- and negative-sequence equivalent circuits shown in Fig. 5.99c. This circuit may be analyzed by determining the impedances $Z_1 = E_1/I_1$ and $Z_2 = E_2/I_2$ for a number of values of the slip s, and then by solving the resultant two-mesh network. The sequence currents I_1 and I_2 can be

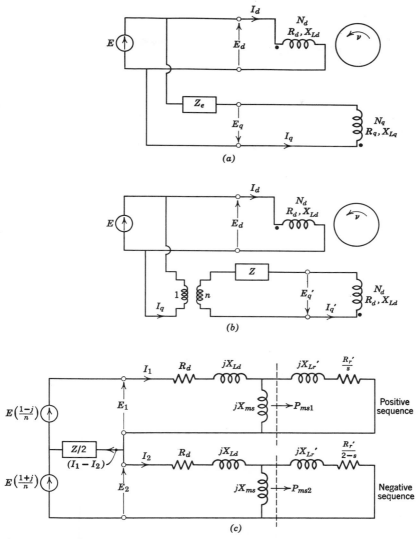

Fig. 5.99 (*a*) Single-phase motor with impedance Z_e in series with quadrature windings. (*b*) Equivalent balanced two-phase motor representation. (*c*) Connection of sequence equivalent circuits.

combined to obtain the direct winding current I_d and the quadrature-winding current $I_q = nI_q'$.

The torque of the machine at any slip s is found by determining the air-gap powers P_{ms1} in the positive-sequence circuit and P_{ms2} in the negative-sequence circuit, and then by inserting them in eq. 5.318. Figure

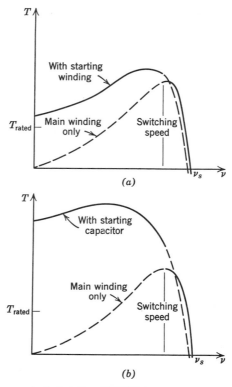

Fig. 5.100   Torque-speed relations for (a) split-phase motor; (b) capacitor-start motor.

5.100 shows typical torque-speed relations for split-phase and capacitor-start motors. As we might expect, the starting torque of the capacitor-start motor is considerably larger than that of the split-phase motor. The choice between these two types of motor is therefore dependent on the load requirements during the starting period. The lower-cost, split-phase motor has adequate starting torque for many domestic appliances and industrial operations. Its starting current is relatively high. The higher starting torque of the capacitor-start motor is required for applications such as the compressors in refrigerators and air conditioners. The starting current of the capacitor-start motor is relatively low. Its power factor at standstill may be nearly unity. Because of the limitations imposed by the source impedance in single-phase supplies, most split-phase and capacitor-start motors have ratings in the fractional horsepower range. The direction of rotation of either type of motor may be reversed by interchanging the connections to either of the stator windings.

Figure 5.101 shows a cross-sectional sketch of a *shaded-pole motor*. This motor has a stator winding around its salient poles. A shorted

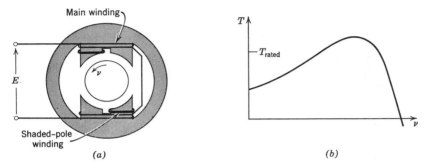

Fig. 5.101   (*a*) Shaded-pole motor. (*b*) Torque-speed relation.

"shading" winding is connected around a part of each pole. Because of the low resistance of the shading winding, the current induced in this winding lags in phase behind the current in the main stator winding. The magnetomotive force thus rises to its maximum value first in the unshaded portion of the pole and then in the shaded portion. The small rotating field component thus produced is sufficient to start the machine. The starting torque is, however, low, and the motor is suitable only for applications such as domestic fans and record players. Since the shading coil is not open circuited in the running condition, the efficiency is generally low, that is, less than 25%. The high internal losses restrict the usual range of ratings to less than 100 watts of mechanical output power.

5.8.5   Two-Phase Control Motors

A speed or position control system requires a motor in which the speed or the torque is proportional to some controlled input variable. Polyphase induction motors operating with a controlled balanced supply are generally not suitable for this purpose, partly because the torque is proportional to the square of the supply voltage and partly because their torque tends to increase as the speed increases. If, however, a constant voltage is applied to one phase of a two-phase motor and a controlled voltage of the same frequency is applied to the other phase—as shown in Fig. 5.102a—useful torque and speed control can be achieved.

Suppose a constant voltage E_d is applied to the direct-axis winding in Fig. 5.102a, while a variable voltage E_q, lagging E_d by 90°, is applied to the quadrature-axis winding. This variable voltage may be obtained from an electronic or magnetic amplifier; provision can often be made within the amplifier to introduce the required phase shift. The symmetrical components of the phase voltages are

$$\begin{bmatrix} E_1 \\ E_2 \end{bmatrix} = \frac{1}{2}\begin{bmatrix} 1 & j \\ 1 & -j \end{bmatrix} \cdot \begin{bmatrix} E_d \\ E_q \end{bmatrix} \tag{5.327}$$

Since E_q lags E_d by $\pi/2$ radians, the magnitudes of the sequence voltages are

$$|E_1| = \tfrac{1}{2}(|E_d| + |E_q|) \tag{5.328}$$

and
$$|E_2| = \tfrac{1}{2}(|E_d| - |E_q|) \tag{5.329}$$

For simplicity in analysis, let us use the form of equivalent circuit in Fig. 5.22b for the positive- and negative-sequence networks of Fig. 5.102b, where

$$X = k^2(X_e + X_r') \tag{5.330}$$

$$R = k^2 R_r' \tag{5.331}$$

and
$$k = \frac{X_{Ls} + X_{ms}}{X_{ms}} \tag{5.332}$$

Then, by analogy with eq. 5.318, the torque produced by the motor is

$$T = \frac{2}{\nu_s}(P_{ms1} - P_{ms2})$$
$$= \frac{2}{\nu_s}\left[\frac{R}{s}\frac{|E_1|^2}{(R/s)^2 + X^2} - \frac{R}{2 - s}\frac{|E_2|^2}{[R/(2 - s)]^2 + X^2} \right] \tag{5.333}$$

At standstill, the slip s equals unity. Substitution from eqs. 5.324 and 5.327 into eq. 5.333 gives the standstill torque as

$$T = \frac{2}{\nu_s}\frac{R}{(R^2 + X^2)}|E_d||E_q| \tag{5.334}$$

Thus, since E_d is maintained constant, the standstill torque is directly proportional to the voltage E_q. Reversal of the phase of the voltage E_q causes the torque to act in the reverse direction.

To insure that the torque is always reduced by an increase in speed, control motors generally have a large rotor resistance. Assuming the reactance X to be negligible, the torque at any slip s is, from eq. 5.333,

$$T = \frac{2}{\nu_s R}[s|E_1|^2 - (2 - s)|E_2|^2] \tag{5.335}$$

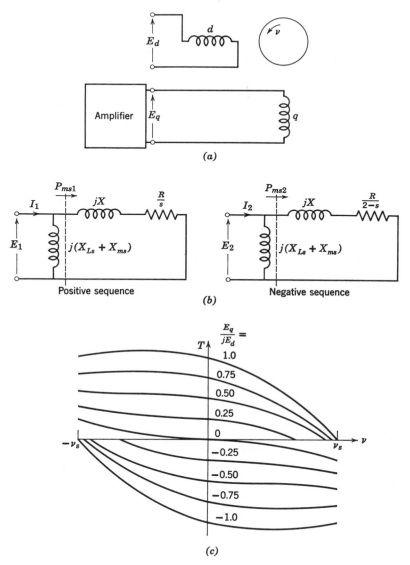

(a)

(b)

$\dfrac{E_q}{jE_d} =$

(c)

Fig. 5.102 (a) Connection of a two-phase control motor. (b) Positive- and negative-sequence equivalent circuits. (c) Torque-speed characteristics for various values of quadrature-axis voltage E_q.

The slope of the torque-slip characteristic is

$$\frac{dT}{ds} = \frac{2}{v_s R}(|E_1|^2 + |E_2|^2)$$

$$= \frac{1}{2v_s R}(|E_d|^2 + |E_q|^2) \qquad (5.336)$$

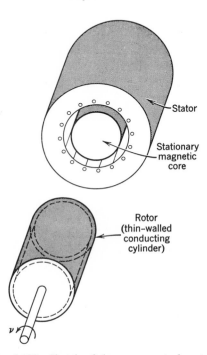

Fig. 5.103   Sketch of drag-cup control motor.

From this expression, we note that with high rotor resistance the torque-slip relation is a straight line for any constant value of E_q. The slope of the relation increases by a factor of two as the voltage E_q is increased from zero to equality with E_d.

Practical control motors are usually constructed with an effective rotor resistance sufficient to produce maximum torque in the balanced condition at a slip of about 1.5. A typical set of torque-speed curves is shown in Fig. 5.102c. As the reactance X is generally not negligible, the curves do not accurately follow the straight-line approximation of eq. 5.336, but they have the same property of an increasing downward slope as the quadrature voltage E_q is increased.

Because power is dissipated in the rotor of the control motor even when producing no torque, the machine has a low average efficiency. Adequate cooling can be easily provided for relatively small motors rated up to a few hundred watts. To obtain rapid mechanical response, the rotor inertia J is made as low as possible. In a squirrel-cage motor with a solid core, the inertia increases roughly as the fourth power of the radius, whereas the power capability increases roughly as the square of the radius. Thus, the rotor is made as small as feasible. Figure 5.103 shows another way in which low rotor inertia can be obtained. In this drag-cup motor, the only moving member is a conducting cylinder. The magnetic material inside the air gap is stationary. Because of the lack of rotor slots, the torque of this type of machine is free from oscillatory reluctance components that vary with rotor position, but the longer air gap of this machine increases its magnetizing current and decreases its efficiency.

The dynamic performance of a control motor may be assessed approximately by linearizing the torque-speed relation of Fig. 5.102c. From eq. 5.334

$$T \approx \frac{2}{v_s} \frac{R\,|E_d|}{(R^2 + X^2)} E_q - k_d v \qquad (5.337)$$

where k_d is the average value of the negative slope of the torque-speed curves over the region considered and E_q is understood to have a sign that changes when its phase is reversed. The machine performance is then described by the differential equation

$$J \frac{dv}{dt} = T - T_L \qquad (5.338)$$

or $\qquad J \dfrac{dv}{dt} + k_d v = \dfrac{2}{v_s} \dfrac{R\,|E_d|}{(R^2 + X^2)} E_q - T_L \qquad$ newton-meters   (5.339)

where J is the polar moment of inertia and T_L is the load torque. This expression is similar to the one developed in Section 4.6.1. for a d-c motor with armature-voltage control.

5.8.6 Alternating-Current Tachometers

In a speed or position control system it is frequently necessary to develop an electrical signal proportional to the speed of a shaft. If the control system uses two-phase control motors, it is generally desirable to have an alternating-voltage signal to represent the speed. The alternating-current tachometer is similar to a two-phase control motor and may, for example, take the form of the drag-cup type shown in Fig. 5.103. A constant-supply voltage E_d is applied to one of the phase windings. When the rotor is rotated at a speed ν, the supply-frequency voltage E_q, which appears on the open-circuited terminals of the other phase winding, is found to be proportional to the speed ν over a wide speed range. A reversal of the speed direction causes a phase reversal in the voltage E_q.

Let us use the method symmetrical components to analyze the performance of this tachometer. If we neglect the leakage reactances and stator resistance, the positive- and negative-sequence behavior of the

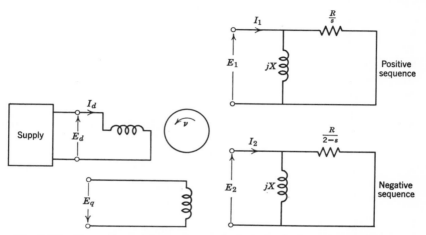

Fig. 5.104 Connections and sequence equivalent circuits for an a-c tachometer.

machine can be represented approximately by the equivalent circuit of Fig. 5.104. Since $I_q = 0$,

$$-jI_1 + jI_2 = 0$$

and
$$I_1 = I_2 \tag{5.340}$$

Then, if $E_1 = Z_1 I_1$ and $E_2 = Z_2 I_2$, the open-circuit quadrature voltage E_q becomes

$$E_q = -jE_1 + jE_2$$
$$= -jZ_1 I_1 + jZ_2 I_2$$
$$= -j(Z_1 - Z_2)I_1 \tag{5.341}$$

Similarly,

$$E_d = E_1 + E_2$$
$$= (Z_1 + Z_2)I_1 \tag{5.342}$$

Thus
$$E_q = -j\left(\frac{Z_1 - Z_2}{Z_1 + Z_2}\right)E_d \tag{5.343}$$

Inserting values of Z_1 and Z_2 from Fig. 5.104 into eq. 5.343 gives, after some manipulation,

$$E_q = \frac{1-s}{(R/X+j)} E_d$$

$$= \frac{E_d}{v_s(R/X+j)} v \qquad \text{volts} \qquad (5.344)$$

With the simplified equivalent circuit used in Fig. 5.104, the quadrature voltage E_q is found to be directly proportional to the speed and to have a phase shift that depends on the relative values of the effective rotor resistance and the magnetizing reactance. A more complete analysis shows that errors are introduced by the effects of stator resistance and leakage reactance, particularly at higher values of speed. By limiting the operating speed range and using precision components, tachometers having errors as low as 0.05% can be produced.

In comparison with d-c, permanent-magnet tachometers, a-c tachometers have lower inertia because only the rotor conductor system is rotated (for example, the drag cup), lower friction because of the absence of commutator brushes, greater freedom from spurious noise in the output signal particularly at low speed, and better inherent accuracy. They are, however, suitable only for systems in which the alternating-voltage signal can be readily utilized.

5.9 SYNCHRONOUS CONTROL DEVICES

In this section we discuss a group of specialized polyphase machines that are useful for the measurement or control of the position of a rotating shaft. These devices are generally known as *synchros*.

5.9.1 Power Synchro System

The system shown in Fig. 5.105a may be used to cause two physically separate shafts to rotate in synchronism with each other. The two identical machines of this system are of essentially the same construction as three-phase, wound-rotor induction motors. Their stator windings are connected to the same supply and their rotor slip-ring terminals are connected in parallel. If the shaft positions of the two machines are equal, the voltages induced in the rotor windings are equal in magnitude and phase. No rotor current flows through the interconnection and the torque is zero. If the angle β_1 of the first machine is increased in the direction of field rotation, the phase angles of the voltages induced in its rotor are retarded. The resulting rotor curents cause torques that tend to increase the angle β_2 of the second machine and tend to prevent the increase of angle β_1 of the first. This system in known as a power synchro.

The relationships between torque, angle, and speed of this system may be determined from an analysis of the equivalent circuit of Fig. 5.105b. This circuit is based on that of the general polyphase machine in Fig. 5.18, assuming equal numbers of rotor and stator turns in each machine. For analysis it is convenient to transfer all the circuit impedances to one side of the ideal polyphase machines, as shown in Fig. 5.105c.

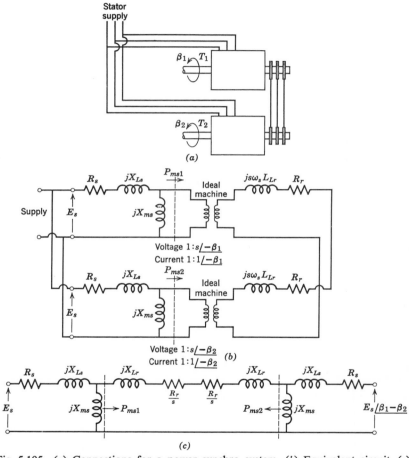

Fig. 5.105   (a) Connections for a power synchro system. (b) Equivalent circuit. (c) Simplified form of equivalent circuit.

The torques T_1 and T_2 on the two machines may be determined by computing the two values of air-gap power P_{ms1} and P_{ms2}. If the winding resistances were negligible, the torques T_1 and T_2 would be equal in magnitude and opposite in direction They would vary as the sine of the difference angle $\beta_1 - \beta_2$. The effect of the losses in the machines is to make the torque produced by the lagging machine somewhat less than that applied to the leading machine. Typical relations between the torques and the angular difference $\beta_1 - \beta_2$ are shown in Fig. 5.106. We note from an examination of Fig. 5.105c that the effect of the rotor resistance is increased as the speed of the two machines increases in the direction of field rotation. At low values of the slip s, the efficiency of power transfer from the leading to the lagging machine becomes low. If possible, the direction of

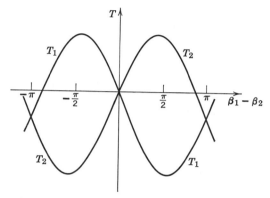

Fig. 5.106 Torques in two machines of a power synchro link as functions of difference in rotor angle.

rotation of the machines is chosen so that it opposes the direction of field rotation, thus producing values of slip greater than unity.

In some situations a pair of power synchros may be used to provide the equivalent of a flexible mechanical coupling between two mechanical systems. The more usual applications are in tandem drives where the speeds of two or more induction machines must be maintained equal. In these applications a power synchro is coupled mechanically to each of the induction machines. The synchros are then connected electrically in parallel and can transfer torque up to the limit of their ratings.

5.9.2 Synchros for Position Indication

The position of a shaft may be indicated at a remote point by use of the system shown in Fig. 5.107. Since the torque requirements in such indicator systems are small, the rotors of both the transmitting and the receiving synchro may be wound for single-phase operation. The two rotor windings are connected to an alternating-voltage source. The three symmetrically distributed stator windings of each synchro are connected in star, and the two sets of stator terminals are connected in parallel.

The voltages induced in the stator windings are in phase but vary in their magnitudes approximately as the cosines of the angles between the axes of the stator windings and the axis of the rotor winding. When the angular positions of the rotors in the two synchros are equal, identical stator voltages are induced in the stator windings of the transmitter and receiver. No stator current flows and there is no torque, but if the rotor angles are not equal, stator currents flow and the resultant torques tend

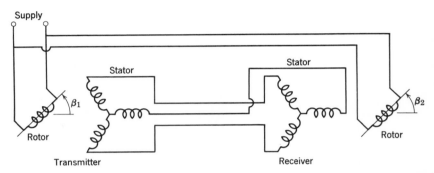

Fig. 5.107   Connection of two single-phase synchros for remote indication β_2 of shaft position β_1.

to align the two rotors. The relation between the torques and the difference in the rotor angles is of the same form, as shown in Fig. 5.106.

The rotor inertias of the two synchros are made small in order to minimize the mechanical disturbance to the shaft whose angle is being measured or indicated. Bearing friction is also minimized, particularly in the receiving synchro, since friction causes an error in alignment. The receiving synchro may also be fitted with mechanical dampers to damp out oscillations in the receiver angle following an abrupt change in the transmitter rotor position. It is sometimes necessary to have an indication of the position of a shaft transmitted to a number of remote points. This may be accomplished by connecting a number of receiving synchros in parallel to a single transmitter.

Occasionally, an indication of the sum or difference to two shaft angles is desired. This may be accomplished by the use of a *differential synchro* in conjunction with a transmitting and a receiving synchro, as shown in Fig. 5.108. The differential synchro is similar to a polyphase phase shifter (Section 5.3.1). The three stator voltages of the transmitting synchro are applied to the stator of the differential synchro. These voltages are dependent in magnitude on the angle β_1. The stator voltages in the differential synchro produce a magnetic field which oscillates with time

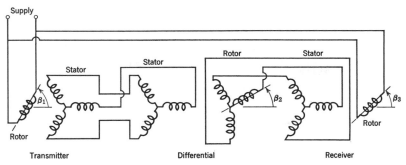

Fig. 5.108 Connections of transmitter, differential and receiver synchros to indicate the difference β_3 between the angles β_1 and β_2 of two shafts.

but is fixed in an angular position that depends on the angle β_1. The induced voltages in the rotor windings of the differential synchro therefore depend on the difference $\beta_1 - \beta_2$ between the angle of the magnetic field axis β_1 and the rotor angle β_2. The torque on the receiving synchro tends to make its angle β_3 equal to $\beta_1 - \beta_2$. The system of Fig. 5.108 may also be operated so that the differential synchro indicates the angular difference β_2 between the angles β_1 and β_3 of two synchro transmitters.

5.9.3 Control Transformers

The difference in angle between two shafts may be measured as a voltage by use of the system shown in Fig. 5.109. This system consists of two synchros: a transmitting synchro with a rotor angle β_1 and another synchro, known as a control transformer, with rotor angle β_2. The rotor of the transmitting synchro is energized from a single-phase supply and produces a pulsating magnetic field that is distributed about the rotor axis. The voltages induced in the transmitter stator are applied to the stator

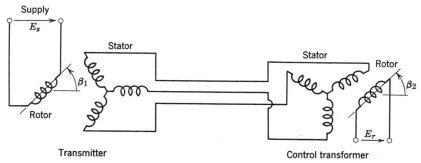

Fig. 5.109 Connection of transmitter and control transformer synchros to produce output voltage E_r proportional to angular difference $\beta_1 - \beta_2$ between two shaft positions.

of the control transformer. If the synchros behave ideally and if their stators are aligned, the magnetic field in the control transformer has the same angular distribution as that of the transmitter. When the rotor is aligned with this magnetic field, its induced voltage is a maximum. When it is displaced $\pi/2$ radians from the field axis, its induced voltage is zero. It is normally desirable to have zero output voltage correspond to equivalence of the angles β_1 and β_2. This may be accomplished by fixing the stator position of the control transformer $\pi/2$ radians behind that of the

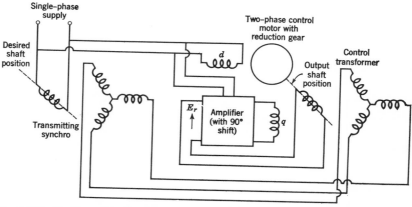

Fig. 5.110   Position control system using control transformer and two-phase control motor.

stator of the transmitter. Then the output voltage for two identical ideal synchros is given by

$$E_r = E_s \sin (\beta_1 - \beta_2) \tag{5.345}$$

If the angle $\beta_1 - \beta_2$ is negative, the phase of the fundamental-frequency output voltage phasor E_r is reversed.

If the difference angle $\beta_1 - \beta_2$ is small, eq. 5.345 may be approximated by

$$E_r = E_s(\beta_1 - \beta_2) \tag{5.346}$$

Thus the system produces an output voltage that is linearly proportional to the angular difference between two shaft positions, provided this difference is reasonably small. Control transformers are constructed with cylindrical rotors to avoid the production of reluctance torque and to make the magnetizing current independent of rotor position.

Figure 5.110 shows a typical application of a control transformer synchro. In this position control system a transmitting synchro is coupled mechanically to the shaft that represents the desired angular position.

The control transformer is coupled to the output shaft and its rotor voltage E_r is a measure of the error between the desired angle and the actual angle of the output shaft. This error voltage is amplified, shifted through a $\pi/2$ phase angle, and applied to the quadrature-axis winding of a two-phase control motor. This produces a torque in such a direction as to reduce the error.

Problems

5.1 A device has one stationary coil with a self-inductance of 0.1 H and one rotatable coil with a self-inductance of 0.04 H. The mutual inductance between the two coils is $0.05 \cos \theta$ H when θ is the angle between the axes of the coils.

(a) Suppose the rotatable coil is rotated at 200 rad/sec. If a current of $10 \sin 200t$ is passed through one of the coils, determine the peak value of the induced voltage in the other coil. *Ans.:* 100 V.

(b) Suppose a current of $10 \sin 200t$ is passed through both coils in series. At what values of speed will this device produce an average torque?

(c) Determine the maximum value of average torque that can be obtained in part (b). *Ans.:* 1.25 newton-m at $v = 400$.

5.2 A sinusoidally-distributed winding of 120 turns is placed on a stator frame, as shown in Fig. 5.4. The frame has an axial length of 10 cm and an air-gap radius of 5 cm. The effective length of the air gap is 1.0 mm. A current of $10 \sin \omega t$ amp is passed through the winding.

(a) Determine the magnetomotive face acting around a closed path at angle θ (Fig. 5.4).

(b) Assuming ideal magnetic material, determine the magnetic flux density in the air gap as a function of angle θ and time t. Sketch a graph of flux density versus angle θ for $\omega t = 0$, $\pi/6$, $\pi/2$, and $2\pi/3$.

(c) Determine the flux linkage of the winding as a function of time.

(d) Determine the self-inductance of the winding. *Ans.:* 0.071 H.

(e) Suppose two other 120-turn sinusoidally distributed windings are placed in the stator slots to make a symmetrical 3-phase winding. Determine the mutual inductance between a pair of these windings.
Ans.: -0.0355 H.

(f) Suppose the 3 phase windings carry currents of $10 \sin \omega t$, $10 \sin (\omega t - 2\pi/3)$ and $10 \sin (\omega t - 4\pi/3)$, respectively. Sketch a graph of the air-gap flux density at $\omega t = 0$, $\pi/6$, $\pi/2$, and $2\pi/3$. Determine the peak value of the flux density. *Ans.:* 1.13 Wb/m².

(g) For the condition of part (f) determine the maximum induced voltage in each of the windings if the frequency is 60 c/s. *Ans.:* 401 V.

5.3   To obtain an assessment of the effects of magnetic saturation in the machine described in Prob. 5.2, let us suppose that the magnetic material can be represented by the idealized B-H model of Fig. 2.7b with $B_k = 2.0 \text{ Wb/m}^2$. Then if the tooth width is equal to the slot width, the flux density averaged over a tooth and slot cannot exceed 1.0 Wb/m^2. Suppose the 3 phase windings carry a balanced set of sinusoidal currents.

(a) Determine the maximum value of peak phase current that can be carried without producing any magnetic saturation.   *Ans.: 8.85 amp.*

(b) Suppose the peak value of each of the phase currents is 17.7 amp. At time $t = 0$, sketch the magnetomotive force and the air-gap flux density as a function of the angle θ. Determine the fundamental component of a Fourier series representation of the flux density.   *Ans.: 1.22 Wb/m².*

(c) Determine the saturated value of the magnetizing inductance per phase for the condition of part (b).   *Ans.: 0.065 mH.*

(d) Repeat parts (b) and (c) for two other values of current in the saturated range and draw a graph relating the peak magnetizing flux linkage λ_{ms} per phase and the peak magnetizing current I_{ms} per phase.

5.4   A small single-base induction motor is to have a single winding of 400 turns. A concentric winding of the type shown in Fig. 5.10 is to be accommodated in 16 slots. Determine the required number of turns in each of the coils.   *Ans.: 76, 65, 44, 15.*

5.5   Consider a 3-phase machine in which the conductor density n for the reference phase is

$$n = \frac{N_s}{2}(\cos\theta + k\cos 3\theta) \qquad \text{conductors/rad}$$

(a) Show that if the winding currents are balanced, the magnetomotive force is sinusoidally distributed.

(b) Find the value of k for which the slots near $\theta = \pi/2$ would have no conductors of the reference phase in them.   *Ans.: 0.333.*

(c) Plot the distribution n for $k = 0.4$. Note the region of essentially zero conductor density. Determine the relative numbers of turns that might be used in each coil of a concentric winding for a 24-slot, 2-pole, 3-phase winding.   *Ans.: N_{coil}/N_s = 0.176, 0.14, 0.083, 0.032.*

(d) Compare the number of turns used in part (c) with the number required for a sinusoidally distributed winding.   *Ans.: About 0.87.*

5.6   The stator of a polyphase machine has 36 slots. The stator coils are identical and each has a span of $\pi/3$ rad.

(a) How many poles does the machine winding have?

(b) List the number of phases m of the symmetrical polyphase windings that can be obtained by connections of these coils.

(c) Assuming a sinusoidally distributed air-gap flux density, determine the ratio of the generated voltage per phase for a 4-phase winding relative to that of a 3-phase winding. *Ans.: 0.706.*

5.7 A 3-phase, 2-pole 2-layer stator winding for a machine is accommodated in 24 slots. Each of the 24 coils has 12 turns. Each coil is short pitched by 2 slots.

(a) Determine the fundamental distribution factor for the winding.

(b) Determine the fundamental pitch factor.

(c) Determine the equivalent number of sinusoidally distributed turns to produce the same fundamental space wave.

Ans.: 113 turns per phase.

(d) On balanced operation, the lowest-order space harmonics will be the 5th and 7th. Determine the winding factors for these two space harmonics. *Ans.: 0.053, 0.04.*

5.8 Suppose the machine of Prob. 5.7 has a radius of 6 cm and an axial length of 10 cm. The air gap has an effective length of 1 mm. The ratio of tooth width to slot width is 1.0. The slots are rectangular in shape and have a slot depth to slot width ratio of 2.5. The slots may be considered to be uniformly filled with conductors.

(a) Assuming the magnetic material to be perfect, determine the magnetizing inductance per phase for blanced operation.

(b) Estimate the slot leakage inductance per phase for balanced operation. Note that because of the short pitching, half the slots carry in-phase currents in the two layers, while in the other half the currents are displaced 60° with respect to each other. *Ans.: 0.437 mH.*

5.9 In Section 4.8 it was shown that the effective volume of the rotor of a commutator machine could be expressed in terms of the air-gap flux density and the linear current density of the winding. Let us derive a similar expression for a polyphase machine. To begin, let us consider a machine with a 2-pole, m-phase set of stator windings, each of which is sinusoidally distributed.

(a) Determine the rms value of the induced voltage per phase in relation to the peak value of air-gap flux density $\hat{B}$ (eq. 5.74).

(b) Determine the total rms current in all the conductors around the stator periphery.

(c) If U is the total Vamp product in all stator windings, ω is the angular frequency, and q is the allowable rms current per meter of circumferential distance around the air gap, show that the volume V of the cylinder bounded by the stator is given by

$$V = \frac{2\sqrt{2}U}{\pi\omega q\hat{B}} \qquad \text{m}^3$$

(d) Show that the volume V for a p-pole machine is $p/2$ times the value given in part (c).

(e) If the stator has a large number (m) of phase windings, each of which consists of one concentrated coil, show that the volume V is reduced to $\pi/4$ of the value given in part (c).

5.10 (a) Using the expressions derived in Prob. 5.9, estimate the axial length and the diameter at the air gap of a 10-MVA, 2300-V (line-to-line), 3-phase, 60-c/s, 6-pole polyphase machine. The axial length may be made equal to one pole pitch. A maximum air-gap flux density of 0.9 Wb/m² and a linear current density of 40,000 amp rms/m of periphery may be used.   *Ans.:* 0.89 m, 1.7 m.

(b) If the stator windings are sinusoidally distributed and connected in star, determine the required number of turns (N_s) per phase.   *Ans.:* 14.

5.11 A 2-pole, 60-c/s machine has 3-phase windings on both stator and rotor. The stator leakage reactance is 0.1 Ω/phase, the rotor leakage reactance is 0.1 Ω/phase and the magnetizing reactance is 2.0 Ω/phase. The turns ratio is unity. All winding resistances are negligible. The machine is used as a phase shifter, the stator being connected to a 220-V line-to-line, 60-c/s supply and output being obtained from the rotor terminals. The rotor angle is β.

(a) Draw a single-phase equivalent circuit for the phase shifter.

(b) Determine the voltage and impedance of a single-phase Thévenin equivalent circuit for the machine as seen from its output terminals.
Ans.: $121\underline{/-\beta}$; $j0.195$ Ω.

5.12 A variable, 3-phase inductive load may be obtained by connecting the stator and rotor windings of a polyphase machine in parallel, as shown in Fig. P5.12. The impedance per phase is controlled by rotating the rotor through an angle β. Use the machine data from Prob. 5.11.

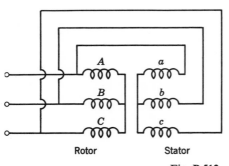 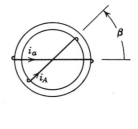

Rotor   Stator

Fig. P.512

(a) Determine the inductive reactance per phase of the system as a function of the angle β between the paralleled stator and rotor windings.

(b) At what angle β should the rotor be set if 25 kVA is to be taken from a 115-V (line-to-line) supply?   *Ans.:* $\pm 31°$.

5.13 Suppose the 3-phase machine described in Prob. 5.11 is connected as an induction regulator as shown in Fig. 5.17. Let the rotor supply voltage be 230-V (line-to-line).

(a) Determine the output voltage per phase on no-load as a function of the rotor angle β.

(b) Determine the effective reactance per phase of the regulator as seen from the output terminals.   *Ans.:* 0.195 Ω.

(c) Draw a Thévenin equivalent circuit for the regulator.

5.14 A 3-phase source of variable frequency is required in an experiment. The frequency is to be controllable over the range 20-150 c/s. The system used consists of a 3-phase, 6-pole, wound-rotor machine with its stator connected to a 440-V, 60-c/s, 3-phase supply. The machine is driven at a controllable speed and the variable frequency output is obtained from its rotor terminals.

(a) Determine the values of rotor speed to give 20 c/s and 150 c/s.

(b) Suppose the open-circuit rotor voltage is 220 V when the rotor is stationary. Determine the rotor voltage available on open-circuit with 20 c/s and with 150 c/s.   *Ans.:* 73.3, 550.

(c) If all losses in the machine are neglected what fraction of the output power is supplied from the stator supply and what fraction is supplied from the shaft at 20 c/s and at 150 c/s?   *Ans.:* 0.4, 0.6 for 150 c/s.

5.15 For comparative purposes, the equivalent circuit parameters of a machine are usually best expressed in per unit of the ratings of the machine. Consider a 3-phase, 60-c/s, 440-V (line-to-line), 10-kVA (total), 6-pole induction machine.

(a) Determine the base values of the voltage (line-to-line), the voltage (line-to-neutral), the phase current, the total power, the power per phase and the synchronous speed.

(b) Determine the base value of the impedance per phase.
Ans.: 19.4 Ω.

(c) Using the base value of power and speed, determine the base value for the shaft torque.   *Ans.:* 79.5 newton-m.

(d) Show that the per unit value of the rated torque is equal to the product of the power factor and the efficiency, divided by the per-unit speed at rated load.

5.16 A 3-phase, 60-c/s, 6-pole, 440-V (line-to-line) wound-rotor machine has the following parameters per phase:

> Stator resistance—negligible
> Stator leakage inductance $= 0.003$ H
> Rotor leakage inductance $= 0.003$ H
> Magnetizing inductance $= 0.1$ H
> Rotor resistance $= 0.3$ Ω
> Turns ratio $1:1$
> Rotational losses negligible

The stator is connected to a supply of rated voltage and frequency:

(a) Determine the standstill torque with a shorted rotor.

Ans.: 85.6 newton-m.

(b) Determine the maximum torque that can be produced with a shorted rotor.   *Ans.:* 322 newton-m.

(c) Determine the speed at which the maximum torue of part (b) occurs.

(d) For operation near synchronous speed, determine the torque produced per unit of slip *s*.   *Ans.:* 4820.

(e) Suppose the machine is used to drive a load requiring a torque of 2 newton-m/rad per sec of speed. Determine the speed of the load.

Ans.: 119 rad/s.

(f) In part (e), determine the frequency of currents in the rotor.

(g) Determine the efficiency of the machine for the operating condition of part (e).

5.17 Consider a polyphase induction machine which produces a maximum torque of $\hat{T}$ at a slip of $s_{\hat{T}}$. If the rotor resistance is independent of rotor frequency and the stator resistance is negligible, show that the torque T produced at any slip s is given by

$$T = \frac{2\hat{T}}{s_{\hat{T}}/s + s/s_{\hat{T}}} \qquad \text{newton-m}$$

5.18 Tests were made on a 440-V (line-to-line), 4-pole, 3-phase, 60-c/s squirrel-cage induction motor to determine its equivalent circuit parameters. When operated at rated supply voltage and frequency with no shaft load, the input current was 3.1 amp per phase and the total input power was 480 W. When operated at standstill with a 60 c/s supply voltage of 110 V line-to-line, the input current was 10.5 amp and the total input power was 1260 W. The resistance measured between a pair of stator terminals with direct current at standstill was 0.61 Ω.

(a) Determine the stator resistance per phase.

(b) Determine the total leakage reactance per phase and the rotor resistance per phase.   *Ans.:* 4.7 Ω; 3.5 Ω.

(c) Determine the magnetizing reactance per phase at rated voltage. *Ans.:* 83.5 Ω.

(d) Estimate the losses due to mechanical friction and eddy currents when operating near synchronous speed. *Ans.:* About 470 W.

(e) Assume that the leakage reactance is equally divided between the stator and the rotor and draw an equivalent circuit of the form shown in Fig. 5.20c.

(f) Compute the input current, the shaft torque, and the efficiency of the machine when operating at rated voltage and frequency at a slip of 0.05 per unit. *Ans.:* 4.7 amp; 11.5 newton-m; 0.77.

(g) Since the standstill test was made at rated frequency, is the prediction of starting torque from the equivalent circuit likely to be more accurate than the prediction of torque in part (f)?

5.19 A 3-phase, 550-V, 60-c/s, 4-pole induction motor has a maximum torque of 100 newton-m at a slip of 0.25. Its rotor resistance is frequency independent and its stator resistance is negligible. It is suggested that this machine will operate satisfactorily on a 400-V, 50-c/s supply.

(a) Compare the new value of maximum torque with the original rated value. *Ans.:* 0.765.

(b) Determine the speed at which the maximum torque of part (a) occurs. *Ans.:* 110 rad/s.

(c) Compare the new value of starting torque with the original rated value of starting torque. *Ans.:* 0.9.

(d) The maximum continuous load on the motor is limited by heating of the rotor. Compare the new value for rated torque with the original rated value. *Ans.:* 0.885.

5.20 An induction motor frame has a large number of stator slots and a squirrel-cage rotor winding. The machine can be wound for various numbers of poles. The maximum flux density, the maximum current density, the supply frequency, and the supply voltage are constant.

(a) Show that the magnetizing Vamp required by the machine are independent of the number of poles.

(b) Show that the rated torque available from the machine is independent of the number of poles if magnetizing current is negligible.

(c) Show that the power conversion capability of the machine is inversely proportional to the number of poles.

(d) If the power factor at rated load of a 4-pole machine is 0.9, estimate the power factor at rated load of the machine if rewound for 8-poles. *Ans.:* About 0.78.

5.21 A turbine at a remote hydroelectric site produces a mechanical power of 1 MW at a speed of about 600–625 r/min. To simplify the control of the system, it is decided to use a 12-pole, 3-phase squirrel-cage induction generator to supply this power to a 4000-V line-to-line, 60-c/s distribution system. A test on the machine at rated voltage, rated frequency, and no-load gives an impedance per phase of approximately $0 + j33\ \Omega$. A test under standstill conditions at rated frequency gives an impedance per phase of $0.5 + j3.0\ \Omega$. The stator resistance may be neglected.

(a) Derive the parameters for an equivalent circuit of the form shown in Fig. 5.22b.

(b) Estimate the per-unit slip at which the generator will operate under full power.   *Ans.*: 0.03.

(c) To reduce the current in the distribution line, it is decided that the terminal power factor of the generating station should be unity under full-load conditions. Determine the required value of capacitance per phase of a star-connected capacitor connected to the stator terminals.
Ans.: 109 μF.

5.22   Consider the wound-rotor induction machine described in Prob. 5.16.

(a) How much resistance should be added in series with each rotor phase to produce maximum torque at standstill?   *Ans.*: 1.93 Ω.

(b) Suppose the motor is used to drive a load requiring a torque of 10 newton-m/rad per sec of speed. If we use the rotor resistance of part (a), at what speed will the load be driven?

(c) What will be the efficiency of the machine in part (b)?
Ans.: 0.245.

5.23   The starting torque of a wound-rotor induction motor can be increased by adding resistances in the rotor circuit. It can be increased still further by adding capacitors in series with the rotor resistances. Suppose a capacitance C in series with a resistance of 2.5 Ω is inserted in each rotor phase of the machine described in Prob. 5.16.

(a) Determine the value of capacitance C to produce maximum air-gap power at standstill.   *Ans.*: 1190 μF.

(b) Determine the starting torque with the value of capacitance found in part (a).   *Ans.*: 519 newton-m.

(c) Sketch the torque-speed curve from standstill to synchronous speed.

(d) Consider the possibility of achieving high torque at standstill and near synchronous speed by connecting a capacitor in parallel with the added rotor resistance.

5.24   The propulsion system of a ship consists of a variable-speed steam turbine driving a synchronous generator, which in turn supplies power to induction motors on each of the two propellers. When the generator is driven at full speed, each induction motor has a synchronous speed of

300 r/min and produces its maximum torque of 10^5 newton-m at 240 r/min. When the synchronous generator is driven at half speed, its terminal voltage and frequency are also reduced to half the full-speed values.

(a) Determine the values of the synchronous speed, the maximum torque, and the speed to produce maximum torque for each induction motor when the generator is driven at half speed. The stator resistances and the magnetizing currents of the induction motors may be neglected.
Ans.: 150; 10^5; 90.

(b) Sketch torque-speed curves for full- and half-turbine speeds.

(c) Suppose each propeller requires a torque of 30,000 newton-m when operating under full-speed conditions and that the propeller torque varies approximately as the square of the propeller speed. Estimate the mechanical power delivered by each induction motor with full- and half-turbine speeds. *Ans.:* 915 kW; 115 kW.

5.25 Two identical 2-pole, 3-phase, wound-rotor induction machines have their shafts coupled together. A 3-phase supply is connected to one stator winding. The rotor terminals of the two machines are connected together and the stator winding of the second machine is short circuited.

(a) Develop an equivalent circuit for the system.

(b) Suppose the rotational losses and the magnetizing currents are negligible in both machines. Show that the no-load speed of the system is equal in magnitude to half the angular frequency of the supply.

(c) If the leakage reactance at rated frequency is 0.1 per unit for each stator and winding and if the winding resistances are ignored, what per-unit resistance must be inserted in each phase of the short-circuited stator winding to produce maximum starting torque? *Ans.:* 0.4 per unit.

(d) Show that the starting torque of part (c) is shared equally by the two machines.

5.26 Suppose the induction motor of Prob. 5.16 has a polar moment of inertia of 15 kg-m². The rotational losses are negligible. The motor is started with no mechanical load, with rated voltage applied to the stator, and with the rotor short circuited.

(a) Estimate the time required for the motor to accelerate from standstill to 0.8 per unit of synchronous speed. *Ans.:* 11 sec.

(b) Repeat part (a) assuming that the motor is driving a load that requires a torque of 2 newton-m/rad per sec of speed. *Ans.:* 30 sec.

(c) Suppose the motor is operating at approximately synchronous speed on no-load. To bring the motor rapidly to standstill, two of the stator supply leads are interchanged. (This operation is known as plugging.) Estimate the time required for the motor to reach standstill.
Ans.: 315 sec.

5.27 Suppose an induction motor is started on no-load. Its polar moment of inertia is J and its rotational losses are negligible.

(a) Show that the total energy loss in the rotor windings during starting is equal to the mechanical energy stored in the rotor inertia at synchronous speed.

(b) A 6-pole, 60-c/s induction motor is rated to supply a continuous mechanical power of 500 kW at a slip of 0.02 per unit. Its polar moment of inertia is 300 kg-m². Suppose the machine is started, disconnected from its electrical supply, stopped mechanically, and subsequently started again. If the average heating of the rotor is not to exceed the value on rated continuous load, what must be the time interval between the two starting times?   *Ans.:* 236 sec.

(c) Suppose the machine in part (b) is to have its speed reversed periodically. This can be accomplished by reversing a pair of the stator supply leads. If the machine has no mechanical load, how often can this reversal be performed each hour without exceeding the rated average rotor heating?
Ans.: 3.8.

5.28 A 3-phase, 6-pole, 60-c/s squirrel-cage induction motor is used to drive a punch press. The load cycle on the motor consists of a constant torque of 200 newton-m for a period of 0.3 sec followed by 3 sec of essentially zero torque. The induction motor is designed to produce a maximum steady-state torque of 200 newton-m at a slip of 0.2 per unit. Its stator resistances can be ignored.

(a) Assume that the rotor resistance of the motor is independent of frequency, and determine the torque per unit of slip when operating near synchronous speed.   *Ans.:* 2000 newton-m per unit.

(b) If the rotor and the punch press mechanism have a combined polar moment of inertia of 20 kg-m², determine the mechanical time constant.
Ans.: 1.256 sec.

(c) Suppose the motor is initially operating at synchronous speed. Determine its per-unit slip at the end of the first 0.3-sec punching period.
Ans.: 0.0213.

(d) Determine the slip at the end of the first 3.0-sec recovery period.
Ans.: 0.00195.

(e) Under continuous punching operation, what are the maximum and minimum values of slip?   *Ans.:* 0.0244; 0.00214.

(f) Determine the average slip.   *Ans.:* 0.0091.

5.29 A source of 3-phase, 400-c/s voltage is required in an industrial operation. The only utility supply available is 3 phase at 60 c/s. The frequency conversion is to be accomplished by use of a synchronous motor driving a synchronous generator. A variation of $\pm 3\%$ about the 400-c/s frequency is permissible. Determine a suitable number of poles for each of the synchronous machines.

5.30 The field winding of a 2-pole, cylindrical-rotor, synchronous machine is to have a total of 240 turns. Six coils each having 40 turns are to be placed in unevenly distributed slots. (See Fig. 5.29.) At approximately what angular positions relative to the field axis should these slots be placed to produce a nearly sinusoidal distribution?
    Ans.: About $34°$, $60°$, $80°$.

5.31 A rough estimate of the dimensions and windings of a 100-MVA, 3-phase synchronous generator is required. The generator is to be driven at 3600 r/min by a steam turbine and is to supply power at 60 c/s and 20,000 V line-to-line. In Prob. 5.9, it was found that the effective rotor volume V of a polyphase machine could be obtained approximately from the relation

$$V \approx \frac{2\sqrt{2}U}{\pi v_s q \hat{B}} \quad \text{m}^3$$

where v_s is the synchronous speed and U is the total Vamp rating. Let us assume that the maximum value $\hat{B}$ of the air-gap flux density is about 1.0 Wb/m². The linear current density q of the stator or rotor winding may be about 80,000 amp rms/m of air-gap periphery for this type of machine. Figure P5.31 shows a sketch of the machine.

(a) Determine the approximate volume of the cylindrical part of the rotor.   *Ans.:* About 3 m³.

(b) Because of mechanical stresses, the velocity of the rotor surface should not exceed about 200 m/sec. Estimate the required radius r and length l.   *Ans.:* $l \approx 3.3$ m.

(c) Suppose the stator winding of this machine is connected in star. Approximately how many turns are required in each phase of the stator winding, assuming the winding to be approximately sinusoidally-distributed?   *Ans.:* About 16.

(d) When each stator winding is carrying rated current, what maximum value of magnetomotive face $\mathscr{F}_\theta$ does it produce in the machine?

(e) Let us suppose that the rotor winding is to be designed to carry a maximum direct current of 500 amp and is to be capable of producing a magnetomotive force equal to that found for the stator winding in part (d). How many sinusoidally distributed turns are required on the rotor?
    Ans.: About 196.

(f) The rotor conductors might be operated at a maximum current density of about 3×10^6 amp/m² of conductor cross section. Using a resistivity of 2×10^{-8} Ω-m, estimate the power dissipation in the rotor winding, and express it as a ratio of the rating of the machine.

Ans.: 0.0005 to 0.001.

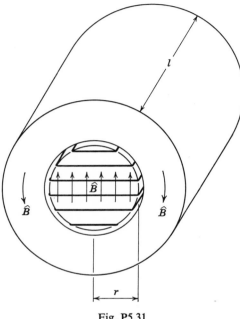

Fig. P5.31

(g) In Fig. P5.31, note that the rotor may be considered as having a uniform flux density $\hat{B}$. Half of the total rotor flux must return on each side of the stator. Allowing for the depth of the stator slots, the maximum flux density in the stator yoke averaged over a cross section might have about the same value $\hat{B}$. Estimate the required overall diameter of the machine.   *Ans.:* About 2.1 m

5.32 A 3-phase, 440-V line-to-line, 10-kVA, wound-rotor machine has the following parameters per phase, measured at its rated frequency of 60 c/s: magnetizing reactance = 48 Ω, stator leakage reactance = rotor leakage reactance = 2.8 Ω, stator resistance = rotor resistance = 0.4 Ω per phase. The turns ratio of the machine is unity. The machine is to be used as a synchronous generator. The field circuit is to be connected as shown in Fig. 5.31a and to be supplied from a d-c source.

(a) Draw an equivalent circuit for the machine.

(b) Determine the field current i_f that is required to produce rated terminal voltage on open circuit when driven at rated speed.

Ans.: 7.49 amp.

(c) Determine the power dissipated in the field winding for the condition of part (b). *Ans.:* 33.6 W.

(d) Determine the synchronous reactance of the machine. Express it in per unit of the base impedance per phase. *Ans.:* 2.63 per unit.

(e) Suppose the machine is used to supply 10 kW to a balanced resistive load at rated terminal voltage. Determine the required value of field current i_f. *Ans.:* 21 amp.

(f) Determine the field power for the condition of part (e) in per unit of the rating of the machine. *Ans.:* 0.025.

5.33 Suppose the machine described in Prob. 5.32 is used as a synchronous motor. The stator terminals are connected to a 440-V line-to-line, 60-c/s supply. The field circuit is connected to a 6-V battery, which has negligible internal resistance. Suppose the machine has 6 poles.

(a) Derive an expression for the electromagnetic torque produced by the machine at synchronous speed as a function of the rotor angle β_0.

(b) Determine the maximum steady-state torque the machine can produce at synchronous speed. *Ans.:* 40.5 newton-m.

(c) Suppose the load torque is gradually increased until it is slightly greater than the value found in part (b). At approximately what value of speed will the load be driven? Note that the battery appears as a short circuit to all frequencies except zero. *Ans.:* About 124 rad/s.

5.34 A 440-V, line-to-line, 50-kVA, 3-phase, 60-c/s, synchronous generator is rotated at rated speed. A field current of 7 amp is required to produce rated terminal voltage on open circuit. A field current of 5.5 amp is required to produce rated terminal current with the stator windings short circuited. The machine may be considered to be magnetically linear.

(a) Determine the synchronous reactance in Ω per phase.

Ans.: 3.04 Ω.

(b) Determine the synchronous reactance in per unit using the machine rating as a base. *Ans.:* 0.785.

5.35 To determine the equivalent circuit parameters for a 4400-V line-to-line, 3-phase, 3000-kVA synchronous machine, an open-circuit test and a zero power-factor load test were made. This last test was made with a capacitive load adjusted to take rated stator current at each value of voltage.

| Field Current | Terminal Voltage (volts, *L-L*) | |
(amp)	Open Circuit	Zero Power Factor
0	50	4750
20	1450	5500
40	2880	6060
60	3960	6420
70	4400	6540
80	4740	6650
100	5300	
120	5680	
140	5920	

(a) Determine the stator leakage reactance in Ω/phase and in per unit of rating.   *Ans.:* 1.16 Ω; 0.18.

(b) Find the value of the current ratio n'.   *Ans.:* 6.6.

(c) Determine the magnetizing reactance in Ω/phase and in per unit when the air-gap voltage E_{ms} is 1.0 per unit.   *Ans.:* 0.85.

(d) Suppose this machine is operated as a generator supplying rated voltage and rated current to a partially inductive load with a power factor of 0.75. Calculate the required field current.   *Ans.:* 137 amp.

(e) Suppose the machine is operated as a motor with rated terminal voltage. The mechanical load and the field current are adjusted so that the machine takes a rated 0.75 power factor capacitive load from the supply. Determine the required field current.   *Ans.:* 137 amp.

5.36 Suppose a balanced capacitive load of 6.0 Ω/phase is connected to the stator terminals of the synchronous generator described in Prob. 5.35 and that the field current is zero. The machine is driven at rated speed.

(a) To what value will the terminal voltage rise?   *Ans.:* 3580 V.

(b) Can the generator deliver power to a resistive load connected in parallel with the capacitor?

5.37 Suppose the machine described in Prob. 5.35 is to be used as a synchronous reactor or condenser. It has no mechanical load and its mechanical losses may be ignored. It is connected to a 4400-V (line-to-line), 3-phase, 60-c/s supply.

(a) Derive a linear approximation for the magnetization characteristic of the machine (eq. 5.169).

(b) What total value of reactive Vamp will be taken by the machine when its field current is reduced to zero?   *Ans.:* 2.54 MVA.

(c) What field current is required when the machine is acting as a 3000-kVA capacitive load on the system?   *Ans.:* 154 amp.

5.38 In Fig. 5.45 it is shown that a synchronous machine, operating with a constant power, may have the same value of stator current for two values of the field current.

(a) For which of the two values would the machine be more likely to remain in synchronism following a disturbance?

(b) For which of the two values of field current would the machine have a greater efficiency?

(c) Suppose the machine is a synchronous generator supplying a variety of loads including induction motors. Which of the values of field current would be used?

(d) Suppose this machine is a synchronous motor operating in an industrial plant with other loads including induction motors. Which of the values of field current would be used?

5.39 A 3-phase, 60-c/s, 60-MVA synchronous generator is connected to a distribution system, the voltage of which is maintained constant at 13.2 kV line-to-line. The synchronous reactance of the generator is 1.2 per unit based on the machine rating and may be considered constant. The losses in the machine may be ignored. Initially, the driving turbine is adjusted to deliver 50 MW of mechanical power to the shaft, and the field current is adjusted to give a terminal power factor of unity.

(a) By what factor can the field current be increased before the stator current exceeds the rated value? *Ans.: 1.37.*

(b) By what factor can the field current be reduced before the rated stator current is exceeded or synchronism is lost? *Ans.: 0.707.*

5.40 A 3-phase, 1000-c/s synchronous generator is to supply power for induction heating of steel for a forging machine. The magnitude and power factor of the load change continually, and it is desired to keep the load voltage constant at 550 V line-to-line. This might be accomplished by automatic control of the field current. An alternative method is to place a capacitor in series with each phase between the load and the machine terminals. Suppose the synchronous reactance of the machine is 0.7 Ω/phase.

(a) Assume the synchronous reactance is constant and that the field current is set to give 550 V line-to-line on no-load. What series capacitance per phase is required to make the load voltage constant under all load conditions? *Ans.: 228 μF.*

(b) Suppose the load varies from 500 kVA at unity power factor to 500 kVA at an inductive power factor of 0.6. Over what range will the voltage of the terminals of the machine vary? *Ans.: 487; 222.*

5.41 Figure P5.41 shows a voltage regulation system for a synchronous generator. It is based on the concept that the field current required to maintain a constant terminal voltage has two contributory components; the first is required to supply the magnetizing current for the machine and the second is required to compensate for the stator curent. In this regulator a current proportional to the terminal voltage is obtained by the use of a capacitive load. This current flows in one primary winding of a current transformer in each phase. A second primary winding on each

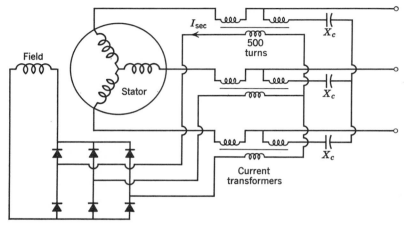

Fig. P5.41

current transformer carries the stator current. The turns ratios are chosen so that the secondary currents of the current transformers, when rectified in a 3-phase bridge rectifier and added, will produce the required field current.

To simplify the analysis of this system, let us ignore the stator resistance and stator leakage reactance. At rated speed, a section of the open-circuit characteristic is given by the following data.

Terminal voltage (volts, L-L)	198	220	242
Field current (amp)	1.1	1.38	1.73

The effective current ratio of the machine (n') is 10.5. The capacitive load has an impedance of $X_c = 15 \ \Omega$ in each phase.

(a) Develop a single-phase equivalent circuit for the system.

(b) For a 3-phase bridge rectifier driven by current sources, show that $i_f = 1.35 I_{\text{sec rms}}$.

(c) Suppose the secondary winding of each current transformer has 500 turns. Determine the appropriate number of turns in each primary winding to maintain rated voltage of 220 V (line-to-line) under all load conditions. Neglect the voltages across the primary windings of the current transformers. *Ans.:* 35, 60.

(d) Compare the operation of this system with that of a compound self-excited d-c generator.

5.42 The parameters of a 440-V, 10-kVA, 60-c/s wound rotor machine are given in Prob. 5.32. Suppose this machine is to be used as a synchronous generator, its field circuit being connected as shown in Fig. 5.31*a*.

(a) Derive an equivalent circuit of the form shown in Fig. 5.48*a*.

(b) Suppose the stator terminals are open circuited and a direct voltage is connected to the field circuit. At what time constant will the field current rise toward its steady-state value? *Ans.:* 0.337 sec.

(c) Suppose the generator is connected to a 3-phase inductor that requires 10 kVA at zero power factor when the terminal voltage is 440 V line-to-line at 60 c/s. The stator resistance may be neglected in this section. If the field source is connected at $t = 0$, approximately what time is required for the terminal voltage to reach 95% of its final rms value? *Ans.:* 0.357 sec.

(d) Suppose the field voltage is adjusted to produce rated terminal voltage on open circuit. If a 3-phase short circuit occurs at the generator terminals, what will be the rms value of the sinusoidal component of the stator current immediately after the short circuit? *Ans.:* 46.6 amp.

(e) At what time constant will the envelope of the sinusoidal component of part (d) decay? *Ans.:* 0.036 sec.

(f) To what steady-state value will the sinusoidal component of the stator current decay? *Ans.:* 5 amp.

(g) What is the maximum value of the unidirectional component of the short-circuit current for the conditions of part (d)? *Ans.:* 66 amp.

(h) At what time constant will the unidirectional component decay? *Ans.:* 0.036 sec.

(i) Estimate the peak value of stator current that can occur in any phase for the conditions of part (d). *Ans.:* 100 amp.

5.43 A synchronous motor has a synchronous reactance of 0.9 per unit and a transient reactance of 0.35 per unit. Its stator resistance may be neglected and it may be considered magnetically linear. The motor is initially synchronized with a balanced supply of 1.0 per unit voltage by adjusting the field current to the value that produces an open circuit voltage of 1.0 per unit.

(a) Suppose the field current is left unchanged as load torque is gradually applied. Find the maximum per-unit torque that can be applied without losing synchronism. *Ans.:* 1.11 per unit.

(b) Let us assume that the transient time constant is large. Estimate the maximum torque that can be applied suddenly after initial synchronization, without losing synchronism. It can be assumed that the torque will be applied for a period that is much less than the transient time constant.

Ans.: 2.05 per unit.

(c) Suppose the load torque is gradually increased to 1.0 per unit and the field current is adjusted to give an input power factor of unity. Approximately how much additional torque can be added suddenly without losing synchronism?   *Ans.:* 1.4 per unit.

5.44 A 2-pole, 100-MVA, 60-c/s, 16-kV line-to-line synchronous generator is brought up to rated speed, and its field current is adjusted to give rated terminal voltage. It is then synchronized to a 16-kV power system which has negligible internal impedance. The transient reactance of the generator is 0.4 per unit based on its rating. Its losses are negligible. The polar moment of inertia of the generator and its driving turbine is 10^4 Kg-m².

(a) Determine the angular velocity of the speed oscillation that follows the application of a small-step increment of turbine torque.

Ans.: 8.13 rad/sec.

(b) When the machine is operated with a shorted field circuit, it is found that the generator operates as an induction generator and produces an output power of 30 MW with a slip of -0.02 per unit. For the condition stated in part (a), determine the angular velocity and relative damping factor of the speed oscillation following an incremental torque change.

Ans.: 8.11; 0.065.

(c) Suppose, that because of improper design of the control gear on the turbine valves, the torque T applied to the generator contains an oscillatory term. If $T = 5000 + 3000 \sin 7t$ newton-m, determine the peak-to-peak value of the continuous oscilation of the rotor angle β_0. Include the damping of part (b).   *Ans.:* 0.036 rad.

5.45 A 6000-hp, 1000-r/min, synchronous motor is supplied from a 13.2-kV line-to-line, 3-phase, 50-c/s, distribution line. The motor has a transient reactance of 14.0 Ω/phase. Its stator resistance may be neglected. The polar moment of inertia of the motor and its load is 6000 kg-m². Initially, the motor is supplying a mechanical power of 4000 kW to its load, and the field current is adjusted to obtain unity power factor at its terminals. When lightning causes a temporary flashover on the distribution line, the circuit breaker connecting the motor to the line opens for 0.45 sec to allow the fault to clear and then recloses.

(a) Derive the transient torque-angle relationships for the machine.

(b) Determine the initial value of the rotor angle.   *Ans.:* -0.312 rad.

(c) Determine the value of the rotor angle after operating 0.7 sec without supply.   *Ans.:* −1.84 rad.

(d) Assuming that the load torque remains unchanged, will the motor remain in synchronism?

5.46 The rotor of a small 3-phase, 400-c/s synchronous generator consists of a solid cylinder of permanent-magnet material as shown in Fig. 5.59. The permanet-magnet material has recoil permeability μ_r of 3.0 and a flux density B_0 of 1.1 Wb/m² at zero magnetic field intensity. The flux density of the magnet can be reduced to 0.9 Wb/m² before some of its permanent magnetism is destroyed (see Fig. 2.25b). The machine has a rotor radius r of 4 cm and a rotor length l of 6 cm. The air gap has an effective length g' of 1.0 mm. The stator has $N_s = 400$ sinusoidally distributed turns per phase.

(a) Suppose the stator current is zero. By use of the circuital law around a path along the axis of the magnet, show that the maximum flux density $\hat{B}$ at the air gap is given by

$$\hat{B} = \frac{B_0}{1 + (g'\mu_r/r)} \qquad \text{Wb/m}^2$$

(b) Assuming the stator magnetic material is perfect, determine the value of the magnetizing reactance X_{ms} per phase. Note that this rectance represents the air gap only (see eq. 5.38).   *Ans.:* 1430 Ω.

(c) In determining the reactance X_0 (Fig. 5.60a) the rotor may be considered as a cylinder of magnetic material having a relative permeability equal to the recoil permeability. Show that $X_0/X_{ms} = g'\mu_r/r$.

(d) Draw an equivalent circuit for the machine. Assume that the stator leakage reactance is $0.05 X_{ms}$ and neglect the stator resistance.

(e) Determine the terminal voltage on no-load.   *Ans.:* 274 V.

(f) Suppose a variable inductive load is connected to the machine terminals. What is the maximum value of rms current per phase that can be taken from the terminals without permanently changing the open-circuit voltage?   *Ans.:* 0.34 amp.

(g) What value of capacitance should be connected in series with each phase to make the voltage across a variable load resistance constant?
Ans.: 2.32 μF.

5.47 One method of assessing the torque-producing capability of a hysteresis motor is to determine the power dissipated as hysteresis loss in the rotor. From this loss power, the air-gap power and the torque may be derived. Consider a small 2-pole, 400 c/s polyphase motor having a cylindrical permanent-magnet rotor of the type shown in Fig. 5.62a. Its rotor radius is 2 cm and its rotor length is 4 cm. The permanent-magnet material has a hysteresis loop that may be approximated by the idealized model of Fig. 2.10 with $B_r = 1.2$ Wb/m^2 and $H_c = 10,000$ amp/m. Suppose the stator voltage and current are sufficient to cause the whole volume of the rotor to make a complete excursion around this B–H loop for each revolution of the stator magnetic field relative to the rotor.

(a) Determine the hysteresis loss in the rotor at standstill.
Ans.: 967 W.

(b) Determine the torque at standstill.   *Ans.:* 0.384 newton-m.

(c) Show that the power dissipated in the rotor is proportional to the slip.

(d) Show that the torque is independent of the slip.

(e) Determine the maximum shaft power the machine can produce.
Ans.: 967 W.

5.48   A 4-pole, 60-c/s, 3-phase reluctance motor has a direct-axis reactance of 8.0 Ω and a quadrature-axis reactance of 3.0 Ω/phase as seen from its stator terminals. Stator resistance and rotational losses may be ignored. The motor is connected to a 550-V line-to-line supply.

(a) Determine the maximum shaft torque which the motor can supply.
Ans.: 167 newton-m.

(b) Since the power factor of reluctance machines is always low, it is advisable to operate the motor at its maximum power factor condition. Determine the power factor and the power output for this condition.
Ans.: 0.455; 28 kW.

5.49   Suppose we wish to obtain a ratio $X_{md}/X_{mq} = k$ for a reluctance machine. The minimum value of the air gap is determined by mechanical considerations. If the air gap is not very large, the flux density in the air gap may be assumed to be radially directed. The analysis of Section 5.6.1

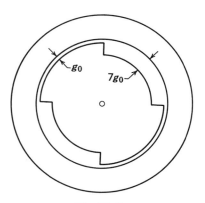

Fig. P5.49

suggests that the inverse of the air-gap length can be expressed by a Fourier series of only two significant terms.

(a) Derive an expression for the air-gap length in terms of the constant k and the minimum gap length g_0.

(b) Sketch the rotor shape for a rotor having a maximum rotor radius $\hat{r} = 30g_0$ and $k = 2.5$. Find the maximum gap length $\hat{g}$.

Ans.: $13g_0$.

(c) Figure P5.49 shows a rotor that consists of two 90° sectors having a gap equal to g_0 and two 90° sectors having a gap of $7g_0$. Compare the value of k for this rotor with that of the rotor in part (b).

Ans.: $k = 2.81$.

5.50 A salient-pole synchronous motor has a direct-axis synchronous reactance of 1.1 per unit and a quadrature-axis synchronous reactance of 0.6 per unit based on the machine rating. It is connected to a rated-voltage supply, and its field current is adjusted to give minimum stator current on no-load.

(a) Determine the per-unit torque produced per radian of rotor angle β_0 when operating near $\beta_0 = 0$. 						*Ans.:* 1.667.

(b) What fraction of the torque in part (a) is reluctance torque?

(c) Estimate the maximum steady-state torque the motor can supply with the above value of field current. 				*Ans.:* 1.11.

(d) Suppose we wish to study small speed oscillations of the machine. If the direct-axis transient reactance of the motor is 0.4 per unit, determine the electromagnetic torque produced per radian of rotor angle when operating in the transient regime near $\beta_0 = 0$. 				*Ans.:* 1.667.

(e) Estimate the maximum transient value of electromagnetic torque that the motor can supply with the same initial excitation as in part (c).

Ans.: 2.68.

5.51 A salient-pole synchronous machine has a direct-axis synchronous reactance of 1.0 per unit and a quadrature-axis synchronous reactance of 0.6 per unit. The machine is operated as a generator with a terminal voltage of 1.0 per unit supplying a current of 1.0 per unit to a load having a lagging power factor of 0.8.

(a) Determine the load angle β_0 of the machine for this condition. As an aid to solution, consider resolving the current components in Fig. 5.74 about an axis at angle β_0. 					*Ans.:* 19°.

(b) Determine the field current required for this load in per unit of the field current required to produce 1.0 per unit terminal voltage on no-load.

Ans.: 1.775.

5.52 A salient-pole synchronous machine is used as a synchronous reactor. It has no mechanical load and negligible losses. It is connected to a supply having a voltage of E_s per phase. Let i_{f0} be the value of field current that produces essentially zero stator current per phase.

(a) Suppose the field current is reduced to zero. Show that the complex power taken per phase is given by

$$U = -j\frac{|E_s|^2}{X_d} \quad \text{Vamp}$$

(b) To increase the inductive load the machine can take, let us consider reversing the direction of the field current. The rotor will remain in synchronism as long as a small shift in rotor angle β_0 away from $\beta_0 = 0$ will produce a torque tending to restore β_0 to zero. Show that the machine can remain in synchronism until the field current is reduced to

$$i_f = -\frac{X_d - X_q}{X_q} i_{f0}$$

(c) Show that the complex power into the machine per phase for the field current of part (b) is

$$U = -j\frac{|E_s|^2}{X_q} \quad \text{Vamp}$$

(d) Devise a method for measuring the direct-axis and quadrature-axis synchronous reactance of a machine.

5.53 A 3-phase commutator motor has an effective turns ratio of 1:1. The parameters of the machine in per unit of rating are $X_{Ls} = X_{Lr} = 0.15$; $X_{ms} = 2.0$; $R_s = 0$; $R_r = 0.02$. The machine is shunt connected with a 3-phase, variable-ratio autotransformer supplying voltage to the rotor brushes. The transformer imperfections may be ignored. The brushes are set for zero phase shift.

(a) Determine the voltage ratio required in the autotransformer to give a no-load speed of 0.8 per unit of synchronous speed.   *Ans.:* 0.186.

(b) Determine the maximum per-unit torque that the motor can produce with the setting found in part (a).   *Ans.:* 0.56.

(c) Repeat parts (a) and (b) for a no-load speed of 1.2 per unit.

5.54 We wish to obtain a 3-phase, 220-V line-to-line supply at a frequency of 5 c/s to supply a low-speed induction motor. A 3-phase, 220-V line-to-line, 60-c/s 2-pole commutator machine having both slip rings and a commutator on its rotor is available. The turns-ratio is unity. The leakage reactances, resistances, and magnetizing current of the machine can be neglected.

(a) Suppose a 220-V, 3-phase, 60-c/s supply is connected to the rotor slip rings. The stator winding is open circuited. At what speed should the rotor be driven to supply the required frequency from the stationary rotor brushes? *Ans.:* 55 or 65 r/sec.

(b) For the connection of part (a), what fraction of the load power is supplied from the source and what fraction from the shaft?

(c) What will be the line-to-line voltage and the frequency in the stator winding for the connection of part (a)? (d) In certain circumstances it may be easier to rotate the brush gear than to rotate the rotor. Determine the required speed of the brush gear if the rotor speed is zero and the supply is connected to the stator winding.

5.55 A 3-phase, 220-V line-to-neutral, 7.5 kVA (total) synchronous generator has a field current that produces rated voltage on no-load. It is used to supply a single resistive load of 10 Ω connected between one phase and neutral. The machine has a synchronous reactance of 0.6 per unit, a negative-sequence reactance of 0.25 per unit, and a zero-sequence reactance of 0.05 per unit based on the machine rating. Its winding resistances may be neglected.

(a) Determine the voltage applied to the load. *Ans.:* 191 V.

(b) Compare the voltage in part (a) with the voltage per phase for a balanced 3-phase star-connected load of 10 Ω per phase.

(c) Determine the voltages of the two unloaded phases with respect to neutral. *Ans.:* 181; 220.

5.56 A 3-phase, 230-V line-to-line, wound-rotor machine is used as a single-phase synchronous generator to supply 230 volts to a resistance of 10 Ω connected between two of its three stator terminals. Direct current is supplied to the rotor through phase A in series with phases B and C connected in parallel. The turns ratio of the machine is 1:1. The stator and rotor leakage reactances are each equal to 2 Ω/phase and the magnetizing reactance is equal to 15 Ω at rated frequency.

(a) Determine the required value of field current. *Ans.:* 29.

(b) Show that a second-harmonic component of current flows in the field-current source.

5.57 A 3-phase 220-V line-to-line, 400-c/s, 2-pole, induction machine has negligible stator resistance, infinite magnetizing reactance, a total leakage reactance of 20 Ω/phase, and a rotor resistance of 4 Ω/phase. Suppose a single-phase, 220-V source is connected between two stator terminals, the third being left open circuited.

(a) Derive an expression for the current taken from the source as a function of the rotor speed. Determine the current at standstill. *Ans.:* 5.4 amp.

(b) Derive an expression for the electromagnetic torque produced by the machine. Sketch a torque-speed curve over the range from synchronous speed in one direction to synchronous speed in the opposite direction. Evaluate the torque at half synchronous speed.

Ans.: 0.0733 newton-m.

5.58 A small, 2-phase, 400-c/s, 6-pole induction motor has a stator resistance of 100 Ω/phase, a total leakage inductance of 0.12 H/phase, and a rotor resistance of 300 Ω/phase. Its magnetizing current is negligible.

(a) Suppose an asymmetrical 2-phase, 400-c/s source (half of a symmetrical 4-phase system) of 115 V rms per phase is applied to the motor. Determine the torque and the current per phase at standstill.

Ans.: 0.0377 newton-m; 0.229 amp.

(b) Suppose the motor is to be started from a single-phase 115-V, 400-c/s source using a resistance in series with one phase (see Fig. 5.97a). What should be the value of this series resistance to produce maximum starting torque?   *Ans.:* 500 Ω.

(c) Determine the starting torque using the value of resistance found in part (b).   *Ans.:* 0.0071 newton-m.

(d) Determine the total supply current at standstill for the condition of part (b).   *Ans.:* 0.344 amp.

(e) Suppose the motor is to be started using a capacitor in series with one phase (see Fig. 5.98a). What should be the value of the capacitance to produce maximum starting torque?   *Ans.:* 0.82 μF.

(f) Determine the starting torque for part (e).   *Ans.:* 0.038 newton-m.

(g) Determine the total supply current at standstill for part (e).

Ans.: 0.416 amp.

(h) Compare the starting torque per Vamp taken from the supply for the conditions of parts a, b, and e.

5.59 Suppose the 2-phase induction motor described in Prob. 5.58 is to be used as a variable-speed control motor with $E_d = 115$ V rms applied to one phase and a variable voltage E_q applied to the other phase.

(a) Determine the standstill torque produced per volt of the winding voltage E_q.   *Ans.:* 3.28 $\times$ 10^{-4} newton-m/V.

(b) Determine the torque at half of synchronous speed for $E_q = 115$ V and for $E_q = 0$.   *Ans.:* 0.0325 newton-m; -0.00064 newton-m.

(c) Sketch the torque-speed curves for the machine for a few values of the voltage E_q.

(d) Suppose the motor has a polar moment of inertia of 10^{-6} kg-m^2 and negligible mechanical losses. If the rotor speed is small relative to synchronous speed, show that the relationship between rotor speed ν and the voltage E_q may be represented approximately by the transfer function

$$\nu_{(s)} = \frac{328}{s + 1.53} E_{q(s)} \qquad \text{rad/sec}$$

where s is the complex frequency variable.

(e) Determine the maximum acceleration this motor can produce at standstill. *Ans.:* 3.77×10^4 rad/sec².

5.60 Suppose the 2-phase induction motor described in Prob. 5.58 is used as an a-c tachometer, one winding being supplied with 115 V rms at 400 c/s and the open-circuit voltage E_q being measured on the other winding.

(a) Derive an expression for the voltage E_q as a function of the rotor speed v.

(b) Determine the voltage E_q per unit of rotor speed for small values of rotor speed relative to synchronous speed. *Ans.:* 0.0825 V-sec/rad.

(c) Suppose the rotor speed is 0.2 per unit of synchronous speed. Compare the voltage E_q per unit of rotor speed with the value found in part (b). *Ans.:* 2% lower.

(d) Show that the linearity of this machine as a tachometer could be improved and the sensitivity increased by increasing the rotor resistance.

5.61 A semiconductor inverter is used to supply the 2-phase voltage required for the small induction motor described in Prob. 5.58. Figure

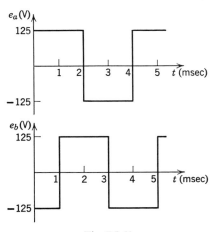

Fig. P5.61

P5.61 shows the waveforms of the phase voltages e_a and e_b provided by the inverter.

(a) Derive Fourier series representations for the phase voltages e_a and e_b.

(b) Determine the phase sequence for each of the pairs of fundamental, third, and fifth harmonic components of the phase voltages.

(c) Determine the synchronous speeds for each of the frequency components in the phase voltages. *Ans.:* 525, −1575, 2625 rad/sec.

(d) Using the principle of superposition, determine the starting torque. *Ans.:* 0.0719 newton-m.

(e) Draw a rough sketch of the torque-speed curve for the machine. Comment on the effects of the higher harmonics in the supply voltages.

5.62 Two identical, 440-V line-to-line, 60-c/s, 2-pole, wound-rotor machines are connected as a power synchro system (see Fig. 5.105). Each machine has the following parameters per phase at rated frequency: $R_s \approx 0$, $X_{Ls} = X_{Lr} = 1.1\ \Omega$, $X_{ms} = 20\ \Omega$, $R_r = 0.4\ \Omega$. Rated voltages are applied at rated frequency to the stator windings of both machines.

(a) Suppose the difference $(\beta_1 - \beta_2)$ between the rotor angles is small. When the speed is near zero, determine the torque produced in each machine per radian of the difference angle $\beta_1 - \beta_2$.   *Ans.:* 10.3.

(b) Determine the maximum shaft torque that can be applied to the lagging machine.   *Ans.:* 86.

(c) Suppose each of the machines has a polar moment of inertia of 0.5 kg-m². Neither machine has a mechanical load. The rotor positions are separated by a small angle (less than 0.1 rad) and then released. At what angular frequency will each rotor oscillate?   *Ans.:* 41.2 rad/sec.

REFERENCES

Adkins, B. and W. J. Gibbs, *Polyphase Commutator Machines*. Cambridge University Press, Cambridge, 1951.

Adkins, B., *The General Theory of Electrical Machines*. Chapman and Hall, London and John Wiley and Sons, New York, 1957.

Alger, P. D., *The Nature of Polyphase Induction Machines*. John Wiley and Sons, New York, 1951.

Clarke, E., *Circuit Analysis of A-C Power Systems*. John Wiley and Sons, New York, 1943.

Concordia, C., *Synchronous Machines*. John Wiley and Sons, New York, 1951.

Copeland, M. A. and G. R. Slemon, "An Analysis of the Hysteresis Motor, Part I: An Analysis of the Idealized Machine." *Transactions, Institute of Electrical and Electronic Engineers* (Power Apparatus and Systems), 1963, 34; "Part II: The Circumferential Flux Machine," *ibid*, 1964, 619.

Crary, S. B., *Power System Stability* (2 volumes). John Wiley and Sons, New York, 1947.

Hanrahan, D. J. and D. S. Toffolo, "Permanent Magnet Generators, Part I, Theory." *Transactions, American Institute of Electrical Engineers*, Part III, **76**, 1957, 1098; "Part II, Optimum Design," Power Apparatus and Systems, **65**, 1963, 68.

Kron, G., *Equivalent Circuits of Electric Machinery*. John Wiley and Sons, New York, 1951.

Lyon, W. V., *Transient Analysis of Alternating Current Machinery: An Application of the Method of Symmetrical Components*. John Wiley and Sons, New York, 1954.

Park, R. H., "Two Reaction Theory of Synchronous Machines, Part I." *Transactions, American Institute of Electrical Engineers*, **48**, 1929, 716. Part II, *ibid*, **52**, 1933, 352.

Puchstein, A. F., T. C. Lloyd, and A. G. Conrad, *Alternating Current Machines* (third edition). John Wiley and Sons, New York, 1954.

Say, M. G., *Performance and Design of A-C Machines*. Pitman, London, 1961.

Slemon, G. R., "Equivalent Circuits for Transformers and Machines Including Nonlinear Effects." *Proceedings, Institution of Electrical Engineers*, Part IV, **100**, 1953, 129.

Tricky, P. H., "Performance Calculations on Polyphase Reluctance Motors," *Transactions, American Institute of Electrical Engineers*, **65**, 1946, 190.

Vienott, C. G., *Theory and Design of Small Induction Motors*. McGraw-Hill, New York, 1959.

Wagner, C. F. and R. D. Evans, *Symmetrical Components*. McGraw-Hill, New York, 1933.

White, D. C. and H. H. Woodson, *Electromechanical Energy Conversion*. John Wiley and Sons, New York, 1959.

Appendix A

CONVERSION FACTORS

Length	1 meter (m)	= 3.281 feet (ft)
		= 39.37 inches (in.)
Angle	1 radian (rad)	= 57.30 degrees
Mass	1 kilogram (kg)	= 0.0685 slugs
		= 2.205 pounds (lb)
		= 35.27 ounces (oz)
Force	1 newton	= 0.2248 pounds (lbf)
		= 7.233 poundals
		= 10^5 dynes
		= 102 grams
Torque	1 newton-meter	= 0.738 pound-feet (lbf-ft)
		= 10^7 dyne-centimeter
		= 1.02×10^4 gram-centimeter
Moment of inertia	1 kilogram-meter^2 (kg-m^2)	= 0.738 slug-feet^2
		= 23.7 pound-feet^2 (lb-ft^2)
		= 5.46×10^4 ounce-inches^2
		= 10^7 gram-centimeter^2 (g-cm^2)
Energy	1 joule	= 1 watt-second
		= 0.7376 foot-pounds (ft-lb)
		= 2.778×10^{-7} kilowatt-hours (kWh)
		= 0.2388 calorie (cal)
		= 9.48×10^{-4} British Thermal Units (Btu)
		= 10^7 ergs
Power	1 watt (W)	= 0.7376 foot-pounds/second
		= 1.341×10^{-3} horsepower (hp)
Resistivity	1 ohm-meter (Ω-m)	= 6.015×10^8 ohm-circular mil/foot
		= 10^8 micro-ohm/centimeter
Magnetic flux	1 weber (Wb)	= 10^8 maxwells or lines
		= 10^5 kilolines

Magnetic flux density	1 weber/meter^2 (Wb/m^2)	$= 10^4$ gauss
		$= 64.52$ kilolines/in.^{2}
Magnetomotive force	1 ampere-(turn)	$= 1.257$ gilberts
Magnetic field intensity	1 ampere/meter	$= 2.54 \times 10^{-2}$ ampere/in.
		$= 1.257 \times 10^{-2}$ oersted

Appendix B
PHYSICAL CONSTANTS

Quantity	Symbol	Value	Unit
Permittivity of free space	ϵ_0	8.854×10^{-12}	coulomb^2/newton-meter^2
Permeability of free space	μ_0	$4\pi \times 10^{-7}$	newton/ampere^2
Gravitation acceleration constant	g_0	9.807	meter/second^2
Magnitude of proton or electron charge	Q_e	1.603×10^{-19}	coulomb
Electron mass	m_e	9.1×10^{-31}	kilogram
Proton mass	m_p	1.67×10^{-27}	kilogram
Bohr magneton	p_{Bohr}	9.27×10^{-24}	ampere-meter^2

Appendix C

RESISTIVITY (ρ_{20}) AND TEMPERATURE COEFFICIENT OF RESISTIVITY (α_{20}) OF SOME CONDUCTIVE MATERIALS

Material	ρ_{20} (ohm-meter)	α_{20} (°C)$^{-1}$
Copper (annealed)	1.72×10^{-8}	3.93×10^{-3}
Copper (hard drawn)	1.78×10^{-8}	3.82×10^{-3}
Aluminum	2.7×10^{-8}	3.9×10^{-3}
Sodium	4.65×10^{-8}	5.4×10^{-3}
Nickel	7.8×10^{-8}	5.4×10^{-3}
Lead	2.2×10^{-7}	4×10^{-3}
Tungsten	5.5×10^{-8}	4.5×10^{-3}
Iron	9.8×10^{-8}	6.5×10^{-3}
Mercury	9.58×10^{-7}	8.9×10^{-4}

Appendix D

SYMBOLS

Symbol	Quantity	Unit
A	Area	meter^2
a	Number of parallel paths	
B	Magnetic flux density	weber/meter^2
C	Capacitance	farad
D	Electric flux density	coulomb/meter^2
d	Distance	meter
	Differential	
∂	Partial differential	
E, e	Electromotive force	volt
	Electric potential difference	volt
$\mathscr{E}$	Electric field intensity	volt/meter
$\mathscr{F}$	Magnetomotive force	ampere
f	Force	newton
	Frequency	cycle/second
G	Conductance	mho
g	Length of air gap	meter
H	Magnetic field intensity	ampere/meter
h	Order of space harmonic	
	Convection coefficient	watts/meter^2-°C
I, i	Current	ampere
J	Current density	ampere/meter^2
	Polar moment of inertia	kilogram-meter^2
j	Operator $= 1 \; \underline{/\pi/2}$	
K, k	Constants	
L	Inductance	henry
l	Length	meter
$\mathscr{M}$	Magnetic moment per unit volume	ampere/meter
m	Number of phases	
N	Number of turns	

Symbol	Quantity	Unit
n	Number of free charges per unit volume	meter^{-3}
	Turns ratio	
	Number of conductors per radian	
P, p	Power	watt
p	Number of poles	
p_m	Magnetic moment	ampere-meter^2
Q, q	Electric charge	coulomb
Q_e	Magnitude of proton or electron charge	coulomb
q	Linear current density	ampere-meter
R	Resistance	ohm
r	Radius, distance	meter
$\mathscr{R}$	Magnetic reluctance	ampere/weber
$\mathscr{R}_e$	Real part of	
s	Complex frequency	second^{-1}
s	Slip	
T	Torque	newton-meter
t	Time	second
U	Complex power	volt-ampere
u	Unit vector	
V	Volume	meter^3
v	Velocity	meter/second
W	Energy, work	joule
w	Energy per unit volume	joule/meter^3
X	Reactance	ohm
x	Distance	meter
Y	Admittance (complex)	ohm
y	Distance	meter
Z	Impedance (complex)	ohm
z	Distance	meter
α	Operator $= 1 \; \underline{/2\pi/3}$	
	Attenuation constant	second^{-1}
	Angle	radian
	Ratio of pole arc to pole pitch.	
β	Angle	radian
γ	Angle	radian
Δ	Increment of . . .	
δ	Angle	radian

Symbol	Quantity	Unit
ϵ_0	Permittivity of free space	coulomb²/newton-meter²
ϵ_r	Relative permittivity	
η	Efficiency	
θ	Angle	radian
λ	Magnetic flux linkage	weber
μ_0	Permeability of free space	newton/ampere²
μ_r	Relative permeability	
ν	Angular velocity	radian/second
ρ	Electrical resistivity	ohm-meter
Σ	Sum of . . .	
τ	Time constant	second
	Time interval	second
Φ, ϕ	Magnetic flux	weber
ω	Angular frequency or velocity	radian/second

INDEX